World catalogue
of maximum observed
floods

Répertoire mondial
des crues maximales
observées

TITLES RECENTLY PUBLISHED BY IAHS

Hydrogeology of Great Sedimentary Basins. Proceedings of the Budapest
Symposium, May–June 1976
Publ. no. 120 (1978), price $7
(co-edition IAHS/Hungarian Geological Institute, Budapest)

Land Subsidence. Proceedings of the Anaheim Symposium, December 1976
Publ. no. 121 (1977), price $30

Erosion and Solid Matter Transport in Inland Waters. Proceedings of the Paris
Symposium, July 1977
Publ. no. 122 (1977), price $20

*Effects of Urbanization and Industrialization on the Hydrological Regime and on
Water Quality.* Proceedings of the Amsterdam Symposium, October 1977
Publ. no. 123 (1977), price $16
(co-edition IAHS/UNESCO. UNESCO Studies and reports in hydrology 24)

Sea Ice Processes and Models. Proceedings of the Seattle Symposium, September
1977
Publ. no. 124 (1980), price $25
(co-edition IAHS/University of Washington Press)

Modelling the Water Quality of the Hydrological Cycle. Proceedings of the
Baden Symposium, September 1978
Publ. no. 125 (1978), price $25

World Glacier Inventory. Proceedings of the Riederalp Workshop, September 1978
Publ. no. 126 (1980), price $20

The Hydrology of Areas of Low Precipitation. Proceedings of the Canberra
Symposium, December 1979
Publ. no. 128 (1979), price $40

Hydrological Forecasting. Proceedings of the Oxford Symposium, April 1980
Publ. no. 129 (1980), price $50

*The Influence of Man on the Hydrological Regime with Special Reference to
Representative and Experimental Basins.* Proceedings of the Helsinki Symposium,
June 1980
Publ. no. 130 (1980), price $50

Sea Level, Ice, and Climatic Change. Proceedings of the Canberra Symposium,
December 1979
Publ. no. 131 (1981), price $40

Erosion and Sediment Transport in Pacific Rim Steeplands. Proceedings of the
Christchurch Symposium, January 1981
Publ. no. 132 (1981), price $45

Erosion and Sediment Transport Measurement. Proceedings of the Florence
Symposium, June 1981
Publ. no. 133 (1981), price $40

**Proceedings of the symposia held during the First IAHS Scientific General
Assembly, Exeter, July 1982**

Advances in Hydrometry
Publ. no. 134, price $30

Optimal Allocation of Water Resources
Publ. no. 135, price $35

*Improvement of Methods of Long Term Prediction of Variations in Groundwater Resources
and Regimes Due to Human Activity*
Publ. no. 136, price $30

Recent Developments in the Explanation and Prediction of Erosion and Sediment Yield
Publ. no. 137, price $35

Hydrological Aspects of Alpine and High-Mountain Areas
Publ. no. 138, price $30

Effect of Waste Disposal on Groundwater and Surface Water
Publ. no. 139, price $30

Hydrology of Humid Tropical Regions. Proceedings of the Hamburg Symposium,
August 1983
Publ. no. 140 (1983), price $37

Dissolved Loads of Rivers and Surface Water Quantity/Quality Relationships.
Proceedings of the Hamburg Symposium, August 1983
Publ. no. 141 (1983), price $37

Ground Water in Water Resources Planning, volumes I and II. Proceedings of the
Koblenz Symposium, August–September 1983
Publ. no. 142 (1983), price $22

World Catalogue of Maximum Observed Floods
Publ. no. 143 (1984), price $30

Challenges in African Hydrology and Water Resources. Proceedings of the Harare
Symposium, July 1984
Publ. no. 144 (1984), price $48

PLEASE SEND ORDERS TO:

Office of the Treasurer IAHS	IUGG Publications Office	IAHS Editorial Office
2000 Florida Avenue, NW	39 ter Rue Gay Lussac	Institute of Hydrology
Washington, DC 20009, USA	75005 Paris, France	Wallingford, Oxon OX10 8BB, UK

WORLD CATALOGUE OF MAXIMUM OBSERVED FLOODS

REPERTOIRE MONDIAL DES CRUES MAXIMALES OBSERVEES

Prepared by
Mis au point par
J.A. RODIER & M. ROCHE
ORSTOM, 70-74 Route d'Aulnay,
93140 Bondy,France

As a contribution to the International
Hydrological Programme of UNESCO
A titre de contribution au Programme
Hydrologique International de l'UNESCO

IHP - II Project A.2.7.2
PHI - II Projet A.2.7.2

 IAHS - AISH Publication No. 143

Published by the International Association of Hydrological Sciences
1984.
IAHS Press, Institute of Hydrology, Wallingford, Oxfordshire
OX10 8BB, UK.
IAHS Publication No. 143.
ISBN 0-947571-00-0.

The camera-ready copy for this publication was produced at ORSTOM,
70-74 Route d'Aulnay, F-93140 Bondy, France.

Table of contents
Table des matières

List of Tables I, II and III country by country
Liste des Tableaux I, II et III pays par pays

Country or State Pays ou Territoire	Table I Tableau I	Table II Tableau II	Table III Tableau III
Ivory Coast/Côte d'Ivoire	121	122	294
Japan/Japon	123	125	295
Jordan/Jordanie	127	128	297
Kenya	129	129	—
Laos Popular Democratic Republic/République Populaire Démocratique du Laos	130	130	—
Liberia	131	131	—
Madagascar	132	133	297
Malawi	135	135	—
Malaysia/Malaisie	136	137	298
Mali	138	139	299
Martinique (France)	140	140	300
Mauritania/Mauritanie	141	142	—
Mexico/Mexique	143	144	300
Morocco/Maroc	145	146	301
Mozambique	147	148	—
Netherlands/Pays Bas	149	149	302
New Caledonia/Nouvelle Calédonie (France)	150	151	303
New Zealand/Nouvelle Zélande	152	154	303
Niger	155	156	304
Nigeria	157	158	304
Norway/Norvège	159	160	305
Pakistan	161	162	306
Panama	163	163	—
Philippines	164	164	—
Poland/Pologne	165	166	307
Portugal	167	168	—
Puerto Rico/Porto Rico (United States of America/Etats Unis d'Amérique)	169	169	—
Republic of Capo Verde Islands/République des Iles du Cap Vert	170	170	—
Republic of Korea/République de Corée	171	172	307
Reunion Island/Ile de la Réunion (France)	173	173	—
Romania/Roumanie	174	176	308
Rwanda	177	177	—
Senegal	178	179	309
Sierra Leone	180	181	—
Socialist Republic of Vietnam/République Socialiste du Vietnam	182	182	—
South Africa/Afrique du Sud	183	186	309
Spain/Espagne	188	191	312
Sri Lanka	195	195	314
Sudan/Soudan	196	196	—
Sweden/Suède	197	199	315
Switzerland/Suisse	201	201	—
Thailand/Thaïlande	202	202	—
Togo	203	204	316
Tunisia/Tunisie	205	206	316
Turkey/Turquie	207	208	317
Uganda/Ouganda	209	209	318
Union of Soviet Socialist Republics/Union des Républiques Socialistes Soviètiques	210	214	318
United Kingdom/Royaume Uni	218	220	329
United States of America/Etats Unis d'Amérique	222	236	330
Upper Volta/Haute Volta	249	250	338
Uruguay	251	251	338
Venezuela	252	253	—
Yugoslavia/Yougoslavie	254	255	339
Zaïre	256	256	340
Zimbabwe	257	258	—

Introduction
(in English)

Knowledge of exceptionally large floods is essential to the solution of many problems in water management and also to assess the susceptibility to flooding of any structure to be constructed in the vicinity of a water course. The choice of a design flood value is generally difficult and delicate. It necessitates (a) the use of the appropriate hydrological method of estimation (if possible several methods and the comparison of results); and (b) good knowledge of the condition of operation of the structure to be studied, in order to choose correctly the risk – which is closely related to frequency – for those cases where it is possible to speak about frequencies. The first step of this study requires that the estimation of discharges of the past floods be properly made, that this information be stored safely and that a minimum of diffusion of this information be insured. During the preparation of the present publication, it was found that in some countries some outstanding interesting floods observed 30 years ago were practically forgotten in these countries and entirely ignored in neighbouring countries.

The purpose of such a world catalogue as this is twofold : to insure in each country the assessment and the safekeeping of data on large floods for at least the main stations and to permit a world review as exhaustive as possible of the largest floods for the different hydrological regimes for adequate and useful comparisons. This necessitates also a description of the main parameters of the basin.

In 1976, in the framework of the International Hydrological Programme, UNESCO published the World Catalogue of very large floods; thirty five countries answered the UNESCO Questionnaire. This publication is very useful to all hydrologists, but its major objective was not specifically the collection of maximum floods; furthermore, the limited time available for the preparation of this catalogue was such that a relatively small number of countries were represented.

This is the reason why, after the preparation of the UNESCO Catalogue, IAHS (which had participated in the production of that publication) launched an inquiry for the publication of a world catalogue of maximum floods which would be a follow-up to the UNESCO Catalogue. This initiative was endorsed by the IHP Council which included this activity in the IHP II Programme as Project A.2.7.2. In this way the project became a joint IAHS/Unesco venture.

Mr. M. Roche, following the instructions of the International Commission on Surface Water of IAHS, had prepared the questionnaire, thus beginning the inquiry at the end of 1976; with the help of the IAHS National Committees and correspondents he collected the first replies. In December 1979, Dr. J.A. Rodier was appointed responsible for fulfilment of this catalogue, since the new responsabilities of Mr. M. Roche did not leave him enough time for the task.

In the implementation of IHP project A.2.7.2 the UNESCO Division of Water Sciences, authorized IAHS to have recourse when necessary to the IHP National Committees and to use the material of the previous UNESCO Catalogue. UNESCO contributed to this project by facilitating contacts with hydrologists of several countries. The inquiry also benefitted from co-operation with several expert hydrologists and consultants.

All this effort permitted collection of data from 95 countries, including 34 of the 35 countries which have already participated in the inquiry for the UNESCO Catalogue. For these latter countries the flood lists were updated, historical floods were also mentioned and for some countries an important number of new gauging stations were used, generally from rivers with high specific flood discharges. IAHS has contacted 110 countries. The questionnaire was not sent to 40 countries because they could not usefully contribute to this catalogue for the following reasons :

(a) Countries of very small area, such as Monaco or Andorra, and where the slope and the precipitation regime are such that large floods of exceptional character are unlikely to occur;

(b) Small islands in the Pacific and Indian Oceans and in the Caribbean. These small islands were too numerous for them all to be included in the Catalogue. A sampling was made on the basis of two criteria :

  (i)   floods with high specific discharge,
  (ii) ease of obtaining flood data.

(c) Arid countries without a hydrometric network or with a very recent network.

Nevertheless, great effort was made to include data from arid or very arid countries or parts of countries (such as the south-west USA, Australia, countries around the Sahara, etc ...)

At the end of the inquiry only six countries contacted, presenting relatively large rivers, were missing; consequently it seems possible to say that this IAHS Catalogue is relatively exhaustive. The maximum observed flood discharge is given for 1400 stations or observation sites.

Table I gives for each of these stations the parameters that are of particular interest for understanding the hydrology in general and the formation of floods. Factors concerning the genesis of snowmelt floods were intentionally neglected, as this aspect has been already dealt with in a precise and exhaustive way in the UNESCO Catalogue; furthermore most of the countries principally concerned by problems of snowmelt were represented in that publication. All details concerning Table I are given in the explanatory note.

Table II provides direct information concerning the maximum flood and generally the second and the third largest floods also. For many of these floods information is given about the procedure used for estimating the flood and about the precision of this estimate. For some of these floods from small and relatively small basins the precipitation causing them is also given.

For many countries, the maximum flood data were compared with values already given in the literature, and often some discussion took place by correspondence to avoid any erroneous value due to a printing error or to a too rough estimation. Nevertheless, all hydrologists know quite well that in such a field it is impossible to avoid all such errors although we hope that they will be few. There are some differences between the discharge values of certain maximum floods already published in the early literature (including the UNESCO Catalogue) and their values given in the present Catalogue. These correspond to a new appraisal of discharges by the contributing countries.

For some states and territories located far from the main part of their country, such as the island of Hawaii, USA, or Tahiti for France, the maximum flood discharges were presented separately.

It seemed useful to publish also a selection of long time series of yearly maximum values, but as these series are less essential for the solution of problems of maximum flood than the maxima, IAHS does not reproduce the 180 series already published by UNESCO in Table II; however, these series were updated as far as possible and were sometimes completed. The present catalogue provides 105 new long time series concerning the main rivers or stations with interesting statistical distributions of annual maxima.

At the end of this publication a short comment is made on the maximum observed floods.

For its main objective study of maximum discharges, this publication should not need any complement as it includes all maxima published in the UNESCO Catalogue.

For the study of long time series of annual maxima, and for the analysis of factors of snowmelt floods, it must be used jointly with the UNESCO Catalogue. For thorough analysis of large flood factors it is recommended that reference be made to the publication of Maurice Pardé (1961) "sur la puissance des crues en diverses parties du monde. Geographica. Enero-Diciembre 1961 Facultad de Letras de Zaragoza" which contains many details about the maximum floods observed in the world before 1961.

The present Catalogue is the result of the work of the IAHS National Committees and correspondents, of the UNESCO IHP National Committees and of many national agencies, expert hydrologists and consultants of 95 countries : Albania, Algeria, Argentina, Australia, Austria, Bangladesh, Belgium, Benin, Bolivia, Brazil, Bulgaria, Cameroon, Canada, Central African Republic, Chad, China, Colombia, Congo, Costa Rica, Cuba, Czechoslovakia, Democratic Kampuchea, Democratic People's Republic of Korea, Dominican Republic, Ecuador, Egypt, Federal Republic of Germany, Finland, France, Gabon, German Democratic Republic, Ghana, Guatemala, Guinea, Guyana, Hungary, Iceland, India, Indonesia, Iran, Iraq, Ireland, Israel, Italy, Ivory Coast, Japan, Jordan, Kenya, Liberia, Laos Popular Democratic Republic, Madagascar, Malawi, Malaysia, Mali, Mauritania, Mexico, Morocco, Mozambique, the Netherlands, New Zealand, Niger, Nigeria, Norway, Pakistan, Panama, Philippines, Poland, Portugal, Republic of Cabo Verde, Republic of Korea, Romania, Rwanda, Senegal, Sierra Leone, Socialist Republic of Vietnam, South Africa, Spain, Sri Lanka, Sudan, Sweden, Switzerland, Thailand, Togo, Tunisia, Turkey, Uganda, Union of Soviet Socialist Republics, United Kingdom, United States of America, Upper Volta, Uruguay, Venezuela, Yugoslavia, Zaire and Zimbabwe. The Association expresses its gratitude to all who, in spite of their duties, found some time to contribute to this Catalogue. We should like to thank those bodies whose contributions were particularly important, such as : the Committee of Co-ordination of investigation of

the lower Mekong Basin; Commonwealth Scientific and Industrial Research Organisation, Australia; Department of Enviromental Affairs of South Africa; Office de la Recherche Scientifique et Technique Outre-Mer, France; United States Geological Survey; USSR State Committee for Hydrometeorology and Control of Natural Environment; Direction Générale des Eaux Intérieures, Canada, Divisao de Controle de Ricursos Hidricos, DNAE Brazil; Institute of Hydrology, Wallingford, United Kingdom and in this last Institute, Mr R.T. Clarke and Mr M. Beran who corrected the English texts and helped edit this book.

Some errors certainly remain in this Catalogue. It is possible that for the contributing countries some important floods are missing; for some large countries, the contribution concerning small or relatively small basins could be greatly enlarged; or countries with interesting rivers are missing. For these reasons all comments or complementary material would be welcomed. The IAHS Secretary General will collect this material for a future edition of the catalogue whose preparation could begin in 1996 or 1997, an interval of twenty years between two editions being reasonable.

It is hoped that this publication will be useful for all scientists or engineers involved in problems of water management.

Introduction
(texte français)

La connaissance des crues exceptionnellement fortes est essentielle pour la solution de nombreux problèmes que pose la réalisation d'aménagements hydrauliques et également pour déterminer les risques d'inondation pour tous les ouvrages à construire au voisinage d'un cours d'eau.

Le choix du débit pour la crue du projet est une opération généralement difficile et délicate. Elle exige:

a) L'emploi d'une méthode hydrologique d'estimation bien adaptée au cas de la rivière à étudier (si possible plusieurs méthodes dont on compare les résultats).

b) Une bonne connaissance des conditions d'exploitation de l'ouvrage à étudier en vue de choisir judicieusement le degré de risque à prendre en considération, lequel est lié étroitement à la fréquence (pour les cas où il est possible de parler de fréquence).

La première étape de cette étude exige que l'estimation des débits des crues qui se sont déjà produites dans le passé soit effectuée correctement, que cette information soit stockée dans de bonnes conditions de sécurité et qu'on lui assure un minimum de diffusion. Au cours de la préparation de la présente publication on a constaté que dans certains pays des crues intéressantes, qui s'étaient produites il y a 30 ans, étaient pratiquement oubliées dans ces pays et tout à fait ignorées dans les pays voisins.

Le but d'un Répertoire mondial est double: assurer dans chaque pays la détermination et la conservation des débits des grandes crues au moins pour les stations principales et permettre de procéder à une revue aussi exhaustive que possible sur le plan mondial des plus fortes crues pour différents régimes hydrologiques, en vue de permettre des comparaisons correctes et utiles. Ceci exige également une description des principaux paramètres du bassin.

En 1976, dans le cadre du Programme Hydrologique International, UNESCO a publié le Répertoire mondial des très fortes crues; trente cinq pays ont répondu au questionnaire UNESCO. Cette publication est très utile pour tous les hydrologues mais son objectif principal n'était pas explicitement la collecte de données sur les crues maximales; en outre, le temps disponible pour la préparation de ce Catalogue était tel qu'un nombre relativement faible de pays étaient représentés.

C'est la raison pour laquelle, après la préparation du Répertoire UNESCO, l'AISH (qui avait participé à la mise au point de ce Répertoire) a lancé une enquête pour la publication d'un Répertoire des crues maximales qui constituerait une suite au Répertoire de l'UNESCO. Cette initiative a reçu l'approbation du Conseil du PHI qui a incorporé cette activité dans le programme PHI II en tant que Projet A.2.7.2.. Dans ces conditions cette opération est devenue une entreprise conjointe AISH/UNESCO.

M.M. Roche, suivant les instructions de la Commission Internationale des Eaux de Surface de l'AISH, a préparé le questionnaire et l'enquête a commencé à la fin de 1976. Avec l'aide des Comités Nationaux et des correspondants de l'AISH, il a rassemblé les premières réponses. En Décembre 1979, le Dr. J.A. Rodier a été nommé responsable pour l'achèvement de ce répertoire car les nouvelles responsabilités que devait assurer M. Roche ne lui laissaient plus assez de temps pour mener à bien cette tâche.

Pour l'exécution du projet A.2.7.2. du PHI II la Division des Sciences de l'Eau de l'UNESCO a autorisé l'AISH à recourir, chaque fois que c'était nécessaire, aux Comités Nationaux du PHI et à utiliser les données du Répertoire de l'UNESCO. Ainsi l'UNESCO a apporté directement une aide importante à ce projet en facilitant les contacts avec les hydrologues de plusieurs pays. Cette enquête a aussi bénéficié de la coopération de plusieurs experts hydrologues et d'ingénieurs conseils.

Tous ces efforts ont permis de rassembler les données de 95 pays y compris 34 des 35 pays qui avaient déjà participé à l'enquête pour le Répertoire de l'UNESCO. Pour ces derniers pays les listes de crues ont été remises à jour, les crues historiques ont également été indiquées et on a utilisé un nombre important de nouvelles stations de jaugeage généralement pour des rivières présentant des débits spécifiques de crue élevés. L'AISH a écrit à 110 pays. Le questionnaire n'a pas été envoyé à 40 pays parce qu'ils ne pouvaient pas apporter une contribution très utile à ce catalogue pour les raisons suivantes :

a)   Pays couvrant de très petites superficies tels que Monaco ou la Principauté d'Andorre et où la pente et le régime des précipitations sont tels qu'il n'est pas vraisemblable que de fortes crues de caractère exceptionnel puissent s'y produire.

b)   Petites îles dans l'Océan Pacifique, l'Océan Indien et la mer des Caraïbes. Ces petites îles étaient trop nombreuses pour être représentées toutes dans le catalogue. On a dû procéder à une sélection d'après les critères suivants :

     i)   Crues avec débits spécifiques élevés
     ii) Données sur les crues faciles à obtenir

c)   Pays arides sans réseaux hydrométriques ou avec un réseau hydrométrique très récent.

Cependant un grand effort a été fait pour présenter dans le catalogue des données provenant des pays arides ou particulièrement arides (tels que le Sud Ouest des Etats-Unis, les pays autour du Sahara, l'Australie, etc ...).

A la fin de l'enquête six pays seulement qui avaient été compris dans cette enquête et qui présentaient des fleuves relativement importants n'y ont pas répondu. Par conséquent, il paraît possible de dire que le Répertoire Mondial de l'AISH est relativement exhaustif. Le débit de crue maximal observé est donné pour 1400 stations ou points d'observations.

Le tableau I donne pour chacune de ces stations les paramètres intéressants pour la bonne compréhension des phénomènes hydrologiques et en particulier pour la formation des crues.

Les facteurs concernant la genèse des crues de fonte des neiges ont été volontairement négligés car cet aspect de l'hydrologie a été traité de façon précise et exhaustive dans le Répertoire de L'UNESCO. En outre, la plupart des pays particulièrement intéressés par ces problèmes de fonte des neiges ont été bien représentés dans cette publication. Tous les détails concernant le tableau I sont donnés dans la notice explicative.

Le tableau II fournit des informations directes sur la crue maximale et en général sur la seconde et la troisième crue les plus fortes. Pour un bon nombre de ces crues, des renseignements sont fournis sur la méthode utilisée pour l'estimation du débit de crue et sur la précision de cette estimation.

Pour certaines de ces crues observées sur des bassins petits ou relativement petits, on indique également les précipitations qui les ont provoquées.

Pour un bon nombre de pays, les données concernant les crues maximales ont été comparées avec les valeurs déjà citées dans la documentation et souvent il y a eu discussion par correspondance en vue d'éviter de reproduire des valeurs erronées qui pourraient être dues à des erreurs d'impression ou des estimations trop sommaires. Cependant tous les hydrologues savent bien que dans un tel domaine il est impossible d'éliminer la totalité des erreurs de ce genre bien que nous espérons qu'elles soient peu nombreuses. Il y a quelques différences entre les valeurs de débits de certaines crues maximales du présent catalogue et celles qui ont déjà été citées dans la documentation existante (y compris le Répertoire de l'UNESCO) pour les mêmes crues. Ceci correspond à de nouvelles estimations des débits de grandes crues par un certain nombre de pays qui ont contribué à l'enquête.

Pour certains états ou territoires situés loin de la partie principale de leur pays, tel que les îles Hawaï pour les Etats-Unis ou Tahiti pour la France, les débits maximaux de crue ont été présentés à part.

Il a semblé utile de publier également une sélection de longues séries temporelles de valeurs annuelles maximales, mais comme ces séries sont moins importantes pour la solution de problèmes concernant les crues maximales que leurs valeurs maximales elles-mêmes, l'AISH n'a pas reproduit les 180 séries déjà publiées dans le Répertoire de l'UNESCO (Tableaux III); cependant elles ont été mises à jour dans la mesure du possible et parfois complétées. Le présent catalogue présente 105 nouvelles longues séries temporelles concernant les cours d'eau principaux ou des stations présentant une intéressante distribution statistique des débits maximaux annuels.

A la fin de cette publication on trouvera un court commentaire sur les crues maximales observées.

Pour son principal objectif l'étude des valeurs maximales des débits, cette publication se suffit à elle-même puisqu'elle contient toutes les valeurs maximales publiées dans le Répertoire de l'UNESCO.

Pour l'étude des longues séries temporelles et l'analyse des facteurs de la formation des crues de fonte des neiges, il doit être utilisé avec le Répertoire de l'UNESCO. Pour une analyse minutieuse des facteurs de formation des grandes crues, il est recommandé de se référer en outre à la publication de Maurice Pardé (1961) "Sur la puissance des crues en diverses parties du monde - Géographica. Enero-Diciembre 1961 Faculdad de Letras de Zaragoza" qui contient de nombreux détails sur les crues maximales observées dans le monde avant 1961.

Le présent catalogue est le résultat du travail des Comités Nationaux et des correspondants de l'AISH, des Comités Nationaux du PHI de l'UNESCO et d'un bon nombre de Services, d'experts hydrologues, et d'ingénieurs conseils de 95 pays : Afrique du Sud, Albanie, Algérie, Argentine, Australie, Autriche, Bangladesh, Belgique, Bénin, Bolivie, Brésil, Bulgarie, Cameroun, Canada, Chine, Colombie, Congo, Costa-Rica, Côte d'Ivoire, Cuba, Equateur, Egypte, Espagne, Etats-Unis d'Amérique, Finlande, France, Gabon, Ghana, Guatemala, Guinée, Guyane, Haute Volta, Hongrie, Inde, Indonésie, Iran, Irak, irlande, Islande, Israel, Italie, Japon, Jordanie, Kampuchea Démocratique Kenya, Liberia, Madagascar, Malaisie, Malawi, Mali, Maroc, Mauritanie, Mexique, Mozambique, Niger, Nigeria Norvège, Nouvelle Zélande, Ouganda, Pakistan, Panama, Pays-Bas, Philippines, Pologne, Portugal, République Centrafricaine, République de Corée, République Démocratique Allemande, République Démocratique Populaire de Corée, République Dominicaine, République du Cap Vert, République Fédérale d'Allemagne, République Populaire Démocratique Lao, République Socialiste du Vietnam, Roumanie, Royaume Uni de Grande Bretagne et d'Irlande du Nord, Rwanda, Senegal, Sierra Leone, Soudan, Sri-Lanka, Suède, Suisse, Tchad, Tchécoslovaquie, Thaïlande, Togo, Tunisie, Turquie, Union des Républiques Socialistes Soviétiques, Uruguay, Venezuela, Yougoslavie, Zaïre, Zimbabwé.

L'Association remercie tous ceux, qui malgré de lourdes charges, ont bien voulu consacrer une partie de leur temps à la préparation de ce catalogue.

Nous aimerions exprimer notre gratitude aux organismes dont la contribution a été particulièrement importante, tels que le Committee of Coordination and of Investigation of the lower Mekong Basin, le Commonwealth Scientific and Industrial Research Organization Australie, le Department of Environmental Affairs of South Africa, l'Office de la Recherche Scientifique et Technique Outre-Mer, l' United States Geological Survey, l'USSR State Committee for Hydrometeorology and Control of Environment, la Direction Générale des Eaux intérieures du Canada, la Divisao de Controle de Recursos Hidricos/DNAE Brésil, l'Institut d'Hydrologie de Wallingford et dans ce dernier Institut Mrs. R.T. Clarke et M. Beran qui ont corrigé les textes anglais et apporté leur concours à l'édition de cet ouvrage.

Il subsiste certainement quelques erreurs dans ce catalogue. Il est possible que pour les pays représentés certaines crues importantes n'y figurent pas; pour certains grands pays, la contribution à cet ouvrage concernant les bassins petits et relativement petits devrait être beaucoup plus importante; enfin quelques pays comportant de grands fleuves ne sont pas représentés. Pour ces raisons, tous les commentaires et les informations complémentaires seront les bienvenus. Le Secrétaire Général de l'AISH collectera ces matériaux pour une future édition du catalogue dont la préparation commencerait en 1996 ou 1997, un intervalle de vingt ans entre deux éditions paraissant le mieux approprié.

On espère que cette publication sera utile à tous les chercheurs et ingénieurs qui s'intéressent aux problèmes d'aménagement des eaux.

Explanatory note

1. Selection of stations or observation sites

The selection was made by contributing countries on the following basis.

(a) As far as possible each hydrological regime is represented by several stations, at least two or three corresponding to basin areas ranging from 3 km² up to 500.000 km² or more. The maximum floods were observed in regular hydrometric stations or at particular sites for which the a posteriori estimation of flood discharge was not too difficult or where the maximum water level was observed.

(b) Rivers with very large floods in relation to the basin area, such as those with high specific maximum discharges, are also represented. In some cases, certain rivers with noteworthy low specific maximum discharge are represented. In some countries the hydrologists had provided maximum discharges from well-equipped stations with records in which they had confidence, and had omitted to provide data on much larger floods from other stations of which they were less confident. For all such cases, data on floods from the latter stations were sought by correspondence, however poor the records.

Particular effort was made to receive data from small and very small basins. Despite such efforts there does remain in these data a tendency to sample from well gauged basins without examples of very large floods.

For countries with networks that have only recently come into service, all efforts were made to obtain information about all the regimes even where observations are as yet of poor quality.

2. Problems related to the lack of information

Frequently maximum floods are not well determined. Furthermore, in many countries the physical characteristics of a basin (such as slope characteristics, and the extent to which permeability varies spatially) have been insufficiently studied to allow their representation by numerical indices. For very large basins, which often contain a very variable set of physical characteristics, it may be misleading to express these characteristics as a set of four or six percentage values. Likewise a single average precipitation cannot encapsulate the spatial variability of this property over an extensive basin. The vegetation cover may have changed radically since the beginning of observation and for this reason also cannot be indexed by a simple single value. It is therefore not unexpected for some of the data requested for the compilation of tables to be missing.

Some characteristics are noted in numerically or alphabetically coded form. In this case it is agreed that lack of information will be indicated by 0 for numeric code, and X for alphabetic code.

In Table II , the letter U indicates that the precision of the discharge estimation is unknown.

3. <u>Explanation of the content of the tables</u>

3.1 <u>Table I</u>

Identification of observation sites and characteristics of basins.

Column 4: Observation site: generally town, village or confluent of a tributary or mileage along road or railway or bridge, waterfall, hydroelectric plant etc. For columns 3 and 4 some abbreviations are entered, such as Br (=bridge); N.F. (=North Fork); M.F. (=Middle Fork).

OBSERVATION SITE							
Site no	River basin	Stream	Observation site		Co-ordinates Lat. Long.	Period	Area km²
1	2	3	4	5	6	7	8

CHARACTERISTICS OF BASIN					
Slope	Soil	Vegetation	Regime	Mean Rainfall mm	Mean annual discharges m³s-1
9	10	11	12	13	14

Column 1: The site number is the national code number or any arbitrary number corresponding to the place of the site in Table I. For some countries where the first figures of the code number are used to define the country and are therefore the same for the whole country, these first figures may be deleted. For other countries, column 1 includes both code numbers and sequence numbers the latters often defining sites not included in the hydrometric network: representative basins or simply sites where the water level was observed only during the flood.

Column 2: River basin: for streams flowing directly into the sea, some countries presented here the name of a bay or of part of the sea or ocean into which it flowed. For small streams in some countries the name of basin remains blank.

Column 3: Stream: for most of the rivers, the world "river" after or before the name was deleted. For instance, Broad (USA) instead of Broad river. But there are some exceptions : in Algeria, for instance. The name of the river is the local name. For some well-known rivers, however, the English or French name was mentioned in brackets.

Column 5: Nature of the observation site: this is given the following numerical code:

1   Regular gauging station;

2   Limnimetric station only (where water levels are observed regularly but where discharge measurements are not made systematically);

3   Site on the river where no regular observations are made;

4   Representative or experimental basin.

Column 6: Co-ordinates of the observation site, latitude and longitude in degrees and minutes, relative to Greenwich meridian. For some countries the answer to our questionnaire did not include this information; the co-ordinates were then determined from available maps and for this case the figures representing the number of minutes are approximate. The given co-ordinates could then be used to locate the site within the country, but not for finding exactly the site again if, for example, the station had been destroyed or discontinued.

Column 7: Period: when a regular gauging or limnimetric station is concerned, the observation period is indicated here. If there are major interruptions during the opération of the station, the several distinct continous periods are mentioned. For the case where these interruptions are numerous, the total duration of the observation period is given here in years.

Column 8: Basin area in km². For a very small number of stations the value of the area is approximate, for some parts of the Nile and for the Brahmaputra basins, for instance.

For large basins lying partly in an arid zone, only the contributing part is mentioned, since for some very large basins the total basin area then has no physical significance.

Column 9: Slope: the purpose of this column is to give a qualitative idea of the relief with a reference to general slopes, longitudinal and transverse, of the basin. Six types of relief have been distinguished, each being coded by a letter :

A: very flat basins: slopes less than 0.1-0.2%;

B: basins in plain regions: small slopes less than 0.5%;

C: slightly rolling basins : moderate slopes 0.5-1%;

D: basins in hilly terrain: rather steep slopes longitudinal between 1 and 2%, transversal greater than 2%;

E hilly basins: relatively steep slopes: longitudinal 2-5%, transverse 8-20%;

F: basins in mountains: steep slope: longitudinal greater than 5%, transverse greater than 20%;

For complex basins every letter code characterizing the relief of a part of the basin considered as homogeneous is sometimes completed by a number giving the percentage of the total area indicated by this letter. For example, the entry B 10; E 60; F 30 applied to a river basin taken at its mouth, means that basin runoff is supplied by a mountainous area comprising 30% of the total area, extending into a still very hilly active area covering 60% of the surface with a hard slope break to a littoral plain.

It must be emphasized that these relief indices are purely qualitative and have been generally chosen without reference to any morphometric measurements in the field. Values mentioned for slopes are only indicative.

Column 10: Soil: soil permeability characteristics are indicated schematically according to the following alphabetic code:

A: karst (fully permeable);

B: very permeable (on a small scale);

C: of average permeability;

D: impermeable or only slightly permeable;

The letters are sometimes followed by an entry showing the approximate percentage of area associated with the letter code. For example, the entry A 25; C 30; D 45 means that 25% of the basin area is karstic; 30% is of average permeability, and 45% is impermeable. For large and very large basins this information is often missing.

Column 11: Vegetation: the vegetal cover is mentioned according to the following alphabetic code:

A: thick forest;

B: sparse forest, wooded savannah;

C: meadows, savannah with few trees or without trees, tundra;

D: cultivated land;

E: bare soil, urban zones.

The percentage of the catchment area covered by various types of vegetation is indicated as in column 10. However, this parameter is dependent upon human influence and in some parts of the world the vegetation cover for large floods occuring one century ago was not the same as the present vegetation cover. For this reason some countries did not supply information for this column.

For the case where lakes or reservoirs have a very significant influence on the maximum flood discharge, foot-notes are generally printed in Table I, sometimes in Table II.

Column 12: Regime: this shows the mean climatic conditions of the basin. The numerical code proposed by R. Hadley, following a request by UNESCO, has been used. This macro-classification, although being established for representative and experimental basins is also suitable for a world catalogue of maximum floods. However, when using the classification several difficulties arose; for example, the entry "long wet season " or "short summer" may demonstrate some element of subjectivity. For this reason the information given by some countries was corrected using the world map published by Hadley. Codes used were as follows:-

00	Humid tropical
10	Savannah with long wet season or two wet seasons
11	Savannah with short wet season
20	Desert
30	Dry subtropical (Mediterranean)
40	Wet subtropical
50	Marine west coast (temperate)
60	Humid continental, long summer
61	Humid continental, short summer
70	Dry continental steppe (semi arid, precipitation > 250 mm)
71	Dry continental arid (precipitation < 250 mm)
80	Subarctic
81	Polar, tundra
82	Polar, icecap
90	Mountainous areas (individual basins should be related to the altitudinal zones)

Column 13: Mean annual precipitation: the sole purpose of this characteristic is to classify the basin from the point of view of rainfall. Estimation of the value entered here did not therefore require detailed study since a precise value was not necessary. For example, if the basin is located in a humid tropical climate it was important from the point of view of extreme floods to know if the mean annual rainfall in this basin is between 1500 and 2000 mm or between 3000 and 4000 mm. For very large basins this parameter may be so spatially variable in that the mean value is meaningless.
Here again, the more homogeneous the area is with regard to rainfall the more useful the information will be. For some basins where precipitation was spatially variable, two figures were mentioned in column 13, the highest and the lowest values of precipitation depth.

Column 14: Mean annual flow: this parameter is entered principally for regular gauging stations. Only an estimate is necessary; it is for this reason that the infor-mation is given even if short discharge records are available. A rough estimate of the annual flow is presented in brackets, but as for column 13, many of the figures are accurate since long time series of precipitation and discharge are available that are of good quality.

3.2 Table II: Floods' characteristics

3.2.1. Generalities

For floods (historic or recent) which have been recons-tituted by various means at sites without continuous observations, only the largest or the two largest floods have been selected. This was also the case for experi-mental and representative basins because of the short observation period. For floods observed at regular stations, the three largest floods have generally been entered.

If the record period is short or if it is clear that the annual maximum discharges that were provided do not correspond to very low frequency, only one or two floods were entered. On the other hand, if the record period is very long, four or five floods were often selected. If several stations of the catalogue are on the same stream or in the same region with very different period lengths, up to five or six floods have been selected for the oldest station so that rank orders for the recent large floods can be compared between stations.

In cases where two maxima would normally be adequate but where these were poorly estimated, we include further lower ranking maxima down to the range where flow estimation is reliable.

As far as possible, effort was made to obtain the dis-charge of historical floods. For very rare cases, less than ten stations, some historical flood values were taken from the literature (generally the review by M. Pardé).

3.2.2   Description of Table II

FLOOD CHARACTERISTICS						
Site number	Stream	Observation Site	Year	Date of the maximum	Maximum discharge	Origin
1	2	3	4	5	6	7

DISCHARGE ESTIMATION			PRECIPITATION		
Condition of discharge estimation	Quality of the section	Precision $\pm m^3 s^{-1}$	Antecedent Precipitation	Precipitation Depth mm	duration days
8	9	10	11	12	13

Column 1: See Table I, column 1.

Column 2: See Table I, column 3. This column and the next one were introduced in order to have them at hand for immediate reference when reading the information concerning the floods themselves.

Column 3: See Table I, column 4. The name of the station is sometimes abbreviated.

Column 4: Year: Calendar year during which the flood took place. If the calendar year is very different to the hydrological year it is possible to encounter two entries in the same calendar year.

Column 5: Month and day of the calendar year on which the maximum discharge occurred. If only one number is entered it corresponds to the month. Sometimes the day and the month are unknown.

Column 6: Value of maximum discharge in $m^3 s^{-1}$. For most cases it is the instantaneous value. For many large basins the mean daily value or the value estimated for a given time of the day is not significantly different from the maximum value, the difference being less than the precision range (Column 10). In some cases column 8 shows whether or not the maximum is the instantaneous value.

Column 7: Climatic origin of each flood: this is indicated by the following code:

1:   rainfall flood

2:   snowmelt flood

3:   flood from glacier melting (with eventual snowmelt)

4:   rainfall flood with snowmelt and/or glacier melting

5:   flood resulting from glacier burst (Iceland)

As far as possible the floods resulting from dam failure, natural or artificial, were eliminated; however, flood discharges having some influence of dam failure upstream are sometimes included, where this failure is not the main cause of the high discharge.

Column 8: Condition of discharge estimation: the appraisal of this characteristic is often extremely delicate and many countries did not give any information on this point. They entail four factors, each represented by a sub-column. Each factor has been coded alternately by alphabetic and numeric codes in order to make clearer the overall information given in column 8.

1st sub-column: Origin of information on water levels (alphabetic code).

A: from a regularly observed station

B: from a survey following a relatively recent flood (with subsequent interrogation of witnesses)

C: historical inquiry involving direct witness

D: historical inquiry carried out through a study of the archives

2nd sub-column: <u>Nature</u> of information on water levels and their variations during the flood (numeric code).

1: data from level recorder, or manual observations providing complete information of the whole flood, especially the maximum level

2: incomplete data (through mechanical failure) or regular observation, but with too large a time interval to provide a complete graph of the flood; but giving, nevertheless, sufficient information to define the maximum level

3: data gathered as in 2 but at a fixed time not permitting definition of the maximum level

4: neither staff gauge nor level recorder was used but an accurate topographic survey of maximum level was made a posteriori

5: approximate estimation of maximum level was made a posteriori

3rd sub-column: <u>Method</u> for estimating maximum discharge.

A: direct measurement of maximum discharge

B: estimation derived from a rating curve without extrapolation or with slight extrapolation

C: estimation derived from a rating curve with much extrapolation

D: estimation by hydraulic runoff formula

E: estimation by level variations in a reservoir

4th sub-column: measurement or computation processes.

1: complete discharge measurement (by tracer or by current meter)

2: surface velocity measurement by current meter

3: surface velocity measurement by floats

4: computation by hydraulic runoff formula for rivers (the "Manning" type) the slope being measured at maximum water line of the flood or at a clear flood mark line observed a posteriori

5: same computation as in 4, but the slope is estimated from the bottom of the river or from low or mean water line

6: computation by hydraulic formula from observed hydraulic discontinuity (eg. rise in level above a bridge, threshold discharge etc ...)

Example 1 : Code A1B1 means that the flood levels have been observed in their entirety, in a regular station where rating curves extend almost to the maximum and which are established from complete discharge measurement (by current meter or tracer). It is obvious that if, in addition, the section benefits from good characteristics (see column 9), flood characteristics mentioned in the catalogue are very likely to be quite reliable.

Example 2: Code D0X0 indicates that the maximum discharge for the flood was found in the archives and that no indication of the way in which it was established is available. In some place instead of D0X0 it is mentioned U (Unknown).

Column 9: Quality of the section; indicated by an alphanumeric code of 3 sub-columns:

1st sub-column: stability of bed (as far as floods are concerned), alphabetic:

A: non shifting bed

B: slightly shifting bed giving an error between 5 and 15% on the rating curve for the discharge corresponding to the middle of the interval

C: noticeably shifting bed (15% < error < 40%)

D: strongly shifting bed (error > 40%)

for the cases where such information was not available the choice of the code letter was more subjective.

2nd sub-column: Level discharge relationships (numeric code).

1: single-branched or so considered

2: multi-valued or loop rating

3rd sub-column: hydraulic behaviour of measurement or computation reach, according to estimation process (alphabetic code).

A: good

B: average

C: poor

If one of these characteristics is unknown, code 0 is indicated in 2nd sub-column and code X in the first and 3rd sub-columns.

Column 10: Precision: this information mostly has only

qualificative value. Precision is given by a confidence interval. Some countries provided information according to the following rule:

Very precise estimation of flood:	5%
Fair estimation:	10%
Rough estimation:	20%

The hydrologists for most of the stations adopted a symmetrical precision interval for instance for a maximal flood of 1550 m^3s^{-1} ±150 (interval 1400-1700 m^3s^{-1}).

For some stations the precision interval is assymetric: for instance; $^{+200}_{-100}$ for the same flood (interval 1450-1750 m^3s^{-1}).

Some countries mentioned often very precise values; this is normal for large or rather large rivers with moderate water speed and regular and stable bed, generally in humid or relatively humid countries. But for some rivers and some countries underestimation of the error is not to be excluded.

On the other hand, it appears that other countries were sometimes pessimistic. It is unfortunately impossible to give a definitive opinion for any particular case without a perfect knowledge of the station and of the quality of the computations. It is necessary to stress here that for the highest flood discharges long discussions generally took place in the service producing the data and between the different services of the countries; this eliminated error of the order of magnitude of 50% for instance. For some of the recent largest floods it was possible to obtain more detail on the estimation process than what is included in Table II (such as for the Amazon maximum flood or for Ouaieme river, for instance).

Column 11: Antecedent precipitation: the object of this column is to indicate wether the flood was generated by an isolated rainfall or occurred after a period of abundant precipitation.

The following code was used:

1: non existent or very slight previous precipitation

2: moderate previous precipitation

3: abundant previous precipitation

these comments were interpreted in the context of the pluviometrical climate of the region. For Mauritania a daily antecedent precipitation of 10 mm is important,

whilst such precipitation is without interest for forested area of Northern Brazil.

Information contained in columns 11, 12, 13 have little significance for most of the large basins.

Column 12: Depth of precipitation: this depth corresponds to the rainy period which actually contributed to flood generation. Generally this information is given for one or several raingauges in or near the basin. For some representative basins and for very few stations it was possible to obtain the spatial mean value.

Column 13: Duration of precipitation: this is given in days or for a fractionnal part of day.

3.3 Table III: Series of yearly maxima

3.3.1 Generalities

This part of the catalogue gives some long time series characteristics of most of the regimes and for the main rivers. Some attempt has been made to present many distributions with large coefficients of variation and of skewness. The information received for this Table III varies broadly from one country to another; some countries gave information for all stations presented in Tables I and II, whilst others presented only a selection. It would be costly to present all annual maximum series received, and a selection was necessary on the basis presented above. Furthermore, since 180 long time series were presented in the UNESCO world catalogue, they are not reproduced here but cross-references are shown except for two countries for which the maximum discharges were revised after the preparation of the UNESCO catalogue.

Where appropriate information had been received by IAHS, the UNESCO long time series were updated in two ways.

(i) only the large floods after 1970 or 1971 were mentioned

(ii) all the yearly maximum after 1970 or 1971 were mentioned

For the case where in the UNESCO catalogue some yearly maximum from long past were missing, they have been mentioned in this catalogue together with their more recent ones. In total 105 new long time series of yearly maxima are presented here.

3.3.2   Description of Table III; series of yearly
         maxima

Table III recapitulates the series of annual maximum
discharges recorded at selected stations. Values derived
from regular observations or reconstituted by various
ways for a relatively recent period will be preceded by
the values of eventual historical floods.

Column 1: Year: in almost all cases the calendar year is
quoted. For almost all cases there is one maximum value
for each year; exceptionally if two very large floods
occur in the same year, both may be mentioned. For
the case where the hydrological year is very different
to the calendar year, there is one maximum for each
hydrological year but a given calendar year may occa-
sionally include two maximum yearly values, as in the
case of Australia.

Column 2: Date in months and days: often the day is
missing, and only the month is quoted.

Column 3: Observations: various comments have been
presented codified in 2 sub-columns:

1st sub-column (alphabetic code):

A: Flood directly observed at a regular station,
    maximum observed

B: Regular station but maximum reconstituted,
    not directly observed

C: Recent maximum flood estimated a posteriori
    (even for a regular station)

D: Recent historical flood

E: Old historical flood

X: Unknown origin of information

2nd sub-column (numeric code):

1: Very reliable value (good rating curve, slight
    extrapolation or direct measurement)

2: Correct estimation but not very precise
    (rating curve relatively poor, appreciable
    extrapolation, water level reconstituted in
    good conditions, estimation on the basis of
    formulae in good or acceptable conditions)

3: rough estimation.

Notice explicative

1. Choix des stations ou du point d'observations:

La sélection des stations a été faite par les pays qui ont contribué à l'établissement de ce catalogue, sur les bases suivantes :

a) Autant que possible chaque régime hydrologique est représenté par plusieurs stations, au moins deux ou trois, contrôlant des bassins de superficies différentes variant de 3 km² à 500.000 km² ou plus. Les crues maximales ont été observées à des stations hydrométriques régulières ou à des sites particuliers pour lesquels l'estimation à posteriori du débit de crue n'était pas trop difficile ou qui ont été l'objet d'observations du niveau maximum de l'eau.

b) On a également représenté des rivières sujettes à de très fortes crues par rapport à la surface de leur bassin. Dans certains cas des rivières présentant des débits spécifiques maximaux remarquablement faibles ont été également sélectionnées. Dans certains pays, les hydrologues avaient donné les débits maximaux pour des stations bien observées avec un excellent équipement sans mentionner les débits maximaux d'autres stations qui avaient subi des crues beaucoup plus violentes mais, pour lesquelles les estimations de débits étaient beaucoup plus mauvaises. Dans tous ces cas on a essayé d'obtenir par correspondance des valeurs pour les estimations relatives à cette dernière catégorie de stations même si la qualité de ces données laissait à désirer.

Ceci est vrai surtout pour les bassins, petits ou relativement petits. Mais malgré les modifications apportées ainsi à la sélection initiale de certains pays, il subsiste dans la liste définitive des stations choisies une certaine influence du choix initial, de très bonnes stations sans crues vraiment fortes.

Pour les pays dont le réseau d'observations est récent, on s'est efforcé d'obtenir des informations sur tous les régimes, même dans le cas où les informations étaient de médiocre qualité.

2. Problèmes liés au manque d'informations:

Il est fréquent que les crues maximales soient assez mal connues. En outre dans beaucoup de pays les caractéristiques physiques des bassins (telles que la perméabilité des différentes parties de ce bassin, les pentes longitudinales et transversales) n'ont pas été suffisamment étudiées pour permettre leur représentation par des index numériques.
Pour de très grands bassins qui souvent présentent une série très variable de caractéristiques physiques, il pourrait être dangereux de représenter ces caractéristiques par un ensemble de 5 ou 6 valeurs d'index suivies d'un pourcentage.

De même, on ne peut pas non plus représenter la variabilité spatiale des précipitations sur un bassin étendu par une simple moyenne pluviométrique. Le couvert végétal peut avoir changé radicalement depuis le début des observations et pour cette raison ne peut pas être représenté par un index avec simplement une seule valeur. On doit s'attendre donc à ce que certaines des données requises pour l'établissement des tableaux n'y figurent pas.

Certaines indications sont portées sous forme codée, numérique ou alphabétique. On conviendra que dans ce cas le manque d'information se traduira par 0 pour le code numérique et X pour le code alphabétique.

Dans le tableau II, la lettre U indique que la précision avec laquelle le débit a été estimé est inconnue.

3. Explications du contenu des tableaux:

3.1 Tableau I

Identification des points d'observations et caractéristiques des bassins:

certaines rivières bien connues, cependant, le nom en anglais ou en français est indiqué entre parenthèses.

Colonne 4: Point d'observations: C'est généralement une ville, un village, le confluent d'un tributaire, le nombre de km le long d'une route ou d'un chemin de fer, un

POINT D'OBSERVATIONS							
N° du point	Bassin Fluvial	Rivière	Point d'observations	Coordonnées Lat. Long.	Période	Superficie km²	
1	2	3	4	5	6	7	8

CARACTERISTIQUES DU BASSIN					
Pente	Sol	Végétation	Régime	Pluie moyenne mm	Module m³s-1
9	10	11	12	13	14

Colonne 1: Le numéro du point d'observations est le numéro du code national ou tout nombre arbitraire correspondant au rang de ce point dans le tableau I. Pour certains pays où les premiers chiffres du numéro de code sont utilisés pour définir le pays et par suite, sont les mêmes pour tout le pays, ces premiers chiffres sont parfois supprimés. Pour d'autres pays, la colonne I comporte à la fois, des numéros de code et des séries de nombres arbitraires, les derniers correspondant souvent à des sites qui ne font pas partie du réseau hydrométrique: bassins représentatifs ou sites auxquels la hauteur d'eau n'a été observée que pendant la crue.

Colonne 2: Bassin fluvial: pour des cours d'eau se jetant directement dans la mer, certains pays ont indiqué ici le nom d'une baie ou d'une partie de la mer ou de l'océan dans laquelle débouchait cette rivière ou ce fleuve. Pour les petits cours d'eau de certains pays, le nom du bassin fluvial est resté en blanc.

Colonne 3: Rivière: pour la plupart des cours d'eau, le mot rivière situé avant ou après le nom a été supprimé. Par exemple: Broad (USA) au lieu de Broad River. Mais il y a des exceptions: en Algérie par exemple. Le nom de la rivière est généralement le nom local, pour

pont, une chûte d'eau, une centrale hydroélectrique, etc ... Pour les colonnes 3 et 4 on a introduit certaines abréviations telle que Br. ou Pt. (pont), N.F. (branche nord), M.F. (branche moyenne).

Colonne 5: Nature du point d'observations: elle est indiquée par le code numérique suivant:

1   Station de jaugeage régulière

2   Station purement limnimétrique (où les hauteurs d'eau sont observées régulièrement mais où les mesures de débit ne sont pas faites systématiquement)

3   Sites sur la rivière sans observations régulières

4   Bassin représentatif ou expérimental

Colonne 6: Coordonnées du point d'observations: latitude et longitude en degrés et minutes par rapport au méridien de Greenwich. Pour certains pays la réponse à notre questionnaire ne comportait pas cette indication; les coordonnées ont été alors déterminées à partir des cartes disponibles et dans ce cas, les chiffres représentant le nombre de minutes sont approximatifs. Les coordonnées indiquées ainsi dans le tableau I peuvent être utilisées pour localiser le site dans le pays mais non pour retrouver exactement le site sur le terrain si, par exemple, la station a été détruite ou abandonnée.

Colonne 7: Période: lorsqu'il s'agit d'une station de jaugeage ou limnimétrique on indique dans cette colonne la période des observations. S'il y a eu des interruptions importantes en cours de fonctionnement, on mentionne ici les différentes périodes continues. Dans le cas où ces interruptions ont été nombreuses, la durée totale des observations est donnée en années.

Colonne 8: Surface du bassin versant en km²: pour un très petit nombre de stations la valeur de la surface est approximative, pour certaines parties du bassin du Nil ou du Brahmapoutre par exemple. Pour de grands bassins dont une partie est située en zone aride, on mentionne seulement la partie du bassin qui contribue à l'écoulement puisque pour certains très grands bassins, la superficie totale n'a pas de signification physique.

Colonne 9: Pente: il s'agit dans cette colonne de donner une idée qualitative du relief en se référant pour fixer les idées aux pentes générales, longitudinales et transversales du bassin. On a distingué six types de relief, représentés chacun par une lettre:

A: bassins très plats : pentes inférieures à 0.1-0.2%

B: bassins de plaine: pentes faibles, inférieures à 0.5%

C: bassins faiblement ondulés: pentes modérées de 0.5 à 1%

D: bassins à ondulations de terrains: pentes assez fortes, pentes longitudinales comprises entre 1 et 2%, pentes transversales supérieures à 2%

E: bassins de collines: pentes fortes: longitudinales entre 2 et 5%, transversales entre 8 et 20%

F: bassins de montagnes: pentes très fortes: longitudinales supérieures à 5%, transversales supérieures à 20%

Pour les bassins complexes chaque lettre de code caractérisant le relief d'une partie du bassin considérée comme homogène est quelquefois suivie par un nombre donnant le pourcentage de la superficie totale représenté par cette lettre. Par exemple, l'indication B 10, E 60, F 30, appliquée à un bassin fluvial considéré à son embouchure signifie qu'il s'agit d'un bassin alimenté

par une zone de montagnes occupant 30% de sa superficie prolongée par un bassin de collines encore très actif couvrant 60% de la surface et débouchant, avec une forte rupture de pente, sur une plaine littorale.

On doit insister sur le fait que ces indices de relief sont purement qualitatifs et ont été généralement choisis sans procéder à aucune mesure morphométrique sur le terrain. Les valeurs de pentes mentionnées dans les définitions de ces indices sont seulement indicatives.

Colonne 10: Sol: les caractères de perméabilité du sol sont indiqués schématiquement au moyen du code alphabétique suivant:

A: karst (perméable en grand)

B: très perméable (en petit)

C: perméabilité moyenne

D: très peu perméable ou imperméable

Ces lettres sont quelquefois suivies par un nombre donnant le pourcentage au moins approximatif de la surface du bassin concerné par la perméabilité ainsi codée. Par exemple, l'indication A 25, C 30, D 45, signifie que 25% du bassin sont occupés par des formations karstiques, 30% par un sol de perméabilité moyenne et 45% sont imperméables. Pour de grands et de très grands bassins, il est fréquent que cette information manque.

Colonne 11: Végétation: le couvert végétal est précisé d'après le code alphabétique suivant :

A: forêt dense

B: forêt clairsemée, savane boisée

C: prairie, savane non ou peu boisée, toundra

D: cultures

E: sol nu, zones urbaines

Les pourcentages du bassin occupés par les différentes couvertures végétales sont indiqués de la la même façon que dans la colonne 10. Cependant, ce paramètre est sous l'influence de l'homme et dans certaines parties du monde, le couvert végétal, pour de très fortes crues qui se sont produites il y a 100 ans, n'était pas le même que la couverture végétale actuelle. C'est pour cette raison que certains pays n'ont pas fourni de renseignements pour cette colonne. Pour le cas où des lacs ou des réservoirs ont une influence très significative sur la crue maximale, des notes ont généralement été présentées dans le tableau I ou le tableau II.

Colonne 12: Régime: il s'agit du régime climatique moyen du bassin. On a employé le code numérique proposé par R. Hadley suivant une demande faite par l'UNESCO. Cette macro-classification bien qu'établie pour le classement en zones naturelles des bassins représentatifs et expérimentaux convient également pour un catalogue mondial des crues maximales. Cependant, à l'usage, quelques difficultés sont apparues: par exemple l'indication "longue saison des pluies" ou "Eté court" peut présenter un caractère quelque peu subjectif. Pour cette raison, les informations données par certains pays ont été modifiées à partir de la carte mondiale publiée par Hadley. Les numéros de codes sont les suivants:

- 00   tropical humide
- 10   savane avec saison des pluies de longue durée ou deux saisons des pluies.
- 11   savane avec saison des pluies de courte durée
- 20   désert
- 30   méditerranéen, subtropical sec
- 40   subtropical humide
- 50   climat tempéré marin des côtes Ouest
- 60   continental humide avec Eté de longue durée
- 61   continental humide avec Eté de courte durée
- 70   steppe continentale sèche (semi-aride, précipitations > 250 mm)
- 71   continental sec aride (précipitations < 250mm)
- 80   subarctique
- 81   climat polaire, toundra
- 82   climat polaire, calottes de glace
- 90   climats de montagne

Colonne 13: Précipitation moyenne annuelle: la valeur portée dans cette colonne est destinée uniquement à situer le bassin sur le plan de la pluviosité. L'estimation de cette valeur n'a pas en général nécessité une étude détaillée puisqu'un chiffre précis n'était pas nécessaire. Par exemple, pour un bassin situé en climat tropical humide, il est important du point de vue des crues extrêmes de savoir s'il est situé dans une bande 1500-2000 mm ou dans une bande 3000-4000 mm. Pour de très grands bassins, la variabilité spatiale de ce paramètre peut être telle que sa valeur moyenne n'a pas de signification. Là encore les indications sont d'autant plus intéressantes que le bassin est plus homogène du point de vue pluviométrique. Pour certains bassins présentant une certaine variabilité spatiale, deux chiffres ont été donnés dans la colonne 13, la valeur la plus élevée et la plus basse de la hauteur de précipitation moyenne annuelle.

Colonne 14: Module hydrométrique: c'est le débit moyen interannuel. Cette indication concerne surtout les stations de jaugeage régulières. Une simple estimation était nécessaire, c'est pour cette raison que cette information est donnée même si une courte série de relevés de débit est disponible. S'il s'agit d'une estimation grossière, elle est donnée entre parenthèses. Mais comme pour la colonne 13, un bon nombre de ces chiffres sont précis puisque de longues séries de débits et de précipitations, de bonne qualité, sont assez souvent disponibles.

3.2   Tableau II: Caractéristiques des crues

3.2.1.   Remarques générales

Pour les crues (historiques ou récentes) qui ont été reconstituées par divers moyens à des sites pour lesquels il n'y a pas d'observations continues, on a choisi seulement la plus forte ou les deux plus fortes crues. Cela a été aussi le cas pour les bassins représentatifs et expérimentaux en raison de la brièveté de la période d'observations. Pour des crues observées aux stations régulières, on a généralement indiqué les trois crues les plus fortes.

Si la période des relevés est courte et s'il est clair que les débits annuels maximaux qui ont été fournis par les pays ne correspondent pas à de très faibles fréquences, seules une ou deux crues ont été citées. Si au contraire la période d'observations est très longue, on a souvent choisi quatre ou cinq crues. Si plusieurs stations du répertoire sont sur la même rivière, ou dans la même région, avec des périodes d'observations très différentes, on a sélectionné jusqu'à cinq ou six crues pour la station la plus ancienne afin qu'on puisse comparer d'une station à une autre les rangs qu'occupent les grandes crues récentes.

Dans le cas où deux valeurs maximales seraient suffisantes, mais lorsque leur estimation est vraiment médiocre, nous avons introduit dans le tableau d'autres valeurs moins rares jusqu'à ce que l'on arrive à des débits de crues dont l'estimation soit acceptable.

Autant que possible on s'est efforcé d'obtenir les débits de crues historiques. Dans de très rares cas, pour moins de dix stations, les valeurs maximales ont été prises dans la documentation (généralement dans le répertoire des crues de M. Pardé).

3.2.2   Description du tableau II

Colonne 7: Origine climatique de chaque crue: elle est

		CARACTERISTIQUES DE LA CRUE				
Numéro du point	Rivière	Point d'observations	Année	Date du Maximum	Débit Maximal	Origine
1	2	3	4	5	6	7

EVALUATION DU DEBIT			PRECIPITATIONS			
Base et mode d'évaluation	Qualité de la section	Précision ± m³s-1	Antécédents		Hauteur mm	Durée Jours
8	9	10	11		12	13

Colonne 1: Voir tableau I, colonne 1.

Colonne 2: Voir tableau I, colonne 3: cette colonne et la suivante ont été placées dans ce tableau en vue de les avoir sous les yeux losqu'on lit la valeur du débit maximal lui-même.

Colonne 3: Voir tableau I, colonne 4: le nom de la station est quelquefois indiqué par une abréviation.

Colonne 4: Année: année calendaire pendant laquelle la crue a été observée. Si cette année calendaire est très différente de l'année hydrologique, il est possible de trouver dans cette colonne deux crues pour la même année calendaire.

Colonne 5: Mois et jour de l'année calendaire où a été observé le débit maximal. S'il n'y a qu'un nombre, il correspond au mois. Parfois le jour et le mois sont inconnus, ou n'ont pas été indiqués par les pays.

Colonne 6: Valeur du débit maximal en m³s-1: pour la plupart des cas c'est la valeur instantanée. Pour un bon nombre de grands bassins, la valeur journalière moyenne ou la valeur estimée pour un moment donné de la journée ne diffèrent pas de façon significative de la valeur maximale instantanée, la différence étant inférieure à la marge de précision (colonne 10). Dans certains cas, la colonne 8 indique si la valeur maximale que l'on donne est ou non la valeur instantanée.

indiquée par le code numérique suivant:

1:   crue pluviale

2:   crue de fonte des neiges

3:   crue glaciaire (avec éventuellement fonte des neiges)

4:   crue pluviale avec fonte de neige et/ou fonte glaciaire

5:   crue résultant de la rupture d'une poche glaciaire (Islande)

Autant que possible les crues provenant de la rupture d'un barrage, naturel ou artificiel, ont été éliminées; cependant certains débits de crues ayant provoqué à l'amont des ruptures de barrage ont été quelquefois pris en compte lorsque cette rupture n'était pas la cause principale de la valeur élevée du débit.

Colonne 8: Base et mode d'évaluation des débits: ce sont souvent des éléments très délicats à apprécier et un bon nombre de pays n'ont pas donné d'information sur ce point. Ils comportent quatre facteurs représentés chacun par une sous-colonne, chaque facteur a été codé alternativement en code alphabétique et numérique pour rendre plus claire l'expression globale donnée dans la colonne 8.

1ère sous-colonne: Origine de la connaissance des hauteurs d'eau de la rivière (code alphabétique)

A: A partir d'une station régulèrement observée

B: A partir d'un contrôle consécutif à une crue relativement récente (en utilisant éventuellement des témoins)

C: Enquête historique par témoignage direct

D: Enquête historique sur archives

2ème sous-colonne: Nature de la connaissance des hauteur et de leurs variations pendant la crue (code numérique)

1:   Relevé limnigraphique ou relevé limnimétrique manuel permettant une connaissance de la totalité de la crue, notamment du maximum.

2:   Relevé limnigraphique incomplet (panne d'appareil) ou limnimétrique régulier mais à heure fixe, ne donnant pas tout le diagramme de la crue mais ayant fonctionné ou étant exécuté de telle manière qu'on puisse garantir le maximum.

3:   Relevé limnigraphique incomplet ou limnimétrique régulier mais à heure fixe ne permettant pas de garantir le maximum.

4:   Ni limnimètre, ni limnigraphe mais relevé topo graphique précis, à posteriori, du maximum.

5:   Estimation approximative à postériori du niveau maximum.

3ème sous-colonne: Méthode d'estimation du débit maximal (code alphabétique)

A: Mesure directe du débit maximum

B: Evaluation d'après une courbe d'étalonnage sans extrapolation ou avec une faible extrapolation

C: Evaluation d'après une courbe d'étalonnage avec forte extrapolation

D: Calcul par une formule hydraulique d'écoulement

E: Estimation par les variations de niveau d'un réservoir

4ème sous-colonne: Procédés de mesure ou de calcul (code numérique)

1:   Jaugeage complet (par traceur ou par exploration du champ des vitesses)

2:   Jaugeage de surface par moulinet

3:   Mesures de vitesse de surface par flotteurs

4:   Calcul par une formule d'écoulement en rivière (type Manning) avec mesure de la pente sur la ligne d'eau au maximum ou à posteriori sur des délaissés de crues nets

5:   Mêmes calculs que 4, mais mesure de la pente sur le fond de la rivière ou sur une ligne d'eau de basses ou moyennes eaux

6:   Calculs par formule d'écoulement sur accident hydraulique (remous de pont, seuil déversant etc...)

Exemple 1 : Le code A1B1 signifie que la crue a été complètement observée en hauteurs, dans une station régulère pour laquelle on dispose d'une courbe d'étalonnage allant pratiquement jusqu'au maximum, établie à partir de jaugeages complets, soit au moulinet, soit par traceur. Il est évident que si de plus la station présente de bonnes conditions (voir colonne 9) les caractéristiques de la crue mentionnée dans le catalogue auront de fortes chances de présenter une bonne garantie.

Exemple 2 : Le code DOXO indique que le débit maximal de la crue a été trouvé dans les archives sans qu'on ait aucune idée de la façon dont il a été établi. Pour certains pays, au lieu de DOXO, on a indiqué U (inconnu).

Colonne 9: Qualité de la section:

1ère sous-colonne: critère de stabilité (uniquement pour les hautes eaux) (code alphabétique)

A: Lit stable

B: Légère instabilité entrainant une erreur en débit comprise entre 5 et 15% sur la courbe d'étalonnage par rapport au débit correspondant au milieu de la fourchette

C: Instabilité notable (15% < erreur < 40%)

D: Forte instabilité (erreur > 40%)

Si on ne dispose pas de telles informations, on pourra évaluer ce critère de façon plus subjective.

2ème sous-colonne: relation hauteur-débit (code numérique)

1:   Univoque ou pouvant être considérée comme telle

2:   Non univoque

3ème sous-colonne: qualités hydrauliques du bief de mesure ou de calcul (code alphabétique)

A   Bonnes

B: Moyennes

C: Mauvaises

Si un de ces éléments n'est pas connu, on l'indiquera par le code 0 pour la 2ème sous-colonne et par le code X pour la 1ère et la 3ème sous-colonne.

Colonne 10: Précision: Cette information n'a, la plupart du temps, qu'une valeur indicative. La précision est indiquée par un intervalle de confiance. Certains pays ont fourni cette information à partir de la règle suivante:

Estimation très précise du débit de crue: 5%
Assez bonne estimation: 10%
Estimation grossière: 20%

Pour la plupart des stations, les hydrologues ont adopté une fourchette de précision symétrique: par exemple pour une crue maximale de 1550 m³s-1 ± 150 (fourchette 1400-1700 m³s-1).

Pour certaines stations la fourchette de précision est dissymétrique: par exemple $^{+200}_{-100}$ pour le même débit de crue (fourchette 1450-1750 m³s-1).

Certains pays ont indiqué des valeurs très précises: c'est normal pour de grands fleuves ou d'assez grands fleuves avec des vitesses modérées et un lit régulier et stable, généralement dans des régions humides ou relativement humides. Mais pour certaines rivières et certains pays, une sous-estimation des erreurs n'est pas à exclure. Il semble que d'autres pays se soient montrés au contraire quelquefois pessimistes. Il est malheureusement impossible d'émettre une opinion définitive pour un cas particulier donné sans avoir une parfaite connaissance de la station et de la valeur des calculs. On doit insister ici sur le fait que, pour les débits très élevés de crues, ces estimations ont donné lieu généralement à de longues discussions dans les services ayant fourni ces données et entre plusieurs services du pays intéressé; ceci élimine des erreurs de l'ordre de 50% par exemple. Pour certaines crues récentes, il a été possible d'obtenir plus de détails que n'en contient le tableau II sur le développement des calculs (pour la crue maximale de l'Amazone ou celle de la Ouaïeme par exemple).

Colonne 11: Pluies-antécédents: Il s'agit dans cette colonne, d'indiquer si la crue est engendrée par un épisode pluvieux isolé ou survenant après une période de précipitations abondantes. On a utilisé le code suivant :

1:   Antécédents faibles ou inexistants
2:   Antécédents modérés
3:   Antécédents abondants

Ces indications s'entendent suivant le climat pluviométrique de la région. Pour la Mauritanie, une précipitation antérieure de 10 mm est importante, alors qu'une telle averse est sans intérêt pour la région forestière au Nord du Brésil.

Les informations dans les colonnes 11, 12, 13 ont peu de signification pour la plupart des grands bassins.

Colonne 12: Hauteur de précipitations en mm: Cette hauteur correspond à la période pluvieuse qui a effectivement contribué à la genèse de la crue. Généralement cette information est donnée pour un ou plusieurs pluviomètres situés dans le bassin ou à proximité. Pour certains bassins représentatifs et pour un très petit nombre de stations, il a été possible d'obtenir la moyenne spatiale de la hauteur.

Colonne 13: Durée de précipitations: Celle-ci est donnée en jours ou en fractions de jours.

3.3 Tableau III: Séries de débits maximaux annuels

3.3.1 Généralités

Cette partie du répertoire donne quelques longues séries temporelles caractéristiques de la plupart des régimes et pour les principaux fleuves. On s'est efforcé de présenter un bon nombre de distributions avec des coefficients de variation et d'asymétrie élevés.

L'information reçue pour établir ces tableaux III varie largement d'un pays à un autre; certains pays ont envoyé des séries complètes pour toutes les stations représentées dans les tableaux I et II alors que d'autres ont fourni seulement une sélection. Il aurait été très coûteux et cela aurait alourdi considérablement le présent ouvrage de présenter toutes les séries de valeur maximale annuelle, et une sélection a été nécessaire sur les bases données plus haut. En outre, puisque 180 longues séries temporelles avaient déjà été présentées dans le catalogue mondial de l'UNESCO, elles n'ont pas été reproduites ici mais on donne des références pour les retrouver, sauf pour deux pays pour lesquels les valeurs maximales des débits ont été revues depuis la préparation de ce Répertoire UNESCO. Chaque fois que les données reçues par l'AISH l'ont permis, les longues séries temporelles du Répertoire UNESCO ont été remises à jour de deux façons:

(i)   seules les grandes crues après 1970 ou 1971 ont été citées

(ii)   toutes les valeurs maximales annuelles après 1970 ou 1971 ont été reproduites

Pour le cas où dans le Catalogue UNESCO certains débits maximaux très anciens manquaient, ils ont été indiqués dans le présent catalogue en même temps que les valeurs les plus récentes. Au total 105 nouvelles longues séries temporelles de valeurs maximales annuelles sont présentées ici.

3.3.2 Description du tableau III: Séries chronologiques de débits maximaux annuels.

Les tableaux III récapitulent les séries chronologiques de débits maximaux annuels relevés aux stations qui ont été sélectionnées. Les valeurs déduites d'observations régulières ou reconstituées par différents procédés pour une période relativement récente, sont précédées éventuellement pas les crues historiques.

Colonne 1: Année: Dans presque tous les cas il s'agit de l'année calendaire. Presque toujours il y a une valeur maximale par année. Exceptionnellement, si deux très grandes crues se produisent au cours de la même année, elles peuvent être indiquées toutes deux, mais certains pays, dans ce cas, n'en ont indiqué qu'une seule. Pour le cas où l'année hydrologique est différente de l'année calendaire, on peut occasionnellement trouver deux valeurs maximales annuelles comme en Australie par exemple.

Colonne 2: Date donnée en mois et en jours: Souvent le jour manque et seul le mois est indiqué.

Colonne 3: Observations: Des commentaires divers sont présentés ici. Ils ont été codifiés en 2 sous-colonnes:

1ère sous-colonne (code alphabétique)

A: Crue directement observée à une station régulière, maximum observé

B: Station régulière, mais maximum reconstitué non directement observé

C: Crue récente évaluée à posteriori (même s'il s'agit d'une station régulière)

D: Crue historique récente

E: Crue historique ancienne

X: Origine non connue

2ème sous-colonne (code numérique)

1: Valeur très sûre (bonne courbe d'étalonnage, faible extrapolation ou mesure directe)

2: Estimation correcte mais pas très précise (courbe d'étalonnage médiocre, forte extrapolation, hauteurs reconstituées dans de bonnes conditions, estimation d'après des formules dans des conditions bonnes ou acceptables)

3: Evaluation sommaire.

ALASKA (UNITED STATES OF AMERICA/ETATS UNIS D'AMERIQUE)

TABLE I : IDENTIFICATION OF OBSERVATION SITES AND CHARACTERISTICS OF BASINS

	OBSERVATION SITES							CHARACTERISTICS OF BASINS					
Site number	River basin	Stream	Observ. site		Coordinates Lat. Long.	Period	Area km²	Slope	Soil	Cover	Regime	Mean precip.	Mean disc
1	2	3	4	5	6	7	8	9	10	11	12	13	14
15036000	Speel	Speel	Juneau	1	N 58:12 W 133:37	1917 18 1961 75	585			A	90 50	1400	73
15085600	South East Alaska	Indian	Hollis	1	N 55:27 W 132:42	1950 63	22.8				50	2400	
15212000	Copper	Copper	Chitina	1	N 61:28 W 144:27	1950 52 1956 80	53400				90 80	300	1060
15389000	Yukon	Porcupine	Fort Yukon	1	N 66:59 W 143:08	1965 79	76400				80	200	403
15468000	Yukon	Yukon	Rampart	1	N 65:30 W 150:10	1956 67	537000				80 90	300	3000
15484000	Yukon	Salcha	Salchaket	1	N 64:28 W 146:55	1949 80	5620				80	300	47
15518350	Yukon	Teklanika	Lignite	1	N 63:55 W 149:30	1965 74	1270				80	400	20
15564900	Yukon	Koyukuk	Hughes	1	N 66:03 W 154:16	1961 80	48400				80	400	400

TABLE II : FLOODS CHARACTERISTICS

	FLOOD CHARACTERISTICS						DISCHARGE ESTIMATION					
Site number	Stream	Observ. site	Year	Date of the max	Maximal dis m^3s-1	Climatic orig.	Condition disc est	Qual. of the sect	Preci. $\pm m^3s-1$	Anteced precip.	Depth mm	Duration days
1	2	3	4	5	6	7	8	9	10	11	12	13
15036000	Speel	Juneau	1918	09-27	1010	1	A0X0					
			1961	08-13	949	1	A1C1					
15085600	Indian	Hollis	1961	10-13	170	1						
			1949	10-13	123	1						
15212000	Copper	Chitina	1971	07-15	7500	2	A1B1					
			1951	07	6230	2						
15389000	Porcupine	Fort Yukon	1973	05-24	8470	2	A1C1					
			1971	05-25	8180	2						
15468000	Yukon	Rampart	1964	06-15	26900	2	A1C1					
			1962	06-07	21700	2						
15484000	Salcha	Salchaket	1967	08-14	2750	1	A4D4					
			1956	06-23	1030	2						
			1957	05-21	799	2						
15518350	Teklanika	Lignite	1967	07-25	937	4	A1C1					
			1970	07-19	476	4						
15564900	Koyukuk	Hughes	1964	06-06	7530	2	A1C1					
			1968	06-08	6600	2						

ALBANIA/ALBANIE

TABLEAU I : IDENTIFICATION DES POINTS D'OBSERVATIONS ET CARACTERISTIQUES DES BASSINS

	POINT D'OBSERVATION							CARACTERISTIQUES DU BASSIN					
N° du point	Bassin fluvial	Rivière	Point d'observ.		Coordonnées Lat. Long.	Période	Surface km²	Relief	Sol	Végét.	Régime	Pluie moyenne	Module m³s-1
1	2	3	4	5	6	7	8	9	10	11	12	13	14
1	Shkumbini	Shkumbini	Papër	1	N 41:03 W 19:57	1956 81	1960	D 75 E 25		C D	30	1410	887
2	Buna	Buna	Shkodër	1	N 42:02 W 19:28		5179				30		
3	Drini	Drini	Vau Dejë	1	N 42:01 W 19:32		13650				30		
4	Erzeni	Erzeni	Sallmanaj	1	N 41:15 W 19:40		755				30		
5	Vjosa	Vjosa	Dorzë	1	N 40:21 W 19:43		5420				30		

ALBANIA/ALBANIE

TABLEAU II : CARACTERISTIQUES DES CRUES

	CARACTERISTIQUES DE LA CRUE						EVALUATION DES DEBITS					
N° du point	Rivière	Point d'observ.	Année	Date du maximum	Débit max m³/s	Origine	Base et mode eval	Qual. de la séch.	Precis. ±m³s-1	Anteced	Hauteur	Durée jours
1	2	3	4	5	6	7	8	9	10	11	12	13
1	Shkumbini	Papër	1971 1962	01-01 11-16	1640 1430	1 1			250	3	137 144	
2	Buna	Shkodër	1963	01-15	2730	1			410			
3	Drini	Vau Dejë	1963	01-13	4920	1			740			
4	Erzeni	Sallmanaj			975	1			150			
5	Vjosa	Dorzë	1971	01-01	3320	1			500			

TABLEAU I : IDENTIFICATION DES POINTS D'OBSERVATIONS ET CARACTERISTIQUES DES BASSINS

N° du point	Bassin fluvial	Rivière	Point d'observ.		Coordonnées Lat. Long.		Période	Surface km²	Relief	Sol	Végét.	Régime	Pluie moyenne	Module m³s-1
1	2	3	4	5	6	7	8		9	10	11	12	13	14
01-26-01	Chéliff	Oued Rhiou	Ammi Moussa	1	N 35:52	E 01:07	1958 78	1890	C35 F65	A50 C50	A15 E85	30	545	4.08
01-34-02	Chéliff	Oued Mina	Oued el Abtal	1	N 35:29	E 00:41	1953 66 1968 78	5400	C80 D10 F10	B10 C90	A60 E40	30	505	5.05
01-30-01	Mina	Oued el Taht	Kef Mahboula	1	N 35:18	E 00:50	1952 56 1967 78	680	A60 F40	C100	A65 E35	30	515	0.57
01-33-02	Mina	Oued el Abd	Aïn Hamara	1	N 35:24	E 00:41	1967 78	2480	C85 F15	A15 C85	A60 E40	30	440	1.21
02-06-09	Côtiers Algérois	Oued Boudouaou	Keddara2	1	N 36:39	E 03:25	1959 65 1968 79	93	B 5 D15 F80	A15 C50 D45	A15 B25 E60	30	920	1.08
02-18-03	Côtiers Algérois	Oued Sebaou	Belloua	1	N 36:43	E 04:05	1949 59 1973 78	1490	B 5 D 5 F90	A 5 C45 D50	A20 B 5 E75	30	1150	17.42
02-20-01	Côtiers Algérois	Oued Sebaou	Baghlia	1	N 36:48	E 03:52	1949 56 1963 78	2390	B15 F85	A 5 C55 D40	A35 E65	30	1080	27.41
02-03-01	Côtiers Algérois	Oued Hachem	Bordj Ghobrini	1	N 36:36	E 02:16	1966 78	215	B20 D50 F30	A 5 C30 D65	A30 B10 E60	30	725	
02-02-07	Côtiers Algérois	Oued Allalia	Sidi Akacha	1	N 36:29	E 01:19	1972 78	295	B10 C75 D15	A 5 C45 D50	A10 F90	30	540	
02-06-29	Côtiers Algérois	Oued Hamiz	Pont D 9	1	N 36:39	E 03:20	1972 75	160	B10 F10	C55 D40	A75 E25	30	830	
02-11-26	Côtiers Algérois	Chiffa	Amont des gorges	1	N 36:23	E 02:46	1969 78	314	B15 C25 F60	A 5 C65 D30	A65 E35	30	725	
02-13-01	Côtiers Algérois	Oued el Hanach	Hammam Melouane	1	N 36:29	E 03:03	1970 78	387	C10 D40 F50	A 5 C65 D30	A40 B40 E20	30	955	
02-14-18	Côtiers Algérois	Oued el Hanach	Baraki	1	N 36:41	E 03:05	1971 76	970	C45 D35 F25	A 5 C75 D20	A30 B25 E45	30	850	
05-01-01	Chott Hodna	Oued el Ham	Aïn N'ssissa	1	N 35:55	E 03:37	1953 56 1966 78	460	A50 C20 F30	B10 C90	A 2 E98	30	460	0.69

TABLEAU I : IDENTIFICATION DES POINTS D'OBSERVATIONS ET CARACTERISTIQUES DES BASSINS

	POINT D'OBSERVATION							CARACTERISTIQUES DU BASSIN					
N° du point	Bassin fluvial	Rivière	Point d'observ.		Coordonnées Lat. Long.		Période Surface km²	Relief	Sol	Végét.	Régime	Pluie moyenne	Module m³s−1
1	2	3	4	5	6	7	8	9	10	11	12	13	14
05-05-01	Chott Hodna	Oued el Ham	Rocade Sud	1	N 35:38	E 04:17	1954 61 1964 74	5600(1) 4000(2)	C90 F10	A45 C55	A 2 B 1 E97	30	300	1.25
05-08-01	Chott Hodna	Oued Lougmane	Ced Fagues	1	N 35:48	E 04:26	1955 56 1957 60 1965 78	334	A60 C30 F30	A20 C80	A45 E55	30	415	0.29
09-05-01	Isser	Oued Isser	Lakhdaria	1	N 36:37	E 03:35	1954 58 1965 78	3615	B20 C10 F70	A12 B 5 C35 D48	A30 B 4 E66	30	610	12.77
15-01-06	Soummam	Oued Eddous	Tilesdit 1	1	N 36:21	E 04:06	1963 78	840	B30 C20 D30 F20	A10 C75 D15	A20 B 5 E75	30	660	4.03
15-09-01	Soummam	Bou Sellam	Sidi Yahia	1	N 36:25	E 04:36	1963 68 1971 78	4050	A25 C10 F65	A20 C70 D10	A10 E90	30	525	7.73
15-10-01	Soummam	Soummam	Sidi Aich	1	N 36:37	E 04:42	1953 74	8420	B20 D25 F55	A20 C75 D 5	A40 E60	30	560	18.12
10-03-01	Kebir Rhumel	Oued Rhumel	Oued Athmania	1	N 36:14	E 06:18	1861 71 1885 1907 1964 78	1130	B85 C10 F 5	A85 C10 D 5	A 1 E99	30	475	0.65
14-06-02	Seybouse	Ressoul	Aïn Berda	1	N 36:41	E 07:36	1959 78	103	B95 C 5	A10 C65 D25	E100	30	1055	0.42
14-05-01	Seybouse	Oued Mellah	Bouchegouf Mellah	1	N 36:27	E 07:43	1948 54 1968 78	550	B15 D25 F60	A10 C50 D40	A55 E45	30	925	4.12
12-01-01	Medjerdah	Medjerdah	Souk Ahras	1	N 36:16	E 07:55	1952 57 1959 61 1968 76	217	B15 D50 F35	B 5 C85 D10	A15 E85	30	805	1.85
03-04-08	Côtiers Constantinois	Djen Djen	Oued Missa	1	N 36:37	E 05:50	1972 77	183	D55 F45	B10 C45 E45	A45 B 5 E50	30	1550	

TABLEAU I : IDENTIFICATION DES POINTS D'OBSERVATIONS ET CARACTERISTIQUES DES BASSINS

	POINT D'OBSERVATION							CARACTERISTIQUES DU BASSIN					
N° du point	Bassin fluvial	Rivière	Point d'observ.		Coordonnées Lat. Long.	Période	Surface km²	Relief	Sol	Végét.	Régime	Pluie moyenne	Module m³s-1
1	2	3	4	5	6	7	8	9	10	11	12	13	14
11-01-01	Macta	Oued Mekerra	El Hacaiba	1	N 34:42 W 00:45	1963 75	955	B10 C80 F10	A50 B10 C40	A20 B70 E10	30	410	0.11
11-02-01	Macta	Oued Mekerra	Sidi Ali Ben Youb	1	N 34:59 W 00:44	1949 62 1966 78	1890	B30 C45 D15 F10	A40 B 5 C55	A35 B45 E20	30	400	0.81
11-03-01	Macta	Oued Mekerra	Sidi bel Abbès	1	N 35:14 W 00:36	1942 62 1968 75	3000	B40 C30 D10 F20	A55 C45	A25 B35 E40	30	455	1.12
11-15-01	Macta	Oued el Hammam	Trois rivières	1	N 35:13 W 00:05	1947 58 1960 77	7440	B65 C15 F20	A 5 B20 C74 D 1	A45 B15 E40	30	440	4.98
16-04-01	Tafna	Oued Tafna	Sebdou	1	N 34:39 W 01:20	1966 78	195	B25 C10 F65	A95 D 5	A20 B60 E20	30	440	0.52
16-06-01	Tafna	Oued Chouly	Chouly	1	N 34:52 W 01:08	1947 78	170	B30 F70	A90 D10	A20 B70 E10	30	720	0.47
16-07-03	Tafna	Oued Isser	Remchi	1	N 35:06 W 01:27	1948 56 1958 62 1963 78	1935	B10 C10 D40 F40	A63 B 2 D35	A15 B25 E60	30	590	3.84
16-08-01	Tafna	Oued Tafna	Pierre du chat	1	N 35:09 W 01:26	1969 80	6900	B25 D20 F50 C 5	A80 B10 D10	A25 B15 C60	30	540	7.50
13-01-01	Sahara	Oued Guir	Djorf Torba	1	N 31:31 W 02:46	1921 33 1941 53 1966 75	22500(1) 22100(2)	B10 C80 E10	A60 C15 D25	E100	20	90	

TABLEAU II : CARACTERISTIQUES DES CRUES

	CARACTERISTIQUES DE LA CRUE						EVALUATION DES DEBITS					
N° du point	Rivière	Point d'observ.	Année	Date du maximum	Débit max m³/s	Origine	Base et mode eval	Qual. de la séch	Précis ±m³s-1	Anteced	Hauteur mm	Durée jours
1	2	3	4	5	6	7	8	9	10	11	12	13
01-26-01	Oued Rhiou	Ammi Moussa	1969 1965 1966	10-02 04-08 10-05	1140 825 746	1 1 1	A1B1	B1B	100 80			
01-34-02	Oued Mina	Oued el Abtal	1965 1955 1961	04-07 01-27 01-15	809 732 577	1 1 1	A1B1	B1B	80 73			
01-30-01	Oued el That	Kef Mahboula	1969 1955	10-02 01-27	231 207	1 1	A1B1	B1A	23 20			
01-33-02	Oued el Abd	Aïn Hamara	1968	06-11	196	1	A1B1	B1B	19			
02-06-09	Oued Boudouaou	Keddara2	1973 1969	02-04 09-26	254 212	1 1	A1B1 A1B1	C1B C1B	25 21			
02-18-03	Oued Sebaou	Belloua	1974 1957	03-31 12-30	2940 2830	1 1	A1B1 A1B1	B1B B1B	290 283			
02-20-01	Oued Sebaou	Baghlia	1974 1972	03-30 01-19	2972 2316	1 1	A1B1 A1B1	B1B B1B	297 231			
02-03-01	Oued Hachem	Bordj Ghobrini	1971	11-27	555	1	A1B1	B1B	50			
02-02-07	Oued Allalia	Sidi Akacha	1976	02-07	495	1	A1B1	B1B	50			
02-06-29	Oued Hamiz	Pont D 9	1974	03-30	453	1	A1B1	B1B	45			
02-11-26	Chiffa	Amont des Gorges	1974	03-30	731	1	A1B1	B1B	70			
02-13-01	Oued el Hanach	Hammam Melouane	1974	03-30	820	1	A1B1	B1B	80			
02-14-18	Oued el Hanach	Baraki	1974	03-30	1620	1	A1B1	B1B	160			
05-01-01	Oued el Ham	Aïn N'ssissa	1955 1976	10-04 09-06	460 313	1 1	A1B1 A1B1	C1B C1B	46 31			
05-05-01	Oued el Ham	Rocade Sud	1957 1972	12-29 01-19	315 282	1 1	A1B1 A1B1	C1C C1C	31 28			
05-08-01	Oued Lougmane	Ced Fagues	1965 1969	09-30 10-05	229 212	1 1	A1B1 A1B1	B1B B1B	22 21			
09-05-01	Oued Isser	Lakhdaria	1974 1972	03-30 01-23	2520 2020	1 1	A1B1 A1B1	B1A B1A	+250 +200			

TABLEAU II : CARACTERISTIQUES DES CRUES

			CARACTERISTIQUES DE LA CRUE				EVALUATION DES DEBITS					
N° du point	Rivière	Point d'observ.	Année	Date du maximum	Débit max m³/s	Origine	Base et mode eval	Qual. de la séch	Précis ±m³s-1	Anteced	Hauteur mm	Durée jours
1	2	3	4	5	6	7	8	9	10	11	12	13
15-01-06	Oued Eddous	Tilesdit I	1972	01-23	734	1	A1B1	C1B	73			
			1967	12-12	702	1	A1B1	C1B	70			
15-09-01	Bou Sellam	Sidi Yahia	1973	01-06	902	1	A1B1	C1B	90			
15-10-01	Soummam	Sidi Aich	1967	12-12	2700	1	A1B1	B1B	270			
			1974	03-31	1820	1	A1B1	B1B	182			
10-03-01	Oued Rhumel	Oued Athmania	1967	11-29	1236	1	A1B1	B1A	120			
			1875-76		700	1			70			
			1898	03-06	600	1			60			
14-06-02	Ressoul	Aïn Berda	1973	03-27	137	1	A1B1	A1A	13			
			1969	12-24	116	1	A1B1	A1A	11			
14-05-01	Oued Mellah	Bouchegouf Mellah	1976	11-18	1011	1	A1B1	B1A	101			
			1951	10-05	610	1	A1B1	B1A	61			
12-01-01	Medjerdah	Souk Ahras	1973	03-28	345	1	A1B1	B1B	34			
			1969	12-24	270	1	A1B1	B1B	27			
03-04-08	Djen Djen	Oued Missa	1973	09-25	902	1	A1B1	C1A	90			
11-01-01	Oued Mekerra	El Hacaiba	1966	10-09	88	1	A1B1	B1B	8			
11-02-01	Oued Mekerra	Sidi Ali Ben Youb	1966	10-10	575	1	A1B1	B1B	57			
			1950	09-18	520	1	A1B1	B1B	52			
11-03-01	Oued Mekerra	Sidi Bel Abbès	1950	12-29	110	1	A1B1	A1A	11			
			1954	04-19	100	1	A1B1	A1A	10			
			1943	10-10	80	1	A1B1	A1A	8			
11-15-01	Oued el Hammam	Trois Rivières	1927	12-29	5000	1	B5D5	B1B	600	3	230	4
			1966	10-06	1400	1	A1B1	B1B	140			
			1948	05-13	728	1	A1B1	B1B	72			
			1953	09-26	715	1	A1B1	B1B	71			
16-4-01	Oued Tafna	Sebdou I	1966	09-13	180	1	A1B1	A1B	18			
16-06-01	Oued Chouly	Chouly I	1954	04-14	148	1	A1B1	B1B	14			
			1973	03-29	138	1	A1B1	B1B	13			
			1974	03-30	95	1	A1B1	B1B	9			
16-07-03	Oued Isser	Remchi	1954	04-16	1140	1	A1B1	B1B	114			
			1973	03-29	1110	1	A1B1	B1B	111			
16-08-01	Oued Tafna	Pierre du chat	1975	04-21	2120	1	A1B1	B1B	212			
13-01-01	Oued Guir	Djorf Torba	1975	04-20	17148	1	A1D6		1714			
			1967	11-17	6241	1	A1D6		624			
			1925	03	5400	1	A1D6		540			

TABLE I : IDENTIFICATION OF OBSERVATION SITES AND CHARACTERISTICS OF BASINS

	OBSERVATION SITES						CHARACTERISTICS OF BASINS						
Site number	River basin	Stream	Observ. site	Coordinates Lat.	Long.	Period	Area km²	Slope	Soil	Cover	Regime	Mean precip. mm	Mean disc. m³s-1
1	2	3	4	5	6	7	8	9	10	11	12	13	14
1	Del Plata	Iguazu	Km 31 o' Tipo	2	S 25:41 W 54:24	1924	70000	D	C	A	40	1750	1620
2	Del Plata	Parana	Posadas	2	S 27:22 W 55:53	1901	975000	D	C	A	10 40	1650	11440
3	Del Plata	Parana	Corrientes	2	S 27:28 W 58:51	1901	1949800	C	B	C	10 40 11 90	1200	16130
4	Del Plata	Parana	Parana	2	S 31:44 W 60:32	1901	2047300	B	B	D	10 40 11 90	950	13670
5	Del Plata	Parana	Rosario	2	S 32:57 W 60:39	1886	2275100	A	B	D	10 40 11 90	950	12070
6	Del Plata	Uruguay	Santo Tomé	2	S 28:33 W 56:03	1907	127500	B	B	C	40	1500	2260
7	Del Plata	Uruguay	Concordia	2	S 31:23 W 58:01	1898	249312	B	B	C	40	1200	4000
8	Del Plata	Uruguay	Paso Hervidero	2	S 31:38 W 58:01	1916	254000				40	1700	4240
9	Paraguay	Pilcomayo	Fortin nuevo Pilcomayo	1	S 23:51 W 60:52	1949	130000	A	B	C	11 90	700	166
10	Paraguay	Bermejo	Zanja del Tigre	1	S 23:06 W 64:13	1944	25000	B	B	B	11 90	700	300
101	Colorado	Atuel	Rincon del Atuel y Angostura	1	S 35:02 W 68:52	1907	3800	C	C	E	70 90	270	31.8
102	Colorado	Colorado	Buta Ranquil	1	S 37:06 W 69:44	1942	15300	C	D	E	70 90	240	150
103	Colorado	Colorado	Pichi-Mahuida	1	S 38:50 W 64:50	1918	22300	C	C	E	70 90	260	134
104	Colorado	De los Patos	Alvarez Condarco	1	S 31:57 W 69:42	1950	3710	F E	C	E	30 90	100	18.5
105	Colorado	De los Patos	La Platéada	1	S 31:53 W 69:41	1909	8500	F E	C	E	30 90	100	52.8

TABLE I : IDENTIFICATION OF OBSERVATION SITES AND CHARACTERISTICS OF BASINS

	OBSERVATION SITE						CHARACTERISTICS OF BASINS						
Site number	River basin	Stream	Observ. site		Coordinates Lat. Long.	Period	Area km²	Slope	Soil	Cover	Regime	Mean precip. mm	Mean disc. m³s-1
1	2	3	4	5	6	7	8	9	10	11	12	13	14
106	Colorado	Diamante	Los Reyunos	1	S 34:34 W 68:34	1917	4150	F E	C	E	71 90	260	36.3
107	Colorado	Mendoza	Guido	1	S 32:51 W 69:16	1956	8180	F E	B	E	71 90	150	35.7
108	Colorado	Mendoza	Usina Cacheuta	1	S 33:01 W 69:07	1909	9040	F E	B	E	71 90	190	50.4
109	Colorado	San Juan	Km 47.3	1	S 31:32 W 68:53	1909	25700	F E	B	E	71 90	90	67.6
110	Colorado	San Juan	La Puntilla	1	S 31:31 W 68:38	1909	26000	F E	B	E	71 90	90	59.7
111	Colorado	Tunuyan	Dique Valle de Oro	1	S 33:47 W 69:15	1909	2380	C	C	E	71 90	200	27
112	Colorado	Tupungato	Punta de Vacas	1	S 32:51 W 69:46	1948	1800	F E	C	E	30 90	200	19.4
1001	Negro	Negro	Primera de Angostura	1	S 40:26 W 63:40	1927	95000	C	C	E	70 71	250	930
1002	Negro	Negro	Paso Roca	1	S 39:05 W 67:38	1922	89000	C	C	E	71	180	1020
1003	Negro	Neuquen	Paso de los Indios	1	S 38:32 W 69:25	1903	30200	D	B	E	71	130	303
1004	Negro	Limay	Paso Limay	1	S 40:32 W 70:26	1903	26400	D	C	C	71	200	725
1005	Negro	Limay	Paso Flores	1	S 40:32 W 70:40	1941	9800	D	C	C	71	200	282
1006	Negro	Limay	Nahuel Huapi	1	S 41:04 W 71:09	1921	3900	D	C	C	61 90	400	211
1007	Santa Cruz	Santa Cruz	Charles Fuhr	1	S 50:16 W 71:54	1955	15550	C	B	E	71	200	748
1008	Santa Cruz	La Leona	La Leona	1	S 49:47 W 72:05	1956	7450	C	B	E	71	200	300
1009	Futaleufù	Futaleufù	Balsa Garzon	1	S 43:08 W 71:35	1948	4650	F E	D	B	61 90	550	296

TABLE II : FLOODS CHARACTERISTICS

	FLOODS CHARACTERISTICS						DISCHARGE ESTIMATION					
Site number	Stream	Observ. site	Year	Date of the max	Maximal disc m^3s^{-1}	Climatic orig.	Condition disc est	Qual. of the sect	Precis. $\pm m^3s^{-1}$	Anteced precip.	Depth mm	Duration days
1	2	3	4	5	6	7	8	9	10	11	12	13
1	Iguazu	Km 31	1936	06-10	24750	1	A3B1	A1A		3		
		0 Tipo	1928	10-20	20540	1	A3B1	A1A		3		
			1927	11-10	10850	1	A3B1	A1A		3		
2	Parana	Posadas	1905	05-25	45000	1	A3B1	A1A		3		
			1936	06-12	34500	1	A3B1	A1A		3		
3	Parana	Corrientes	1905	06-05	43070	1	A3C1	A1B		3		
			1966	03-01	39100	1	A3C1	A1B		3		
4	Parana	Parana	1905	06-15	29900	1	A3C1	A1B		3		
			1966	03-17	27870	1	A3C1	A1B		3		
5	Parana	Rosario	1905	06-21	27490	1	A3C1	A1B		3		
			1966	04-01	26780	1	A3C1	A1B		3		
6	Uruguay	Santo	1972	09-01	23040	1	A3B1	A1B		3		
		Tomé	1923	06-24	22800	1	A3B1	A1B		3		
7	Uruguay	Concordia	1959	04-16	36600	1	A3B1	A1A		3		
			1941	05-13	29900	1	A3B1	A1A		3		
8	Uruguay	Paso	1959	04-15	39300	1	A3C1	A1B		3		
		Hervidero	1941	05-13	30500	1	A3C1	A1B		3		
9	Pilcomayo	Fortin nuevo	1961	02	1230	1	A1B1	A1A		3		
		Pilcomayo	1959	03	1150	1	A1B1	A1A		3		
10	Bermejo	Zanja del	1955	03-10	7980	1	A1B3	B1B		3		
		Tigre	1960	03-30	6735	1	A1B3	B1B		3		
101	Atuel	Rincon del	1921	01	165	2	A1A1	A1A		1		
		Atuel y	1919	03	159	2	A1A1	A1A		1		
		Angostura										
102	Colorado	Buta	1972	12-21	876	2	A1A1	A1A		1		
		Ranquil	1963	12	691	2	A1A1	A1A		1		
103	Colorado	Pichi	1953	12-16	818	2	A1A1	A1A		1		
		Mahuida	1920	01-05	780	2	A1A1	A1A		1		
104	De los Patos	Alvarez Condorco	1963	12-25	190	2	A1A1	A1A		1		
			1953	12-17	160	2	A1A1	A1A		1		
105	De los Patos	La Plateada	1963	12	387	2	A1A1	A1A		1		
			1965	12	291	2	A1A1	A1A		1		
106	Diamante	Los Reyunos	1919	12-25	255	2	A1A1	A1A		1		
			1954	01-01	210	2	A1A1	A1A		1		
107	Mendoza	Guido	1964	01	214	2	A1A1	A1A		1		
			1966	01	157	2	A1A1	A1A		1		

TABLE II : FLOODS CHARACTERISTICS

	FLOODS CHARACTERISTICS						DISCHARGE ESTIMATION					
Site number	Stream	Observ. site	Year	Date of the max	Maximal disc m³s-1	Climatic orig.	Condition disc est	Qual. of the sect	Precis. ±m³s-1	Anteced precip.	Depth mm	Duration days
1	2	3	4	5	6	7	8	9	10	11	12	13
108	Mendoza	Usina Cacheuta	1920 1915 1941	02-02 01-20 12-26	509 489 387	2 2 2	A1A1 A1A1	A1A A1A		1 1		
109	San Juan	Km 47.3	1972 1953	12-23 12-19	474 462	2 2	A1A1 A1A1	A1A A1A		1 1		
110	San Juan	La Puntilla	1919 1915 1941	12-29 01-22 12-26	1097 842 681	2 2 2	A1A1 A1A1 A1A1	A1A A1A A1A		1 1 1		
111	Tunuyan	Dique Valle de Oro	1963 1944	12-29 12-21	192 136	2 2	A1A1 A1A1	A1A A1A		1 1		
112	Tupungato	Punta de Vacas	1973 1964	01-21 01	119 99	2 2	A1A1 A1A1	A1A A1A		1 1		
1001	Negro	Primera de Angostura	1949 1932	06-26 08-18	3405 3355	1 1	A1B1 A1B1	B1A B1A		3 3		
1002	Negro	Paso Roca	1945 1932	06-02 08-11	5975 5090	(1) 1 1	A1B1 A1B1	B2A B2A		3 3		
1003	Neuquen	Paso de Los Indios	1945 1972	05-31 05-29	5060 4990	1 1	A1B1 A1B1	B2A B2A		3 3		
1004	Limay	Paso Limay	1922 1906	07 06	4865 4825	1 1	A1B1 A1B1	A1A A1A		3 3		
1005	Limay	Paso Flores	1958 1971	06-20 06-10	1115 1085	1 1	A1B1 A1B1	A1A A1A		3 3		
1006	Limay	Nahuel Huapi	1958 1949	06-24 05-26	658 511	1 1	A1B1 A1B1	A1A A1A		3 3		
1007	Santa Cruz	Charles Fuhr	1966 1963	02-28 03-01	2260 2250	1 1	A1B1 A1B1	A1A A1A		3 3		
1008	La Leona	La Leona	1960 1959	02-20 03-07	914 670	3 3	A1B1 A1B1	A1A A1A				
1009	Futaleufu	Balsa Garzon	1958 1966	06 07	1870 1331	1 1	A1B1 A1B1	A1A A1A				

(1) A flood of 10000 m³/s is mentioned in July 1899 by Mr. Pardé on the Rio Negro for a basin area of about 40000 km².

TABLE I : IDENTIFICATION OF OBSERVATIONS SITES AND CHARACTERISTICS OF BASINS

		OBSERVATIONS SITES			Coordinates		Period	Area km²	CHARACTERISTICS OF BASIN				Mean precip mm	Mean disc m³s-1
Site number	River basin	Stream	Observ. site		Lat.	Long.			Slope	Soil	Cover	Reg.		
1	2	3	4	5		6	7	8	9	10	11	12	13	14

QUEENSLAND

Site number	River basin	Stream	Observ. site	5	Lat. S	Long. E	Period	Area km²	Slope	Soil	Cover	Reg.	Mean precip mm	Mean disc m³s-1
915004	Flinders	Flinders	Richmond	1	20:50	144:11	1969 81	108780	B			11	450	4.9
919311	Mitchell	Walsh	Flatrock	1	17:11	144:54	1968 81	71795	D C B			10	800	28.2
925001	Wenlock	Wenlock	Moreton	1	12:28	142:38	1958 81	7575	B			10	1300	44.4
105001B	Normanby	Hann	Sandy Ck	1	15:14	143:51	1958 81	24605	B C			10	1080	7.8
118101	Ross	Ross	Gleesons Weir	1	19:19	146:45	1915 61	1815	D			10	1030	8.8
120006	Burdekin	Burdekin	Clare	1	19:48	147:14	1949 81	129860	D C B			10 11	640	352
122003	Proserpine	Proserpine	Dam Site	1	20:22	148:23	1956 81	2480	E D			10	1485	3.5
125001	Pioneer	Pioneer	Pleystowe	1	21:09	149:03	1915 71	1490	E D A			10	1175	27.3
130001	Fitzroy	Fitzroy	Yaamba	1	23:09	150:22	1915 70	142645	E D C B A			10	690	189
133001	Boyne	Boyne	Annondale	1	24:03	151:19	1938 81	2540	E D			10	1020	11.5
143001	Brisbane	Brisbane	Savages Crossing	1	27:26	152:40	1909 81	13560	E D C B			10	865	29.7
002101	Diamantina	Diamantina	Birdsville	1	25:55	139:22	1948 81	158000	C B A			11 20	200	49
003101	Coopers	Coopers Ck	Currareva	1	25:20	142:44	1939 81	296000	C B A			11 20	420	106
011203	Bulloo	Bulloo	Quilpie	1	26:37	144:17	1966 81	78220	B			11 20	350	13.6

TABLE I : IDENTIFICATION OF OBSERVATIONS SITES AND CHARACTERISTICS OF BASINS

	OBSERVATION SITES						CHARACTERISTICS OF BASIN						
Site number	River basin	Stream	Observ. site		Coordinates Lat. Long.	Period	Area km²	Slope	Soil	Cover	Reg.	Mean precip mm	Mean disc m³s-1
1	2	3	4	5	6	7	8	9	10	11	12	13	14
422201	Condamine Culgoa	Balonne	St. Georges	1	S 28:02 E 148:38	1920 81	150220	D C B A			11 10	610	35.3
423001	Warrego	Warrego	Charleville	1	S 26:24 E 146:14	1975 78	64700	D C B			11	550	4.8
NEW SOUTH WALES													
203004	Richmond	Richmond	Casino	1	S 28:52 E 153:03	1943 82	1790	D10 C30 B60			10	1110	24
204007	Clarence	Clarence	Lilydale	1	S 29:31 E 152:41	1923 82	16690	F25 E25 D25 C15 B10			10	1050	122
206011	Macleay	Macleay	Turnersflat	1	S 31:01 E 152:43	1945 82	9980	F30 E20 D10 C30 B10			40	900	59
210001	Hunter	Hunter	Singleton	1	S 32:34 E 151:10	1891 1982	16400	F30 E20 D10 C20 B20			40	750	29
211001	Macquarie Tuggerah	Wyee	Wyee	1	S 33:10 E 151:29	1958 79	19.8	F25 E25 B50			40	1200	0.2
211005	Lakes	Ourimbah	Tuggerah	1	S 33:20 E 151:24	1965 82	153	F E B			40	1200	1.7
212201	Hawkesbury	Nepean	Penrith	1	S 33:45 E 150:51	1891 1982	11000	F30 E30 D10 C10 B20			40	800	45
215001	Shoalhaven	Shoalhaven	Welcome Reef	1	S 35:10 E 150:00	1909 76	2770	F E D B			40	700	19
418001	Gwydir	Gwydir	Paliamallawa	1	S 29:28 E 150:08	1892 1931 1951 82	12300	E D C B A			40 70 11	700	26

TABLE I : IDENTIFICATION OF OBSERVATIONS SITES AND CHARACTERISTICS OF BASINS

OBSERVATION SITES							CHARACTERISTICS OF BASIN						
Site number	River basin	Stream	Observ. site		Coordinates Lat. Long.	Period	Area km²	Slope	Soil	Cover	Reg.	Mean precip. mm	Mean disc m³s−1
1	2	3	4	5	6	7	8	9	10	11	12	13	14
421001	Macquarie-Bogan	Macquarie	Dubbo	1	S 32:16 E 148:36	1885 1982	19600	F E D B			40 70	650	36
412002	Lachlan	Lachlan	Cowra	1	S 33:50 E 148:41	1892 1982	11100	D C B			40 70	700	27
410004	Murrum-bidgee	Murrum-Bidgee	Gungadai	1	S 35:05 E 148:06	1886 1982	21100	F E D C B			90 40	800	110
425001	Darling	Darling	Menindee	1	S 32:23 E 142:25	1881 1982	570000				70 20 40 10 11	(200)	100

VICTORIA

222200	Snowy	Snowy	Jarrahmond	1	S 37:41 E 148:22	1889 1982	13420	F20 E25 C55			50 90	1000	57.8
226200	Latrobe	Latrobe	Rosedale	1	S 38:09 E 146:48	1889 1982	4145	F E C A			50	1200	27.2
228200	Bunyip	Bunyip	Tona	1	S 38:05 E 145:45	1907 82	600	D C			50	1300	4.8
401201	Upper Murray	Murray	Jingellic	1	S 35:56 E 147:43	1890 1982	6525	F E D			90 70	900	79.2
409207	Murray-Riverina	Murray	Torrumbarry	1	S 35:57 E 144:28	1893 1982	54400	F E D B			70 30		177

SOUTH AUSTRALIA

426901	Lower Murray	Murray	Morgan	1	S 34:02 E 139:41	1886 1981	(1000000)	B A			70 30 20		700
504501	Torrens	Torrens	Gorge Weir	1	S 34:51 E 138:44	1884 1981	343	C B			30	750	0.5

WESTERN AUSTRALIA

605012	Frankland	Frankland	Mount Frankland	1	S 34:54 E 116:47	1940 82	5800	C B			30	800	5

TABLE I : IDENTIFICATION OF OBSERVATIONS SITES AND CHARACTERISTICS OF BASINS

	OBSERVATION SITES						CHARACTERISTICS OF BASIN						
Site number	River basin	Stream	Observ. site		Coordinates Lat. Long.	Period	Area km²	Slope	Soil	Cover	Reg.	Mean precip. mm	Mean disc m³s-1
1	2	3	4	5	6	7	8	9	10	11	12	13	14
609025	Blackwood	Blackwood	Daradup	1	S 34:04 E 115:37	1956 80	20500	C B				30	700	19.2
611049	Preston	Preston	Beelerup	1	S 33:34 E 115:53	1955 75	603	C				30	950	2.6
614006	Murray W.A.	Murray	Hughes Bridge	1	S 32:46 E 116:05	1939 81	6840	C				30	650	9.5
702001	Murchison	Murchison	Emu Springs	1	S 27:51 E 114:33	1967 80	82300	C B A				20 30	250	6.4
704193	Gascoyne	Gascoyne	Fishy Pool	1	S 24:57 E 114:39	1964 80	70200	D C B A				20	200	17.4
708003	Fortescue	Fortescue	Jimbeenyinoo Pool	1	S 21:20 E 116:09	1968 80	48900	E D C B A				11	250	8.8
710229	De Grey	Shaw	North Pole Mine	1	S 21:06 E 119:19	1966 80	6530	D C B				11	300	6.5
802055	Fitzroy	Fitzroy	Fitzroy Crossing	1	S 18:12 E 125:35	1957 80	45300	E D C B				11	650	106
809302	Ord	Ord	Coolibah Pocket	1	S 16:08 E 128:44	1955 69	46100	D C B A				11	575	145

NORTHERN TERRITORY

811007	Victoria	Victoria	Coolibah HS	1	S 15:32 E 130:57	1952 82	44900	D B C A				10 11	610	92.5
814040	Daly	Daly	Mount Nanear	1	S 13:50 E 130:44	1969 82	46600	B A				10	990	192
818035	Mary	Mary	Mt. Bundey	1	S 12:54 E 131:39	1958 82	5700	B A				10	1250	56
821009	East Alligator	Magela Ck	Downstream Jabiru	1	S 12:38 E 132:54	1971 82	605	C B				10	1250	14.9

AUSTRALIA/AUSTRALIE

TABLE I : IDENTIFICATION OF OBSERVATIONS SITES AND CHARACTERISTICS OF BASINS

OBSERVATION SITES							CHARACTERISTICS OF BASIN						
Site number	River basin	Stream	Observ. site		Coordinates Lat. Long.	Period	Area km²	Slope	Soil	Cover	Reg.	Mean precip. mm	Mean disc m³s-1
1	2	3	4	5	6	7	8	9	10	11	12	13	14
903250	Roper	Roper	Red Rock	1	S 14:42 E 134:25	1965 82	47400	B A			10	760	93.2
006009	Todd	Todd	Wills Terrace	1	S 23:42 E 133:53	1952 82	445	E			20	250	0.27
TASMANIA													
306002	Huon	Huon	Frying Ck Pan	1	S 43:02 E 146:50	1948 81	2090	F E			50	2080	90.5
310008	Pieman	Pieman	Heemskirk	1	S 41:48 E 145:14	1955 81	2540	E D			50	2640	136
316001	Mersey	Mersey	Kimberley	1	S 41:24 E 146:30	1922 81	1440	E D C			50	1400	44.5
318001	Tamar	South Esk	Launceston	1	S 41:28 E 147:07	1901 81	9000	E D B			50	760	70.2

TABLE II : FLOODS CHARACTERISTICS

	FLOODS CHARACTERISTICS							DISCHARGE ESTIMATION				
Site number	Stream	Observ. site	Year	Date of the max	Maximal dis m³s-1	Climatic origine	Condition disc est	Qual. of the sect	Precis. ±m³s-1	Anteced precip.	Depth mm	Duration days
1	2	3	4	5	6	7	8	9	10	11	12	13

QUEENSLAND

915004	Flinders	Richmond	1981	01-19	595	1			60			
			1974	01-22	555	1			55			
919311	Walsh	Flatrock	1977	03-07	2670	1			270			
			1979	01-05	2510	1			250			
925001	Wenlock	Moreton	1979	01-13	990	1			100			
			1979	04-12	895	1			90			
105001B	Hann	Sandy Ck	1974	02-11	755	1			75			
			1979	02-03	635	1			60			
118101	Ross	Gleesons Weir	1946	03-03	4555	1			250			
			1927	02-11	4450	1			250			
			1946	02-10	2640	1			130			
120006	Burdekin	Clare	1958	04-13	36000	1			3600			
			1974	01-25	26620	1			2700			
122003	Proserpine	Dam Site	1970	01-19	4640	1			460			
			1979	03-02	1475	1			150			
125001	Pioneer	Pleystowe	1918	01-23	9840	1			1000			
			1958	02-18	9440	1			950			
			1956	03-31	6690	1			700			
130001	Fitzroy	Yaamba	1918	02-01	32620	1			3300			
			1954	02-18	22960	1			2300			
			1951	01-20	10540	1			1000			
133001	Boyne	Annondale	1947	02-12	8200	1			820			
			1973	12-20	6150	1			620			
			1971	01-31	4050	1			400			
143001	Brisbane	Savages Crossing	1974	01-28	7710 (1)				770	(1) 9900 m³s-1		
			1963	02-06	5580	1			560	02-05-1893		
			1955	03-30	5360	1			540	Mr. Brunt		
002101	Diamantina	Birdsville	1974	02-08	4690	1			470			
			1980	03-23	4090	1			410			
			1976	02-26	2770	1			280			
003101	Coopers	Currareva	1974	02-02	5420	1			540			
			1951	01-21	4370	1			440			
			1955	03-20	4180	1			420			
011203	Bulloo	Quilpie	1974	01-16	630	1			60			
			1971	12-29	625	1			60			
422201	Balonne	St. Georges	1950	07-31	2710	1			270			
			54	02-19	2230	1			220			
			50	11-29	2010	1			200			

TABLE II : FLOODS CHARACTERISTICS

	FLOODS CHARACTERISTICS						DISCHARGE ESTIMATION					
Site number	Stream	Observ. site	Year	Date of the max	Maximal dis m^3s-1	Climatic origine	Condition disc est	Qual. of the sect	Precis. $\pm m^3s-1$	Anteced precip.	Depth mm	Duration days
1	2	3	4	5	6	7	8	9	10	11	12	13
423001	Warrego	Charleville	1956	04-03	1270	1			130			
			56	02-09	990	1			100			
			50	11-27	920	1			90			

NEW SOUTH WALES

Site number	Stream	Observ. site	Year	Date of the max	Maximal dis m^3s-1	Climatic origine	Condition disc est	Qual. of the sect	Precis. $\pm m^3s-1$	Anteced precip.	Depth mm	Duration days
203004	Richmond	Casino	1954	02-21	4250	1			800			
			56	02	2300	1			230			
204007	Clarence	Lilydale	1954	02-21	18300	1			1800			
			46	03-25	17700	1			1800			
			50	06-24	16800	1			1700			
206011	Macleay	Turners Flat	1949	08	14300	1			2800			
			63	05	12000	1			2400			
			46	03-26	7000	1			1400			
210001	Hunter	Singleton	1955	02	12500	1			2500			
			1971	02-01	5400	1			550			
			13	05-16	5100	1			500			
211001	Wyee	Wyee	1963	04	35	1			7			
			64	06-10	34	1			7			
211005	Ourimbah	Tuggerah	1977	03	270	1			55			
			67	08-07	210	1			40			
212201	Nepean	Penrith	1867		21000 (1)	1	(1) 6740 m^3s-1 february 1898 at Pheasants Nest 710 km^2 A. French and W. Wolson	U				
			1900	07-06	15600	1		U				
			25	06-21	13400	1		U				
			61	11-20	11300	1						
215001	Shoalhaven	Welcome Reef	1925	05-11	8900	1			1800			
			59	10-21	4600	1			900			
			16	10-05	3700	1			750			
418001	Gwydir	Paliamallawa	1955	02	6000	1			U			
			56	02	4000	1			U			
			76	02-11	3700	1			700			
421001	Macquarie	Dubbo	1955	02-26	5900	1			1200			
			56	03-17	3900	1			400			
			50	04-05	3400	1			350			
412002	Lachlan	Cowra	1870		8000 (2)	1	(2) 9300 m^3s-1 1870 at Wyangala 8300 km^2	U				
			1952	06-17	5400	1		1100				
			16	10-06	4700	1		940				
			1900	07	4200	1		840				
410004	Murrum-Bidgee	Gungadai	1853		10500	1			U			
			1852		10000	1			U			
			1870		10000	1			U			
			1925	05	6200 (3)	1	(3) 11000 m^3s-1 1925 at Burrinjuck 12900 km^2 V.T. England A. Morrison	620				
			74	08-29	5500	1		550				
			50	03-23	4200	1		420				

TABLE II : FLOODS CHARACTERISTICS

	FLOODS CHARACTERISTICS						DISCHARGE ESTIMATION					
Site number	Stream	Observ. site	Year	Date of the max	Maximal dism³s-1	Climatic origine	Condition disc est	Qual. of the sect	Precis. ±m³s-1	Anteced precip.	Depth mm	Duration days
1	2	3	4	5	6	7	8	9	10	11	12	13
425001	Darling	Menindee	1890	06	2840	1			570			
			1956	09	1550	1			310			
			1976	04	1470	1			290			
VICTORIA												
222200	Snowy	Jarrahmond	1971	02-06	7500	1						
			74	01-08	6940	1						
			78	06-04	4830	1						
226200	Latrobe	Rosedale	1934	12-01	3510	1						
			54	06-17								
			78	06-04	1475	1						
228200	Bunyip	Tona	1934	12-01	825	1						
			37	10-18	525	1						
			24	08-26	350	1						
401201	Murray	Jingellic	1974	10-18	1600	1						
			75	10-26	1460	1						
			17	10-21	1415 (1)	1	(1) 3540 m³s-1 observed 1917 at Corowa 16820 km²					
409207	Murray	Torrumbarry	1916	10-03	1100 (2)	1	(2) significant part of the flood discharge flows upstream of the station towards Edwards and Wakool rivers.					
			75	11-03	630	1						
			81	09-02	610							
SOUTH AUSTRALIA												
426901	Murray	Morgan	1956	09-05	3940	1			600			
			31	08-25	2220	1			330			
			17	12-11	2160	1			320			
504501	Torrens	Gorge Weir	1889	09-21	485	1			95			
			1923	09-28	405	1			40			
			17	07-18	350	1			35			
WESTERN AUSTRALIA												
605012	Frankland	Mount Frankland	1982	01	500	1			100			
			64	08-06	238	1			12			
609025	Blackwood	Daradup	1982	01-27	1140	1			115			
			64	08-04	1100	1			110			
			63	08-24	654	1			35			
611049	Preston	Beelerup	1964	08-03	170	1			34			
			67	07-15	152	1			30			
614006	Murray W.A.	Hughes Bridge	1945	06-26	720	1			140			
			64	08-05	555	1			55			
702001	Murchison	Emu Springs	1975	03-01	1080 (1)	1	(1) 1330 m³s-1 03.16.1960 estimated		110			
			80	07-01	695	1			35			

TABLE II : FLOODS CHARACTERISTICS

| | | | | FLOODS CHARACTERISTICS | | | | | DISCHARGE ESTIMATION | | | |
Site number	Stream	Observ. site	Year	Date of the max	Maximal dism³s-1	Climatic origine	Condition disc est	Qual. of the sect	Precis. ±m³s-1	Anteced precip.	Depth mm	Duration days
1	2	3	4	5	6	7	8	9	10	11	12	13
704193	Gascoyne	Fishy Pool	1980	06-22	9180 (2)	1	(2) Two floods of the same order as June 1980 observed in Feb 1960 1961.		1800			
			74	07-15	4170	1			400			
708003	Fortescue	Jimbeenyino Pool	1975	12-12	3240	1			320			
			71	02-05	2160	1			215			
710229	Shaw	North Pole Mine	1971	02-04	3470	1			700			
			80	02-02	3240	1			650			
802055	Fitzroy	Fitzroy Crossing	1967	02-17	12200	1			2400			
			1981	02	12000	1			2400			
809302	Ord	Coolibah Pockett	1956	02-27	30800	1			6000			
			59	01-11	30000	1			6000			

NORTHERN TERRITORY

811007	Victoria	Coolibah H S	1974	03-09	20000	1			8000			
			56	03-01	13000	1			2600			
			57	03-08	10400	1			2000			
814040	Daly	Mount Nanear	1957	03-13	8400	1			850			
			76	03-26	6260	1			310			
818035	Mary	Mt. Bundey	1977	03-23	3270	1			325			
			80	02-06	3050	1			300			
821009	Magela C K	Downstream Jabiru	1980	02-04	1550	1			155			
903250	Roper	Red Rock	1940	01	7400	1			1480			
			63	04	5000	1			1000			
			67	03-19	2260	1			225			
006009	Todd	Wills Terrace	1910	03	900	1			180			
			20	12	750	1			150			
			21	02	620	1			120			

TASMANIA

306002	Huon	Frying Pan Ck	1948	05-28	2200	1			110			
			75	05-18	1970	1			100			
			60	04-23	1910	1			95			
310008	Pieman	Heemskirk	1975	05-18	2620	1			260			
			58	05-03	2275	1			230			
			62	06-17	2205	1			220			
316001	Mersey	Kimberley	1970	08-25	1810	1			180			
318001	South Esk	Launceston	1929	04-06	3965	1			400			
			1969	06-01	2670	1			135			
			1926	10-14	2040	1			400			

TABLE I : IDENTIFICATION OF OBSERVATION SITES AND CHARACTERISTICS OF BASINS

OBSERVATION SITES								CHARACTERISTICS OF BASINS					
Site number	River basin	Stream	Observ. site		Coordinates Lat. Long.	Period	Area km²	Slope	Soil	Cover	Regime	Mean precip. mm	Mean disc. m³s-1
1	2	3	4	5	6	7	8	9	10	11	12	13	14
207183	Donau (Danube)	Donau	Wien	1	N 48:16 E 16:26	1828	101700	A20 B20 C20 D15 E15 F10	A20 B20 C30 D30	A20 B10 C20 D40 E10	61 90	900	1920
212571	Donau	Drau	Villach	1	N 46:37 E 13:51	1852	5266	C10 D15 E15 F60	A10 B20 C30 D40	A20 B10 C30 D20 E20	90	1400	150
212787	Drau	Gail	Federaun	1	N 46:34 E 13:49	1877	1305	D10 E10 F80	A20 B30 C30 D20	A20 B10 C20 D30 E20	90	1750	50
211375	Drau	Mur	Landscha	1	N 46:46 E 15:34	1855	8340	A10 B10 C10 D25 E25 F20	A10 B10 C40 D40	A40 B20 C10 D10 E20	90	1200	140
201525	Donau	Inn	Innsbruck	1	N 47:16 E 11:24	1849	5794	D 5 E 5 F90	A10 B10 C40 D40	A15 B15 D10 E60	90	900	165
205542	Donau	Traun	Wels	1	N 48:09 E 14:02	1895	3499	B30 D 5 E 5 F60	A20 B20 C50 D10	A35 B20 D30 E15	90 (61)	1500	125

TABLE II : FLOODS CHARACTERISTICS

	FLOODS CHARACTERISTICS						DISCHARGE ESTIMATION					
Site number	Stream	Observ. site	Year	Date of the max	Maximal discm³s-1	Climatic orig.	Condition disc est	Qual. of the sect	Precis. ±m³s-1	Anteced precip.	Depth mm	Duration days
1	2	3	4	5	6	7	8	9	10	11	12	13
207183	Donau (Danube)	Wien	1501	08	14000	1	D5D4	BOC	400	3		
			1787	11-01	11800	1	D5D4	BOC	200	3		
			1899	09-18	10500	1	A1B1	B1A	100	3	150	7
			1862	02-04	9850	4	A1C1	B1C	200	3		
212571	Drau	Villach	1966	08-19	1900	1	A1B1	B1A	100	3	200	4
			1965	09-04	1550	1	A1B1	B1A	100	3	170	4
212787	Gail	Federaun	1966	11-05	850	1	A1B1	B1A	50	3	230	4
			1926	11-23	750	1	B2B1	B1A	50			
211375	Mur	Landscha	1938	05-23	1450	1	A1C1	C2B	200			
			1966	08-20	1150	1	A1C1	C2B	150			
201525	Inn	Innsbrück	1855	06-17	1350	1	C4D5	XOX	-150			
			1871	06-19	1210	1	A2C1	BOC	100			
			1851	08-02	1120	1	C4D5	XOX	+100			
205542	Traun	Wells	1899	09-13	1660	1	A2C1	C1X	100	3	300	7
			1959	08-13	1430	1	A1C1	C1B	50	3	280	15

TABLE I : IDENTIFICATION OF OBSERVATION SITES AND CHARACTERISTICS OF BASINS

	OBSERVATION SITES							CHARACTERISTICS OF BASINS					
Site number	River basin	Stream	Observ. site	Coordinates Lat. Long.		Period	Area km²	Slope	Soil	Cover	Regime	Mean precip. mm	Mean disc. m³s−1
1	2	3	4	5	6	7	8	9	10	11	12	13	14
1	Brahmaputra Brahmaputra		Bahadurabad 1	N 25:09	E 89:40	1956 1975	(800000)	B10 D20 E20 F50			00 90		
2	Ganges	Ganges	Hardings Bridge	1 N 23:04	E 89:02	1934 1975	(950000)				00 90	1100	
3	Brahmaputra Meghna		Bhairab Bazar	1 N 24:02	E 90:60	1956 1972	20700				00 90	3180	

TABLE II : FLOODS CHARACTERISTICS

	FLOODS CHARACTERISTICS						DISCHARGE ESTIMATION					
Site number	Stream	Observ. site	Year	Date of the max	Maximal discm³s−1	Climatic orig.	Condition disc est	Qual. of the sect	Precis. ±m³s−1	Anteced precip.	Depth mm	Duration days
1	2	3	4	5	6	7	8	9	10	11	12	13
1	Brahmaputra	Bahadurabad	1974 1970 1966	08−06 07−28 08−26	81000 76600 69100	4 4						
2	Ganges	Hardings Bridge	1973 1961 1969	08−21 09−01 08−27	74060 73200 54700	4 4						
3	Meghna	Bhairab Bazar	1966	09−03	14400	1						

BELGIUM/BELGIQUE

TABLEAU I : IDENTIFICATION DES POINTS D'OBSERVATIONS ET CARACTERISTIQUES DES BASSINS

	POINT D'OBSERVATION							CARACTERISTIQUES DU BASSIN					
N° du point	Bassin fluvial	Rivière	Point d'observ.		Coordonnées Lat. Long.		Période	Surface km²	Relief	Sol	Végét.	Régime	Pluie moyenne mm	Module m³s-1
1	2	3	4	5	6		7	8	9	10	11	12	13	14
713	Meuse	Meuse	Ampsin Neuville	1	N 50:31	E 05:18	1966 77	16400	D E	C	B C	50	920	250
326	Escaut	Escaut	Kain	1	N 50:37	E 03:22	1966 77	5091	B C	C	C	50	700	20

BELGIUM/BELGIQUE

TABLEAU II : CARACTERISTIQUES DES CRUES

	CARACTERISTIQUES DE LA CRUE						EVALUATION DES DEBITS					
N° du point	Rivière	Point d'observ.	Année	Date du maximum	Débit max m³s-1	Origine	Base et mode evalla	Qual.de séch	Précis. ±m³s-1	Anteced	Hauteur mm	Durée jours
1	2	3	4	5	6	7	8	9	10	11	12	13
713	Meuse	Ampsin- Neuville	1967	01-03	2000	4	A1C1	A2A	120			
			1966	12-14	1700	4	A1C1	A2A	80			
			1970	02-23	1580	4	A1C1	A2A	70			
326	Escaut	Kain	1967	01-01	170	1	A1C1	A2A	15			
			1968	01-16	159	1	A1C1	A2A	10			

TABLEAU I : IDENTIFICATION DES POINTS D'OBSERVATIONS ET CARACTERISTIQUES DES BASSINS

			POINT D'OBSERVATION						CARACTERISTIQUES DU BASSIN					
N° du point	Bassin fluvial	Rivière	Point d'observ.		Coordonnées Lat. Long.		Période	Surface km^2	Relief	Sol	Végét.	Régime	Pluie moyenne mm	Module m^{3}s-1
1	2	3	4	5	6		7	8	9	10	11	12	13	14
400-107	Mono	Mono	Athiémé	1	N 06:34	E 01:40	1944 81	21500	B50 A50	C	B50 C50	10	1500 1100	125
450-119	Oueme	Oueme	Pont de Savé	1	N 08:00	E 02:35	1942 81	23600	C 8 B92	C	B	10	1300 1100	140
450-117	Oueme	Oueme	Sagon	1	N 07:10	E 02:26	1951 81	37980	C 5 B95	C	B	10	1300 1100	182?
151-103	Niger	Alibori	Route Kandi Banikouara	1	N 11:10	E 02:41	1952 81	8150	B	C	B	10	1300 900	(29)

TABLEAU II : CARACTERISTIQUES DES CRUES

			CARACTERISTIQUES DE LA CRUE				EVALUATION DES DEBITS					
N° du point	Rivière	Point d'observ.	Année	Date du maximum	Débit max m^{3}s-1	Origine	Base et mode eval	Qual. de la séch	Précis. ±m^{3}s-1	Anteced précip.	Hauteur mm	Durée jours
1	2	3	4	5	6	7	8	9	10	11	12	13
400-107	Mono	Athiémé	1949 1963	09-06 09-07	911 904	1 1	A2C1 A2C1	A1C A1C	100 100			
450-119	Ouémé	Pont de Savé	1949 1957	08-28 09-15	2650 2040	1 1	A3C1 A2C1	A1A A1A	150 150			
450-117	Ouémé	Sagon	1957 1963	09-16 09-06	1090 1054	1 1	A2C1 A2C1	A1B A1B	100 100			
151-103	Alibori	Route Kandi Banikouara	1962 1953	09-03 09-04	685 553	1 1	A3B1 A3B1	A1A A1A	25 25			

TABLE I : IDENTIFICATION OF OBSERVATION SITES AND CHARACTERISTICS OF BASSINS

	OBSERVATION SITES							CHARACTERISTICS OF BASIN						
Site number	River basin	Stream	Observ. site		Coordinates Lat. Long.		Period	Area km²	Slope	Soil	Cover	Regime	Mean precip. mm	Mean disc. m³s-1
1	2	3	4	5	6		7	8	9	10	11	12	13	14
1	Rio Mamoré (Amazon)	Rio Grande	Abapo	1	S 18:51	W 63:28	1945 74	59000	F	C	B20 C50 D20 E10	90 10		
2	Rio Mamoré	Rio Grande	Puente Arle	1	S 18:36	W 63:09	1945 74	58230	F	C	C70 D20 E10	90 10		
3	Rio Madeira	Rio Beni	Angosto Del Bala	1	S 14:33	W 67:33	1967 73 1975 80	67770	F85 E15	C	C50 D10 A20 E20	90 10		2080
4	Rio del Plata	Rio Pilcomayo	Villa Montes	1	S 21:16	W 63:30	1941 46 1949 55	25300	F	C	C60 D30 E10	90 10		185

TABLE II : FLOODS CHARACTERISTICS

	FLOODS CHARACTERISTICS						DISCHARGE ESTIMATION					
Site number	Stream	Observ. site	Year	Date of the max	Maximal disc m³s-1	Climatic Orig.	Condition disc est	Qual. of the sect	Précis. ±m³s-1	Anteced précip.	Depth mm	Duration days
1	2	3	4	5	6	7	8	9	10	11	12	13
1	Rio Grande	Abapo	1949 1968 1950		11360 9240 9080	1 1 1	A1C	B1C				
2	Rio Grande	Puente Arle	1968 1960		8610 8140	1 1	A1C	B1C				
3	Rio Beni	Angosto Del Bala	1978 1972	02-05 01-22	23370 17500	1 1	A1C	B1C				
4	Rio Pilcomayo	Villa Montes	1955 1950 1949		2580 2420 1940	1 1 1	A1C	B1C				

TABLE I : IDENTIFICATION OF OBSERVATION SITES AND CHARACTERISTICS OF BASINS

	OBSERVATION SITES							CHARACTERISTICS OF BASINS						
Site number	River basin	Stream	Observ. site		Coordinates Lat. Long.		Period	Area km²	Slope	Soil	Cover	Regime	Mean precip. mm	Mean disc. m³s-1
1	2	3	4	5	6	7	8		9	10	11	12	13	14
17050001	Amazonas	Amazonas	Obidos	1	S 01:54	W 55:30	1928 47 1968 79	4640300			A	00 90		160000
18850000	Amazonas	Xingu	Altamira	1	S 03:12	W 52:13	1968 79	446570			A B	00 10		7675
22350000	Tocantins	Tocantins	Porto Nacional	1	S 10:42	W 48:26	1949 77	175360			A B	00 10		2050
27500000	Tocantins	Araguaïa	Conceiçao do Araguaïa	1	S 08:17	W 49:15	1949 77	320290			A B	00 10		3950
29200000	Tocantins	Tocantins	Itupiranga	1	S 05:08	W 49:21	1969 77	727900			A B	00 10		9895
34060000	Atlantico Sul (Norte-Nordeste)	Parnaiba	Ribeiro Gonçalves	1	S 07:32	W 45:15	1965 78	32700			B	10 11		223
34880000	Atlantico Sul (Norte-Nordeste)	Parnaiba	Porto Formoso	1	S 03:26	W 42:24	1963 78	282000	B40 C60	C	B	10 11	1100	770
3869092(a)	Atlantico Sul (Norte-Nordeste)	Capibaribe	S.Lourenço da Mata	1	S 08:01	W 35:03	1956 77	7200	D50 E50	D	C50 D50	11	900	18.2
44500000	Sao Francisco	Sao Francisco	Manga	1	S 14:45	W 43:56	1932 75	200790			B	10		2110
48020000	Sao Francisco	Sao Francisco	Juazeiro	1	S 09:25	W 40:31	1929 78	510800			B	10		2680
49660000	Sao Francisco	Sao Francisco	Traipu	1	S 09:58	W 36:59	1938 78	622600			B	10		2940
54150000	Atlantico Sul (Leste)	Jequitinhonha	Porto Mandacaru	1	S 16:30	W 42:30	1945 78	16340			B	10 00		144
54500000	Atlantico Sul (Leste)	Araçuai	Araçuai	1	S 16:52	W 42:05	1931 78	14620			B	10 00		95
54950000	Atlantico Sul (Leste)	Jequitinhonha	Itapebi	1	S 15:57	W 39:32	1972 78	67770			B	10 00		360
58099000	Altantico Sul (Leste)	Paraiba do Sul	Santa Branca	1	S 23:22	W 45:54	1952 79	4935				10 00		73.4

TABLE I : IDENTIFICATION OF OBSERVATION SITES AND CHARACTERISTICS OF BASINS

	OBSERVATION SITES							CHARACTERISTICS OF BASINS						
Site number	River basin	Stream	Observ. site		Coordinates Lat.	Period Long.		Area km²	Slope	Soil	Cover	Regime	Mean precip. mm	Mean disc. m³s−1
1	2	3	4	5	6	7		8	9	10	11	12	13	14
58630002	Atlantico Sul (Leste)	Paraiba do Sul	Arita	1	S 22:02	W 42:59	1930 78	29820				1000		483
58972000	Atlantico Sul (Leste)	Paraiba do Sul	Guarus	1	S 21:44	W 41:20	1955 74	55080				1000		708
58974000	Atlantico Sul (Leste)	Paraiba do Sul	Campos	1	S 21:45	W 41:20	1934 78	55080				1000		829
64843000	Parana	Parana	Guaira DNAEE Itaipu	1	S 24:04	W 54:15	1921 1980	802200				10		9150
65035000	Parana	Iguaçu	Porto Amazonas	1	S 25:33	W 49:53	1935 78	3660				40		59.7
65310000	Parana	Iguaçu	Uniao da Victoria	1	S 26:14	W 51:04	1930	24210				40		417
65985000	Parana	Iguaçu	Estreito do Iguaçu	1	S 25:33	W 53:46	1968 78	62240				40		1520
67050000	Parana	Paraguai	Fecho dos Morros	1	S 21:25	W 57:53	1965 72	470000				10		1100
70700000	Uruguai	Pelotas	Passo Socorro	1	S 28:22	W 50:48	1940 78	9010				40		182
73200000	Uruguai	Uruguai	Ita	1	S 27:17	W 52:20	1950 78	43900				40		950
74100000	Uruguai	Uruguai	Irai	1	S 27:11	W 53:15	1941 78	62200				40		1360
85650000	Atlantico Sul (Sudeste)	Jacui	Cachoeira	1	S 30:03	W 52:54	1934 56	30210				40		560
85900000	Atlantico Sul (Sudeste)	Jacui	Rio Pardo	1	S 29:59	W 52:21	1940 78	36100				40		703
86470000	Atlantico Sul (Sudeste)	Antas	Ponte do Rio das Antas	1	S 29:04	W 51:35	1970 78	12690				40		304
86510000	Atlantico Sul (Sudeste)	Taquari	Muçum	1	S 29:11	W 51:52	1940 78	16150				40		305
87035000	Atlantico Sul (Sudeste)	Jacui	Sao Jeronimo−	1	S 29:56	W 51:41	1972 76	68260				40		1520

TABLE II : FLOODS CHARACTERSTICS

	FLOODS CHARACTERISTICS						DISCHARGE ESTIMATION					
Site number	Stream	Observation site	Year	Date of the max.	Maximal discm³s-1	Climatic orig.	Condit. disc est	Qual of the sec	Preci ±m³s-1	Anteced precip.	Depth mm	Duration days
1	2	3	4	5	6	7	8	9	10	11	12	13
17050001	Amazonas	Obidos	1953	06	370000	1	C4BC1	A1A	25000			
			1963	06	250000	1						
			1976	06-19	239600	1	A1B1	A1A	10000			
18850000	Xingu	Altamira	1974	04-07	32670	1						
22350000	Tocantins	Porto Nacional	1977	02-06	16300	1						
			1964	02	15450	1						
			1968	03	14980	1						
27500000	Araguaia	Conceiçao do Araguaia	1957	04-21	18600	1						
			1974	04	16700	1						
			1977	03	16670	1						
29200000	Tocantins	Itupiranga	1974	04-02	38780	1						
34060000	Parnaiba	Ribeiro Gonçalves	1977	12-30	930	1						
34880000	Parnaiba	Porto Formoso	1974	04-26	7130	1	A1B	B1A	400			
3869092(a)	Capibaribe	S.Lourenço da Mata	1975	07-17	3440	1	A2C4	A1A	300			
			1966	06-13	2400	1	A4C4	A1A	200			
44500000	Sao Francisco	Manga	1949	02-13	11260	1						
			1946	01	10810	1						
48020000	Sao Francisco	Juazeiro	1949	03-14	13265	1	A1					
			1946	02	11570	1	A1					
49660000	Sao Francisco	Traipu	1960	04-01	15890	1						
			1949	03	15680	1						
54150000	Jequitinhonha	Porto Mandacaru	1948	12-26	2345	1						
54500000	Araçuai	Araçuai	1942	12-05	2365	1						
			1943	12	1931	1						
54950000	Jequitinhonha	Itapebi (1)	1978	02-16	7212	1						
58099000	Paraiba do Sul	Santa Branca	1959	02-18	608	1						
			1967	02	605	1						
58630002	Paraiba do Sul	Anta	1947	03-15	5355	1						
			1966	01	4365	1						
58972000	Paraiba do Sul	Guarus	1966	01-15	7945	1						
			1961	02	6410	1						

(1) Were observed 9340 m³s^{-1} in 1943 at Itamarati (62000 km²)

TABLE II : FLOODS CHARACTERISTICS

		FLOODS CHARACTERISTICS					DISCHARGE ESTIMATION					
Site number	Stream	Observation site	Year	Date of the max.	Maximal discm³s-1	Climatic orig.	Condit. disc est	Qual of the sec	Preci. ±m³s-1	Anteced precip.	Depth mm	Duration days
1	2	3	4	5	6	7	8	9	10	11	12	13
58974000	Paraiba do Sul	Campos	1943	01-23	5210	1						
			1967	02-21	4710	1						
			1937	02	4620	1						
			1947	03	4620	1						
64843000	Parana	Guaira	1983	07-15	40260	1						
			1929	03-03	32900	1						
			1905		(32500)	1						
			1931	02	30960	1						
			1977	02	28375	1						
65035000	Iguaçu	Porto Amazonas	1983	07-16	919	1						
			1970	12	633	1						
65310000	Iguaçu	Uniao da Victoria	1983	07-18	4960	1						
			1935	10-17	2790	1						
			1957	08	2396	1						
65985000	Iguaçu	Estreito (6) do Iguaçu	1983	07-10	20200	1						
			1936(2)		?	1						
67050000	Paraguai	Fecho dos Morros	1905(3)			1						
			1983	05-30	5200	1						
70700000	Pelotas	Passo (4) Socorro	1954	09-24	4800	1						
			1977	08-17	3735	1						
73200000	Uruguai	Ita	1983	07-08	23200	1						
			1965	08-19	20650	1						
			1977	08	13330	1						
74100000	Uruguai	Irai	1983	07-08	32800	1						
			1965	08-20	30790	1						
85650000	Jacui	Cachoeira	1936	10-09	13000	1						
			1941	05-06	9960	1						
			1942	05	5290	1						
85900000	Jacui	Rio Pardo	1941	05-07	7310	1						
			1965	09	5700	1						
86470000	Antas	Ponto do Rio das Antas	1983	07-06	11000 ?	1						
			1977	08-17	8920	1						
8651000	Taquari	Muçum	1941	05-05	12500 ?	1						
			1965	08-19	11500	1						
			1946	01-26	10300	1						
			1983	07-06	10170	1						
87035000	Jacui (5)	Sao Jeronimo Jusante	1972	08-29	9220	1						

(2) The 1936 maximum before the observation period would have been 15000-20000 m³s⁻¹ (see Argentina).
(3) The 1905 maximum at Puerto Sastre (450000 km² instead of 470000 km²), would have been 6500 m³s-1 ?
(4) The 1965 large flood happened durinf a gap of observations.
(5) The 1941 and 1936 floods occured before the observations period.
(6) 32500 m³s-1 at Salto Cataratas 68950 km².

TABLE I : IDENTIFICATION OF OBSERVATION SITES AND CHARACTERISTICS OF BASINS

OBSERVATION SITES								CHARACTERISTICS OF BASIN					
Site number	River basin	Stream	Observ. site		Coordinates Lat. Long.		Period	Area km²	Slope	Soil	Cover	Regime	Mean precip. mm	Mean disc. m³s−1
1	2	3	4	5	6		7	8	9	10	11	12	13	14
1	Iskar	Malak Iskar	Etropole	1	N 42:47	E 23:58	1946 70	54.3	F	C		30 90	1080	0.98
2	Danube	Iskar	Oriahovitza	1	N 43:37	E 24:24	1935 1970	8370	F E D C B		A33 D67	30 90	730	53.80
3	Vit	Belivit	Teteven	1	N 42:54	E 24:12	1938 70	315	F	C	A90 D10	30 90	1040	3.8
4	Danube	Osim	Gradiste	1	N 43:21	E 25:07	1929 70	1770	F E D C B	C	A51 D49	30 90	780	12.6
5	Yantra	Rositza	Sevlievo	1	N 43:02	E 25:05	1922 70	1090	F E D C	C	A33 D67	30 90	875	9.82
6	Danube	Yantra	Ciolokovitzi	1	N 43:03	E 25:37	1932 70	1290	F E D C B	C	A34 D66	30 90	880	9.65
7	Danube	Yantra	Rodanovo	1	N 43:20	E 25:40	1936 65	6570	F E D C B	C	A19 D81	30 90	760	40
8	Rus Lom	Tscherni Lom	Sirokovo	1	N 43:32	E 25:56	1948 70	1380	D C B	D C	A11 D89	30	600	2.49
9	Maritza	Maritza	Kota 1400	1	N 42:11	E 23:38	1950 70	39.9	F	C	A99 D 1	30 90	1100	0.96
10	Maritza	Maritza	Belovo	1	N 42:15	E 23:55	1912 70	741	F E D	C	A75 D25	30 90	750	8.58
11	Maritza	Topolnitza	Lesichevo	1	N 42:21	E 24:07	1911 62	1620	F E D C	C	A57 D43	30 90	680	9.25
12	Maritza	Maritza	Plovdiv	1	N 42:09	E 24:42	1912 73	7930	F E D C	C	A57 D43	30 90	695	50.3

TABLE I : IDENTIFICATION OF OBSERVATION SITES AND CHARACTERISTICS OF BASINS

	OBSERVATION SITES							CHARACTERISTICS OF BASIN					
Site number	River basin	Stream	Observ. site		Coordinates Lat. Long.		Period	Area km²	Slope	Soil	Cover	Regime	Mean precip. mm	Mean disc. m³s⁻¹
1	2	3	4	5	6		7	8	9	10	11	12	13	14
13	Maritza	Striama	Klisura	1	N 42:42	E 24:20	1952 70	49.5	F	C		30 90	810	0.72
14	Maritza	Striama	Bania	1	N 42:30	E 24:52	1913 73	833	F E D	C D	A68 D32	30 90	795	7.39
15	Maritza	Tchepelarska	Batchkovo	1	N 41:57	E 24:53	1911 73	825	F		A81 D19	30 90	795	10.3
16	Maritza	Maritza	Harmanli	1	N 41:54	E 25:57	1912 73	19700	F E D C B		A50 D50	30 90	665	103
17	Maritza	Elhovska	Rudovem	1	N 41:27	E 24:47	1951 66	83.7	F	C	A100	30 90	1010	1.59
18	Maritza	Virbitza	Djebel	1	N 41:33	E 25:23	1950 70	1150	F E D	C	A34 D66	30 90	905	19.3
19	Struma	Struma	Rajdavitza	1	N 42:25	E 22:47	1950 70	2170	F	C	A32 D68	30 90	805	10.2
20	Struma	Elesnitza	Vaksevo	1	N 42:10	E 22:52	1950 70	315	F	C	A55 D45	30 90	830	2.84
21	Struma	Strumesnitza	Mitino	1	N 41:26	E 23:13	1937 70	1890	F	C	A45 D55	30 90	680	10.6

TABLE II : FLOODS CHARACTERISTICS

	FLOODS CHARACTERISTICS						DISCHARGE ESTIMATION					
Site number	Stream	Observ. site	Year	Date of the max	Maximal dism^3s-1	Climatic orig.	Condition disc est	Qual. of the sect	Preci. ±m^3s-1	Anteced precip.	Depth mm	Duration days
1	2	3	4	5	6	7	8	9	10	11	12	13
1	Malak Iskar	Etropole	1960	06-12	52	1						
2	Iskar	Oriahovitza	1957	06-29	940	1						
3	Belivit	Teteven	1964	09-24	323	1						
4	Osim	Gradiste	1954	07-16	280	1						
5	Rositza	Sevlievo	1957	06-28	1160	1						
6	Yantra	Ciolokovitzi	1966	06-04	1190	1						
7	Yantra	Rodanovo	1957	06-29	1340	1						
8	Tscherni Lom	Sirokovo	1955	06-25	170	1						
9	Maritza	Kota 1400	1957	06-29	18.6	1					140	
10	Maritza	Belovo	1957	09-05	710	1					107	
11	Topolnitza	Lesichevo	1957	09-05	510	1					83	
12	Maritza	Plovdiv	1957	06-29	1270	1					118	
13	Striama	Klisura	1957	06-27	150	1						
14	Striama	Bania	1951	08-25	320	1						
15	Tchepelarska	Batchkovo	1961	11-06	530	1						
16	Maritza	Harmanli	1963	02-07	1800	2						
17	Elhovska	Rudovem	1961	11-06	300	1						
18	Virbitza	Djebel	1963	02-03	2640	2						
19	Struma	Rajdavitza	1955	01-10	354	2						
20	Elesnitza	Vaksevo	1954	06-19	350	1						
21	Strumesnitza	Mitino	1963	02-05	318	2						

TABLEAU I : IDENTIFICATION DES POINTS D'OBSERVATIONS ET CARACTERISTIQUES DES BASSINS

	POINT D'OBSERVATION								CARACTERISTIQUES DU BASSIN					
N° du point	Bassin fluvial	Rivière	Point d'observ.		Coordonnées Lat. Long.		Période	Aire km²	Relief	Sol	Végét.	Régime	Pluie moyenne mm	Module m³s-1
1	2	3	4	5	6		7	8	9	10	11	12	13	14
05173803	Bénoué	Louti	Figuil	1	N 09:46	E 13:56	1955 56 1971 79	5540	E30 D70	C	C D	11	900 1100	(40)
05170106	Niger	Bénoué	Garoua	1	N 09:18	E 13:23	1930 79	64000	E10 D10 C30 B30 A20	C	B38 C D	11	1130	380
05230103	Sanaga	Sanaga	Edea	1	N 03:46	E 10:04	1943 79	1315000	E D C	D	A B D	10 00	1630	2080
05600121	Nyong	Nyong	Mbalmayo	1	N 03:31	E 11:30	1951 79	13555	D C	D	A	00	1550	150
05900120	Wouri	Wouri	Yabassi	1	N 04:28	E 09:58	1951 79	8250	F30 E40 D30	C	A70 B30	00	2000 4000	311
05401005	Côtier	Lokoundje	Lolodorf	1	N 03:14	E 10:44	1951 79	1150	D C B	D	A100	00	1860	31

TABLE II : FLOODS CHARACTERISTICS

		FLOODS CHARACTERISTICS						DISCHARGE ESTIMATION				
Site number	Stream	Observ. site	Year	Date of the max	Maximal disc $m^3s{-1}$	Climatic orig.	Condition disc est	Qual. of the sec.	Preci. $\pm m^3s{-1}$	Anteced precip.	Depth mm	Duration days
1	2	3	4	5	6	7	8	9	10	11	12	13
05173803	Louti	Figuil	1975	09-02	1800	1	A1C1	B1B	200			
			1955	?	>1200	1	B5C1	B1B				
			1977	08-26	900	1	A1B1	B1B				
05170106	Bénoué	Garoua	1916	?	>6000	1						
			1948		6000	1	A2C1	A1B				
			1935		4410	1	A2B1	A1B				
			1946		4390	1	A2B1	A1B				
			1975	09-06	4340	1	A2B1	A1B				
			1960		4300	1	A2B1	A1B				
05230103	Sanaga	Edea	1969	10-07	7700	1) 1	A2B1	A1B				
			1955	10-18	7570	1	A2B1	A1B				
			1949	10-30	7450	1	A2B1	A1B				
			1961	10-21	7440	1	A2B1	A1B				
05600121	Nyong	Mbalmayo	1964	11-10	575	1	A2B1	A1B				
			1966	11-20	506	1	A2B1	A1B				
			1970	11-07	482	1	A2B1	A1B				
			1957	11-12	469	1	A2B1	A1B				
05900120	Wouri	Yabassi	1965	10-01	1845	1	A2B1	A1B				
			1978	09-30	1841	1	A3B1	A1B				
			1960	08-25	1825	1	A2B1	A1B				
			1967	08-30	1799	1	A2B1	A1B				
05401005	Lokoundje	Lolodorf	1954	06-09	220	1	A2B1	A1B				
			1976	10-28	220	1	A2B1	A1B				
			1964	11-09	200	1	A2B1	A1B				
			1970	11-04	183	1	A2B1	A1B				

1) Reconstitued natural flow.

TABLE I : IDENTIFICATION OF OBSERVATION SITES AND CHARACTERISTICS OF BASINS

OBSERVATION SITES							CHARACTERISTICS OF BASIN						
Site number	River basin	Stream	Observ. site		Coordinates Lat. Long.	Period	Area km²	Slope	Soil	Cover	Regime	Mean precip. mm	Mean disc. m³s-1
1	2	3	4	5	6	7	8	9	10	11	12	13	14
YUKON TERRITORY													
09AB008	Yukon	M'clintock	White Horse	1	N 60:36 W 134:27	1955 79	1700	F *		A	80 90		10.0
09AE001	Yukon	Teslin	Teslin	1	N 60:29 W 133:18	1944 79	30300	F * E D		A	80 90		304
09DC002	Yukon	Stewart	Mayo	1	N 63:35 W 135:08	1947 79	31600	F * E D			80 90		370
BRITISH COLUMBIA													
08CG001	Stikine	Iskut	Below Johnson r.	1	N 56:44 W 131:40	1959 79	9350	F E			50		432
08EF001	Skeena	Skeena	Usk	1	N 54:38 W 128:26	1928 31 1936 79	42200	F * E D		A	50 90		919
08KB001	Fraser	Fraser	Shelley	1	N 54:01 W 122:37	1950 79	32400	F E D		A	50 90 61		829
08MA001	Fraser	Chilko	Redstone	1	N 52:04 W 123:32	1927 79	6940	F * E D		A C	50 90		89
08LF051	Fraser	Thompson	Spences Bridge	1	N 50:21 W 121:23	1951 79	54900	F * E D		A C	50 90 61		780
08MG005	Fraser	Lilloet	Pemberton	1	N 50:20 W 122:48	1923 79	2160	D *			50 90		126
08MF005	Fraser	Fraser	Hope	1	N 49:23 W 121:27	1912 79	217000	F * E D C			50 90		2730
08MH076	Fraser	Kanaka	Webster Corners	1	N 49:12 W 122:32	1960 79	47.7	F		A C D	61 50		2.84
08MH016	Fraser	Chilliwack	Outlet Chilliwack Lake	1	N 49:05 W 121:27	1923 51 1957 79	329	F *		A	90 50		19
08NB005	Columbia	Columbia	Donald	1	N 51:29 W 117:11	1944 79	9710	F E			61 90		175
08NJ009	Columbia	Kootenay	Nelson	1	N 49:30 W 117:17	1894 79	45300	F * E			61 90		756

* influence of lakes

TABLE I : IDENTIFICATION OF OBSERVATION SITES AND CHARACTERISTICS OF BASINS

	OBSERVATION SITES						CHARACTERISTICS OF BASIN						
Site number	River basin	Stream	Observ. site		Coordinates Lat. Long.	Period	Area km²	Slope	Soil	Cover	Regime	Mean precip. mm	Mean disc. m³s-1
1	2	3	4	5	6	7	8	9	10	11	12	13	14
08NJ013	Columbia	Slocan	Crescent Valley	1	N 49:27 W 117:34	1913 79	3290	F * E			61 90		87.4
08NN013	Columbia	Kettle	Ferry	1	N 48:59 W 118:46	1928 79	5700	F E		C D	61 90		42.3
08HD003	Campbell	Campbell	Campbell River	1	N 50:02 W 125:17	1949 70	1460	F E D			50		98.9
08GA030	Seymour	Seymour	North Vancouver	1	N 49:20 W 123:00	1928 79	176	F E D			50		16.6
10BE004	Mackenzie	Toad	Above Nonda	1	N 58:51 W 125:23	1961 79	2570	F E		A	80		43.1
10AC002	Mackenzie	Dease	Macdame	1	N 59:11 W 129:12	1957 79	6940	F E D		A	80		102
NORTHEN TERRITORIES													
10EC001	Mackenzie	South Nahanni	Above Clausen Creek	1	N 61:15 W 124:02	1959 79	33400	F E D		A	80		427
10GC001	Mackenzie	Mackenzie	Fort Simpson	1	N 61:52 W 121:20	1933 79	1270000				80 61		6760
10KA001	Mackenzie	Mackenzie	Norman Wells	1	N 65:17 W 126:51	1943 56 1960 79	1570000				80 61		8550
ALBERTA													
07FD002	Mackenzie	Peace	Taylor	1	N 56:08 W 120:40	1944 79	97400	F E D C			61 90		1400
07AG001	Mackenzie	Mac Leod	Near Wolf Creek	1	N 53:59 W 116:17	1913 31 1957 79	6320	F E D		A	70 90		38.9
07AD002	Mackenzie	Athabasca	Hinton	1	N 53:25 W 117:35	1961 79	9790	F E D		A	70 90		176
07BE001	Mackenzie	Athabasca	Athabasca	1	N 54:43 W 113:17	1913 31 1938 79	74100	F E D C		A	70 90		436
05AA022	Nelson	Castle	Near Beaver Mines	1	N 49:29 W 114:09	1945 79	826	F E		A	70 90		16.8

CANADA

TABLE I : IDENTIFICATION OF OBSERVATION SITES AND CHARACTERISTICS OF BASINS

	OBSERVATION SITES						CHARACTERISTICS OF BASIN						
Site number	River basin	Stream	Observ. site		Coordinates Lat. Long.	Period	Area km²	Slope	Soil	Cover	Regime	Mean precip. mm	Mean disc. m³s-1
1	2	3	4	5	6	7	8	9	10	11	12	13	14
05DB001	Nelson	Clearwater	Rocky Mountain House	1	N 52:21 W 114:56	1914 31 1944 75	3210	F E D		A	70 90		25.6
05DB006	Nelson	Clearwater	Dovercourt	1	N 52:15 W 114:51	1975 79	2230	F E		A	70 90		15.0
05DC001	Nelson	North Saskatchewan	Rocky Mountain House	1	N 52:23 W 114:56	1913 31 1944 79	11000	E D			70 90		141
05DF001	Nelson	North Saskatchewan	Edmonton	1	N 53:32 W 113:29	1911 79	28000	E D			70 90		215
SASKATCHEWAN													
05HG001	Nelson	South Saskatchewan	Saskatoon	1	N 52:08 W 106:39	1911 79	141000	E D C			70 90 61		268
MANITOBA													
05KJ001	Nelson	Saskatchewan	Le Pas	1	N 53:50 W 101:11	i913 79	347000	E D C *			61 70		669
05MH005	Nelson	Assiniboine	Holland	1	N 49:42 W 98:54	1954 79	152000	D C			61		76.8
05ØC001	Nelson	Red	Emerson	1	N 49:00 W 97:13	1912 79	104000	C B *			61		94.3
05ØD031	Nelson	Sprague	Sprague	1	N 48:59 W 95:40	1928 79	355	B A		A	61		1.70
ONTARIO													
04LJ001	Moose	Missinaibi	Mattice	1	N 49:37 W 83:16	1920 79	8940	B A		A	80		105
02AD008	St Lawrence	Nipigon	Pine Portage	1	N 49:19 W 88:17	1950 79	24600	B			80		368
02BD003	St Lawrence	Magpie	Michipicoten	1	N 47:56 W 84:50	1939 79	1930	C B		A	61		28
02CF005	St Lawrence	Junction	Sudbury	1	N 46:29 W 80:59	1958 79	89.1	B		A	61		1.51
02GA010	St Lawrence	Nith	Canning	1	N 43:11 W 80:27	1913 26 1947 79	1030	A B		C D	60		10.8
02HC013	St Lawrence	Highland	West Hill	1	N 43:47 W 79:10	1956 79	88.1	A B		C D	60		0.89

CANADA

TABLE I : IDENTIFICATION OF OBSERVATION SITES AND CHARACTERISTICS OF BASINS

	OBSERVATION SITES				Coordinates		Period		CHARACTERISTICS OF BASIN						
Site number	River basin	Stream	Observ. site		Lat.	Long.		Area km²	Slope	Soil	Cover	Regime	Mean precip. mm	Mean disc. m³s-1	
1	2	3	4	5	6		7	8	9	10	11	12	13	14	
02JE012	St Lawrence	Ottawa	La Cave Rapids	1	N 46:22	W 78:43	1952 79	47900	A B			61		693	
QUEBEC															
041301	Des Outaouais (Ottawa)	Coulonge	Fort Coulonge	1	N 45:52	W 76:41	1926 80	5150				61		73.2	
040601	Des Outaouais	Du Lièvre	Mont Laurier	1	N 46:32	W 75:30	1924 80	5130				61		97.1	
030901-05	Saint-Laurent	Chateaugay	Amont Chateaugay	1	N 45:20	W 73:46	1920 80	2500				61		33.7	
020 A016	Saint-Laurent	Saint-Laurent	La Salle	1	N 45:24	W 73:37	1880 1979	960000				61		8340	
030203	Saint-Laurent	Saint-François	Drummond-Ville	4	N 45:52	W 72:27	1925 80	9610				61		190	
023402	Saint-Laurent	Chaudière	Saint-Lambert	1	N 46:35	W 71:12	1915 80	5830				61		116	
022502-13	Saint-Laurent	Du Loup	Rivière Du Loup	1	N 47:49	W 69:31	1923 80	1040				61		18.9	
021601	Saint-Laurent	Matane	8,5 km Amont Matane	1	N 48:46	W 67:32	1927 80	1650				61		39.4	
052219	Saint-Laurent	L'Assomption	Joliette	1	N 46:01	W 73:26	1922 80	1340				61		23.4	
050115	Saint-Laurent	Saint-Maurice	Grand-Mère	4	N 46:37	W 72:41	1919 80	42000				61 80		711	
050401	Saint-Laurent	Sainte-Anne	Saint-Alban	4	N 46:42	W 72:05	1919 80	1800				61		52	
050801	Saint-Laurent	Jacques Cartier	Saint-Gabriel	1	N 46:53	W 71:32	1924 80	2010				61		62	
051001	Saint-Laurent	Montmorency	Boischatel	1	N 46:54	W 71:09	1924 39 1965 80	1100				61		36.1	
051502	Saint-Laurent	Malbaie	Clermont	1	N 47:42	W 70:13	1969 80	1700				80		36.1	
061901	Saguenay	Chamou-chouane	Saint-Félicien	1	N 48:41	W 72:29	1953 80	15300				80		306	
062101	Saguenay	Mistassibi	Mistassibi	1	N 48:54	W 72:13	1953 80	9320				80		197	

CANADA

TABLE I : IDENTIFICATION OF OBSERVATION SITES AND CHARACTERISTICS OF BASINS

	OBSERVATION SITES							CHARACTERISTICS OF BASIN						
Site number	River basin	Stream	Observ. site		Coordinates Lat. Long.		Period	Area km²	Slope	Soil	Cover	Regime	Mean precip. mm	Mean disc. m³s-1
1	2	3	4	5	6		7	8	9	10	11	12	13	14

QUEBEC

062901	Saint-Laurent	Saguenay	Isle Maligne	4	N 48:35	W 71:38	1913 80	73000				80		1460
071001	Saint-Laurent	Aux Outardes	Chûte aux Outardes	4	N 49:09	W 68:24	1923 80	18900				80		385
073301	Saint-Laurent	Au Tonnerre	Rivière au Tonnerre	1	N 50:17	W 64:47	1949 80	684				80		20.5
020802	Golfe Saint-Laurent	Madeleine	5,1 km de la Rivière Madeleine	1	N 49:12	W 65:18	1954 80	1220				61		29.1
011201	Baies des Chaleurs	Nouvelle	Nouvelle	1	N 48:09	W 66:21	1964 80	1140				61		27.3
080101	Baie James	Harricana	Amos	1	N 48:38	W 78:07	1915 80	3680				61		60.3
080701	Baie James	Nottoway	Lac Soscumica	1	N 50:08	W 77:25	1956 80	57500				61		1020
081001-02	Baie James	De Rupert	Lac Nemiscau	1	N 51:27	W 76:52	1950 80	40900				80		863
090601	Baie James	East-Main	Gorges de Basile	1	N 52:15	W 78:04	1958 80	44300				80		895
092704	Baie D'Hudson	La Grande Rivière	Près Embouchure	1	N 53:44	W 78:34	1958 78	96600				80		1700
093801	Baie D'Hudson	Grande Rivière de La Baleine	Près Embouchure	1	N 55:14	W 76:59	1961 80	36300				80		533
102001	Baie Ungava	Arnaud	Amont de la Hamelin	1	N 59:59	W 71:54	1955 80	26900				80		343
103602-05	Baie Ungava	Aux Mélèzes	Près Embouchure	1	N 57:40	W 69:37	1962 80	42700				80		641
103702	Baie Ungava	Caniapiscau	Près Embouchure	1	N 57:26	W 69:15	1962 80	86800				80		1660
104801	Baie Ungava	George	Près Embouchure	1	N 58:09	W 65:51	1962 79	35200				80		746

NEW BRUNSWICK

01AD002	St John	St John	Fort Kent	1	N 47:15	W 68:35	1926 79	14700	B C		A	61		274
01AD003	St Francis	St Francis	Outlet Glasier Lake	1	N 47:12	W 68:57	1951 79	1350	B C		A	61		25.2

TABLE I : IDENTIFICATION OF OBSERVATION SITES AND CHARACTERISTICS OF BASINS

| | OBSERVATION SITES | | | | | | CHARACTERISTICS OF BASIN | | | | | | |
Site number	River basin	Stream	Observ. site		Coordinates Lat. Long.	Period	Area km²	Slope	Soil	Cover	Regime	Mean precip. mm	Mean disc. m³s-1
1	2	3	4	5	6	7	8	9	10	11	12	13	14

NOVA SCOTIA

01ER001	Clam Harbour	Clam Harbour	Birchtown	1	N W 45:28 61:27	1957 79	45.1	A B		A	61		1.64
01FB001	Northeast Margaree	Northeast Margaree	Margaree Valley	1	N W 46:22 60:58	1916 79	368	A B		A	61		17.2

NEWFOUNDLAND AND LABRADOR

02ZK001	Rocky	Rocky	Colinet	1	N W 47:13 53:34	1949 79	285	A B C		A	80		11
02YL001	Upper Humber	Upper Humber	Near Reidville	1	N W 49:14 57:22	1928 79	2110	A * B C		A	80		83.2
03ØE001	Lake Melville	Churchill	Above upper Muskrat Falls	1	N W 53:14 60:47	1948 50 1953 79	92500	A * B C		A	80		1700

CANADA

TABLEAU II : CARACTERISTIQUES DES CRUES

	CARACTERISTIQUES DE LA CRUE						EVALUATION DES DEBITS					
N° du point	Rivière	Point d'observ.	Année	Date du maximum	Débit max m³/s	Origine	Base et mode eval	Qual. de la séc.	Préci. ±m³s-1	Anteced	Haut. mm	Durée jours
1	2	3	4	5	6	7	8	9	10	11	12	13

YUKON

N° du point	Rivière	Point d'observ.	Année	Date du maximum	Débit max m³/s	Origine	Base et mode eval	Qual. de la séc.	Préci. ±m³s-1	Anteced	Haut. mm	Durée jours
09AB008	Mac Clintock	White Horse	1972	06-01	113	2	A1B1					
			1957	05-22	92	2	A3B1					
09AE001	Teslin	Teslin	1962	06-27	1840	2	A3B1					
			1964	06-18	1710	2	A3B1					
09DC002	Stewart	Mayo	1964	06-10	4110	2	A1C					
			1975	06-07	3140	2	A1B1					

BRITISH COLUMBIA

N° du point	Rivière	Point d'observ.	Année	Date du maximum	Débit max m³/s	Origine	Base et mode eval	Qual. de la séc.	Préci. ±m³s-1	Anteced	Haut. mm	Durée jours
08CG001	Iskut	Below Johnson r.	1961	10-15	7930	1	A1C1					
			1974	10-09	5150	1	A1C1					
08EF001	Skeena	Usk	1948	05-26	9340	2	A1B1					
			1972	06-12	8100	2	A1B1					
			1964	06-11	7530	2	A1B1					
08KB001	Fraser	Shelley	1972	06-14	5010	2	A1B1					
			1967	06-04	4130	2	A1B1					
08MA001	Chilko	Redstone	1950	06-20	479	2	A1B1					
08LF051	Thompson	Spences Bridge	1972	06-15	4130	2	A1B1					
08MG005	Lilloet	Pemberton	1940	10-19	900	4?	A3B1					
			1975	11-05	858	4?	A1B1					
08MF005	Fraser	Hope	1948	05-31	15200	2						
			1972	06-16	13000	2	A1B1					
08MH076	Kanaka	Webster Corner	1979	12-14	146	1	A1B1					
08MH016	Chilliwack	Outlet of Chilliwack Lake	1972	06-10	116	2	A1B1					
			1974	06-20	109	2	A1B1					
08NB005	Columbia	Donald	1972	06-12	1320	2	A1B1					
08NJ009	Kootenay	Nelson	1916	06-27	4020	1	A1B1					
			1933	06-23	3880	1	A1B1					
08NJ013	Slocan	Crescent Valley	1961	06-07	719	2	A1B1					
			1974	06-20	708	2	A1B1					
08NN013	Kettle	Ferry	1948	05-29	600	2	A1B1					
			1942	05-27	515	2	A1B1					
08HD003	Campbell	Campbell r.	1953	11-15	835	1	A1B1					
			1961	01-17	640	1	A1B1					

CANADA

TABLEAU II : CARACTERISTIQUES DES CRUES

	CARACTERISTIQUES DE LA CRUE						EVALUATION DES DEBITS					
N° du point	Rivière	Point d'observ.	Annee	Date du maximum	Débit max m³/s	Origine	Base et mode eval	Qual. de la séc.	Préci. ±m³s-1	Anteced	Haut. mm	Durée jours
1	2	3	4	5	6	7	8	9	10	11	12	13
08GA030	Seymour	North Vancouver	1961 1955	01-15 11-03	583 544	1 1	A1C A1B1					
10BE004	Toad	Above Nonda	1975 1974	06-28 07-17	762 597	2 2	A1B1 A1B1					
10AC002	Dease	Mac Dame	1972 1962	05-31 06-16	968 821	4 4	A1B1 A1B1					
NORTHWEST TERRITORY												
10EC001	South Nahanni	Above Clausen Creek	1962 1975	06-17 06-04	8210 3280	2 2	A1C A1B1					
10GC001	Mackenzie	Fort Simpson	1961 1977	05-30 06-06	23500 23000	2 2	A3B1 A1B1					
10KA001	Mackenzie	Norman Wells	1975 1977	05-24 05-17	30300 28300	2 2	A3B1 A3B1					
ALBERTA												
07FD002	Peace	Taylor	1948 1964 1954	05-30 06-13 05-28	11500 10000 9430	2 2 2	A1B1 A1B1 A1B1					
07AG001	Mac Leod	Near Wolf Creek	1954 1969	06-08 08-07	2270 2020	2 4	A1B1 A1B1					
07AD002	Athabasca	Hinton	1972 1974	06-13 06-25	1270 1080	2 2	A1B1 A1B1					
07BE001	Athabasca	Athabasca	1954 1944	06-10 06-18	5660 5040	2 2	A1B1 A1B1					
05AA022	Castle	Near Beaver Mines	1975 1964	06-20 06-08	736 510	4 4	A1B1 A1B1					
05DB001	Clearwater	Near Rocky Mountain House	1915 1965 1972	06-27 06-19 06-26	1110 524 467	4 4 4	A3B1 A1B1 A1B1					
05DB006	Clearwater	Dovercourt	1978	06-07	111	4	A1B1					
05DC001	North Saskatchevan	Rocky Mountain House	1915 1952	06-27 06-23	4110 1990	2 2	A1C A1B1					
05DF001	North Saskatchevan	Edmonton	1915 1952 1944	06-28 06-25 06-16	5800 3740 3570	2 2 2	A1C A1B1 A1B1					
SASKATCHEVAN												
05HG001	South Saskatchevan	Saskatoon	1953 1923	06-15 06-07	4190 3650	2 2	A1B1 A1B1					
MANITOBA												
05KJ001	Saskatchevan	Le Pas	1948 1916	06-11 07-19	3000 2920	2 2	A3B1 A3B1					

CANADA

TABLEAU II : CARACTERISTIQUES DES CRUES

	CARACTERISTIQUES DE LA CRUE						EVALUATION DES DEBITS				
N° du point	Rivière	Point d'observ.	Année	Date du maximum	Débit max m³/s	Origine	Base et mode éval	Qual. de la séch	Préci. ±m³s-1	Anteced précip.	Haut. mm	Durée jours
1	2	3	4	5	6	7	8	9	10	11	12	13
05MH005	Assiniboine	Holland	1976	04-20	1470	2	A1B1					
05ØD001	Red	Emerson	1950	05-13	2670	2	A3B1					
			1979	05-01	2630	2	A1B1					
05ØD031	Sprague	Sprague	1974	04-22	72,5	2	A1B1					
			1942	09-01	58,6	1	A1B1					
ONTARIO												
04LJ001	Missinaibi	Mattice	1979	05-12	1790	2	A1B1					
			1939	05-10	1480	2	A3B1					
02AD008	Nipigon	Pine Portage	1964	08-23	640	1	A1B1					
			1968	07-29	629	1	A1B1					
02BD003	Magpie	Michipicoten	1979	05-12	381	2	A1B1					
			1976	04-24	309	2	A1B1					
02CF005	Junction	Sudbury	1963	03-30	37.9	4	A1B1					
			1974	08-18	34.5	1	A1B1					
02GA010	Nith	Canning	1954	10-17	428	1	A1B1					
			1948	03-21	422	1	A1B1					
02HC013	Highland	Westhill	1977 ?	03-13	?							
			1973	03-11	63.1	4	A1B1					
02JE012	Ottawa	La Cave Rapids	1960	05-15	3650	2	A1B1					
			1979	05-05	2760	2	A1B1					
QUEBEC												
041301	Coulonge	Fort Coulonge	1979	04-30	656	2	A1C1	A1A	35			
			1951	04-15	583	2	A2C1	A1A	30			
040601	Du Lièvre	Mont Laurier	1936	05-13	742	2	A2C1	A1A	35			
			1947	05-30	742	2	A2C1	A1A	35			
			1928	05-12	688	2	A2C1	A1A	35			
030901-05	Chateaugay	Amont Chateaugay	1944	03-28	787	2	A2B1	B1A	80			
			1922	03-20	767	2	A2B1	B1A	75			
020A016	Saint-Laurent	La Salle	1943	05-13	14870	2	A1B1					
			1976	04-02	14600	2	A1B1					
			1951	04-17	14570	2	A1B1					
030203	Saint-François	Drummondville	1936	03-19	2420	2	A206	A0X	240			
			1928	04-07	2360	2	A206	A0X	235			
023402	Chaudière	Saint-Lambert	1917	07-31	3500	1			U			
			1933	05-04	1680	2	A2B1	A1A	85			
			1974	04-30	1680	2	A1B1	A1A	85			
			1947	05-07	1650	2	A2B1	A1A	80			
022502 022513	Du Loup	Rivière du Loup	1927	11-20	340	4	A2C1	A1A	15			
			1942	05-06	340	2	A2C1	A1A	15			

TABLEAU II : CARACTERISTIQUES DES CRUES

	CARACTERISTIQUES DE LA CRUE						EVALUATION DES DEBITS					
N° du point	Rivière	Point d'observ.	Année	Date du maximum	Débit max m³/s	Origne	Base et mode eval	Qual. de la séch	Préci. ±m³s-1	Anteced	Haut. mm	Durée jours
1	2	3	4	5	6	7	8	9	10	11	12	13
021601	Matane	8,5 km amont Matane	1979 1961	04-30 05-29	807 600	2 2	A3C1 A2B1	A1A A1A	160 30			
052219	L'Assomption	Joliette	1970 1928	05-03 05-06	351 323	2 2	A1B1 A2B1	A1A A1A	15 15			
050115	Saint-Maurice	Grand-Mère	1974 1947	05-17 05-24	5130 5100	2 2	A2D6 A2D6	A0X A0X	510 510			
050401	Sainte-Anne	Saint-Alban	1924 1943 1932	10-01 05-27 10-07	1272 855 714	1 2 1	A2D6 A2D6	A0X A0X	U 85 70			
050801	Jacques Cartier	Saint-Gabriel	1924 1979	10-01 04-28	1130 918	1 2	A2C1 A1C1	A1A A1A	220 45			
051001	Montmorency	Boischatel	1928 1927	05-25 11-18	564 549	2 1	A2B1 A2B1	A1A A1A	30 25			
051502	Malbaie	Clermont	1979	04-28	610	2	A1C1	A1A	30			
061901	Chamouchouane	Saint-Félicien	1960 1974 1979	05-12 05-17 04-30	2810 2400 2040	2 2 2	A2B1 A1B1 A1B1	A1A A1A A1A	140 120 100			
062101	Mistassibi	Mistassibi	1976 1979	05-21 05-01	1560 1480	2 2	A1B1 A1B1	A1A A1A	80 75			
062901	Saguenay	Isle Maligne	1928 1920 1976	05-31 05-30 05-22	9260 9060 8950	2 2 2	A2D6 A2D6 A2D6	A0X A0X A0X	930 910 900			
071001	Aux Outardes	Chûte aux Outardes	1943 1928	05-29 05-29	2830 2430	2 2	A2D6 A2D6	A0X A0X	280 240			
073301	Au Tonnerre	Rivière au Tonnerre	1959 1950 1966	10-27 12-13 11-04	782 470 281	2 4 4	B5X0 A2C1 A2C1	A1A A1A A1A	160 50 15			
020802	Madeleine	5,1 km de Rivière Madeleine	1977 1979	05-24 04-30	640 520	2 2	A1C1 A3X1	A1A A1A	15 100			
011201	Nouvelle	Nouvelle	1979 1966	04-30 05-30	510 370	2 2	A1B1 A2B1	B1A B1A	25 20			
080101	Harricana	Amos	1960 1947	05-11 05-26	340 320	2 2	A1B1 A1B1	A1A A1A	15 15			
080701	Nottoway	Lac Soscumica	1974 1962	06-07 06-06	4730 3280	2 2	A1B1 A1B1	A1A A1A	250 160			
081001 02	De Rupert	Lac Nemiscau	1974 1979	06-07 05-16	1890 1890	2 2	A1B1 A2B1	A1A A1A	95 380			

CANADA

TABLEAU II : CARACTERISTIQUES DES CRUES

	CARACTERISTIQUES DE LA CRUE						EVALUATION DES DEBITS					
N° du point	Rivière	Point d'observ.	Année	Date du maximum	Débit max m³/s	Origine	Base et mode eval	Qual. de la séch	Préci. ±m³s-1	Anteced	Haut. mm	Durée jours
1	2	3	4	5	6	7	8	9	10	11	12	13
090601	East Main	Gorges de Basile	1977	06-01	3680	2	A1B1	A1A	185			
			1960	05-25	3450	2	A1B1	A1A	170			
092704	La Grande Rivière	Près embouchure	1973	05-19	6710	2	A1B1	A1A	335			
			1966	06-03	5300	2	A1B1	A1A	265			
093801	Grande Rivière De La Baleine	Près embouchure	1967	05-25	1850	2	A1B1	A1A	90			
			1965	07-03	1810	1	A1B1	A1A	90			
102001	Arnaud	Amont de la Hamelin	1965	06-17	3110	2	A1C1	A1A	155			
			1974	06-10	2760	2	A1C1	A1A	140			
103602 3605	Aux Mélèzes	Près embouchure	1966	05-30	7500	2	A2C1	A1A	1500			
			1965	06-11	7360	2	A2C1	A1A	1500			
			1968	05-22	6090	2	A1C1	A1A	300			
103702	Caniapiscau	Près embouchure	1979	05-24	13500	2	A1C1	A1A	700			
			1975	07-09	10400	1	A1C1	A1A	500			
104801	George	Près embouchure	1979	05-23	7960	2	A1C1	A1A	400			
			1975	06-08	7900	2	A1C1	A1A	400			
			1970	06-25	7050	2	A1C1	A1A	350			

NEW BRUNSWICK

01AD002	St John	Fort Kent	1979	04-30	4280	4	A1B1					
			1973	04-30	3850	4	A1B1					
01AD003	St Francis	Outlet Glasier Lake	1979	04-30	428	4	A1B1					
			1969	05-12	368	4	A1B1					

NOVA SCOTIA

01ER001	Clam Harbour	Birchtown	1969	11-09	134	1	A1B1					
			1968	08-31	79.6	1	A1B1					
01FB001	Northeast Margaree	Margaree Valley	1968	08-26	569	1	A1B1					
			1967	11-24	558	1	A1B1					

NEWFOUNDLAN AND LABRADOR

02ZK001	Rocky	Colinet	1974	08-31	237	1	A1B1					
			1962	02-11	187	4	A1B1					
02YL001	Upper Humber	Near Reidville	1935	11-30	813	1	A3B1					
			1948	05-23	799	4 ?	A3B1					
			1954	12-23	776	1	A1B1					
030E001	Churchill	Above upper Muskrat Falls	1957	06-27	6820	4	A1B1					
			1966	06-17	6710	4 ?	A1B1					
			1956	07-03	6630	4 ?	A1B1					

CENTRAL AFRICAN REPUBLIC/REPUBLIQUE CENTRAFRICAINE

TABLEAU I : IDENTIFICATION DES POINTS D'OBSERVATION ET CARACTERISTIQUES DES BASSINS

	POINT D'OBSERVATION							CARACTERISTIQUES DU BASSIN					
N° du point	Bassin fluvial	Rivière	Point d'observ.		Coordonnées Lat. Long.	Période	Surface km²	Relief	Sol	Végét.	Régime	Pluie moyenne mm	Module m³s-1
1	2	3	4	5	6	7	8	9	10	11	12	13	14
1	Oubangui	Oubangui	Bangui	1	N E 04:22 18:35	1880 1980	500000	A B C	C D	A B	00 10	1560	4300
2	Oubangui	Lobaye	M'bata	1	N E 03:39 18:18	1950 75	30000	A B	C D	A B	00 10	1520	355

CENTRAL AFRICAN REPUBLIC/REPUBLIQUE CENTRAFRICAINE

TABLEAU II : CARACTERISTIQUES DES CRUES

	CARACTERISTIQUES DE LA CRUE						EVALUATION DES DEBITS					
N° du point	Rivière	Point d'observ.	Année	Date du maximum	Débit max m³s-1	Origine	Base et mode éval	Qual. de la séch.	Précis. ±m³s-1	Anteced	Hauteur mm	Durée jours
1	2	3	4	5	6	7	8	9	10	11	12	13
1	Oubangui	Bangui	1916	10-23	15800	1	A1B1	A1A	400			
			1891	11-19	14500	1	A3B1	A1A	1000			
			1961	11-02	14400	1	A1B1	A1A	400			
2	Lobaye	M'bata	1955	10-18	650	1	A1C1	A1A	60			
			1950	?	640	1	C4B1	A1A	50			
			1969	10-04	630	1	A1B1	A1A	30			
			1966	10-29	607	1	A1B1	A1A	30			

TABLEAU I : IDENTIFICATION DES POINTS D'OBSERVATION ET CARACTERISTIQUES DES BASSINS

		POINT D'OBSERVATION						CARACTERISTIQUES DU BASSIN					
N° du point	Bassin fluvial	Rivière	Point d'observ.		Coordonnées Lat. Long.	Période	Surface km²	Relief	Sol	Végét.	Régime	Pluie moyenne mm	Module m³s-1
1	2	3	4	5	6	7	8	9	10	11	12	13	14
46020121	Lac Tchad	Chari	N'Djamena	1	N 12:07 E 15:02	1906 08 1932 38 1953 77	600000	A40 B C D	D90 C10	B C	10 11	1040 (1)	1200
46030160	Chari	Logone	Logone Birni	1	N 11:47 E 15:06	1952 60 1966 77	74000	A B C D	D80 C20	B C	10 11	1300	381
46020118	Chari	Chari	Sahr	1	N 09:09 E 18:25	1938 40 1942 43 1950 77	193000	A50 B C D	D90 C10	B C	10 11	1080	287
46030157	Chari	Logone	Laï	1	N 09:24 E 16:18	1948 77	56700	A B C D	D C	B C	10 11	1370	512
46030172	Chari	Logone	Moundou	1	N 08:32 E 16:04	1935 77 avec lacunes	33970	B C D	D	B	10 11	1390	370
46021906	Chari	Barh Sara	Moissala	1	N 08:20 E 17:46	1951 78	67600	C D	D	B	10 11	1440	498
46031805	Logone	M'béré	M'béré	1	N 07:26 E 15:27	1951 70	7430	C D	D	B	10	1470	115
9	Logone	Nya	Badé	4	N 08:31 E 15:41	1963 64	316	B	B	B	10	1215	1.0
10	Bénoué	Mayo Ligan	Route Fianga Léré	4	N 09:52 E 14:40	1961 1964 1965	41	C	D	B	11	900	0.33
46400109	Lac Fitri	Batha	Ati	1	N 13:12 E 18:19	1955 74	46000	A B C D	C D	C	11	590	18.5
11	Lac Tchad	Ouadi Enné	Biltine	3	N 14:37 E 21:00	1959 61	527	A B C D	B C D	C	11	340	0.11
12	Enneri Salaa	Bachikélé	Bassin représentatif	4	N 16:30 E 22:17	1958 59	20	D E	C D	E	20	115	0.012
13	Sahara	Zoumri	Bardaï	3	N 21:30 E 17:00	1954 62	4050	F E D	B C D	E	20	30	

1) La moyenne n'a pas de signification physique rapportée aux 600.000 km².

TABLEAU II : CARACTERISTIQUES DES CRUES

	CARACTERISTIQUES DE LA CRUE						EVALUATION DES DEBITS					
N° du point	Rivière	Point d'observ.	Année	Date du maximum	Débit max m³s-1	Origine	Base et mode eval	Qual. de la séch.	Précis. ±m³s-1	Anteced	Hauteur mm	Durée jours
1	2	3	4	5	6	7	8	9	10	11	12	13
46020121	Chari	N'Djamena	1961	11-09	5160	1	A1B1	A1A	200			
			1955	11-10	4730	1	A1B1	A1A	190			
46030160	Logone	Logone Birni	1970	10-24	1060	1	A1B1	B1A	40			
			1969	11-04	984	1	A1B1	B1A	40			
			1955	11-12	932	1	A1B1	B1A	37			
46020118	Chari	Sahr	1961	10-17	2090	1	A1B1	B1A	80			
			1962	10-23	1650	1	A1B1	B1A	70			
			1955	10-21	1600	1	A1B1	B1A	60			
46030157	Logone	Laï	1955	10-09	3730	1	A1B1	B1A	150			
			1969	09-25	3330	1	A1B1	B1A	130			
			1970	09-08	3330	1	A1B1	B1A	130			
46030172	Logone	Moundou	1956	10-07	3640	1	A3B1	B1A	150			
			1948	08-26	3290	1	A3B1	B1A	130			
			1935	09-05	2970	1	A3B1	B1A	130			
46021906	Bahr Sara	Moïssala	1955	09-22	3680	1	A1B1	B1A	150			
			1961	10-01	2960	1	A1B1	B1A	120			
46031805	Mbéré	Mbéré	1964	09-03	1930	1	A3C1	B1A	80			
			1963	08-16	1880	1	A3C1	B1A	70			
9	Nya	Badé	1964	09-24	5.6	1	A1B1	B1A	05		90	1
10	Mayo Ligan	Route Fianga Léré	1965	08-10	137.5	1	A1B1	B1A	10		42	1
46400109	Batha	Ati	1961	09-07	794	1	A1B1	B1A	80			
11	Ouadi Enné	Biltine	1958	été	160	1	B5C1	B1A	30			
			1961	08-06	120	1	A1C1	B1A	20			
12	Bachikélé	Bassin Représentatif	1958	07-26	114	1	A1B1	B1A	10		39	1
13	Zoumri	Bardaï	1954	été	425	1	D5DC25	C1B	50			

TABLE I : IDENTIFICATION OF OBSERVATION SITES AND CHARACTERISTICS OF BASINS

	OBSERVATION SITES						CHARACTERISTICS OF BASIN						
Site number	River basin	Stream	Observ. site		Coordinates Lat. Long.	Period	Area km²	Slope	Soil	Cover	Regime	Mean precip. mm	Mean disc. m³s−1
1	2	3	4	5	6	7	8	9	10	11	12	13	14
HEILONG JIANG													
1	Songhua	Songhua	Harbin	1	N 45:46 E 126:35	1898 1980	391000	A10 C10 D40 E20 F20	D	A50 B30 C20	61	580	1190
JILIN													
2	Songhua	Songhua	Jilin	1	N 43:50 E 126:32	1933 39 1944 71	44100	D E F			61	710	466
HEBEI													
3	Luanhe	Luanhe	Luanxian	1	N 39:44 E 118:45	1929 44 1946 79	44100	D40 E60	D	B	60	550	148
BEIJING													
4	Haihe	Yongding	Guanting	1	N 40:14 E 115:36	1925 52	42500				60 70	420	43
SHANXI													
5	Huanghe	Jinghe	Zhangjiashan	1	N 34:38 E 108:36	1933 72	43200				90 71	570	51
6	Changjiang	Hanjiang	Ankang	1	N 32:41 E 109:01	1935 74	41400				90	830	620
HENAN													
7	Huanghe	Yiluo	Heishiguan	1	N 34:43 E 112:56	1936 72	18600				90	550	109
8	Huanghe	Huanghe	Shanxian	1	N 34:49 E 111:09	1919 43 1946 58	688000	C10 D65 E25	C	C20 E80	90 70 71	450	1350
SICHUAN													
9	Changjiang	Wujiang	Gongtan	1	N 28:54 E 108:21	1939 78	58300	F			90 40	1200	1160
HUBEI													
10	Changjiang	Changjiang	Yichang	1	N 30:40 E 111:14	1877 1978	1010000	B 5 D35 E30 F30	D	B	90 40	1140	14300
JIANGXI													
11	Changjiang	Ganjiang	Jian	1	N 27:06 E 114:59	1931 1935 1943 1945 78	56200				40	1500	1500
ZHEJIANG													
12	Qiantang	Qiantang	Lucibu	1	N 29:42 E 119:40	1931 35 1938 41 1947 68	31500				40	1710	925
FUJIAN													
13	Minjiang	Minjiang	Zhuqi	1	N 26:09 E 119:06	1934 40 1942 78	54500	D20 E80	D	B	40	1750	1760

TABLE I : IDENTIFICATION OF OBSERVATION SITES AND CHARACTERISTICS OF BASINS

	OBSERVATION SITES						CHARACTERISTICS OF BASIN						
Site number	River basin	Stream	Observ. site		Coordinates Lat. Long.	Period	Area km²	Slope	Soil	Cover	Regime	Mean precip. mm	Mean disc. m³s-1
1	2	3	4	5	6	7	8	9	10	11	12	13	14
GUANGXI													
14	Zhujiang	Yujiang	Nanning	1	N 22:48 E 108:22	1938 72	75500				10	1330	1290
15	Zhujiang	Xijiang	Wuzhou	1	N 23:29 E 111:18	1900 44 1946 79	330000	D60 E40	A30 C60	B	90 40 10	1400	7200
GUANGDONG													
16	Zhujiang	Dongjiang	Boluo	1	N 23:10 E 114:18	1954 72	25300				40 10	1750	710
TAIWAN													
29-H-24	Choshui	Choshui	Tung-ton	1	N 23:29 E 120:39		259	F E	D	A	40		
29-H-21	Choshui	Choshui	Chichi	1	N 23:49 E 120:45	1941 79	2304	E D	D85 C15	A B	40	2600	133
29-H-29	Choshui	Choshui	Hsilo	1	N 23:48 E 120:27		2976	E D	D C	A D	40		
3-H-29	Tamshui	Tamshui	Taipei-Bridge	1	N 25:03 E 121:30		2110	E D	D C	A D	40		
3-H-58	Tamshui	Tamshui	Wutu	1	N 25:04 E 121:41		204	E	D	A	40		
51-H-26	Kaoping	Kaoping	Chiu Chu Tang	1	N 22:39 E 120:25		3076	E D	D C	A D	40		
51-H-31	Kaoping	Kaoping	Lao nung	1	N 23:05 E 120:39		812	E	D	A D	40		
30-H-24	Hualien	Hualien	Hualien Bridge	1	N 23:55 E 121:35		1500	E D	D C	A	40		

TABLE II : FLOODS CHARACTERISTICS

	FLOODS CHARACTERISTICS						DISCHARGE ESTIMATION					
Site number	Stream	Observ. site	Year	Date of the max	Maximal disc m³s-1	Climatic origine	Condition disc est	Qual. of the sect	Préci. ±m³s-1	Anteced precip.	Depth mm	Duration days
1	2	3	4	5	6	7	8	9	10	11	12	13
HEILONG JIANG												
1	Songhua	Harbin	1957	09-06	12200	1	A1A1	B1B		1		
			1956	08-15	11700	1	A1A1	B1B		1		
			1932	08-12	11500	1	A2C	B1B		2		
JILIN												
2	Songhua	Jilin	1909	07-24	12900	1						
			1923	08-14	11000	1						
			1953	08-22	7720	1						
HEBEI												
3	Luanhe	Luanxian	1886	08	35000							
			1962	07-27	35000	1	C4B	C2B		2		
			1949	08-15	34000	1	A1B	C2B				
					28500	1	B2B	C2B				
BEIJING												
4	Yongding	Guanting	1801		9400	1						
			1893		6300	1						
			1924		5000	1						
SHANXI												
5	Jinghe	Zhangjiashan	1843or1847		18800	1						
			1911	08-03	14700	1						
			1933	08-08	9200	1						
6	Hanjiang	Ankang	1583		40000	1						
			1867		33000	1						
			1921		27500	1						
HENAN												
7	Yiluo	Heishiguan	1935	07-08	10200	1						
			1958	07-17	9450	1						
			1937	08-06	8950	1						
8	Huanghe	Shanxian	1843		36000	1	C4D	C2B		2		
			1933	08-20	22000	1	A1C	C2B		1		
			1942	08-04	17000	1	A1C	C2B		1		
SICHUAN												
9	Wujiang	Gongtan	1830		24700	1						
			1909	07-05	20000	1						
			1935		16600	1						
HUBEI												
10	Changjiang	Yichang	1870	07-20	110000	1	C4C	B2B				
			1860	07-18	92500	1	C4C	B2B				
			1788	07-23	86000	1	C4C	B2B				
			1896	09-04	71100	1	A1B	B2B		2		
JIANGXI												
11	Ganjiang	Jian	1915		23000	1						
			1876		20800	1						
			1899		19800	1						
ZHEJIANG												
12	Qiantang	Lucibu	1901	06-20	26500	1						
			1942	06-18	23300	1						
			1929	06-21	21100	1						
FUJIAN												
13	Minjiang	Zhuqi	1900	06-29	29400	1	C4D4	B2B		2		
			1968	06-19	29400	1	A1A3	B2B		2		
			1962	06-29	27000	1	A1A3	B2B		3		

TABLE II : FLOODS CHARACTERISTICS

	FLOODS CHARACTERISTICS						DISCHARGE ESTIMATION					
Site number	Stream	Observ. site	Year	Date of the max	Maximal disc m³s-1	Climatic origine	Condition disc est	Qual. of the sect	Précis. ±m³s-1	Anteced precip.	Depth mm	Duratio jours
1	2	3	4	5	6	7	8	9	10	11	12	13

GUANGXI

14	Yujiang	Nanning	1936	09-12	15200	1						
			1968	08-18	13300	1						
			1970	08-21	12300	1						
15	Xijiang	Wuzhou	1915	07-10	54500	1	A3D4	A1A		2		
			1949	07-05	49900	1	A3D4	A1A		3		
			1924	07-13	47700	1	A2B	A1A		3		
			1914	06-20	46100	1	A2B	A1A		1		
			1944	06-28	44200	1	A1A3	A1A		3		

GUANGDONG

16	Dongjiang	Boluo	1959	06-16	12200	1						
			1940	07-30	10300	1						
			1966	06-24	10200	1						

TAIWAN

29-H-24	Choshui	Tong-ton	1979	08-24	7780	1	A1C3					
			1965		4670	1	A1C3					
29-H-21	Choshui	Chi-chi	1960	08-01	10500	1	A1C3	D2B		1	657	3
			1956		9900	1	A1C3			1	598	4
29-H-29	Choshui	Hsilo	1969		12800	1	A1C3					
			1970		11300	1	A1C3					
3-H-29	Tamshui	Taipei-bridge	1963	09-11	16700	1	A1C3					
			1948		15520	1	A1C3					
3-H-58	Tamshui	Wutu	1977		1380	1	A1C3					
			1978		1370	1	A1C3					
51-H-26	Kaoping	Chin chu tang	1959	08-08	18000	1	A1C3					
			1976	07	16300	1	A1C3					
51-H-31	Kaoping	Lao-nung	1960	08-01	6160	1	A1C3					
			1959		4940	1	A1C3					
30-H-24	Hualien	Hualien bridge	1973		11900	1	A1C3					
			1971		9060	1	A1C3					

TABLEAU I : IDENTIFICATION DES POINTS D'OBSERVATION ET CARACTERISTIQUES DES BASSINS

	POINT D'OBSERVATION								CARACTERISTIQUES DU BASSIN					
N° du point	Bassin fluvial	Rivière	Point d'observ.		Coordonnées Lat. Long.		Période	Surface km²	Relief	Sol	Végét.	Régime	Pluie moyenne mm	Module m³s−1
1	2	3	4	5	6		7	8	9	10	11	12	13	14
1107701	Atrato	Atrato	Bellavista	1	N 06:34	W 76:52	1969 1973 76	17267	B30 D40 E30	B25 C75	A	10 00 90	5900	2420
5408701	San Juan	San Juan	Noamana	1	N 04:40	W 76:53	1969 1976	8902	B25 D35 E40	B 5 C90 D 5	A	10 00 90	5400	1450
3501702	Orinoco	Meta	Puerto Lleras	1	N 04:45	W 72:57	1973 76	8358	A50 C10 D10 E30	B50 C25 D25	B50 D50	90 10 11	2950	433
2113701	Magdalena	Magdalena	Purificacion	1	N 03:51	W 74:56	1960 76	26115	B30 D50 E20	C50 D50	A15 B35 D50	90 10 11	1620	698
2617703	Magdalena	Cauca	La Virginia	1	N 04:53	W 75:53	1965 76	22814	B20 D40 E40	B30 C20 D50	B10 C20 D70	90 10 11	1730	600
2309703	Magdalena	Magdalena	Puerto Berro	1	N 06:30	W 74:23	1936 63 1965 76	74410	B30 D35 E35	B 5 C60 D35	A 5 B35 D60	90 10 11	1950	2480
2903702	Magdalena	Magdalena	Calamar	1	N 10:16	W 74:55	1941 76	257438	A10 B20 C 5 D35 E30	B15 C50 D35	B20 C10 D70	10 11 90	2020	7320

TABLEAU II : CARACTERISTIQUES DES CRUES

		CARACTERISTIQUES DE LA CRUE					EVALUATION DES DEBITS					
N° du point	Rivière	Point d'observ.	Année	Date du maximum	Débit max m³s-1	Origine	Base et mode éval.	Qual. de la séch	Précis. ±m³s-1	Anteced	Hauteur mm	Durée jours
1	2	3	4	5	6	7	8	9	10	11	12	13
1107701	Atrato	Bellavista	1969	10-06	4200	1	A2C1	X1B	U			
5408701	San Juan	Noamana	1971	11-10	3860	1	A1B1	X1A	U			
3501702	Meta	Puerto Lleras	1973	07-11	1300	1	A1B1	A1A	100	2/3	1500	200
2113701	Magdalena	Purificacion	1975	12-19	4190	1	A1B1	B1A	400	2	550	70
			1974	02-15	4100	1	A1B1	B1A	400			
2617703	Cauca	La Virginia	1971	03-27	2170	1	A1B1	B1AB	200			
			1973	11-16	2100	1	A1B1	B1AB	200	2	400	60
2309703	Magdalena	Puerto Berro	1942	05-06	6850	1	A1B1	B1B/C	500			
			1970	11-01	6570	1	A1B1	B1B/C	500			
2903702	Magdalena	Calamar	1975	11-(20)	14700	1	A5C1	B1B	+300 -1200			
			1974	11-(28)	14400	1	A5C1	B1B	+600 -1600			

TABLEAU I : IDENTIFICATION DES POINTS D'OBSERVATION ET CARACTERISTIQUES DES BASSINS

	POINT D'OBSERVATION							CARACTERISTIQUES DU BASSIN					
N° du point	Bassin fluvial	Rivière	Point d'observ.		Coordonnées Lat. Long.		Période	Surface km²	Relief	Sol	Végét.	Régime	Pluie moyenne mm	Module m³s-1
1	2	3	4	5	6		7	8	9	10	11	12	13	14
1	Congo (Zaïre)	Congo	Brazzaville Beach	1	S 04:16	E 15:19	1902 1980	3475000			A B C	00 10	1550	43000
28	Congo	Sangha	Ouesso	1	S 01:36	E 16:02	1947 80	158350	C D	C	A B	00 10	1600	1715
8	Congo	Nkeni	Gamboma	1	S 01:54	E 15:51	1951 80	6200	C	B	C	00	1860	206
3	Congo	Foulakary	Kimpanzou	1	S 04:15	E 14:56	1947 80	2980	C D	C	B C	00	1440	57
68	Kouilou	Comba	Comba	1	S 04:14	E 14:17	1966 80	90	E	C	B30 C70	00	1470	1.30
68-1	Kouilou	Mazoumbou	Abattoirs	4	S 04:19	E 14:16	4 ans	3.25	F	C	B	00	1620	0.08
68-2	Kouilou	Affluent Mazoumbou	Déversoir	4	S 04:18	E 14:16	3 ans	1.18	E	D	C	00	1560	0.02
42	Kouilou	Niari	Loudima	1	S 04:07	E 13:05	1951 80	23385	C D	D C	B C	00	1455	380
40	Kouilou	Kouilou	Kibangou	1	S 03:33	E 12:20	1952 80	48990	C D	B C D	A B C	00	1520	855
39 37	Kouilou	Kouilou	Sounda- Kakamoeka	1 1	S 04:06 04:09	E 12:04 12:04	1955 80 1952 80	55010 55340	C D	B C D	A B C	00	1500 1500	935 940
69	Nyanga	Nyanga	Donguila	1	S 02:52	E 11:58	1954 80	5800	B C	C D	A	00	1795	217
80	Songolo	Tchinouka	Pointe Noire	1	S 04:47	E 11:52	1 an	10.7	B	B	E40 C60	00	1250	0.15

TABLEAU II : CARACTERISTIQUES DES CRUES

	CARACTERISTIQUES DE LA CRUE						EVALUATION DES DEBITS					
N° du point	Rivière	Point d'observ.	Année	Date du maximum	Débit max m³s-1	Origine	Base et mode éval	Qual. de la séch.	Précis. ±m³s-1	Anteced	Hauteur mm	Durée jours
1	2	3	4	5	6	7	8	9	10	11	12	13
1	Congo (Zaïre)	Brazzaville Beach	1961	12-27	76900	(2) 1	A1C1	A1A	2000			
			1962	12-20	73250	1	A1C1	A1A	2000			
			1964	12-10	69450	1	A1C1	A1A	2000			
			1967	12-05	67100	1	A1B1	A1A	2000			
28	Sangha	Ouesso	1960	11-06	4730	1	A1B1	A1A	400			
			1962	11-02	4720	1	A1B1	A1A	400			
			1957	10-25	4660	1	A1B1	A1A	400			
8	Nkeni	Gamboma	1974	09-11	324	1	A1D1	B1B	20			
			1967	03-29	295	1	A1D1	B1B	20			
3	Foulakary	Kimpanzou	1966	05-02	470	1	A2C1	B1A	50			
			1957	04-27	428	1	A2C1	B1A	50			
68	Comba	Comba	1977	11-11	202	1	A1B1	A1A	10			
			1973	04-16	183	1	A1B1	A1A	10			
68-1	Mazoumbou	Abattoirs	1973	04-16	51.3	1	A1C1	B1A	5	3	138	1
68-2	Mazoumbou Affluent	Déversoir	1974	04-14	22.4	1	A1C1	A1A	2	3	60	1
42	Niari	Loudima	1967	03-25	1790	1	A1C1	A1A	200			
			1966	05-03	1760	1	A1C1	A1A	200			
40	Kouilou	Kibangou	1966	05-09	3500	1	A1C1	A1A	300			
			1953	04-25	3010	1	A1C1	A1A	300			
39 37	Kouilou	Sounda	1950	05-?	4090	1	A1C1	A1A	300			
			1966	05-10	3560	1	A1B1	A1A	250			
			1952	12-06	3180	1	A1B1	A1A	250			
69	Nyanga	Donguila	1966	05-03	893	1	A1C1	A1A	80			
			1961	03-11	849	1	A1C1	A1A	80			
80	Tchinouka	Pointe Noire	1959 (1)	03-28	7.59	1	A1B1	A1A	1	3	252	1

(1) Période de retour voisine de 10 ans.
(2) Courbe de tarage congolaise, jaugeages à Maluku Tréchaud.

COSTA RICA

TABLE I : IDENTIFICATION OF OBSERVATION SITES AND CHARACTERISTICS OF BASINS

	OBSERVATION SITES							CHARACTERISTICS OF BASIN						
Site number	River basin	Stream	Observ. site		Coordinates Lat. Long.	Period	Area km²	Slope	Soil	Cover	Regime	Mean precip. mm	Mean disc. m³s-1
1	2	3	4	5	6	7	8	9	10	11	12	13	14
73.09.03	Reventazon Parismina	Reventazon	Angostura	1	N 09:53 W 83:39	1954 80	1337	D E	C	A56 D20	00	3780	107
98.31.01	Grande de Terraba	Grande de Terraba	Palmar	1	N 08:57 W 83:28	1962 80	4765	D E	C	A25 D75	00	3360	328
84.24.11	Grande de Tarcoles	Grande de Tarcoles	Alumbre	1	N 09:55 W 84:29	1969 80	1745	D E	C	A20 D41 E37	00	2460	87.2
74.19.01	Tempisque	Tempisque	Guardia	1	N 10:34 W 85:36	1958 69 1980	955	C	C	A53 D46 E 1	00	2040	28.7

COSTA RICA

TABLE II : FLOODS CHARACTERISTICS

	FLOODS CHARACTERISTICS						DISCARGE ESTIMATION					
Site number	Stream	Observ. site	Year	Date of the max	Maximal discm³s-1	Climatic orig.	Condition disc est	Qual. of the sect	Preci. ±m³s-1	Anteced precip.	Depth mm	Duration days
1	2	3	4	5	6	7	8	9	10	11	12	13
73.09.03	Reventazon	Angostura	1970 1955	04-09 10-14	3800 1670	1 1	A4D4	BOB	400 150	3	447	4
98-31-01	Grande de Terraba	Palmar	1973 1971	08-29 09-19	7300 4960	1 1	A1C2	BOB	700 500	3		
84-24-11	Grande de Tarcoles	Alumbre	1969	11-25	4400 (?)	1	A1C4	BOB	400	3		
74-19-01	Tempisque	Guardia	1960	10-27	2060	1	A1C4	BOB	200	3		

CUBA

TABLEAU I : IDENTIFICATION DES POINTS D'OBSERVATION ET CARACTERISTIQUES DES BASSINS

	POINT D'OBSERVATION				Coordonnées			CARACTERISTIQUES DU BASSIN					
N° du point	Bassin fluvial	Rivière	Point d'observ.		Lat.	Long	Période	Surface km²	Relief	Sol	Végét.	Régime	Pluie moyenne mm	Module m³s-1
1	2	3	4	5	6		7	8	9	10	11	12	13	14
1	Toa	Toa	El Aguacate	1	N 20:22	W 74:41	1965 79	753	E	B55 C45	B C	40	2000	24.3
2	Cauto	Bayamo	La Bayamesa	1	N 20:24	W 76:40	1965 68 1973 79	540	E	A60 C25 D15	C D	40	1820	14.0
3	Toa	Toa	El Toro	1	N 20:17	W 74:51	1956 58 1960 62 1964 79	326	E	B55 C45	B C	40	1980	10.6
4	Toa	Jaguani	Arroyo Prieto	1	N 20:27	W 74:48	1966 70 1973 79	182	E	B55 C45	B C	40	2710	10.6
5	Saga la Chica	Camajuani	Paso Ibarra	1	N 22:29	W 79:45	1967 79	154	D	B70 C30	B D	40	1400	2.39
6	Mani Mani	Mani Mani	Martires de Guajaibon	1	N 22:51	W 83:13	1967 79	79	E	B30 C70	C D	40	1860	1.98
7	Buey	Buey	San Miguel	1	N 20:08	W 76:45	1960 79	73	E	A30 C60 D10	B C	40	2150	2.68
8	San Juan Y Martinez	San Juan Y Martinez	El Tabaco	1	N 22:17	W 83:51	1969 79	62	E	B65 C35	C D	40	1800	1.68
9	Gua	Jibacoa	Praga	1	N 20:04	W 77:01	1968 77	42	E	A30 B20 C50	B C	40	2000	1.52
10	San Cristobal	Santa Cruz	Santa Ana	1	N 22:43	W 83:08	1966 79	28	E	B30 C70	C D	40	1990	1.57

CUBA

TABLEAU II : CARACTERISTIQUES DES CRUES

	CARACTERISTIQUES DE LA CRUE						EVALUATION DES DEBITS					
N° du point	Rivière	Point d'observ.	Année	Date du maximum	Débit max m³s-1	Origine	Base et mode éval	Qual. de la séch	Précis. ±m³s-1	Anteced	Hauteur	Durée jours
1	2	3	4	5	6	7	8	9	10	11	12	13
1	Toa	El Aguacate	1977	11-14	2760	1	A1B2	A1A	280			
			1965	11-03	2244	1	A1B2	A1A	220			
2	Bayamo	La Bayamesa	1977	05-30	3015	1	A1B2	A1A	300			
			1979	04-25	1655	1	A1B2	A1A	160			
3	Toa	El Toro	1963	10-	2160	1	A3D4	A1A	440			
			1961	10-19	1600	1	A1B2	A1A	160			
			1972	05-21	1185	1	A1B2	A1A	120			
4	Jaguani	Arroyo Prieto	1977	11-14	1532	1	A1B3	C2B	300			
			1970	07-29	746	1	A1B3	C2B	140			
5	Camajuani	Paso Ibarra	1978	10-18	2750	1	A1B2	A1A	540			
			1973	08-08	393	1	A2D4	A1A	40			
6	Mani Mani	Martires de Guajaibon	1972	06-18	655	1	A1B2	B1A	60			
			1967	06-17	630	1	A1B2	B1A	60			
7	Buey	San Miguel	1963	10-07	2060	1	A3D4	B1X	410			
			1973	10-18	588	1	A1B2	B1X	60			
			1966	09-30	542	1	A1B2	B1X	50			
8	San Juan y Martinez	El Tobaco	1967	06-16	684	1	A1B2	A1A	70			
			1979	04-24	667	1	A1B2	A1A	70			
9	Jibacoa	Praga	1977	05-30	803	1	A1B3	A1B	90			
10	Santa Cruz	Santa Ana	1972	06-17	380	1	A1B3	A1A	40			
			1971	10-12	211	1	A1B3	A1A	20			

TABLE I : IDENTIFICATION OF OBSERVATION SITES AND CHARACTERISTICS OF BASINS

	OBSERVATION SITES						CHARACTERISTICS OF BASIN						
Site number	River basin	Stream	Observ. site		Coordinates Lat. Long.	Period	Area km²	Slope	Soil	Cover	Regime	Mean precip. mm	Mean disc. m³s⁻¹
1	2	3	4	5	6	7	8	9	10	11	12	13	14
1	Odra	Smedava	Bily Potok	1	N 50:51 E 15:14	1956 81	26.1	F		A90 D10	90 61	1470	0.85
2	Ostravice	Celadenka	Celadna	1	N 49:50 E 18:20	1952 81	31.1	C D		A100	90 61	1320	0.83
3	Odra	Ostravice	Sance	1	N 49:30 E 18:24	1926 81	146	C D		A100	90 61	1200	3.11
4	Labe (Elbe)	Kamenice	Josefuv dul	1	N 50:46 E 15:14	1911 81	26	F		A90 D10	90 61	1420	0.93
5	Labe	Cidlina	Novy Bydzov	1	N 50:14 E 15:30	1932 81	452	D E		A20 D80	61	640	1.98
6	Vltava	Berounka	Krivoklat	1	N 50:01 E 13:53	1886 1981	7422	D E		A30 D65 E 5	90 61	590	31.8
7	Labe	Vltava	Kamyk na Vltavou	1	N 49:38 E 14:15	1877 1954	12200	C D E		A34 D66	90 61	690	77.8
8	Labe	Labe	Decin	1	N 50:47 E 14:13	1851 1981	51100	C D E		A30 D62 E 8	90 61	680	306
9	Becva	Zdechovka	Zdechov	1	N 49:16 E 18:05	1928 81	4.08	F		A 6 D90 E 4	61	970	0.06
10	Morava	Becva	Teplice	1	N 49:32 E 17:44	1920 81	1280	C D E F		A47 D53	61	890	15.3
11	Danube	Morava	Kromeriz	1	N 49:18 E 17:24	1916 81	7010	C D E F		A36 D64	61	720	49.3
12	Morava	Dyje	Dolni Vestonice	1	N 48:53 E 17:39	1921 81	11700	B C D		A27 D73	61	590	41.5
13	Danube	Vah	Lubochna	1	N 49:20 E 19:10	1921 81	2130	C D E F		A60 D13 E27	90 61	1020	38
14	Vah	Lubochnianka	Lubochna	1	N 49:20 E 19:10	1931 81	118	F		A90 E10	90 61	1180	2.38
15	Vah	Turiec	Martin	1	N 49:04 E 18:56	1931 81	827	D E		A60 D30 E10	90 61	945	10.7
16	Vah	Kysuca	Cadca	1	N 49:26 E 18:47	1920 81	484	D E		A50 D15 E35	61	910	8.4

TABLE II : FLOODS CHARACTERISTICS

		FLOOD CHARACTERISTICS							DISCHARGE ESTIMATION				
Site number	Stream	Observ. site	Year	Date of the max	Maximal dis $m^3 s{-}1$	Climatic origine	Condition disc est	Qual. of the sect	Preci. $\pm m^3 s{-}1$	Anteced precip.	Depth mm	Duration days
1	2	3	4	5	6	7	8	9	10	11	12	13
1	Smedava	Bily potok	1958	07-04	118	1						
			1977	08-01	97.8	1						
2	Celadenka	Celadna	1960	07-26	83	1						
			1966	07-25	63							
3	Ostravice	Sance	1958	06-29	270	1						
			1940	05-31	220	1						
4	Kamenice	Josefuv dul	1958	07-04	126	1						
			1948	08-14	106	1						
5	Cidlina	Novy Bydzov	1946	02-09	57.1	2						
			1967	12-25	54.6	2						
6	Berounka	Krivoklat	1890	09-03	1300	1						
			1909	02-05	897	2						
			1947	03-15	854	2						
7	Vltava	Kamyk Vlatou	1890	09-04	2310	1						
			1954	07-09	1970	1						
8	Labe	Decin	1845	03-30	5600	2						
			1890	09-06	4450	1						
			1876	02-20	4140	2						
9	Zdechovka	Zdechov	1938	09-15	14.7	1						
			1944	06-30	13.	1						
10	Becva	Teplice	1939	07-27	660	1						
			1937	09-13	650	1						
11	Morava	Kromeriz	1938	09-03	725	1						
			1937	09-14	681	1						
12	Dyje	Dolni Vestonice	1941	03-12	820	2						
			1947	03-23	815	2						
13	Vah	Lubochna	1958	06-30	840	1						
			1960	07-26	618	1						
14	Lubochnianka	Lubochna	1960	07-26	60.5	1						
			1958	06-29	51.3	1						
15	Turiec	Martin	1960	07-26	327	1						
			1974	10-22	188	1						
16	Kysuca	Cadca	1925	08-03	506	1						
			1970	07-19	433	1						

DEMOCRATIC KAMPUCHEA/KAMPUCHEA DEMOCRATIQUE

TABLE I : IDENTIFICATION OF OBSERVATION SITES AND CHARACTERISTICS OF BASINS

		OBSERVATION SITES							CHARACTERISTICS OF BASIN					
Site number	River basin	Stream	Observ. site		Coordinates Lat. Long.		Period	Area km²	Slope	Soil	Cover	Regime	Mean precip. mm	Mean disc. m³s-1
1	2	3	4	5	6		7	8	9	10	11	12	13	14
1	Mékong	Mékong	Kratie	1	N 12:29	E 106:01	1924 68	646000	A B C D E F		A30 B70	90 00 10	1500 2500	14000

DEMOCRATIC KAMPUCHEA/KAMPUCHEA DEMOCRATIQUE

TABLE II : FLOODS CHARACTERISTICS

	FLOOD CHARACTERISTICS						DISCHARGE ESTIMATION					
Site number	Stream	Observ. site	Year	Date of the max	Maximal dism³s-1	Climatic origine	Condition disc est	Qual. of the sect	Precis. ±m³s-1	Anteced precip.	Depth mm	Duration days
1	2	3	4	5	6	7	8	9	10	11	12	13
1	Mékong	Kratié	1939	09-03	66700	1	A1B1	B2B	10000	3		

DEMOCRATIC PEOPLE'S REPUBLIC OF KOREA/REPUBLIQUE POPULAIRE DEMOCRATIQUE DE COREE

TABLE I : IDENTIFICATION OF OBSERVATION SITES AND CHARACTERISTICS OF BASINS

OBSERVATION SITES								CHARACTERISTICS OF BASIN					
Site number	River basin	Stream	Observ. site		Coordinates Lat. Long.	Period	Area km²	Slope	Soil	Cover	Regime	Mean precip. mm	Mean disc. m³s-1
1	2	3	4	5	6	7	8	9	10	11	12	13	14
909	Amnokgang	Amnokgang	Kumchang	1	N 41:32 E 127:08	1965 80	18245	D10 E90	A10 C90	B	90 60	820	156
205	Chongchongang	Daeryonggang	Pakchon	1	N 39:45 E 125:34	1956 80	3020	D30 E70	C50 D50	B	60	1310	86
101	Taedonggang	Taedonggang	Mirim	1	N 39:01 E 125:47	1958 80	12175	C10 D50 E40	A15 C85	B	60	1055	305
505	Ryesonggang	Ryesonggang	Kumchon	1	N 38:10 E 126:28	1960 80	2500	C30 D60 E10	A10 C85 D 5	B	60	1400	60.5

DEMOCRATIC PEOPLE'S REPUBLIC OF KOREA/REPUBLIQUE POPULAIRE DEMOCRATIQUE DE COREE

TABLE II : FLOODS CHARACTERISTICS

FLOOD CHARACTERISTICS							DISCHARGE ESTIMATION					
Site number	Stream	Observ. site	Year	Date of the max	Maximal dis m³s-1	Climatic origine	Condition disc est	Qual. of the sect	Preci. ±m³s-1	Anteced precip.	Depth mm	Duration days
1	2	3	4	5	6	7	8	9	10	11	12	13
909	Amnokgang	Kumchang	1979	08-18	5660	1	A1B2	A1A	500	3	55	4
			1965	08-07	4510	1	A1B2	A1A	300	3	235	6
205	Daeryonggang	Pakchon	1975	08-12	13500	1	A1B2	A1A	1000	3	227	3
			1965	07-29	13130	1	A1B2	A1A	1000	3	198	4
			1978	08-13	12800	1	A1B2	A1A	900	3	154	4
101	Taedonggang	Mirim	1967	08-29	29000	1	A1B2	A1A	2000	3	154	5
			1963	08-19	18000	1	A1B2	A1A	1200	3	362	4
505	Ryesonggang	Kumchon	1965	08-16	6560	1	A1B2	A1A	400	3	527	3
			1973	09-01	4300	1	A1B2	A1A	300	3	254	4
			1979	08-02	4120	1	A1B2	A1A	270			

TABLEAU I : IDENTIFICATION DES POINTS D'OBSERVATION ET CARACTERISTIQUES DES BASSINS

	POINT D'OBSERVATION						CARACTERISTIQUES DU BASSIN						
N° du point	Bassin fluvial	Rivière	Point d'observ.	Coordonnées Lat. Long.		Période	Surface km²	Relief	Sol	Végét.	Régime	Pluie moyenne mm	Module m³s-1
1	2	3	4	5	6	7	8	9	10	11	12	13	14
1	Yaque del Norte	Yaque del Norte	Boma	N (1) 19-17	W (1) 70-43		710	F					17.8
2	Yaque del Norte	Yaque del Norte	Jimanagao	19-34	70-58		2535	F E					27
3	Yuna	Yuna	Los Quemados	18-52	70-28		363	F					17.9
4	Nizao	Nizao	La Peñita	18-27	70-17		786	F E					20.0
5	Bani	Bani	El Recodo	18-18	70-20		63	F E					11.60
6	Ocoa	Ocoa	El Limon	18-28	70-30		402	F					2.4

(1) Le chiffre des minutes de ces coordonnées est approximatif

DOMINICAN REPUBLIC / REPUBLIQUE DOMINICAINE

TABLEAU II : CARACTERISTIQUES DES CRUES

	CARACTERISTIQUES DE LA CRUE						EVALUATION DES DEBITS					
N° du point	Rivière	Point d'observ.	Année	Date du maximum	Débit max m³/s	Origine	Base et mode eval	Qual. de la séch.	Precis. ±m³s-1	Anteced	Hauteur	Durée jours
1	2	3	4	5	6	7	8	9	10	11	12	13
1	Yaque del Norte	Boma	1979 (1)	09-01	5080	1						
2	Yaque del Norte	Jimanagao	1979 (1)	09-01	3410	1						
3	Yuna	Los Quemados	1979 (1)	09-01	1210	1						
4	Nizao	La Peñita	1979 (1)	09-01	3780	1						
5	Bani	El Recodo	1979 (1)	09-01	405	1						
6	Ocoa	El Limon	1979 (1)	09-01	1400	1						

(1) Cyclone David

ECUADOR/EQUATEUR

TABLEAU I : IDENTIFICATION DES POINTS D'OBSERVATION ET CARACTERISTIQUES DES BASSINS

	POINT D'OBSERVATION							CARACTERISTIQUES DU BASSIN					
N° du point	Bassin fluvial	Rivière	Point d'observ.		Coordonnées Lat. Long.		Période	Surface km²	Relief	Sol	Végét.	Regime	Pluie moyenne mm	Module m³s-1
1	2	3	4	5	6	7	8	9	10	11	12	13	14
45-28	Guayas	Quevedo	Quevedo	1	S 01:01	W 79:37	1963 77	3510	F60 D40	A60 B40	A70 D30	00	2900	230
27-03	Chone	Carrizal	Calceta	1	S 00:51	W 80:10	1963 77	546	D	C	C	00	1900	12,1
61-42	Pastaza	Pastaza	Banos	1	S 01:23	W 78:25	1963 77	7820	F	B25 D10 C65	C	90	950	120
62-14	Paute	Paute	D.J. Palmira	1	S 02:38	W 78:33	1965 77	5110	F	C	C	90	1600	126
61-49	Pastaza	Yanayacu	Puente Pucarà	1	S 01:05	W 78:28	1963 77	256	F	C	C	90	1300	10
60-05	Napo (Amazone)	Coca	San Rafael	1	S 00:06	W 77:35	1973 77	3950	F80 D20	D	A	90 00	4000	360

ECUADOR/EQUATEUR

TABLEAU II : CARACTERISTIQUES DES CRUES

	CARACTERISTIQUES DE LA CRUE						EVALUATION DES DEBITS					
N° du point	Rivière	Point d'observ.	Année	Date du maximum	Débit max m³s-1	Origine	Base et mode éval	Qual. de la séch.	Préci. ±m³s-1	Anteced	Hauteur	Durée jours
1	2	3	4	5	6	7	8	9	10	11	12	13
45-28	Quevedo	Quevedo	1973 1969	02-09 03-28	2600 1520	1 1	A1C1 A1C1	B1B B1B	400 200			
27-03	Carrizal	Calceta	1977	05-19	269	1	A1C1	B1B	30			
61-42	Pastaza	Banos	1974	07-07	1200	1	A1C1	B1B	200			
62-14	Paute	D.J. Palmira	1974 1970	07-08 07-03	2560 1320	1 1	A1C1 A1C1	C1B C1B	500 200			
61-49	Yanayacu	Puente Pucara	1976	07-19	133	1	A1C1	C1B	25			
60-05	Coca	San Rafaël	1974 1976	07-07 07-08	5120 3590	1 1						

EGYPT/EGYPTE

TABLE I : IDENTIFICATION OF OBSERVATION SITES AND CHARACTERISTICS OF BASINS

	OBSERVATION SITES							CHARACTERISTICS OF BASIN					
Site number	River basin	Stream	Observ. site		Coordinates Lat. Long.	Period	Area km²	Slope	Soil	Cover	Regime	Mean precip. mm	Mean disc. m³s-1
1	2	3	4	5	6	7	8	9	10	11	12	13	14
	Nile	Nile	Aswan	1	N 24:05 E 32:55	1870 1977	1500000 (1)		No physical signification				

(1) Active part of the basin, rough estimation.

EGYPT/EGYPTE

TABLE II : FLOODS CHARACTERISTICS

	FLOOD CHARACTERISTICS						DISCHARGE ESTIMATION					
Site number	Stream	Observ. site	Year	Date of the max	Maximal discm³s-1	Climatic origine	Condition disc est.	Qual. of the sect	Precis. ±m³s-1	Anteced precip.	Depth mm	Duration days
1	2	3	4	5	6	7	8	9	10	11	12	13
	Nile	Aswan	1878	09-25	13200	1	A1CO	A1A	700			
			1892	09-12	12640	1	A1CO	A1A	600			
			1874	09-03	12640	1	A1CO	A1A	600			
			1964	(1)	12500	1			1000			
			1887	09-05	12040	1	A1CO	A1A	600			

(1) Rough estimation of natural discharge after estimation of influence of irrigation upstream and evaporation losses. This influence is negligible less than 2 %, before 1900.

TABLE I : IDENTIFICATION OF OBSERVATION SITES AND CHARACTERISTICS OF BASINS

	OBSERVATION SITES						CHARACTERISTICS OF BASIN						
Site number	River basin	Stream	Observ. site		Coordinates Lat. Long.	Period	Area km²	Slope	Soil	Cover	Regime	Mean precip. mm	Mean disc. m³s-1
1	2	3	4	5	6	7	8	9	10	11	12	13	14
1	Rhein	Rhein	Maxau	1	N 49:02 E 08:18	1921 78	50345	E70 F30	C	A40 D60	90 50	940	1250
2	Rhein	Neckar	Heidelberg	1	N 49:24 E 08:42	1946 78	13810				50		132
3	Rhein	Wolf	Oberwolfach	1	N 48:25 E 08:20	1906 78	126				50		4.16
4	Rhein	Main	Frankfuhrt Osthafen	1	N 50:06 E 08:42	1957 78	24765				50		170
5	Rhein	Mosel	Cochem	1	N 50:09 E 07:10	1817 1978	27100				50		296
6	Rhein	Rhein	Rees	1	N 51:46 E 06:24	1921 78	159685	B10 D20 E50 F20	C	A25 D75	90 50	760	2270
7	Weser	Weser	Intschede	1	N 52:58 E 09:08	1901 78	37790	C	C	D40 B60	50	646	324
8	Elbe	Elbe	Neu-Darchau	1	N 53:14 E 10:53	1937 78	131950	B	C	D	50	800	722
9	Ems	Ems	Rheine	1	N 52:17 E 07:26	1875 1978	3700	A	C	D90 B10	50	760	35.6
10	Donau (Danube)	Donau	Hofkirchen	1	N 48:40 E 13:07	1925 78	47495	E80 F20	C	D	90 50	1137	635

TABLE II : FLOODS CHARACTERISTICS

	FLOOD CHARACTERISTICS						DISCHARGE ESTIMATION					
Site number	Stream	Observ. site	Year	Date of the max	Maximal dism^3s^{-1}	Climatic origine	Condition disc est	Qual. of the sect	Precis. ±m^3s^{-1}	Anteced precip.	Depth mm	Duration days
1	2	3	4	5	6	7	8	9	10	11	12	13
1	Rhein	Maxau	1882	12-28	4620	4	A1B1	B	460			
			1944	11-26	4420	4	A1B1	B	135	3	20-330	5
			1970	02-25	4400	4	A1B1	B	135			
			1955	01-15	4340	4	A1B1	B	130	3	60-250	7
2	Neckar	Heidelberg	1824	10-30	4000	1	B4C5	A	300			
			1882	12-28	3000	4	A1C5	A	200			
			1970	02-23	2300	4	A1C1	A	50			
3	Wolf	Oberwolfach	1951	08-03	169	1	A1C1	B	10			
			1947	12-28	155	4	A1C1	B	10			
			1919	12-24	155	4	A1C1	B	10			
4	Main	Frankfuhrt-Osthafen	1342	07-21	4000	1	C5C5	C	300			
			1882	11-27	2450	4	A4C5	C	100			
			1920	01-16	2050	4	A1C1	B	50			
5	Mosel	Cochem	1925	12-31	4100	4	A1C1	B	200			
			1920	01-15	4020	4	A1C1	B	200			
			1948	01-01	3740	4	A1C1	B	200			
			1882	11-28	3640	1	A1C5	B	200			
6	Rhein	Rees	1926	01-03	12200	4	A1B1	B	370	2	60-250	14
			1970	02-27	9950	4	A1B1	B	300	2	30-250	10
			1955	01-21	9500	4	A1B1	B	285	2	30-350	11
7	Weser	Intschede	1841	01-21	4650	4	A1B1	B	465			
			1891	01-29	4300 (1)	4	A1B1	B	430			
			1881	02-16	3760 (1)	4	A1B1	B	375			
8	Elbe	Neu-Darchau	1895	04-07	3840	4	A1B1	B	385			
			1940	04-01	3690	4	A1B1	B	110			
			1947	03-27	3500	4	A1B1	B	105			
9	Ems	Rheine	1946	02-10	1030	4	A1B1	B	31	3	50-350	13
			1961	12	483	4	A1B1	B	14			
10	Donau	Hofkirchen	1845	03-31	4470	4	A1B1	B	450			
			1954	07	3880	4	A1B1	B	115			
			1920	01	3000	4	A1B1	B	90			

(1)   Influenced by ice.

FINLAND/FINLANDE

TABLE I : IDENTIFICATION OF OBSERVATION SITES AND CHARACTERISTICS OF BASINS

| OBSERVATION SITES | | | | | | CHARACTERISTICS OF BASIN | | | | | | | |
Site number	River basin	Stream	Observ. site		Coordinates Lat. Long.	Period	Area km²	Slope	Soil	Cover	Regime	Mean precip. mm	Mean disc. m³s-1
1	2	3	4	5	6	7	8	9	10	11	12	13	14
35:10450	Kokemäenj	Kokemäenj	Harjavalta Power station since 1939	1	N 61:20 E 22:07	1931 75	26025	A20 B70 C10	B10 C70 D20	A60 B15 D25	61	590	206
65:00450	Kemijoki	Kemijoki	Taivalkoski Power station since 1949	1	N 65:47 E 24:33	1911 75	50820	A10 B20 C40 D30	B10 C85 D 5	A20 B50 C29 D 1	80	490	530
67:2201	Tornionjoki	Tornionjoki	Karunki	1	N 65:58 E 24:03	1911 75	29450	A10 B20 C30 D30 E10	B 5 C90 D 5	A30 B50 C17 D 3	80	460	366
4:11750	Vuoksi	Vuoksi	Imatra	1	N 61:13 E 28:47	1847 1975	61265	A10 B70 C20	B15 C80 D 5	A70 B20 D10	61	580	553
14:09550	Kymijoki	Kymijoki	Kuusankoski Power station Since 1940	1	N 60:54 E 26:38	1909 75	36050	A15 B40 C35 D10	B10 C85 D 5	A85 C 5 D10	61	580	279

FINLAND/FINLANDE

TABLE II : FLOODS CHARACTERISTICS

| FLOOD CHARACTERISTICS | | | | | | | DISCHARGE ESTIMATION | | | | | |
Site number	Stream	Observ. site	Year	Date of the max	Maximal dism³s-1	Climatic origine	Condition disc est	Qual. of the sect	Precis. ±m³s-1	Anteced precip.	Depth mm	Duration days
1	2	3	4	5	6	7	8	9	10	11	12	13
35:10450	Kokemäenj	Harjavalta	1966	05-05	918	2	Power stat.		20	2		
			1974	12-24	863	1	Power stat.		20	3	355	120
			1936	04-25	846	2	A1B1	A1A	40	2		
65:00450	Kemijoki	Taivalkoski	1973	05-26	4824	2	Power stat.		200	3	280	205
			1967	05-25	4156	2	Power stat.		200	3	325	235
			1917	06-10	4131	2	A1B1	A1A	300	2		
67:2201	Tornionjoki	Karunki	1968	06-11	3667	2	A1B1	B1A	200			
			1917	06-09	3185	2	A1B1	B1A	180			
			1935	06-18	3100	2	A1B1	B1A	180			
4:11750	Vuoksi	Imatra	1899	08-26	1162	4	A1B1	A1A	50	3		
		Power station	1924	07-21	1146	4	A1B1	A1A	50	3	885	445
		Since 1929	1955	04-10	1137	2	Power stat.		25	3	740	285
14:09550	Kymijoki	Kuusankoski	1924	01-02	704	4	A1B1	A1A	35	3	310	120
		Power station	1975	01-17	677	4	Power stat.		20	3	615	200
		Since 1940	1929	01-31	636	4	A1B1	A1A	30	3	520	245

TABLEAU I : IDENTIFICATION DES POINTS D'OBSERVATIONS ET CARACTERISTIQUES DES BASSINS

	POINT D'OBSERVATION						CARACTERISTIQUES DU BASSIN						
N° du point	Bassin fluvial	Rivière	Point d'observ.		Coordonnées Lat. Long.	Période	Surface km²	Relief	Sol	Végét.	Régime	Pluie moyenne mm	Module m³s-1
1	2	3	4	5	6	7	8	9	10	11	12	13	14
1	Rhône	Rhône	Lyon Pt. Morand	1	N 45:46 E 04:50	1877 1979	20300	E5 F95	A33 D66		90 50		600
2	Rhône	Rhône	Beaucaire	1	N 43:48 E 04:40	1877 1979	96500	B5 C10 D5 E30 F50	A20 B10 C20 D50		90 50		2000
3	Rhône	Isère	Grenoble	1	N 45:12 E 05:44	1877 1979	5720	C10 F90	A10 C10 D80		90	1800	178
4	Isère	Drac	Le Sautet	1	N 44:49 E 05:56	1904 1979	990	F100	A30 D70		90	1490	32.3
5	Rhône	Drôme	Livron	1	N 44:46 E 04:52		1640	F100	A25 C75		90 30		26.5
6	Rhône	Durance	Pt. Mirabeau	1	N 43:41 E 05:40	1904 1979	11900	E25 F75	A25 C45 D30		90 30		195
7	Rhône	Ardèche	Aubenas	1	N 44:36 E 04:26	1877 1979	470	E100	D		30		63.15
8	Vidourle	Vidourle	Sommières	1	N 43:46 E 04:05		630	E100	C	B D	30	800 1000	9.5
9	Herault	Herault	Gignac	1	N 43:39 E 03:33	1875 1979	1238	F10 E90	D25 A50 C25	B D	30	1250	32
10	Têt	Têt	Perpignan	1	N 42:42 E 02:53	1876 1979	1300	F75 E25	C50 D50	B D	30		36.1
11	Tech	Tech	Pas du Loup	1	N 42:25 E 02:36	1935 40	236	F100	C50 D50	B	30	600 800	3.94
12	Tech	Canideil	Prats de Mollo	3	N 42:25 E 02:28		11.6	F100	C50 D50	B	30	600 800	
13	Rhin	Bruche	Volxheim	1	N 48:32 E 7:32	1891 1979	3615	E100	C5 D95		90 50		
14	Rhin	Moselle	Epinal	1	N 48:11 E 06:28	1952 79	1220	D20 E80	D		90 50		36.35
15	Seine	Seine	Paris Austerlitz	1	N 48:50 E 02:24	1732 1869 1873 1982	44300	B10 C40 D40 E10	A40 B20 C30 D10		50		270

FRANCE

TABLEAU I : IDENTIFICATION DES POINTS D'OBSERVATIONS ET CARACTERISTIQUES DES BASSINS

		POINT D'OBSERVATION						CARACTERISTIQUES DU BASSIN					
N° du point	Bassin fluvial	Rivière	Point d'observ.		Coordonnées Lat. Long.	Période	Surface km²	Relief	Sol	Végét.	Régime	Pluie moyenne mm	Module m³s-1
1	2	3	4	5	6	7	8	9	10	11	12	13	14
16	Seine	Marne	Noisiel	1	N 48:53 E 02:40	1956 79	12600	B15 C45 D40	A45 B25 C20 D10		50		96
17	Elorn	Elorn	Kerfaven	1	N 48:29 W 04:12		202	D	D		50		3.47
18	Penzé	Penzé	Penhoat	1	N 48:37 W 03:57		141	D	D		50		2.44
19	Loire	Loire	Gien	1	N 47:49 E 02:40	1825 1979	35900	B15 C20 D50 E15	C25 D75		50	845	335
20	Loire	Mayenne	Chambellay	1	N 47:41 W 00:41	1881 1979	4250	B25 C50 D25	C20 D80		50	780	38.4
21	Loire	Vienne	Nouatre	1	N 47:03 E 00:32		19700	B10 C15 D25 E50	C25 D75		50		(200)
22	Loire	Allier	Moulins	1	N 46:34 E 03:20	1790 1979	13000	B20 C20 D30 E30	C20 D80		50 90	850	(135)
23	Loire	Loire	Bas en Basset	1	N 45:19 E 04:08		3300	B10 C40 D40 E10	B20 C10 D70		50 90	875	41
24	Loire	Lignon du Velay	Tence la Valette	1	N 45:07 E 04:17		400	B25 C25 D40 E10	C20 D80		50 90		5.85
25	Dordogne	Corrèze	Tulle	1	N 45:16 E 01:44		370	C10 D30 E60	D		50		10
26	Garonne	Garonne	Agen	1	N 44:13 E 00:36		34900	C15 D50 E25 F10	A10 B20 C50 D20		50 90	915	460
27	Garonne	Gers	Auch	1	N 43:21 E 00:36		475	D	C		50 90		2.5
28	Garonne	Tarn	Montauban	1	N 44:05 E 01:21		9720	B10 D50 E40	A25 C25 D50		50		160
29	Garonne	Ariège	Foix	1	N 42:58 E 01:36	1906 79	1340	E20	A10 D90		50	895	37.9

TABLEAU II : CARACTERISTIQUES DES CRUES

				CARACTERISTIQUES DE LA CRUE			EVALUATION DES DEBITS					
N° du point	Rivière	Point d'observ.	Année	Date du maximum	Débit max m³s-1	Origine	Base et mode éval	Qual. de la séch.	Précis. ±m³s-1	Anteced	Hauteur mm	Durée jours
1	2	3	4	5	6	7	8	9	10	11	12	13
1	Rhône	Lyon Pt Morand	1856 1928 1944	05-31 02-16 11-25	4500 4400 4250	4 1 1	C4B1 A1B1 A1B1	A1B A1B A1B	300 200 200			
2	Rhône	Beaucaire	1856 1840 1935	05-31 11-05 11-14	12000 11000 9600	4 1 1	C4C1 A1C1 A1B1	B1B B1B B1B	1000 1000 500			
3	Isère	Grenoble	1651 1740 1800 1968	11-11 12-20 11-02 09-22	2500 2000 1800 1000	1 1 1 1	D5C1 D5C1 C5B1 A1B1	B1B B1B B1B B1B	300 250 200 150			
4	Drac	Sautet	1928 1928 1955	09-28 10-22 06-07	850 800 540	1 1 4	A1C1 A1C1 A1C1	B1B B1B B1B				
5	Drôme	Livron	1842 1955 1954	09 11-13 12-09	1300 1000 790	1 1 1	C4C1 A1C1 A1B1	B1B B1B B1B				
6	Durance	Pt. Mirabeau	1882 1886 1906	10-25 10-24 11-04	5100 4040 3700	1 1 1	C4C1 C4C1 A1B1					
7	Ardèche	Aubenas	1890	09-22	3000	1			500		600	4
8	Vidourle	Sommières	1958	10-04	1400	1	B3C		100	3	230	1
9	Hérault	Gignac	1875 1890 1907	09-13 09-21 09-26	3750 3150 3050	1 1 1	D5C D5C D5C					
10	Têt	Perpignan	1940 1892 1920	10-18 11-09 02-20	3600 2080 1860	1 1 1	B5D D5D D5D		500 300 200	3 3	323 136	1 1
11	Tech	Pas du Loup	1940 1962	10-18 11-05	3400 220	1 1	A2B5 A1A1		500 20	3 3	1500	4
12	Canideil	Prats de Mollo	1940	10-18	400	1	B5C5			3	1500	4
13	Bruche	Volxheim	1959	12-24	157	1						
14	Moselle	Epinal	1947	12-29	1100	1						
15	Seine	Paris Austerlitz	1658 1910	02-27 01-28	2500 2180	1 1	D5D A1B1	B1B A1B	300 100			
16	Marne	Noisiel	1910	01	853	1	A1C1					
17	Elorn	Kerfaven	1974	02-11	43	1						

TABLEAU II : CARACTERISTIQUES DES CRUES

	CARACTERISTIQUES DE LA CRUE						EVALUATION DES DEBITS					
N° du point	Rivière	Point d'observ.	Année	Date du maximum	Débit max m³s-1	Origine	Base et mode éval	Qual. de la séch.	Précis. ±m³s-1	Anteced	Hauteur mm	Durée jours
1	2	3	4	5	6	7	8	9	10	11	12	13
18	Penzé	Penhoat	1974	02-11	71	1						
19	Loire	Gien	1856	06-02	8500	1	D5D		600			
			1866	09-27	8500	1	D5D		600			
			1846	10-20	7900	1	D5D		600			
20	Mayenne	Chambellay	1974	11-17	1500	1	A1C1					
			1966	10-26	715	1	A1B1					
21	Vienne	Nouâtre	1792	07-16	4000	1	D5D		600			
			1910	05-14	2100	1	A1C1					
22	Allier	Moulins	1790	11	7000	1	D5D		800			
			1856	05	4700	1	D5D		400			
23	Loire	Bas en Basset	1846	10	2650	1			200			
			1907	10-07								
			1866	09								
			1980	09								
24	Lignon du Velay	Tence la Valette	1980	09	900	1	B4D		150			
			1890	09								
			1878	10-8								
25	Corrèze	Tulle	1960	10-04	450	1						
26	Garonne	Agen	1875	06	8500	1	D5D					
			1930	03	7700	1	A1C1					
			1952	02	7000	1	A1C1					
27	Gers	Auch	1977	07-08	1000	1	A1A4		100		170	0.62
			1770	04	800-1000				200			
			1897	07	800				100			
28	Tarn	Montauban	1930	03-03	6300	1						
29	Ariège	Foix	1910	05-23	480	4	A1C1					
			1928	11-24	386	1	A1C1					
			1908	05-13	310	4	A1C1					

TABLEAU I : IDENTIFICATION DES POINTS D'OBSERVATION ET CARACTERISTIQUES DES BASSINS

	POINTS D'OBSERVATION						CARACTERISTIQUES DU BASSIN						
N° du point	Bassin fluvial	Rivière	Point d'observ.		Coordonnées Lat. Long.	Période	Surface km²	Relief	Sol	Végét.	Régime	Pluie moyenne mm	Module m³s-1
1	2	3	4	5	6	7	8	9	10	11	12	13	14
60411915	Maroni	Tampoc	Dégrad Roche	1	N 03:25 W 55:50	1951 80	7650	E	C	A	00	2100	168
60410121	Maroni	Maroni	Langa Tabiki	1	N 04:59 W 54:26	1952 80	60900	D E	C	A	00	2500	1770
60450124	Oyapock	Oyapock	Saut Maripa	1	N 03:49 W 51:53	1953 80	25100	D E	C	A	00	2800	870
60480145	Sinnamary	Sinnamary	Saut Tigre	1	N 04:58 W 53:02	1968 80	5150	E	C	A	00	2800	230
60489031	Sinnamary	Crique Grégoire	Station 1	4	N 05:06 W 53:04	1968 76	8.4	E	C	A	00	3680	0.57
6	Mahury	Crique Virgile	Station 1	4	N 04:31 W 52:19	1959 61	7.6	E	D	A	00	4000	0.55
7	Mahury	Crique Cacao	Station 1	4	N 04:34 W 52:28	1965 66	13	E	B C	A	00	3500	0.8

FRENCH GUYANA/GUYANE FRANCAISE

TABLEAU II : CARACTERISTIQUES DES CRUES

	CARACTERISTIQUES DE LA CRUE						EVALUATION DU DEBIT					
N° du point	Rivière	Point d'observ.	Année	Date du maximum	Débit max m³s-1	Origine	Base et mode éval	Qual. de la séch	Précis. ±m³s-1	Anteced	Hauteur	Durée jours
1	2	3	4	5	6	7	8	9	10	11	12	13
60411915	Tampoc	Dégrad Roche	1969	05-21	1047	1	A1B1	A1B	50			
			1971	04-03	1020	1	A1B1	A1B	50			
60410121	Maroni	Langa Tabiki	1968	06-02	7000	1	A1B1	A1A	250			
			1960	06-04	6840	1	A3B1	A1A	250			
60450124	Oyapock	Saut Maripa	1967	05-24	3700	1	A3B1	A1A	200			
			1971	04-06	3680	1	A3B1	A1A	200			
60480145	Sinnamary	Saut Tigre	1977	04-26	1340	1	A1B1	A1A	75			
			1976	04-29	1130	1	A1B1	A1A	75			
60489031	Crique Grégoire	Station 1	1974	04-03	37.6	1	A1B1	A1A	2		80	0.20
			1973	05-20	30.5	1	A1B1	A1A			11.1	0.25
6	Crique Virgile	Station 1	1960	04-01	25.0 (1)	1	A1B1	A1A	2		169	1
7	Crique	Station 1	1965	06-07	25.0 (2)	1	A1B1	A1A	2		111	1

(1) crue décennale évaluée à 38 m³/s.   (2) crue décennale évaluée à 38 m³/s

FRENCH POLYNESIA/POLYNESIE FRANCAISE

TABLEAU I : IDENTIFICATION DES POINTS D'OBSERVATIONS ET CARACTERISTIQUES DES BASSINS

	POINTS D'OBSERVATION						CARACTERISTIQUES DU BASSIN						
N° du point	Bassin fluvial	Rivière	Point d'observ.		Coordonnées Lat. Long.	Période	Surface km²	Relief	Sol	Végét.	Régime	Pluie moyenne mm	Module m³s-1
1	2	3	4	5	6	7	8	9	10	11	12	13	14
TAHITI													
15.01	Papeiha	Papeiha	Cote 10	1	S 17:39 W 149:19	9 ans	30.7	F	B 6 C94	A85 B10 C 5	00	7500	7
17.01	Papenoo	Papenoo	Cote 45	1	S 17:34 W 149:26	38 ans	78	F	B 3 C97	A85 B10 C 5	00	5000	12
20.02	Punaruu	Punaruu	Cote 50	1	S 17:38 W 149:35	15 ans	38.5	F	B12 C88	A80 B15 C 5	00	3500	3

FRENCH POLYNESIA/POLYNESIE FRANCAISE

TABLEAU II : CARACTERISTIQUES DES CRUES

	CARACTERISTIQUES DE LA CRUE						EVALUATION DES DEBITS					
N° du point	Rivière	Point d'observ.	Année	Date du maximum	Débit max m³s-1	Origine	Base et mode éval	Qual. de la séch	Précis. ±m³s-1	Anteced	Hauteur	Durée jours
1	2	3	4	5	6	7	8	9	10	11	12	13
TAHITI												
15.01	Papeiha	Cote 10	1983	04-12	880	1						
			1977	04-18	470	1	A1B2	B1B				
17.01	Papenoo	Cote 45	1983	04-12	2200	1						
			1944		1500	1	B4C4		300			
			1968		1400	1	B0X0		280			
			1981	03-10	1125	1	A4C4	B1B	200			
			1978	05-19	925	1	A4C4	B1B	100			
20.02	Punaruu	Cote 50	1981	03-10	460	1	A2B3	C1B	100			
			1968	02	330	1	B0X0	C1B	70			

GABON

TABLEAU I : IDENTIFICATION DES POINTS D'OBSERVATIONS ET CARACTERISTIQUES DES BASSINS

		POINTS D'OBSERVATION							CARACTERISTIQUES DU BASSIN					
N° du point	Bassin fluvial	Rivière	Point d'observ.		Coordonnées Lat. Long.		Période	Surface km²	Relief	Sol	Végét.	Régime	Pluie moyenne mm	Module m³s-1
1	2	3	4	5	6		7	8	9	10	11	12	13	14
1	Ogooué	Ogooué	Lambaréné	1	S 00:42	E 10:13	1929 81	204000	B C D	B C D	A75 C25	00	1850	5500
2	Ogooué	Ivindo	Makokou	1	N 00:34	E 12:52	1953 81	35800	B C	D	A	00	1700	620
3	Nzemé	Nzemé III	Bassin représentatif	1	N 00:22	E 09:48	1970 73	3.26	B C	D	A	00	2500	(.14)
4	Noya	Nzang	Bassin représentatif	1	N 00:34	E 10:15	1962 64	9.2	E F	C D	A	00	2500	(.38)

GABON

TABLEAU II : CARACTERISTIQUES DES CRUES

		CARACTERISTIQUES DE LA CRUE					EVALUATION DES DEBITS					
N° du point	Rivière	Point d'observ.	Année	Date du maximum	Débit max m³s-1	Origine	Base et mode éval	Qual. de la séch	Précis. ±m³s-1	Anteced	Hauteur mm	Durée jours
1	2	3	4	5	6	7	8	9	10	11	12	13
1	Ogooué	Lambaréné	1961 1934 1939	11-18 11-19 12-07	13600 13400 13000	1 1 1	A1A1 A1A1 A1A1	A1A A1A A1A	500 500 500			
2	Ivindo	Makokou	1966 1962	12-05 11-07	2090 2040	1 1	A1B1 A1B1	A1A A1A	150 150			
3	Nzemé III	Bassin Représentatif	1973	10-20	10.2	1	A1B1	A1B	1.5	3	155	1
4	Nzang	Bassin Représentatif	1962	12-06	70.7	1	A1B1	B1B	5	1	78	1

TABLE I : IDENTIFICATION OF OBSERVATIONS SITES AND CHARACTERISTICS OF BASINS

	OBSERVATIONS SITE							CHARACTERISTICS OF BASIN					
Site number	River basin	Stream	Observ. site		Coordinates Lat. Long.	Period	Area km²	Slope	Soil	Cover	Regime	Mean precip. mm	Mean disc. m³s-1
1	2	3	4	5	6	7	8	9	10	11	12	13	14
66202	Oder	Mandau	Zittau	1	N E 50:54 14:48	1912 83	295	D	D	A20 D80	61 90	735	2.95
66016	Oder	Lausitzer Neisse	Goerlitz Hischwinkel	1	N E 51:10 15:00	1913 83	1620	C50 D50	D	A50 D50	61 90	825	18.5
60308	Oder	Oder	Hohensaaten Finow	1	N E 52:53 14:09	1853 1983	109560	A20 B45 C15 D15 E 5	B50 C35 D15	A40 C10 D50	61	600	535
50106	Elbe	Elbe	Dresden	1	N E 51:03 13:44	1776 1983	53100	C50 D35 E15	C20 D80	A35 D65	90 61	670	320
55094	Elbe	Mueglitz	Dohna	1	N E 50:58 13:51	1912 83	195	E	D	A60 D40	90 61	780	2.57
56002	Elbe	Mulde	Golzerh	1	N E 51:15 12:46	1909 83	5440	C25 D50 E25	D	A35 D65	90 61	810	62
57652	Elbe	Weisse Elster	Gera-Langenberg	1	N E 50:56 12:02	1945 83	2190	C30 D40 E30	D	A40 D60	90 61	720	15.8
57740	Elbe	Erlbach	Gera-Thieschitz	1	N E 50:54 12:02	1973 83	109	C	D	D	61	620	0.80
57462	Elbe	Apfel-staedt	Georgen-thal	1	N E 50:50 10:38	1944 83	77.5	E	D	A	61 90	1045	1.12
58366	Elbe	Vetschauer Muehlenfliess	Stradow	1	N E 51:49 14:05	1964 83	92	A50 B50	B	A20 D80	61	600	0.34

TABLE II : FLOODS CHARACTERISTICS

					FLOOD CHARACTERISTICS			DISCHARGE ESTIMATION				
Site number	Stream	Observ. site	Year	Date of the max	Maximal disc m^3s^{-1}	Climatic origine	Condition disc est	Qual. of the sect	Precis. $\pm m^3s^{-1}$	Anteced precip.	Depth mm.	Duration days.
1	2	3	4	5	6	7	8	9	10	11	12	13
66202	Mandau	Zittau	1887	05-17	407	1	D4D4	X1X	80	3	70	0.33
			1981	07-20	304	1	A1CO	A1X	50	2	169	1.5
66016	Lausitzer Neisse	Goerlitz Hischwinkel	1981	07-21	710	1	A1BO	B1X	70	2	172	1.5
60308	Oder	Hohensaaten Finow	1888	04	3110	4	A1D4	B1X	500	0		
50106	Elbe	Dresden	1890 (1)	09-06	4350	1	A1CO	X1X	500	0		
55094	Mueglitz	Dohna	1927	07-08	330	1	A1CO	X1X	60	0	164	0.125
56002	Mulde	Golzern	1573	08-14	2200	1	D5XO	XOX	500	0		
57652	Weisse Elster	Gera-Langenberg	1954	07-11	667	1	A1CO	C1X	80	2	165	3
57740	Erlbach	Gera-Thieschitz	1981	08-10	200	1	B4D5	B1X	50	2	177	0.7
57462	Apfelstaedt	Georgenthal	1981	08-10	58	1	A1CO	X1X	10	2	159	0.75
58366	Vetschauer Muehlenfliess	Stradow	1977	06-21	9.3	1	A1A1	X1X	0.5	3	91	0.3

(1) The 1845 flood was not recorded.

TABLE I : IDENTIFICATION OF OBSERVATION SITES AND CHARACTERISTICS OF BASINS

	OBSERVATION SITES						CHARACTERISTICS OF BASIN						
Site number	River basin	Stream	Observ. site		Coordinates Lat. Long.	Period	Area km²	Slope	Soil	Cover	Regime	Mean precip. mm	Mean disc. m³s-1
1	2	3	4	5	6	7	8	9	10	11	12	13	14
1	Volta	Volta	Yeji	2	N 08:14 W 00:39	13 Years	284000	B	C	B50 D50	10 11	1170	605
2	Volta	Volta	Senchi Halcrow	1	N 06:12 E 00:06	40 Years	394000	B	C	B50 D50	10 11	1245	1085
3	Volta	White Volta	Pwalugu	1	N 10:35 W 00:51	26 Years	63300	B	C	B50 D50	10 11	1065	110
4	Volta	White Volta	Yapei	2	N 09:09 W 01:10	17 Years	102000	B	C	B50 D50	10 11	1145	261
5	Volta	White Volta	Nawuni (Dalon)	2	N 09:42 W 01:05	27 Years	92900	B	C	B50 D50	10 11	1145	212
6	Volta	White Volta	Yarugu	1	N 10:59 W 00:24	15 Years	41500	B	C	B50 D50	10 11	890	83
7	White Volta	Kulpawn	Wiasi	1	N 10:20 W 01:26	19 Years	9420	B	C	B50 D50	10	1090	26
8	Volta	Red Volta	Nangodi	1	N 10:52 W 00:37	21 Years	16800	B	C	B50 D50	10 11	1040	24
9	Volta	Black Volta	Bamboi	2	N 08:09 W 02:02	29 Years	134000	B	C	B50 D50	10 11	1145	240
10	Volta	Black Volta	Lawra	1	N 10:28 W 02:55	29 Years	94000	B	C	B50 D50	10 11	1145	102
11	Volta	Oti	Kpetchu	2	N 07:56 E 00:04	13 Years	70600	B	C	B50 D50	10	1335	572
12	Volta	Oti	Saboba	1	N 09:36 E 00:19	27 Years	50300	B	C	B50 D50	10	1195	289
13	Bia	Bia	Dadieso	2	N 06:08 W 03:04	16 Years	6200	B	C	A75 D25	00	1440	27
14	Tano	Tano	Jomuro	2	N 05:46 W 02:34	23 Years	10800	B	C	A75 D25	00	1440	55
15	Tano	Tano	Alenda	2	N 05:07 W 02:45	22 Years	15800	B	C	A75 D25	00	1540	143
16	Tano	Tano	Wiawso	1	N 06:14 W 02:29	22 Years	8440	B	C	A75 D25	00	1425	42
17	Ankobra	Ankobra	Prestea	1	N 05:27 W 02:07	24 Years	4260	B	C	A75 D25	00	1710	49

TABLE I : IDENTIFICATION OF OBSERVATION SITES AND CHARACTERISTICS OF BASINS

| | OBSERVATION SITES | | | | | | | CHARACTERISTICS OF BASIN | | | | | | |
Site number	River basin	Stream	Observ. site		Coordinates Lat. Long.		Period	Area km²	Slope	Soil	Cover	Regime	Mean precip. mm	Mean disc. m³s⁻¹
1	2	3	4	5	6		7	8	9	10	11	12	13	14
18	Ankobra	Ankobra	Dominasi	2	N 05:00	W 02:11	17 Years	6620	B	C80 B20	A75 D25	00	1840	57
19	Pra	Pra	Twifo Praso	1	N 05:36	W 01:33	36 Years	20800	B	C	A60 D40	00	1600	174
20	Pra	Pra	Daboasi	1	N 05:10	W 01:38	25 Years	22700	B	C	A60 D40	00	1520	229
21	Pra	Pra	Brenasi	1	N 06:12	W 01:10	24 Years	2110	B	C	A60 D40	00	1650	15
22	Pra	Obuo	Mampong	1	N 05:33	W 01:33	36 Years	378	B	C	A60 D40	00	1625	5
23	Pra	Birim	Oda	1	N 05:57	W 00:59	25 Years	3290	B	C	A60 D40	00	1655	44
24	Pra	Ofin	Dunkwa	1	N 05:59	W 01:47	22 Years	8530	B	C	A60 D40	00	1545	74
25	Ochi Amissa	Ochi Amissa	Mankesim	2	N 05:16	W 01:00	24 Years	1250	B	C	A80 B20	00	1145	11
26	Ayensu	Ayensu	Oketsew	1	N 05:38	W 00:37	19 Years	728	C	C	A80 B20	00	1460	6
27	Ayensu	Ayensu	Okyereko (Winneba Road)	1	N 05:23	W 00:36	17 Years	640	B	C	A30 B30 D40	00	1410	11
28	Densu	Densu	Manhia	1	N 05:46	W 00:22	12 Years	821	B	C	A70 B30	00	1490	12
29	Todzie	Todzie	Todzienu Tove	1	N 06:05	E 00:45	15 Years	1073	C	B	A60 D40	00	1160	9

GHANA

TABLE II : FLOODS CHARACTERISTICS

		FLOOD CHARACTERISTICS					DISCHARGE ESTIMATION					
Site number	Stream	Observ. site	Year	Date of the max	Maximal dism³s-1	Climatic origine	Condition disc est	Qual. of the sect	Precis. ±m³s-1	Anteced precip.	Depth mm	Duration days
1	2	3	4	5	6	7	8	9	10	11	12	13
1	Volta	Yeji	1963	09-19	6175	1	A1C1	B1B	30			
			1955	10-06	4365	1	A1C1	B1B	30			
			1952	10-16	4350	1	A1C1	B1B	30			
2	Volta	Senchi	1963	09-23	14260	1	A1C1	B1B	70			
			1947	09-24	12400	1	A1C1	B1B	60			
			1931	10-11	12030	1	A1C1	B1B	60			
			1952	10-14	10130	1	A1C1	B1B	50			
3	White-Volta	Pwalugu	1962	09-16	1610	1	A1B1	B1A	10			
			1969	09-13	1520	1	A1B1	B1A	10			
4	White-Volta	Yapei	1963	09-09	2995	1	A1B1	B1A	14			
			1962	09-22	2505	1	A1B1	B1A	14			
5	White-Volta	Nawuni	1963	09-05	2050	1	A1B1	B1A	11			
			1969	09-19	2000	1	A1B1	B1A	11			
6	White-Volta	Yarugu	1962	09-09	1940	1	A1B1	B1A	11			
			1964	07-28	1910	1	A1B1	B1A	11			
7	Kulpawn	Wiasi	1966	08-22	391	1	A1B1	B1A	6	3	21	2
			1968	07-22	387	1	A1B1	B1A	6			
8	Red Volta	Nangodi	1964	09-19	503	1	A1B1	B1A	5	3	65	1
			1969	09-11	430	1	A1B1	B1A	5	3	80	3
9	Black Volta	Bamboi	1963	09-17	3190	1	A1B1	B1A	11	3	15.5	1
			1968	09-14	2560	1	A1B1	B1A	11	3	15.2	1
10	Black Volta	Lawra	1963	09-23	934	1	A1B1	B1A	6	3	92	3
			1951	10-20	880	1	A1B1	B1A	6			
11	Oti	Kpetchu	1963	09-13	4470	1	A1B1	A1A	30			
			1962	10-01	4290	1	A1B1	A1A	30			
12	Oti	Saboba	1957	10-01	2870	1	A1B1	A1A	40			
			1962	09-18	2840	1	A1B1	A1A	40			
13	Bia	Dadieso	1968	08-18	143	1	A1B1	A1A	5	3	108	4
			1976	07-05	142	1	A1B1	A1A	5	3	59	2
14	Tano	Jomuro	1968	09-25	778	1	A1B1	A1A	6	3	82	4
			1959	07-05	523	1	A1B1	A1A	6	3	167	6
15	Tano	Alenda	1971	06-30	550	1	A1B1	A1A	5	3	29	2
			1968	10-01	548	1	A1B1	A1A	5	3	143	9
16	Tano	Wawso	1968	09-11	320	1	A1B1	A1A	3	3	63.5	5
17	Ankobra	Prestea	1968	09-26	680	1	A1B1	A1A	6	3	110	4
			1961	07-22	610	1	A1B1	A1A	6	3	96	3

TABLE II : FLOODS CHARACTERISTICS

	FLOOD CHARACTERISTICS						DISCHARGE ESTIMATION					
Site number	Stream	Observ. site	Year	Date of the max	Maximal dis m^3s-1	Climatic origine	Condition disc est	Qual. of the sect	Precis. $\pm m^3s-1$	Anteced precip.	Depth mm	Duration days
1	2	3	4	5	6	7	8	9	10	11	12	13
18	Ankobra	Dominasi	1964	06-26	645	1	A1B1	A1A	6	3	63	5
19	Pra	Twifo	1968	09-20	2000	1	A1B1	A1A	40			
		Praso	1963	10-13	1390	1	A1B1	A1A	20			
20	Pra	Daboasi	1968	08-31	1560	1	A1B1	A1A	14			
			1963	10-09	1335	1	A1B1	A1A	14			
21	Pra	Brenasi	1957	07-10	235	1	A1B1	A1A	2	3	90	3
22	Obuo	Mampong	1960	05-09	90	1	A1B1	A1A	1	3	184	6
			1956	05-31	85	1	A1B1	A1A	1	3	75	2
23	Birim	Oda	1968	07-19	475	1	A1B1	A1A	6	3	32	3
			1962	07-02	405	1	A1B1	A1A	6	3	44	2
24	Ofin	Dunkwa	1968	09-17	980	1	A1B1	A1A	10	3	77	4
			1963	10-10	670	1	A1B1	A1A	10	3	29	2
25	Ochi	Mankesim	1962	07-18	270	1	A1B1	A1A	5	3	254	7
	Amissa		1961	07-02	230	1	A1B1	A1A	5	3	88	2
26	Ayensu	Oketsew	1968	07-05	130	1	A1B1	A1A	2	3	88.4	4
			1961	07-22	120	1	A1B1	A1A	2	3		
27	Ayensu	Okyereko	1968	07-04	160	1	A1B1	A1A	3	3	80	4
			1974	06-27	135	1	A1B1	A1A	3	3	36	4
28	Densu	Manhia	1974	06-26	130	1	A1B1	A1A	3	3	97	3
			1968	06-30	120	1	A1B1	A1A	3	3	103	2
29	Todzie	Todzienu	1968	08-03	135	1	A1B1	A1A	6	3	13	1
		Tove	1965	06-25	100	1	A1B1	A1A	6	3	20	1

GUATEMALA

TABLE I : IDENTIFICATION OF OBSERVATION SITES AND CHARACTERISTICS OF BASINS

		OBSERVATION SITES							CHARACTERISTICS OF BASIN					
Site number	River basin	Stream	Observ. site		Coordinates Lat. Long.		Period	Area km²	Slope	Soil	Cover	Regime	Mean precip. mm	Mean disc. m³s⁻¹
1	2	3	4	5	6	7		8	9	10	11	12	13	14
181001H	Los Esclavos	Tapalapa	Poza Escondadida	1	N 14:26	W 90:08	1962 75	50.1	F	C	A	90	1550	.87
180101H	Los Esclavos	Los Esclavos	La Sonrisa	1	N 14:16	W 90:15	1966 75	977	E70 D20 B10	C90 B10	C90 D10	10	1485	10.6
180801H	Maria Linda	Aguacapa	Agua Caliente	1	N 14:17	W 90:30	1962 75	345	E	C	C	10	1815	10.6
050201H	Maria Linda	Maria Linda	Guacanayas	1	N 14:09	W 90:38	1968 75	654	E60 D30 C10	C90 B10 B10	C75 D20 E 5	10	1500	15.8
3.2	Achiguate	Achiguate	Carretera CA-2	3	N 14:16	W 90:54		188	F60 E35 D 5	D80 C20	E80 D20	90	3200	4.
3.3	Achiguate	Guacalate	Carretera CA-2	3	N 14:16	W 90:49		580	F60 E35 D 5	D60 C40	E60 D40	90	2000	9.
3.1	Coyolate	Pantaléon	Carretera CA-2	3	N 14:20	W 91:00		109	F60 E35 D 5	D	E	90	3300	4.
170202H (1)	Suchiate	Suchiate	Suchiate II	1	N 14:41	W 92:09	1954 73	1185	E15 D15 C70	C	D70 B30	90	4000	84.1
3.4	Samala	Samala	Santa Maria	3	N 14:43	W 91:31		780	E60 D10 C30	C70 B30	C70 D30	90	1210	9.
130901H	Samala	Samala	Candelaria	1	N 14:39	W 91:34	1964 75	858	E60 D10 C30	C70 B30	C70 D30	90	1210	9.04
030602H	Madre Vieja	Madre Vieja	Panibaj	1	N 14:41	W 91:05	1962 75	167	E	C	A	90	1320	1.46
190801H	Nahualate	Yatza	Paquib	1	N 14:41	W 91:29	1967 75	38.1	F	C	A	90	1480	.63
191301H	Nahualate	Nahualate	Santa Catarina	1	N 14:46	W 91:21	1962 74	144	F	C	A	90	1840	2.
220701H	Motagua	Sunzapote	Pasabien	1	N 15:03	W 89:41	1965 74	78.6	F	C	B	90	1565	2.11
020301H	Motagua	Motagua	Concua	1	N 14:53	W 90:36	1966 74	2594	E	C	C60 E40	10	900	47.1

TABLE I : IDENTIFICATION OF OBSERVATION SITES AND CHARACTERISTICS OF BASINS

| | OBSERVATION SITES | | | | | | CHARACTERISTICS OF BASIN | | | | | | |
Site number	River basin	Stream	Observ. site		Coordinates Lat. Long.	Period	Area km²	Slope	Soil	Cover	Regime	Mean precip. mm	Mean disc. m³s-1
1	2	3	4	5	6	7	8	9	10	11	12	13	14
010301H	Rio Dulce	Cahabon	Chajcar	1	N 15:29 W 90:11	1963 74	882	D	A90 C10	B	10	2240	25.1
010701H	Rio Dulce	Cahabon	Cahaboncito	1	N 15:28 W 89:33	1968 75	2626	E60 D40	A90 C10	B	10	2935	160
141001H	Salinos	Chixoy	Chisiguan	1	N 15:18 W 91:04	1969 74	2245	E30 D70	C	B40 D60	11	870	29.2
020601H	Chixoy	Salama	San Jeronimo	1	N 15:04 W 90:15	1968 74	144	F	C	B80 D20	90	1215	4.5
020603H	Salama	San Jeronimo	Las Astras	1	N 15:04 W 90:13	1966 74	127.5	E	C	B	90	1235	3.6
020602H	Chixoy	Las Flautas	Matanzas	1	N 15:06 W 90:11	1967 75	90.2	E	C	B	90	1285	1.9
020101H	Polochic	Chilasco	Chilasco	1	N 15:07 W 90:07	1964 74	67.5	E	C	B	90	2000	1.7
020202H	Chixoy	Blanco	Calà	1	N 15:13 W 90:35	1972 74	337	E70 D30	C90 A10	B	10	1045	5.6
020203H	Chixoy	Chicruz	Panxic	1	N 15:12 W 90:35	1972 74	484	E40 D60	C	B40 D60	11	740	5.2
141501H	Salinos	Chixoy	Los Torres	1	N 15:22 W 90:40	1962 74	5698	E40 D60	C90 A10	B10 C60 D10 E20	11	875	54.3
141502H	Salinas	Chixoy	San Augustin Chixoy	1	N 16:04 W 90:26	1971 73	10910	E60 D40	A60 C40	A40 B40 C20	00 10 11	2045	516
111103H (1)	Usumacinta	Salinas	El Cedro	1	N 16:26 W 90:26	1966 73	12730	E60 D40	A60 C40	A40 B40 C20	00 10	2075	575
111101H	Usumacinta	Pasion	El Porvenir	1	N 16:31 W 90:29	1970 73	11875	C	A60 C40	A40 B40 C20	00 10	2160	284.3
140301H	Lacantun	Xalbal	Xalbal	1	N 15:48 W 91:05	1972 73	750.3	E80 D20	A20 C80	A40 B40 C20	00	3010	<98.9
M 04 H (1)	Lacantun	Xalbal	Chajul	1	N 16:06 W 90:57	1968 73	1270	E80 D20	A20 C80	A40 B40 C20	00	3010	98.9

GUATEMALA

TABLE I : IDENTIFICATION OF OBSERVATION SITES AND CHARACTERISTICS OF BASINS

		OBSERVATION SITES							CHARACTERISTICS OF BASIN					
Site number	River basin	Stream	Observ. site		Coordinates Lat. Long.		Period	Area km²	Slope	Soil	Cover	Regime	Mean precip. mm	Mean disc. m³s⁻¹
1	2	3	4	5	6	7		8	9	10	11	12	13	14
072701H	Lacantun	Ixcan	Yulquisis	1	N 15:51	W 91:09	1972 73	1415	E80 D20	A20 C80	A40 B40 C20	00	2725	67.0
M 03 H (1)	Lacantun	Ixcan	Ixcan	1	N 16:06	W 91:05	1966 73	2192	E80 D20	A20 C80	A40 B40 C20	00	3375	188
M 06 H (1)	Usumacinta	Lacantun	Agua Verde	1	N 16:27	W 90:45	1965 73	20550	E80 D20	A10 C90	A40 B40 C20	00	2420	771
110302H (1)	Usumacinta	Usumacinta	El Tigre	1	N 16:37	W 90:40	1965 73	45910	E60 D40	A60 C40	A40 B40 C20	00 10	2190	1630
M 08 H (1)	Usumacinta	Usumacinta	Boca del Cerro	1	N 17:26	W 91:29	1949 72	51540	E60 D40	A60 C40	A40 B40 C20	00 10	2170	1776
M 09 H (1)	Usumacinta	San Pedro	San Pedro Tabasc	1	N 17:48	W 91:09	1953 72	14490	C	A40 C40 D20	A40 B30 C30	10	1610	74.3
070401H	Selegua	Selegua	Xemal	1	N 15:24	W 91:42	1964 75	464	E	C	B	90	1290	10.7

GUATEMALA

TABLE II : FLOODS CHARACTERISTICS

	FLOOD CHARACTERISTICS						DISCHARGE ESTIMATION					
Site number	Stream	Observ. site	Year	Date of the max	Maximal dis m³s-1	Climatic origine	Condition dis est	Qual. of the sect	Preci. ±m³s-1	Anteced precip.	Depth mm	Duration days
1	2	4	4	5	6	7	8	9	10	11	12	13
181001H	Tapalapa	Poza Escondadida	1966	10-15	41.5	1	A1C1	BOX				
180101H	Los Esclavos	La Sonrisa	1966	06-28	596	1	A1C1	BOX				
180801H	Aguacapa	Agua Caliente	1969 1974	09-06 09-20	1495 363	1 1	A1C1 A1C1	BOX BOX		3 3	125	2
050201H	Maria Linda	Guacanayas	1969	09-05	197	1	A1D4	BOX	U	3	337	2
3.2	Achiguate	Carretera CA-2	1969	09-05	1733	1	B5D4	DOX	U	3	337	2
3.3	Guacalate	Carretera CA-2	1969	09-05	1723	1	B5D4	DOX	U	3	337	2
3.1	Pantaleon	Carretera CA-2	1971	09-24	518	1	B4D4	DOB	130	2	50	1
170202H	Suchiate	Suchiate II	1973	08-31	2330	1	A1X1	BOX	U	2	149	1
3.4	Samala	Santa Maria	1949	10	1560	1	DOXO	BOX	U	3	>150	3
130901H	Samala	Candelaria	1974	09-20	287	1	A1C1	BOX		3		
030602H	Madre Vieja	Panibaj	1963		59	1	A1C1	BOX				
190801H	Yatza	Paquib	1970	09-17	2.64	1	A3C1	BOX				
191301H	Nahualate	Sta Catarina	1963		62	1	A1C1	BOX				
220701H	Sunzapote	Pasabien	1971	11-21	146	1	A3C1	BOX				
020301H	Motagua	Concua	1966 1969	10-19	>1520 1280	1 1	A2C1 A2C1	BOX				
010301H	Cahabon	Chajcar	1974 1973	09-19	400 152	1 1	A1C1 A1C1	BOX				
010701H	Cahabon	Cahaboncito	1974 1968	09-19	3300 1700	1 1	A1C1 A1C1	BOX BOX				
141001H	Chixoy	Chisiguan	1969	09-09	1710	1	A1C1	BOX				
020601H	Salama	San Jeronimo	1969 1970	08-23	231 120	1 1	A1C1 A1C1	BOX		3		
020603H	San Jeronimo	Las Astras	1969	07-03	133	1	A3C1	BOX				
020602H	Las Flautas	Matanzas	1971	09-21	29.3	1	A3C1	BOX		3	60	2

GUATEMALA

TABLE II : FLOODS CHARACTERISTICS

	FLOOD CHARACTERISTICS						DISCHARGE ESTIMATION					
Site number	Stream	Observ. Site	Year	Date of the max	Maximal dis m³s-1	Climatic origine	Condition dis est	Qual. of the sect	Preci. ±m³s-1	Anteced precip.	Depth mm	Duration days
1	2	3	4	5	6	7	8	9	10	11	12	13
020101H	Chilasco	Chilasco	1968	06-18	29.5	1	A1C1	BOX				
020202H	Blanco	Calà	1973	07-27	105	1	A3C1	BOX				
020203H	Chicruz	Panxic	1973	07-26	155	1	A3C1	BOX				
141501H	Chixoy	Las Torres	1973	08-29	1140	1	A1C1	BOX		3		
			1969	09-09	1100	1	A1C1	BOX				
141502H	Chixoy	San Augustin Chixoy	1973	10-08	2180	1	A1C1	BOX				
111103H	Salinas	El Cedro	1973	10-11	2980	1	A2X1	BOX				
			1970		2840	1	A2X1	BOX				
111101H	Pasion	El Porvenir	1972	08-10	1165	1	A1C1	BOX				
140301H	Xalbal	Xalbal	1973	08-31	418	1	A3C1	BOX	U			
MO4H	Xalbal	Chajul	1971	09-22	1150	1	A1X1	BOX				
072701H	Ixcan	Yulquisis	1973	08-29	414	1	A3C1	BOX		3	100	3
MO3H	Ixcan	Ixcan	1965	06-05	2140	1	A1X1	BOX				
			1973		2000	1	A1X1	BOX				
MO6H	Lacantun	Aguaverde	1966	07-01	5520	1	A1X1	BOX				
			1973		4160	1	A1X1	BOX				
110302H	Usumacinta	El Tigre	1972	08-03	7325	1	A1X1	BOX				
			1973		6755	1	A1X1	BOX				
MO8H	Usumacinta	Boca del Cerro	1967	10-23	6600	1	A1X1	BOX				
			1969		6150	1	A1X1	BOX				
			1972		6100	1	A1X1	BOX				
MO9H	San Pedro	San Pedro Tabasc.	1955	11-01	655	1	A2X1	BOX				
			1966		650	1	A2X1	BOX				
070401H	Selegua	Xemal	1973	08-13	590	1	A1C1	BOX				

TABLEAU I : IDENTIFICATION DES POINTS D'OBSERVATION ET CARACTERISTIQUES DES BASSINS

	POINT D'OBSERVATION								CARACTERISTIQUES DU BASSIN					
N° du point	Bassin fluvial	Rivière	Point d'observ.		Coordonnées Lat. Long.		Période	Surface km²	Relief	Sol	Végét.	Régime	Pluie moyenne mm	Module m³s-1
1	2	3	4	5	6	7	8		9	10	11	12	13	14
50105	Konkouré	Konkouré	Pont de Télimélé	1	N 10:30	W 12:54	1948 59 1967 78	10250	E	D	B	10	2000	368
150120	Niger	Niger	Kouroussa	1	N 10:39	W 09:52	1945 78	16560	C	C	B	10	1650	238
151805	Niger	Niandan	Baro	1	N 10:36	W 09:44	1947 78	12770	C	C	B	10	1800	261
151705	Niger	Milo	Kankan	1	N 10:22	W 09:20	1947 78	9620	C	C	B	10	1900	200

TABLEAU II : CARACTERISTIQUES DES CRUES

	CARACTERISTIQUES DE LA CRUE						EVALUATION DES DEBITS					
N° du point	Rivière	Point d'observ.	Année	Date du maximum	Débit max m³s-1	Origine	Base et mode éval	Qual. de la séch	Précis. ±m³s-1	Anteced	Hauteur	Durée jours
1	2	3	4	5	6	7	8	9	10	11	12	13
150105	Konkouré	Pont de Télimélé	1958	09-06	2930	1	A1B1	A1A	200			
			1955	07-31	2890	1	A1B1	A1A	200			
			1950	08-09	2780	1	A1B1	A1A	200			
150120	Niger	Kouroussa	1955	09-30	1710	1	A1B1	A	100			
			1951	11-12	1640	1	A1B1	A	100			
			1967	10-11	1534	1	A1B1	A	80			
151805	Niandan	Baro	1962	08-31	1960	1	A1B1	A	100			
			1967	09-30	1511	1	A1B1	A	50			
			1955	09-20	1490	1	A1B1	A	50			
151705	Milo	Kankan	1967	10-01	1040	1	A1B1	A	100			
			1975	09-24	1010	1	A1B1	A	100			
			1962	09-23	935	1	A1B1	A	80			
			1955	10- 2	920	1	A1B1	A	80			

GUYANA/GUYANE

TABLE I : IDENTIFICATION OF OBSERVATION SITES AND CHARACTERISTICS OF BASINS

	OBSERVATION SITES								CHARACTERISTICS OF BASIN						
Site number	River basin	Stream	Observ. site		Coordinates Lat. Long.		Period	Area km²	Slope	Soil	Cover	Regime	Mean precip. mm	Mean disc. m³s-1
1	2	3	4	5	6		7	8	9	10	11	12	13	14
1	Mazaruni	Mazaruni	Apaïkwa	1	N 06-22	W 60-23	1950 72	14000	B C	C D	A	00	2915	746
2	Essequibo	Potaru	Kaieteur	1	N 05-09	W 59-29	1950 72	2640	C	C D	A	00	4140	196
3	Demerara	Demerara	Great Falls	1	N 05-19	W 58-32	1950 72	2460	B C	C D	A	00	2360	75.5
4	Demerara	Demerara	Saka	1	N 05-34	W 58-22	1950 72	4040	B C	C D	A	00	2370	114.2

GUYANA/GUYANE

TABLE II : FLOODS CHARACTERISTICS

	FLOODS CHARACTERISTICS						DISCHARGE ESTIMATION					
Site number	Stream	Observ. site	Year	Date of the max	Maximal dism³s-1	Climatic origine	Condition disc est	Qual. of the sect	Precis. ±m³s-1	Anteced precip.	Depth mm	Duration days
1	2	3	4	5	6	7	8	9	10	11	12	13
1	Mazaruni	Apaïkwa	1971	07-04	2640	1						
			1954	06-22	2610	1						
2	Potaru	Kaieteur	1968	06-18	1120	1						
			1950	06-18	985	1						
3	Demerara	Great Falls	1955	07-27	365	1						
			1972	06-16	365	1						
4	Demerara	Saka	1951	07-02	447	1						
			1955	08-04	425	1						

HAWAII ISLANDS/ILES HAWAI (UNITED STATES OF AMERICA)/(ETATS UNIS D'AMERIQUE)

TABLE I : IDENTIFICATION OF OBSERVATION SITES AND CHARACTERISTICS OF BASINS

| | OBSERVATION SITES | | | | | | CHARACTERISTICS OF BASIN | | | | | | |
Site number	River basin	Stream	Observ. site		Coordinates Lat. Long.	Period	Area km²	Slope	Soil	Cover	Regime	Mean precip. mm	Mean disc. m³s−1
1	2	3	4	5	6	7	8	9	10	11	12	13	14
16060000	Wailua	South Fork Wailua	Lihue (Kauai)	1	N 22:02 W 159:23	1914 80	58.0			A	00		3.3
16400000	Halawa	Halawa	Halawa (Molokai)	1	N 21:10 W 156:46	1918 25 1928 31 1938 80	12.0				10		0.8
16587000	Honopou	Honopou	Huelo (Mauai)	1	N 20:53 W 156:15	1910 80	1.7				00		0.13
16704000	Wailuku	Wailuku	Piihonua (Hawai)	1	N 19:43 W 155:09	1929 80	596				00		8.1

HAWAII ISLANDS/ILES HAWAI (UNITED STATES OF AMERICA)/(ETATS UNIS D'AMERIQUE)

TABLE II : FLOODS CHARACTERISTICS

| | FLOOD CHARACTERISTICS | | | | | | DISCHARGE ESTIMATION | | | | | |
Site number	Stream	Observ. site	Year	Date of the max	Maximal dism³s−1	Climatic origine	Condition disc est	Qual. of the sect	Precis. ±m³s−1	Anteced precip.	Depth mm	Duration days
1	2	3	4	5	6	7	8	9	10	11	12	13
16060000	S.F.Wailua	Lihue	1963 1955 1920	04−15 11−12 01−16	2470 1320 1270	1 1 1	A1C4					
16400000	Halawa	Halawa	1965 1961 1948	02−04 01−01 04−02	762 309 277	1 1 1	A4D4					
16587000	Honopou	Huelo	1930 1922 1950	11−18 02−01 04−27	162 75 60.6	1 1 1	A1XO					
16704000	Wailuku	Piihonua	1940 1979 1956	08−11 11−17 08−11	2270 1700 1330	1 1 1	A1C1					

TABLE I : IDENTIFICATION OF OBSERVATION SITES AND CHARACTERISTICS OF BASINS

| OBSERVATION SITES | | | | | | | | CHARACTERISTICS OF BASIN | | | | | | |
Site number	River basin	Stream	Observ. site		Coordinates Lat. Long.		Period	Area km²	Slope	Soil	Cover	Regime	Mean precip. mm	Mean disc. m³s-1
1	2	3	4	5	6		7	8	9	10	11	12	13	14
10-017	Duna (Danube)	Duna	Budapest	1	N 47:29	E 19:03	1823 1975	185200	A16 B63 C21	A 6 B14 C80	A15 B16 C17 D52	60	590	2300
10-031	Duna	Duna	Mohacs	1	N 46:00	E 18:42	1852 1975	209100	A24 B58 C18	A 5 B12 C83	A12 B14 C15 D59	60	630	2370
14-017	Duna	Raba	Arpas	1	N 47:31	E 17:24	1875 1975	6610	A68 B32	B20 C80	A17 B 8 C12 D63	60	630	42
40-003	Duna	Drava	Barcs	1	N 45:55	E 17:28	1872 1975	33980	A82 B18	B25 C75	A 8 B15 C 9 D68	60	770	487
40-006	Drava	Mura	Letenye	1	N 46:25	E 16:42	1891 1975	13030	A76 B24	B22 C78	A14 B 8 C11 D67	60	795	192
50-005	Duna	Tisza	Zahony	1	N 48:	E 22:	1860 1975	32780	A87 B13	B10 C90	A 5 B10 C15 D70	60	685	418
50-021	Duna	Tisza	Szolnok	1	N 47:10	E 20:14	1854 1975	73110	A90 B10	B12 C88	A 4 B 9 C14 D73	60	685	530
50-028	Duna	Tisza	Szeged	1	N 46:16	E 20:13	1833 1975	138400	A94 B 6	B13 C87	A 4 B 8 C14 D74	60	550	936
54-001	Tisza	Szamos	Csenger	1	N 47:51	E 22:42	1875 1975	15280	A100	B 7 C93	B10 C15 D75	60	600	138
60-001	Tisza	Bodrog	Felsöberecki	1	N 48:21	E 21:42	1931 75	12390	A95 B 5	B11 C89	A10 B 5 C10 D75	60	610	112
65-006	Tisza	Sajo	Felsözsolca	1	N 48:06	E 20:51	1879 1975	6440	A90 B10	B16 C84	A10 B 7 C13 D70	60	560	32
67-001	Sajo	Hernad	Hidasnemeti	1	N 48:30	E 21:13	1893 1975	4515	A91 B 9	B14 C86	A10 B 8 C12 D70	60	590	32

TABLE I : IDENTIFICATION OF OBSERVATION SITES AND CHARACTERISTICS OF BASINS

	OBSERVATION SITES						CHARACTERISTICS OF BASIN						
Site number	River basin	Stream	Observ. site		Coordinates Lat. Long.	Period	Area km²	Slope	Soil	Cover	Regime	Mean precip. mm	Mean disc. m³s-1
1	2	3	4	5	6	7	8	9	10	11	12	13	14
70-008	Tisza	Zagyva	Jasztelek	1	N 47:29 E 20:00	1898 1975	4207	A100	C100	A 5 B18 D77	60	590	8,6
82-002	Tisza	Fekete-Koros	Sarkad	1	N 46:43 E 21:23	1930 75	4302	A95 B 5	B21 C79	A10 B10 C25 D55	60	570	44
81-001	Tisza	Feher-Koros	Gyula	1	N 46:36 E 21:17	1873 1975	4251	A95 B 5	B21 C79	A10 B10 C25 D55	60	560	34
84-001	Tisza	Sebes-Koros	Körösszakal	1	N 47:03 E 21:36	1873 1975	2489	A96 B 4	B20 C80	A 5 B10 C25 D60	60	590	25
90-002	Tisza	Maros	Mako	1	N 46:12 E 20:27	1864 1975	30150	A91 B 9	B15 C85	A10 B15 C15 D60	60	580	211

TABLE II : FLOODS CHARACTERISTICS

		FLOODS CHARACTERISTICS					DISCHARGE ESTIMATION					
Site number	Stream	Observ. site	Year	Date of the max	Maximal dis m³s-1	Climatic origine	Condition disc est	Qual. of the sect	Precis. ±m³s-1	Anteced precip.	Depth mm	Duration days
1	2	3	4	5	6	7	8	9	10	11	12	13
10-017	Duna (Danube)	Budapest	1965	06-15	8310	1	A1B1	A1B	415	2	X	X
			1954	07-18	7960	1	A1B1	A1B	310	2	X	X
			1956	03-10	7490	4	A1B1	A1B	300	2	X	X
10-031	Duna	Mohacs	1956	03-13	8750	4	A1B1	B1B	348	2	X	X
			1965	06-19	8244	1	A1B1	B1B	412	2	X	X
			1954	07-23	6858	1	A1B1	B1B	340	2	X	X
14-017	Raba	Arpas	1965	04-25	970	1	A1B1	B1B	48	3	X	X
			1963	03-15	513	4	A1B1	B1B	26	3	X	X
			1972	07-19	471	1	A1B1	B1B	33	3	X	X
40-003	Drava	Barcs	1972	07-19	3090	1	A1B1	B1B	154	3	X	X
			1975	12-05	2573	1	A1B1	B1B	150	3	X	X
41-006	Mura	Letenye	1972	07-18	1580	1	A1B1	B1B	63	3	X	X
			1975	07-03	1334	1	A1B1	B1B	60	3	X	X
50-005	Tisza	Zahony	1941	02-19	3608	4	A1B1	B1B	190	1	X	X
			1970	05-17	3360	1	A1B1	B1B	165	2	X	X
			1932	04-09	3343	1	A1B1	B1B	160	2	X	X
50-021	Tisza	Szolnok	1932	04-17	3314	1	A1B1	B1B	166	2	X	X
			1940	04-08	3160	1	A1B1	B1B	158	2	X	X
			1967	03-22	3030	4	A1B1	B1B	150	2	X	X
50-028	Tisza	Szeged	1932	04-15	4348	1	A1B1	B1B	174	2	X	X
			1924	04-11	3864	1	A1B1	B1B	154	2	X	X
			1970	05-31	3825	1	A1B1	B1B	153	2	X	X
54-001	Szamos	Csenger	1970	05-14	3360	1	A1B1	B1B	134	3	X	X
			1974	06-15	2150	1	A1B1	B1B	86	3	X	X
			1932	04-07	1458	1	A1B1	B1B	73	3	X	X
60-001	Bodrog	Felsöberecki	1940	04-03	1012	1	A1B1	B1B	50	3	X	X
			1941	02-23	980	4	A1B1	B1B	50	1	X	X
			1974	10-25	835	1	A1B1	B1B	42	3	X	X
65-006	Sajo	Felsözsolca	1974	10-24	545	1	A1B1	B1B	33	3	X	X
			1963	03-14	515	4	A1B1	B1B	31	3	X	X
			1940	03-29	500	1	A1B1	B1B	30	3	X	X
67-001	Hernad	Hidasnemeti	1974	10-23	653	1	A1B1	B1B	33	3	X	X
			1948	06-09	552	1	A1B1	B1B	30	X	X	X
			1960	07-28	461	1	A1B1	B1B	28	3	X	X
70-008	Zagyva	Jasztelek	1963	03-14	304	4	A1B1	B1B	18	3	X	X
			1940	03-26	286	1	A1B1	B1B	17	3	X	X
			1919	04-24	229	1	A1B1	B1B	14	3	X	X
82-002	Fekete- körös	Sarkad	1962	04-02	599	1	A1B1	B1B	36	3	X	X
			1974	06-15	580	1	A1B1	B1B	35	3	X	X
			1932	04-04	572	1	A1B1	B1B	34	3	X	X

TABLE II : FLOODS CHARACTERISTICS

		FLOODS CHARACTERISTICS							DISCHARGE ESTIMATION				
Site number	Stream	Observ. site	Year	Date of the max	Maximal dism³s-1	Climatic origine	Condition disc est	Qual. of the sect	Precis. ±m³s-1	Anteced precip.	Depth mm	Duration days
1	2	3	4	5	6	7	8	9	10	11	12	13
81-001	Feher-körös	Gyula	1974	06-15	626	1	A1B1	B1B	31	3	X	X
			1939	11-01	600	1	A1B1	B1B	30	3	X	X
			1957	05-31	560	1	A1B1	B1B	34	3	X	X
84-001	Sebes-körös	Körösszakal	1970	06-13	690	1	A1B1	B1B	34	3	X	X
			1974	07-23	613	1	A1B1	B1B	31	3	X	X
			1962	04-02	596	1	A1B1	B1B	36	3	X	X
90-002	Maros	Mako	1970	05-20	2440	1	A1B1	B1B	98	3	X	X
			1975	07-10	2319	1	A1B1	B1B	93	3	X	X
			1932	04-10	1811	1	A1B1	B1B	90	3	X	X

TABLE I : IDENTIFICATION OF OBSERVATIONS SITES AND CHARACTERISTICS OF BASINS

OBSERVATION SITES						CHARACTERISTICS OF BASIN							
Site number	River basin	Stream	Observ. site		Coordinates Lat. Long.	Period	Area km²	Slope	Soil	Cover	Regime	Mean precip mm	Mean disc m³s-1
1	2	3	4	5	6	7	8	9	10	11	12	13	14
1	Ellidaar	Ellidaar	Heyvad	1	N 64:06 W 21:45	1929 81	270				50	900	5.02
20	Jökulsa à Fjöllum	Jökulsa à Fjöllum	Dettifoss	1	N 65:50 W 16:25	1940 81	7000				81	(500)	185
30	Thjorsa	Thjorsa	Urridafoss	1	N 63:56 W 20:38	1948 81	7200				50	900	367
45	Hnausakvist	Vatnsdalsa	Forsaeludalur	1	N 65:18 W 20:06	1949 81	450				81	500	8.52
51	Kolka	Hjaltadalsa	Sleitustadir	1	N 65:47 W 19-18	1957 81	297				81	500	9.28
64	Olfusa	Olfusa	Selfoss	1	N 63:56 W 21:01	1951 81	5760				50	900	375
149	Geithellnaa	Geithellnaa	Gamla Bru	1	N 64:35 W 14:36	1971 81	184				50	2000	19.5
150	Djupa	Djupa	Bru	1	N 63:57 W 17:39	1969 81	260				50	2000?	27.2
88	Skeidara Sandgigjukvisi	Skeidara	Skeidara	3	N 64 W 17		1700				50	2000?	

TABLE II : FLOODS CHARACTERISTICS

FLOODS CHARACTERISTICS							DISCHARGE ESTIMATION					
Site number	Stream	Observ. site	Year	Date of the max	Maximal dism^3s-1	Climatic origine	Condition disc est	Qual. of the sect	Precis. $\pm m^3s-1$	Anteced precip.	Depth mm	Duration days
1	2	3	4	5	6	7	8	9	10	11	12	13
1	Ellidaar	Heyvad	1968	02-28	220	4 (1)						
20	Jökulsa à Fjollum	Dettifoss	1949	06-20	1720	2						
30	Thjorsa	Urridafoss	1948	03-05	3500	4						
45	Vatnsdalsa	Forsaeludalur	1959	02-03	212	4						
51	Hjaltadalsa	Sleitustadir	1971	07-13	140	1						
64	Olfusa	Sellfoss	1968	02-29	2520	4						
149	Geithellnaa	Gamla Bru	1980	10-31	454	4						
150	Djupa	Bru	1980	10-31	298	4						
88	Skeidara	Skeidara	1954	07-18	10500	5 (2)						

(1) dam failure has increased the natural large flood.
(2) Glacier burst.

TABLE I : IDENTIFICATION OF OBSERVATIONS SITES AND CHARACTERISTICS OF BASINS

	OBSERVATIONS SITE						CHARACTERISTICS OF BASIN						
Site number	River basin	Stream	Observ. site		Coordinates Lat. Long.	Period	Area km²	Slope	Soil	Cover	Regime	Mean precip. mm	Mean disc. m³s⁻¹
1	2	3	4	5	6	7	8	9	10	11	12	13	14
1	Luni	Jojri	Bisalpur	3	N 26:30 E 73:19		1160	C	D	C	11	400	
2	Rann of Kutch	Machhu	Machhu Dam II	3	N 22:47 E 70:51		1900				10-11	570	
3	Cambay Gulf	Mahi	Chandangarh	1	N 23:12 E 75:00		4320						
4	Narmada	Narmada	Garudeshwar	1	N 21:45 E 73:55	1948 80	88000	D C B A			10	1320	1170
5	Narmada	Taïrhia	Br. n° 253	1	N 22:52 E 79:50	1966 74	114	D C		A84 D10 E06	10		5.3
6	Tapi	Tapi	Kathoré/Ghalla	1	N 21:17 E 72:57	1940 80	64000				10	760	540
7	Tapi	Uma	Br. n° 394	1	N 20:46 E 77:29	1958 59 1961 75	350				10		9.7
8	Couvery	Couvery	Billigundlu	1	N 12:25 E 77:27		35570						
9	Pennar	Pennar	Somasila	1	N 14:33 E 78:45		38660						
10	Krishna	Krishna	Vijayawada	1	N 16:31 E 80:37	1894 1980	255000	D C B A			10	1390	1750
11	Krishna	Bhima	Yadgir	1	N 16:48 E 77:08		69860						
12	Krishna	Bhooga Vagu	Br. n° 642	1	N 17:23 E 80:11	1958 59 1961 66	326	D		A50 D30 E20	10		9.4
13	Godavari	Godavari	Dolaishwaram Polavaram	1	N 16:55 E 81:47	1901 60 1965 80	309000	C B A			10	1120	3250
14	Godavari	Indravati	Barthagudem	1	N 19:00 E 80:17		40000						

TABLE I : IDENTIFICATION OF OBSERVATIONS SITES AND CHARACTERISTICS OF BASINS

| | OBSERVATIONS SITE | | | | | | CHARACTERISTICS OF BASIN | | | | | | |
Site number	River basin	Stream	Observ. site		Coordinates Lat. Long.	Period	Area km²	Slope	Soil	Cover	Regime	Mean precip. mm	Mean disc. m³s⁻¹
1	2	3	4	5	6	7	8	9	10	11	12	13	14
15	Godavari	Kulbera	Br. n° 228	1	N 21:58 E 78:57	1966 73	503	E		A25 D40 E35	10		17.5
16	Yamsadhara	Yamsadhara	kasi Nagar	1	N 19:11 E 83:54		7820						
17	Mahanadi	Mahanadi	Baramul/Munduli	1	N 20:30 E 84:50	1946 70	127000				10	1410	1750
18	Mahanadi	Mahanadi	Tikarpara	1	N 20:38 E 84:37	1972 80	107000				10		
19	Mahanadi	Lilagar	Br. n° 12	1	N 22:02 E 82:20	1959 65	647	D			10		26
20	Mahanadi	Mahanadi	Kantamal	1	N 21:35 E 82:27		19600						
21	Brahmani	Brahmani	Bolani	1	N 22:06 E 85:00		18070						
22		Baitarni	Anandapur	1	N 21 ? E 86 ?		8570						
23	Damodar	Damodar	Rhondia	1	N 22:48 E 88:07	1934 60 1965 74	19900				10		305
24	Ganga	Ganga	Farrakka	1	N 25:00 E 87:55	1948 80	935000				90 10	1100	11800
25	Ganga	Kosi	Sunakhambhi Khola	1	N 26:55 E 87:06	1947 67	66900	F E D C B			90 10	1670	1650
26	Ganga	Sone	Koelwar	1	N 25:00 E 84:40		67870						
27	Sone	Bankinadi	Br. n° 171	1	N 24:19 E 83:51	1958 67	373	E		A75 D22 E03	10		14.2
28	Ganga	Gogra	Turtipar	1	N 26:30 E 83:00		113000						
29	Ganga	Tons	Meja Road	1	N 25:00 E 81:50		17400						
30	Ganga	Yamuna	Pratappur	1	N 25:15 E 81:30		366500						

TABLE I : IDENTIFICATION OF OBSERVATIONS SITES AND CHARACTERISTICS OF BASINS

	OBSERVATIONS SITE						CHARACTERISTICS OF BASIN						
Site number	River basin	Stream	Observ. site		Coordinates Lat. Long.	Period	Area km²	Slope	Soil	Cover	Regime	Mean precip. mm	Mean disc. m³s⁻¹
1	2	3	4	5	6	7	8	9	10	11	12	13	14
31	Yamuna	Betwa	Sahijna	1	N 25:55 E 79:40		43870						
32	Yamuna	Chambal	Udi	1	N 26:00 E 77:00		136800						
33	Ganga	Ganga	Rishikesh	1	N 30:00 E 78:25		21800						
34	Brahmaputra	Brahmaputra	Pandu	1	N 26:12 E 91:30	1955 74	404000	F E D C B A				90 10	2400	15700
35	Brahmaputra	Kalajani	Br. n° 242	1	N 26:41 E 89:25	1961 62 1968 69	230	F		A60 D20 E20	90 10		28.5
36	Brahmaputra	Gish	Br. n° 91	1	N 26:53 E 88:37	1966 68	133	F	D	A95 D02 E03	90 10		14.1
37	Brahmaputra	Chell	Br. n° 95	1	N 26:57 E 88:38	1964 66 67	119	F	D	A78 D08 E14	90 10		12.8
38	Indus	Ravi	Mukesar	1	N 32:30 E 75:54	1965 1974	5700	F E D					(250)

TABLE II : FLOODS CHARACTERISTICS

	FLOOD CHARACTERISTICS						DISCHARGE ESTIMATION					
Site number	Stream	Observ. site	Year	Date of the max	Maximal disc m³s-1	Climatic origine	Condition disc est	Qual. of the sect	Precis. ±m³s-1	Anteced precip.	Depth mm.	Duration days.
1	2	3	4	5	6	7	8	9	10	11	12	13
1	Jojri	Bisalpur	1979	07-17	6530	1	U		U		360	2
2	Machhu	Machhu Dam II	1979	08-11	>14000	1	U		U	3	372	2
3	Mahi	Chadangarh	1977	06-28	8160 (6)	1						
4	Narmada	Garudeshwar	1970 1968 1973	09-06 08-06 08-31	69400 58000 58000	1 1 1						
5	Tairhia	Br. n° 253	1973	08-30	646	1						
6	Tapi	Kathoré	1970 (1) 1959 1944	09-06 09-18 08-24	36500 ? 29600 ? 25500	1 1 1						
7	Uma	Br. n° 394	1962	09-19	820	1						
8	Couvery	Billigundlu	1975	08-16	4430 (6)	1	*					
9	Pennar	Somasila	1975	10-28	4710 (6)	1						
10	Krishna	Vijayawada	1903 1914 1949	10-07 08-11 09-24	39000 33900 32500	1 1 1	*					
11	Bhima	Yadgir	1969	09-07	10250	1						
12	Bhooga Vagu	Br. n° 642	1961	07-23	397	1						
13	Godavari	Dolaïshwaram	1907 1959 1953 1958	07 09-17 08-16 09-04	>80000 78700 78000 64000	1 1 1 1						
14	Indravati	Bartha Gudem	1976	07-21	24860 (6)	1						
15	Kulbera	Br. n° 228	1968 73	09-14 07-23	1910 1520	1 1						
16	Yamsadhara	Kasi Nagar	1972	09-23	6590 (6)	1						
17	Mahanadi	Baramul	1946 (2) 1947 1960	08-25 09-02 08-17	39400 39200 36300	1 1 1	*					
18	Mahanadi	Tikarpara	1980 1978	09-21 08-29	36100 30900	1 1	*					

(1) 41700 in 1968 in several publications : probably erroneous.
(2) 42000 in 1872 (Pr. M. Pardé).
(6) Recent records only taken into consideration.

* More or less regulated

TABLE II : FLOODS CHARACTERISTICS

					FLOOD CHARACTERISTICS			DISCHARGE ESTIMATION					
Site number	Stream	Observ. site	Year	Date of the max	Maximal discm³s-1	Climatic origine	Condition disc est	Qual. of the sect	Precis. ±m³s-1	Anteced precip.	Depth mm.	Duration days.	
1	2	3	4	5	6	7	8	9	10	11	12	13	
19	Lilagar	Br. n° 12	1963	08-11	940	1							
20	Mahanadi	Kantamal	1977	09-13	15400 (6)	1							
21	Brahmani	Bolani	1974	08-17	13570 (6)	1							
22	Baitarni	Anandapur	1975	08-19	10400 (6)	1							
23	Damodar	Rhondia	1935	08-12	18100	1							
			1941	10-10	17900	1							
			1938	09-06	12000	1							
24	Ganga	Farrakka	1954	08-22	72900	4							
			1980	09-06	71300	4							
			1971	08-23	70500	4							
25	Kosi	Sunakhambhi Kola	1954	07-27	17400	4							
			1948	07-13	11400	4							
26	Sone	Koelwar	1971	07-20	36800	1							
			1934		35000	1							
27	Bankinadi	Br. n° 171	1962	09-23	427	1							
28	Gogra	Turtipar	1972	09-21	29700 (6)	4 ?							
29	Tons	Meja Road	1971	07-21	10800 (6)	1							
30	Yamuna	Pratappur	1964	09-28	37900	4 ?							
			1861		37500	4 ?							
31	Betwa	Sahijna	1971	07-26	43800 (6)	1							
32	Chambal	Udi	1976	08-07	21600 (6)	1							
33	Ganga	Rishikesh	1924		16000 ?	4							
			1978	03-09	10450	4							
34	Brahmaputra	Pandu	1962	08-24	72700	4							
			1958	08-29	62000	4							
35	Kalajani	Br. n° 242	1968	06-20	250	1							
36	Gish	Br. n° 91 (5)	1968	07-13	1170	1							
37	Chell	Br. n° 95	1967	07-18	787	1							
38	Ravi	Mukesar	1966 (4)	09-09	11330 (3)	4							
			1971	08-09	9740 (3)	4							

(3) Mean daily discharge.
(4) We do not receive information about the 1955 flood largely exceeding the 1966 flood.
(5) For small stream it is possible to find in the litteratur more large floods than this Gish flood.
(6) Recent records only taken into consideration.

TABLE I : IDENTIFICATION OF OBSERVATION SITES AND CHARACTERISTICS OF BASINS

	OBSERVATION SITES							CHARACTERISTICS OF BASIN						
Site number	River basin	Stream	Observ. site		Coordinates Lat. Long.		Period	Area km²	Slope	Soil	Cover	Regime	Mean precip. mm	Mean disc. m³s−1
1	2	3	4	5	6		7	8	9	10	11	12	13	14
BALI														
1	Anda	Anda	Klungkung Bridge	3	S 08:32	E 115:25		205	E			00		
JAVA														
2	Cipetakam	Cipanas	Leuwibunder	1	S 06:38	E 108:03	1938 41	62	F E			00		
3	Citarum	Gimandur	Bantarkarang	1	S 06:49	E 107:20	1938 40	132	F E			00		
4	Citarum	Citarum	Palumbon	1	S 06:43	E 107:20	19 Years	4232	F E D			00		
5	Ciliwung	Cianten II	Kracak	1	S 06:38	E 106:38	25 Years	126	F E			00		
6	Cimanuk	Cimanuk	Cijeungjing	1	S 06:49	E 108:07	1939 40	1608	F E D			00		
7		Celis	Kudus	1	S 06:48	E 110:51	40 Years	40				00		
8		Sempor	Bojong Weir	3	S 07:36	E 109:31		46.6				00		
9	Serayu	Serayu	Garung	1	S 07:17	E 109:56	34 Years	56.4	F E			00		
10	Serayu	Tulis	Sokaraja	1	S 07:22	E 109:46	10 Years	106				00		
11	Serayu	Serayu	Singomerto Weir	3	S 07:24	E 109:40		710	F E D			00		
12	Serayu	Serayu	Banyumas	1	S 07:31	E 109:18	1969 71	2642	F E D			00		
13		Tuntang	Glapan	1	S 07:07	E 110:41	25 Years	514	E D			00		
14	Bengawan Solo	Bengawan Solo	Kedungareng	1	S 07:51	E 110:56	1966 81	957	D C			00		
15	Bengawan Solo	Bengawan Solo	Juranggempal	1	S 07:48	E 110:56		1442	D C			00		
16	Bengawan Solo	Bengawan Solo	Bojonegoro	3	S 07:09	E 111:53		12429	D C			00		

TABLE I : IDENTIFICATION OF OBSERVATION SITES AND CHARACTERISTICS OF BASINS

	OBSERVATION SITES							CHARACTERISTICS OF BASIN					
Site number	River basin	Stream	Observ. site		Coordinates Lat. Long.	Period		Area km²	Slope	Soil	Cover	Regime	Mean precip. mm	Mean disc. m³s-1
1	2	3	4	5	6	7	8	9	10	11	12	13	14

SUMATERA
(Sumatra)

17		Kr. Aceh	Kpg Darang	1	N 05:25 E 95:20			1185	D E			00	
18		Kr. Baro	Keumala Dalan	1	N 05:13 E 95:51			230	E F			00	
19	Batang Hari	Sangir	Sungaltarab	1	S 01:42 E 101:21	7 Years		285	E F			00	
20	Batang Hari	Asam	Dusun Tobat	1	S 01:23 E 101:44	3 Years		240	E F			00	
21	Batang Hari	Tembesi	Muara Inum	1	S 02:18 E 102:23	3 Years		1520	F E D			00	
22	Batang Hari	Tembesi	Limbur Tembesi		S 02:15 E 102:31	2 Years		1720	F E D			00	
23	Musi	Klingi	Lubuk-Linggau		S 03:17 E 102:51	5 Years		400	E			00	

SULAWESI
(Celebes)

24		Baibunta	Baibunta	1	S 02:35 E 120:17	2 Years		9	F E			00	

TABLE II : FLOODS CHARACTERISTICS

			FLOODS CHARACTERISTICS						DISCHARGE ESTIMATION			
Site number	Stream	Observ. site	Year	Date of the max	Maximal dis $m^3s{-}1$	Climatic origine	Condition disc est	Qual. of the sect	Precis. $\pm m^3s{-}1$	Anteced precip.	Depth mm	Duration days
1	2	3	4	5	6	7	8	9	10	11	12	13
BALI												
1	Anda	Klungkung Bridge	1964	02	2500	1	B4D5		U			
JAVA												
2	Cipanas	Leuwibunder	1939	02-12	698	1	A		U			
			1940	03-12	660	1						
3	Gimandur	Bantarkarang	1938	11-12	590	1	A		U			
4	Citarum	Palumbon	1940	03-06	2733	1	A2C		400			
			1969	01-28	1800	1			U			
5	Cianten II	Kracak	1930	06-08	666	1	A2C		120			
6	Cimanuk	Cijeungjing	1940	03-06	910	1	A		U			
7	Celis	Kudus			390	1	A		U			
8	Sempor	Bojong Weir	1954	11	900	1	B4D		U			
9	Serayu	Garung	1916		267	1	A2C		50			
			1928		193	1	A2C		40			
10	Tulis	Sokaraja	1925	03-16	480	1	A		U			
11	Serayu	Singomerto Weir	1922	06	2500	1	B4D		U			
			1973	05	1700	1	B4D		U			
12	Serayu	Banyumas	1970		1274	1	A2C		U			
13	Tuntang	Glapan	1980	01-22	1200	1	A		U			
14	Bengawan Solo	Kedungareng	1966	03-16	4300	1	A		U			
15	Bengawan Solo	Jurangyempal	1975 (1)		2336	1	B2C		400			
16	Bengawan	Bojonegoro	1961		4754	1	B2C		900			
SUMATERA												
17	Kr. Aceh	Kpg Darang	1953		2080	1	A		U			
18	Kr. Baro	Keumala Dalan	1976	12-16	1050	1	A2D		U			
19	Sangir	Sungaltarab	1932	01-23	1200	1	A		U			
20	Asam	Dusun Tobat	1940	01-02	2130	1	A3C		U			

(1) 3800 m^3/sec 03-15 1966 ?

TABLE II : FLOODS CHARACTERISTICS

	FLOODS CHARACTERISTICS						DISCHARGE ESTIMATION					
Site number	Stream	Observ. site	Year	Date of the max	Maximal dism³s-1	Climatic origine	Condition disc est	Qual. of the sect	Precis. ±m³s-1	Anteced precip.	Depth mm	Duration days
1	2	3	4	5	6	7	8	9	10	11	12	13
21	Tembesi	Muara Inum	1940	09-21	2700	1			U			
			1939	04-13	1500	1			U			
22	Tembesi	Limbur Tembesi	1978	03-01	4100	1	A		U			
23	Klingi	Lubuk Klingau	1937	10-23	1000	1			U			
			1936	10-12	560	1			U			
SULAWESI												
24	Baibunta	Baibunta	1939	08-06	270	1			U			
			1938	12-24	112	1			U			

TABLE I : IDENTIFICATION OF OBSERVATION SITES AND CHARACTERISTICS OF BASINS

| | OBSERVATION SITES | | | | | | Period | Area km² | CHARACTERISTICS OF BASIN | | | | | |
Site number	River basin	Stream	Observ. site		Coordinates Lat.	Long.			Slope	Soil	Cover	Regime	Mean precip. mm	Mean disc. m³s-1
1	2	3	4	5	6		7	8	9	10	11	12	13	14
1	Karun	Karun	Ahwaz	1	N 31:20	E 48:41	1894 1970	60800	F E D C			90 70	525	

TABLE II : FLOODS CHARACTERISTICS

| | FLOODS CHARACTERISTICS | | | | | | DISCHARGE ESTIMATION | | | | | |
Site number	Stream	Observ. site	Year	Date of the max	Maximal dis m³s-1	Climatic origine	Condition disc est	Qual. of the sect	Precis. ±m³s-1	Anteced precip.	Depth mm	Duration days
1	2	3	4	5	6	7	8	9	10	11	12	13
1	Karun	Ahwaz	1924	01	11700	4						

TABLE I : IDENTIFICATION OF OBSERVATION SITES AND CHARACTERISTICS OF BASINS

	OBSERVATION SITES							CHARACTERISTICS OF BASIN						
Site number	River basin	Stream	Observ. site		Coordinates Lat. Long.		Period	Area km²	Slope	Soil	Cover	Regime	Mean precip. mm	Mean disc. m³s-1
1	2	3	4	5	6	7	8	9	10	11	12	13	14	
1	Digla (Tigris)	Digla	Baghdad (Saraï)	1	N 33:18	E 44:23	1931 1975	134000	A B C D E F		B C D E	90 30 70	900	1140
2	Alfurat (Euphrates)	Alfurat	Hits	1	N 33:59	E 42:49	1924 75	264100	A B C D E F		B C D E	90 30 70		920

TABLE II : FLOODS CHARACTERISTICS

	FLOODS CHARACTERISTICS						DISCHARGE ESTIMATION					
Site number	Stream	Observ. site	Year	Date of the max	Maximal dism³s-1	Climatic origine	Condition disc est	Qual. of the sect	Precis. ±m³s-1	Anteced precip.	Depth mm	Duration days
1	2	3	4	5	6	7	8	9	10	11	12	13
1	Digla	Baghdad	1941	02-12	7640	4						
2	Alfurat	Hits	1969	05-13	7366 (1)	4	AOXO	C1B				
			1968		6654 (1)		AOXO	C1B				
			1967		6092 (1)		AOXO	C1B				
			1954	04-28	4730	4	A1A1	C1B				
			1952	04-18	4570	4	A1A1	C1B				

(1) These values may be overestimated as a result of the bedshifting , but there is good reasons for the superiority of the floods of 1969 and 1968 relatively to the flood of 1954.

TABLE I : IDENTIFICATION OF OBSERVATIONS SITES ANS CHARACTERISTICS OF BASINS

OBSERVATIONS SITE							CHARACTERISTICS OF BASIN							
Site number	River basin	Stream	Observ. site		Coordinates Lat. Long.	Period	Area km²	Slope	Soil	Cover	Regime	Mean precip. mm	Mean disc. m³s⁻1
1	2	3	4	5	6	7	8	9	10	11	12	13	14
07	Boyne	Boyne	Slane Castle	1	N 53:42 W 06:34	1942 79	2410				50	900	32
09	Liffey	Liffey	Celbridge	1	N 53:22 W 06:29	1933 39 1943 60 1962 78	1565				50	850	15
18	Blackwater	Blackwater	Ballyduff	1	N 52:09 W 08:03	1940 54 1956 81	2340				50	1150	56
25	Shannon	Shannon	Killaloe	1	N 52:48 W 08:26	1893 1981	11690				50	1050	174
30	Corrib	Corrib	Galway	1	N 53:16 W 09:03	1939 81	3115				50	1350	94
34	Moy	Moy	Rahans	1	N 54:05 W 09:09	1939 65 1968 79	1911				50	1300	50
36	Erne	Erne	Ballyshannon	1	N 54:30 W 08:10	1900 50 1951 81	4375				50	1100	98

TABLE II : FLOODS CHARACTERISTICS

	FLOOD CHARACTERISTICS						DISCHARGE ESTIMATION					
Site number	Stream	Observ. site	Year	Date of the max	Maximal disc m^3s^{-1}	Climatic origine	Condition disc est	Qual. of the sect	Precis. $\pm m^3s^{-1}$	Anteced precip.	Depth mm.	Duration days.
1	2	3	4	5	6	7	8	9	10	11	12	13
07	Boyne	Slane Castle	1954	12-09	360	1	A1C1	A2A	35			
			78	12-28	312	1	A1C1	A2A	30			
			48	01-05	242	1	A1C1	A2A	25			
09	Liffey	Celbridge	1937	03-17	280	4	A1C1		55			
			36	01-07	260	1	A1C1		50			
			54	12-10	260	1	A1B1	A1A	26	Reservoir built in 1940-42		
18	Blackwater	Ballyduff	1946	08-13	445	1	A3C1	A1A	66	Staff gauge up to 1954		
			1980	11-01	395	1	A1C1	A1A	40			
			1969	01-10	380	4	A1C1	A1A	38			
25	Shannon	Killaloe	1960	01-01	750	1			75			
			25	01-07	733	1			73			
			30	01-16	721	1			72			
			54	12-15	701	1			70			
30	Corrib	Galway	1975	04-25	395	1	A1C1	A1B	40	Staff gauge up to 1950		
			39	12-10	345	1	A3C1	A1B	70			
			54	12-09	335	1	A1C1	A1B	33			
34	Moy	Rahans	1968	11-02	340	1	B4D4	A1A	85	Staff gauge up to 1951		
			1965	01-18	187	1	A1B1	A1A	19			
36	Erne	Ballyshannon (1)	1977	02-20	325	1			32			
			1965	01-22	320	4			32			
			1944	12-15	317	1			32			

(1) As a matter of fact 3 stations with the same basin area
(Beleek, Mullans and Cathleen Falls).

113

TABLE I : IDENTIFICATION OF OBSERVATION SITES AND CHARACTERISTICS OF BASINS

OBSERVATION SITES							CHARACTERISTICS OF BASIN						
Site number	River basin	Stream	Observ. site		Coordinates Lat. Long.	Period	Area km²	Slope	Soil	Cover	Regime	Mean precip. mm	Mean disc. m³s-1
1	2	3	4	5	6	7	8	9	10	11	12	13	14
30120	Upper Jordan	Snir	Near Ma'ayan Baruch	1	N 33:14 E 35:37	1939 76	623	F	A80 B20	B50 D30 E20	30	1145	4.3
30125	Upper Jordan	Hermon	Near Shear Yashuv	1	N 33:13 E 35:39	1939 76	141	F	A40 B10 D50	B50 D30 E20	30	1010	3.7
8130	Quishon	Hashofet	Near Hazorea	1	N 32:38 E 35:06	1965 76	12	E	B100	B20 C70 D10	30	660	0.086
13125	Taninim	Ada	Near Givat Ada	1	N 32:31 E 35:00	1945 76	18	E	B90 D10	B20 C20 D50 E10	30	595	0.097
15120	Alexander	Alexander	Near Elyashiv	1	N 32:22 E 34:55	1939 76	492	E	A50 B30 D20	B30 C30 D20 E20	30	565	0.25
17140	Yarkon	Natuf	Near Lod	1	N 31:50 E 34:54	1940 76	251	E	A65 B10 D25	B40 C30 D10 E20	30	583	0.13
23127	Bsor	Beer Sheva	Beer Sheva	3	N 31:14 E 34:48	1944 64	1090	E30 C70	A10 B50 C20 D20	C30 D40 E30	20	270	0.32
55165	Zin	Mamshith	Near Oron	1	N 30:57 E 35:02	1955 76	64	B	B10 C90	E100	20	115	0.02
25180	El Arish	El Arish	Ruweifa Dam	3	N 30:49 E 34:08	1968 76	20000	F20 C60 A20	B20 C80	E100	20	30	0.07

TABLE II : FLOODS CHARACTERISTICS

	FLOODS CHARACTERISTICS						DISCHARGE ESTIMATION					
Site number	Stream	Observ. site	Year	Date of the max	Maximal dism³s-1	Climatic origine	Condition disc est	Qual. of the sect	Precis. ±m³s-1	Anteced precip.	Depth mm	Duration days
1	2	3	4	5	6	7	8	9	10	11	12	13
30120	Snir	Near Ma'ayan Baruch	1940 1944 1969	01-29 01-19 01-17	250 208 185	1 1 1	A1B1	B	15			
30125	Hermon	Near Shear Yashuv	1955 1952 1969	12-18 02-04 01-22	95 80 78	1 1 1	A1B1	A	7	2	48	1
8130	Hashofet	Near Hazorea	1969	01-23	29	1	A1B4	A	2	3	111	2
13125	Ada	Near Givat Ada	1961 1969 1974	12-13 01-23 01-14	30 18 13	1 1	A1B4	A	3	2	95	1
15120	Alexander	Near Eliashiv	1958 1966 1951	01-30 12-19 12-21	260 145 140	1	A1B4	A	20	2	108	2
17140	Natuf	Near Lod	1951 1942 1969	12-21 10-18 03-22	340 306 211	1	A1B4	A	30	3	173	2
23127	Beer Sheva	Beer Sheva	1965 1944	01-19 11-11	1000 780	1	B2D4	C	200	3	37.5	2
55165	Mamshit	Near Oron	1968 1956	11-25 04-16	52 37	1	A1D6	B	10	2	25	1
25180	El Arish	Dam Ruweifa	1975	02-21	1650 (1)	1	A1D6	A	150	1	60	1

(1) Return period 50 - 100 years ?

TABLEAU I : IDENTIFICATION DES POINTS D'OBSERVATION ET CARACTERISTIQUES DES BASSINS

	POINT D'OBSERVATION							CARACTERISTIQUES DU BASSIN						
N° du point	Bassin fluvial	Rivière	Point d'observ.		Coordonnées Lat.	Long.	Période	Surface km²	Relief	Sol	Végét.	Rég.	Pluie moy. mm	Module m³s-1
1	2	3	4	5	6	7	8	9	10	11	12	13	14
1	Brenta	Brenta	Barbiza (Bassano)	1	N 45:46	E 11:42	1922 41 1950 1970	1570	F E C			90 30	1300	72
2	Adige	Adige	Trento	1	N 46:04	E 11:05	1921 1970	9770	F60 E30 B10	A45 C30 D25	D90 E10	90 30	900	210
3	Po	Adda	Fuentes	1	N 46:09	E 09:25	1921 43 1948 70	2600	F E D		A	90 30	1120	86
4	Po	Ticino	Miorina	1	N 45:42	E 08:40	1921 70	6600	F lacs E D C			90 30	1695	290
5	Sesia	Mastallone	Ponte Folle	1	N 45:50	E 08:12	1935 44 1946 65	149	F E			90	1935	7.55
6	Po	Sesia	Vercelli	1	N 45:19	E 08:27	1930 1935	2275	F E B			90 30	1635	67
7	Sesia	Strona di Cossato	Vallemosso	3	N 45:50?	E 08:10?		32	F			90	1200	
8	Po	Dora Baltea	Tavagnasco	1	N 45:32	E 07:50	1925 70	3315	F E D		A C D	90	950	96.5
9	Tanaro	Orba	Ortiglietto	3	N 44:37	E 08:32		141				90 30		
10	Po	Tanaro	Montecastello	1	N 44:57	E 08:43	1923 70	7985	F E D C		A D	90 30	1000	127
11	Po	Scrivia	Isola del Cantone	1	N 44:39	E 08:57	1930 35	214	F E			90 30	1750	8
12	Po	Po	Becca	1	N 45:10	E 09:18	1948 70	36770	F E B		A C D	90 30	1110	760
13	Po	Po	Pontelagoscuro	1	N 44:53	E 11:36	1918 44 1953 70	70090	F30 E40 B30	B30 D70	D90 E10	90 30	1100	1470

TABLEAU I : IDENTIFICATION DES POINTS D'OBSERVATION ET CARACTERISTIQUES DES BASSINS

	POINT D'OBSERVATION						CARACTERISTIQUES DU BASSIN						
N° du point	Bassin fluvial	Rivière	Point d'observ.		Coordonnées Lat. Long.	Période	Surface km²	Relief	Sol	Végét.	Rég.	Pluie moy. mm	Module m³s-1
1	2	3	4	5	6	7	8	9	10	11	12	13	14
14	Nervia	Nervia	Isola Bona	1	N 43:52 E 07:38	1929 1939 1941 43 1951 1955 1957 70	123	F E			90 30	1100	2.4
15		Teiro	Pero	3	N 44:25? E 08:28		22	F			90 30	1300	
16	Leiro	Leiro	Foce	3	N 44:28 E 08:50		28	F E			30	1500	
17	Polcevera	Polcevera	Foce	3	N 44:27 E 08:54		138	F E		A C D	30	1700	(4)
18	Bisagno	Bisagno	Foce	3	N 44:25 E 08:58		93	F E		C D	30	1700	(3)
19	Magra	Magra	Calamazza	1	N 44:13 E 09:57	1930 44 1946 70	940	F E D		A D	30	1750	40.6
20	Frigido	Frigido	Canevara	1	N 44:03 E 10:10	1949 70	46	F E			90 30	2200	6.44
21	Arno	Arno	Subbiano	1	N 43:34 E 11:52	1930 42 1949 70	738	F E			30	1300	18.9
22	Arno	Arno	San Giovanni Alla Vena	1	N 43:41 E 10:35	1924 43 1946 70	8185	F20 E60 B20	B10 D90	D90 E10	30	1040	100
23	Ombrone	Ombrone	Sasso d'Ombrone	1	N 42:56 E 11:20	1926 42 1949 70	2660	F E D			30	920	27.3
24	Tevere	Tevere	Roma	1	N 41:54 E 12:30	1921 70	16545	F10 E70 B20	B30 D70	D90 E10	90 30	1050	236
25	Pescara	Pescara	Sta Teresa	1	N 42:25 E 14:11	1922 30 1936 42 1945 61 1965 70	3125	F E D B C			90 30	900	53

TABLEAU I : IDENTIFICATION DES POINTS D'OBSERVATION ET CARACTERISTIQUES DES BASSINS

	POINT D'OBSERVATION						CARACTERISTIQUES DU BASSIN						
N° du point	Bassin fluvial	Rivière	Point d'observ.		Coordonnées Lat. Long.	Période	Surface km²	Relief	Sol	Végét.	Rég.	Pluie moy. mm	Module m³s⁻¹
1	2	3	4	5	6	7	8	9	10	11	12	13	14
26	Garigliano	Garigliano	Suio	1	N 41:17 E 13:54	1933 35	4765	F E D B C			90 30	1300	(120)
27	Volturno	Volturno	Ponte Annibale (Cancello Anone)	1	N 41:08 E 14:16 (C.A.)	1924 1935 1931 60	5550	F E D B C			90 30	1130	100
28	Agri	Agri	Tarangelo	1	N 40:17 E 16:00	1926 60	507	F E			30	1100	10.7
29	Ancinale	Ancinale	Razzona	1	N 38:40 E 16:25	1925 34 1937 70	116	F E			30	1720	3.8

SICILIA

30	Simeto	Simeto	Biscari	1	N 37:27 E 14:56	1925 64 1966	696	F E			90 30	900	8.5
31	Simeto	Dittaino	Bozzetta	1	N 37:36 E 14:23	1950 68	79.2	F E			30	730	0.57

SARDEGNA

32	Flumendosa	Flumendosa	Gadoni M.P.	1	N 39:54 E 09:12	1924 38 1949 70	423	F E			30	1080	6.7

TABLEAU II : CARACTERISTIQUES DES CRUES

	CARACTERISTIQUES DE LA CRUE						EVALUATION DES DEBITS					
N° du point	Rivière	Point d'observ.	Année	Date du maximum	Débit max m³s-1	Origine	Base et mode éval	Qual. de la séch.	Préci. ±m³s-1	Anteced	Hauteur	Durée jours
1	2	3	4	5	6	7	8	9	10	11	12	13
1	Brenta	Barbiza (Bassano)	1966 1928	11-04 11	2800 1900	4						
2	Adige	Trento	1882 1966	09-17 11-04	2500 2320	1 4						
3	Adda	Fuentes	1911 1927 1960	08-22	1190 1160 1070	1 1 1						
4	Ticino	Miorina	1868 1928 1926	10-02 11	5000 2140 1910	1						
5	Mastallone	Ponte Folle	1968 1948	11-02 09-04	1050 781	1						
6	Sesia	Vercelli	1968 1934	11-02 04-23	3900 2970							
7	Strona di Cossato	Vallemosso	1968	11-02	704							
8	Baltea Dora	Tavagnasco	1948 1957 1954	09-04	1950 1310 1210	1 1 1						
9	Orba	Ortiglietto	1935	08-13	2200	1						
10	Tanaro	Montecastello	1951 1935	11-11 08-13	3170 3000	1 1						
11	Scrivia	Isola del Cantone	1970	10-08	1050	1						
12	Po	Becca	1951	11-13	11250	1						
13	Po	Pontelagoscuro	1951 1917 1926 1928	11-14 06-04	10300 8900 8850 8770	4 1 1 1	A1B1	B	1000	2	214	7
14	Nervia	Isolabona	1966	10-24	1330	1						
15	Teiro	Pero	1968	11-01	580	1						
16	Leiro	La Foce	1970	10-07	510	1						
17	Polcevera	La Foce	1970	10-08	1660	1						
18	Bisagno	La Foce	1970	10-08	950	1						

TABLEAU II : CARACTERISTIQUES DES CRUES

	CARACTERISTIQUES DE LA CRUE						EVALUATION DES DEBITS					
N° du point	Rivière	Point d'observ.	Année	Date du maximum	Débit max m³s-1	Origine	Base et mode éval	Qual. de la séch.	Préci. ±m³s-1	Anteced	Hauteur	Durée jours
1	2	3	4	5	6	7	8	9	10	11	12	13
19	Magra	Callamazza	1960	10-15	3480	1						
			1934		3100	1						
			1940		3100	1						
20	Frigido	Canevara	1965	08-23	785	1						
21	Arno	Subbiano	1966	11-04	2250	1						
			1968		1050							
22	Arno	San Giovanni alla Vena	1966	11-04	2290	1	A1B1	B	10	3	164	3
			1949	11-27	2270							
23	Ombrone	Sasso d'Ombrone	1944	11-02	3120	1						
			1966	11-04	3110	1						
			1940	10-25	2380	1						
24	Tevere	Roma	1900	12-02	3300							
			1937	12-17	2800	1						
			1923		2350							
25	Pescara	Sta Teresa	1934	10-11	900	1						
			1959	04-02	796	1						
			1953		660	1						
26	Garigliano	Suio	1959		1950	1						
			1968	12-19	1900	1						
27	Volturno	Ponte Annibale	1949	10-02	3200	1						
			1915	01-05	2400	1						
			1935		2260							
28	Agri	Tarangelo	1935	03-01	430	1						
			1952		419	1						
29	Ancinale	Bazzona	1935	11-22	1650	1						
SICILIA												
30	Simeto	Biscari	1948	09-15	2100	1						
31	Dittaino	Bozzetta	1959	11-30	1300	1						
			1964		330	1						
SARDEGNA												
32	Flumendosa	Gadoni M.P.	1940	10-18	2320	1						
			1930	02-10	1590	1						

TABLEAU I : IDENTIFICATION DES POINTS D'OBSERVATION ET CARACTERISTIQUES DES BASSINS

	POINT D'OBSERVATION						CARACTERISTIQUES DU BASSIN						
N° du point	Bassin fluvial	Rivière	Point d'observ.		Coordonnées Lat. Long.	Période	Surface km²	Relief	Sol	Végét.	Régime	Pluie moyenne mm	Module m³s-1
1	2	3	4	5	6	7	8	9	10	11	12	13	14
09550106	Cavally	Cavally	Taï	1	N 05:52 W 07:27	1955 80	13800	E50 D50	C	A	00	1400 2300	190
09552003	Cavally	Nce	Taï	1	N 05:55 W 07:36	1955 80	1240	D C	C	A	00	1800	
09250106	Sassandra	Sassandra	Guessabo	1	N 06:45 W 06:59	1953 79	35400	E20 D50 C30	C	A25 B65 D10	10	1200 1700	281
09011006	Bandama	Marahoué	Bouaflé	1	N 06:59 W 05:45	1954 80	19800	D10 C50 B40	B	B85 D15	10	1000 1500	81
09012515	Bandama	Nzi	Zienoa	1	N 06:00 W 04:49	1953 80	35000	C70 B30	B	A20 B70 D10	10	900 1500	77
09010154	Bandama	Bandama	Tiassalé	1	N 05:54 W 04:49	1954 80	95500	D10 C70 B20	B	A15 B70 D15	10	1000 1600	189
09040109	Comoé	Comoé	Aniassue	1	N 06:39 W 03:41	1953 80	66500	C60 B40	B	A20 B65 C10 D 5	10 00	800 1400	222
09450105	Bia	Bia	Ayamé	1	N 05:36 W 03:10	1949 58 1961 80	9320	E30 D70	C	A	00	1200 1800	67
09851003	San Pedro	San Pedro	Prise d'eau	1	N 04:45 W 06:50	8 ans	3310	B C	C	A	00		
09161206	Niger	Bagoé	Kouto	1	N 09:52 W 06:22	13 ans	4740	B C	B	B C D	10		
1	Bandama	Lozerigue	Bassin Représentatif Korhogo	4	N 09:25 W 05:35	1962 71	3.6	D	C	D	10	1400	0.07
2	Sassandra	Loué	Bassin Représentatif	4	N 07:23 W 07:36	1958 59	18.4	F	C	A	00	2000	0.35
3	Agneby	Manso	Bassin Représentatif Guessigué	4	N 05:38 W 04:06	1959 62	88.2	C	C D	A	00	1700	1.6

TABLEAU II : CARACTERISTIQUES DES CRUES

		CARACTERISTIQUES DE LA CRUE					EVALUATION DES DEBITS					
N° du point	Rivière	Point d'observ.	Année	Date du maximum	Débit max m³s-1	Origine	Base et mode éval	Qual. de la séch	Précis. ±m³s-1	Anteced	Hauteur	Durée jours
1	2	3	4	5	6	7	8	9	10	11	12	13
09550106	Cavally	Taï	1980	09-18	1370	1	A3B1	A1A	30			
			1966	10-12	1300	1	A3B1	A1A	30			
09552003	Nce	Taï	1966	10-05	285	1	A3B1	A1A	10			
09250106	Sassandra	Guessabo	1957	09-25	1900	1	A3B1	A1A	50			
			1966	10-05	1870	1	A3B1	A1A	50			
			1971	09-12	1800	1	A3B1	A1A	50			
09011006	Marahoué	Bouaflé	1964	09-16	970	1	A3B1	A1A	50			
			1957	10-04	960	1	A3B1	A1A	50			
09012515	Nzi	Zienoa	1968	10	820	1	A3C1	A1B	50			
			1957	10-17	690	1	A3B1	A1B	30			
09010154	Bandama	Tiassalé	1957	10-07	2930	1	A3B1	A1A	100			
			1959	10-06	2560	1	A3B1	A1A	100			
09040109	Comoe	Aniassué	1954	09-29	2370	1	A3B1	A1B	100			
			1968	10-04	2200	1	A3B1	A1B	100			
			1963	10-05	2170	1	A3B1	A1B	100			
09450105	Bia	Ayamé	1959	07-04	640	1	A2C1	A1B	40			
			1951	10-25	540	1	A3B1	A1B	40			
09851003	San Pedro	Prise d'eau	1969	08	510	1	A3B1	A1B	40			
09161206	Bagoé	Kouto	1970	09-02	510	1	A3B1	B1B	40			
	Lozerigué	Bassin Représentatif	1966	08-12	39.8	1	A1B1	B1B	5			
	Loué	Bassin Représentatif	1958	09-26	43.5	1	A1B1	A1A	5		112	0.08
	Manso	Bassin Représentatif	1959	09-28	100	1	A1B1	A1A	10		86	<1

TABLE I : IDENTIFICATION OF OBSERVATION SITES AND CHARACTERISTICS OF BASINS

	OBSERVATION SITES						CHARACTERISTICS OF BASIN						
Site number	River basin	Stream	Observ. site		Coordinates Lat. Long.	Period	Area km²	Slope	Soil	Cover	Regime	Mean precip. mm	Mean disc. m³s-1
1	2	3	4	5	6	7	8	9	10	11	12	13	14
1	Ishikari	Ishikari	Ishikari Ohhashi (Bridge)	1	N 43:07 E 141:32	1954 81	12700	F 5 E15 D50 B30	B15 C80 D 5	A50 D40 E10	90 61 60	1300	434
2	Tokachi	Tokachi	Moiwa (Bridge)	1	N 42:48 E 143:31	1954 81	8210	F10 E10 C60 B20	B 5 C90 D 5	A40 D50 E10	90 60	1100	207
3	Kitakami	Kitakami	Kozenji	1	N 38:55 E 141:10	1955 77	7060	F80 B20	B35 C60 D 5	A40 B10 D40 E10	90 60	1500 1200	284
4	Mogami	Mogami	Shimono	1	N 38:25 E 140:20	1956 77	3530	F80 B20	B25 C70 D 5	A50 B10 D30 E10	90 60	1500 2500	179
5	Tone	Tone	Yattajima	1	N 36:15 E 139:15	1936 80	5110	C10 A90	B25 C70 D 5	A90 D 5 E 5	40	1400	160
6	Tone	Takara	Takara Gawa	1	N 36:51 E 139:01	1939 64	19	F	C	A	40	1400	
7	Ara	Shakuji	Nemura Bashi	1	N 35:45 E 139:30	1958 77	48	A	C50 D50	D50 E50	40	1400	
8	Fuji	Fuji	Shimizubata	1	N 35:32 E 138:27	1922 80	2120	E 3 E 7 A90	C95 D 5	A90 D 5 E 5	90 40	1400	60
9	Agano	Agano	Maoroshi	1	N 37:44 E 139:16	1951 81	7710	B20 D80	B	A83 D15 E 2	90 60	2000	400
10	Shinano	Shinano	Ojiya	1	N 37:01 E 138:48	1954 81	9720	F90 B10	C	A90 D10	90 60	2000	481
11	Tenryu	Tenryu	Kashima	1	N 34:51 E 137:48	1939 80	4880	E93 B 7		A93 D 7	40	1770	250
12	Toyo	Toyo	Ishida	1	N 34:53 E 137:30	1946 80	545	E80 B20		A71 D26 E 3	40	2070	59
13	Kiso	Kiso	Inuyama	1	N 35:23 E 136:57	1951 1980	4685	E93 B 7		A85 D15	40	1680	311
14	Kiso	Nagara	Chusetsu	1	N 35:25 E 136:45	1954 80	1610	E74 B26		A81 D15 E 4	40	1970	118

TABLE I : IDENTIFICATION OF OBSERVATION SITES AND CHARACTERISTICS OF BASINS

	OBSERVATION SITES						CHARACTERISTICS OF BASIN						
Site number	River basin	Stream	Observ. site		Coordinates Lat. Long.	Period	Area km²	Slope	Soil	Cover	Regime	Mean precip. mm	Mean disc. m³s-1
1	2	3	4	5	6	7	8	9	10	11	12	13	14
15	Yodo	Yodo	Hirakata	1	N 34:48 E 135:39	1898 1981	7280	A	B15 C40 D45	A20 D40 E40	40	1790	285
16	Kizu	Kizu	Kamo	1	N 34:15 E 135:53	1899 1981	1455	B	B10 C50 D40	A40 D50 E10	40	1610	47
17	Kino	Kino	Funado	1	N 34:15 E 135:19	1951 81	1560	A	B10 C45 D45	A50 D30 F20	40	1770	62
18	Shingu	Shingu	Oga	1	N 33:44 E 135:59	1937 81	2350	B	B 5 C35 D60	A80 D15 E 5	40	2810	160
19	Gouno	Gouno	Ozekiyama	1	N 34:48 E 132:50	1956 80	3870	F89 E 6 D 5	C11 D89	A90 D10	40	1740	77
20	Cota	Cota	Kumura	1	N 34:29 E 132:31	1953 80	1960	F80 B17 A 3	B95 D 5	A85 D10 E 5	40	1900	70
21	Yoshino	Yoshino	Iwazu	1	N 34:04 E 134:12	1961 80	3750	F20 E68 B12	A 4 C96	A87 D 6 E 7	40	2000	112
22	Niyodo	Niyodo	Ino	1	N 33:33 E 133:25	1961 80	1560	F95 B 5	C	A95 D 5	40	2500	106
23	Chikugo	Chikugo	Senoshita	1	N 33:19 E 130:30	1950 79	2315	C	C	B	40	2020	110
24	Ono	Ono	Shiratakibashi	1	N 33:09 E 131:39	1950 79	1380	C	C	B	40	2210	60

TABLE II : FLOODS CHARACTERISTICS

	FLOODS CHARACTERISTICS						DISCHARGE ESTIMATION					
Site number	Stream	Observ. site	Year	Date of the max	Maximal dism³s-1	Climatic origine	Condition disc est	Qual. of the sect	Preci. ±m³s-1	Anteced precip.	Depth mm	Duration days
1	2	3	4	5	6	7	8	9	10	11	12	13
1	Ishikari	Ishikari Ohhashi	1981	08-06	11330	1	A1B3	B1A	100	1	282	3
			1975	08-24	7530	1	A1B3	B1A	80	1	173	3
2	Tokachi	Moiwa	1932	08-25	9390	1	C4C6	B1A	U	2	161	3
			1981	08-06	8050	1	A1B3	B1A	80	1	221	3
			1962	08-04	5380	1	A1B3	B1A	50	2	116	3
3	Kitakami	Kozenji	1947	09-16	7900	1	A1C4	A1B	100	3	183	2
			1948	09-17	5700	1	A1C4	A1B	100	1	148	2
			1981	08-24	5300	1	A1B1	A1B	50			
4	Mogami	Shimono	1967	08-28	3900	1	A1C4	A1B	100	1	175	2
			1976	08-06	3400	1	A1C4	A1B	100			
5	Tone	Yattajima	1947	09-15	16900	1	A1B3	B1A	2500	1	317	3
			1949	09-01	9700	1	A1B3	B1A	1500	1	204	3
			1958	09-18	9700	1	A1B3	B1A	1500	1	168	3
6	Takara	Takara Gawa	1950	07-28	112	1	A1B3	A1B	20	1	75	3
			1959	09-26	108	1	A1B3	A1B	15	1	116	3
7	Shakuji	Nemura Bashi	1977	08-19	169	1	A1B1	B1A	25	1	142	3
			1973	07-02	116	1	A1B1	B1A	20	1	42	2
8	Fuji	Shimizubata	1947	09	7300	1	A1B3	B1A	1000	1	292	2
			1959	08-14	5600	1	A1B3	B1A	800			
9	Agano	Maoroshi	1958	09-18	8930	1	A1B3	B1A	1000	3	114	2
			1956	07-17	8030	1	A1C3	B1B	1000	2	139	2
			1978	06-26	7870	1	A1B3	B1A	1000	3	224	4
10	Shinano	Ojiya	1914	08-14	9000	1						
			1958	09-18	6250	1	A1B3	C1B		2	130	2
			1969	08-12	6106	1	A1B3	C1A		3	200	4
11	Tenryu	Kashima	1968	08	10010	1	A1B3	B1A		3	220	1
			1969	08	8670	1	A1B3	B1A		3	321	1
			1961	06	8440	1	A1B3	B1A		3	337	1
12	Toyo	Ishida	1969	08	4570	1	A1B3	B1A		2	278	1
			1979	10	4360	1	A1B3	B1A		2	208	1
13	Kiso	Inuyama	1961	06	11150	1	A1B3	B1A		3	380	1
			1972	07	9580	1	A1B3	B1A		3	285	1
			1967	07	8930	1	A1B3	B1A		3	313	1
14	Nagara	Chusetsu	1960	08	6710	1	A1B3	B1A		3	290	1
			1976	09	6390	1	A1B3	B1A		1	333	1
			1959	05	5560	1	A1B3	B1A		3	310	1
15	Yodo	Hirakata	1959	09-27	7970	1	A1B3	A1A	800	1	212	2
			1953	09-25	7800	1	A1B3	A1A	750	1	250	2
			1961	10-28	7200	1	A1B3	A1A	700	3	261	3

TABLE II : FLOODS CHARACTERISTICS

	FLOODS CHARACTERISTICS						DISCHARGE ESTIMATION					
Site number	Stream	Observ. site	Year	Date of the max	Maximal dis $m^3 s^{-1}$	Climatic origine	Condition disc est	Qual. of the sect	Preci. $\pm m^3 s^{-1}$	Anteced precip.	Depth mm	Duration days
1	2	3	4	5	6	7	8	9	10	11	12	13
16	Kizu	Kamo	1959	09-26	6200	1	A1B3	A1A	600	2	332	2
			1953	09-25	5400	1	A1B3	A1A	550	2	251	2
17	Kino	Funado	1959	09-26	7650	1	A1B3	A1A	750	2	310	2
			1953	09-25	7360	1	A1B3	A1A	700	2	306	2
			1972	09-16	5875	1	A1B3	A1A	600	2	190	2
18	Shingu	Oga	1959	09-26	19025	1	A1B3	A1A	1900	2	381	2
			1953	09-25	18000	1	A1B3	A1A	1800			
			1958	08-24	16540	1	A1B3	A1A	1600	2	481	2
			1962	07-26	14655	1	A1B3	A1A	1500	2	426	2
19	Gouno	Ozekiyama	1972	07-12	6900	1	A1A3	B1B	200	3	532	5
			1965	07-23	4786	1	A1A3	B1B	100	3	248	3
			1980	08-03	4621	1	A1A3	B1B	100	3	231	4
20	Oota	Kumura	1972	07-12	6800	1	A1B3	B1B	200	1	419	4
			1943	09-20	6700	1	A1B3	B1B	200			
			1976	09-13	5800	1	A2C3	B1B	100	3	201	3
21	Yoshino	Iwazu	1974	09-09	14470	1	A1B3	B1A	200	2	342	3
			1975	08-23	13870	1	A1B3	B1A	200			
			1970	08-21	12820	1	A1B3	B1A	200	2	329	3
			1961	09-16	11960	1	A1B3	B1A	200	2	420	3
22	Niyodo	Ino	1963	08-09	13510	1	A1B3	B1B	400	1	504	3
			1975	08-17	13460	1	A1B3	B1B	400	1	520	3
			1971	08-30	9530	1	A1B3	B1B	400	1	448	3
23	Chikugo	Senoshita	1953	06-26	6070	1	A1B3	B1A	300	3	420	2
			1979	06-30	5060	1	A1B3	B1A	250	3	700	5
			1965	06-20	3700	1	A1B3	B1A	180	3	330	2
24	Ono	Shiratakibashi	1964	07-24	7570	1	A1B3	B1A	380	3		
			1974	09-09	6560	1	A1B3	B1A	330	3	140	2
			1966	09-09	5560	1	A1B3	B1A	280	3	230	2

TABLE I : IDENTIFICATION OF OBSERVATION SITES AND CHARACTERISTICS OF BASINS

	OBSERVATION SITES							CHARACTERISTICS OF BASIN						
Site number	River basin	Stream	Observ. site		Coordinates Lat. Long.		Period	Area km²	Slope	Soil	Cover	Regime	Mean precip. mm	Mean disc. m³s−1
1	2	3	4	5	6		7	8	9	10	11	12	13	14
1	Jordan	Yarmouk	Adasiya	1	N 32:41	E 35:38	1954 72	6790	E D C B		E C	30	405	7.02
2	Jordan	Yarmouk	Maqarin	1	N 32:44	E 35:52	1961 72	5950	E D C		E C	30	427	2.87
3	Jordan	Wadi Zerqa	Deir Alla	1	N 32:12	E 35:40	1959 72	3400	E D C		E C	30	271	1.06
4	Jordan	Zerqa	Jerash Bridge	1	N 32:12	E 35:50	1963 72	3100	E D C		E C	30	342	0.71
5	Jordan	Zerqa	Sukhneh	1	N 32:08	E 36:04	1971 72	870	E D C		E	30 20	163	0.35
6	Jordan	Zerqa	Dhuleil	1	N 32:09	E 36:04	1972	1640	E D C		E	30 20	100	0.10
7	Dead Sea	Wala	Bridge	1	N 31:33	E 35:46	1965 72	1810	D C		E C	30 20	240	0.53
8	Dead Sea	Mojib	Kerak road Bridge	1	N 31:27	E 35:49	1965 72	4380	D C		E	30 20	157	0.51

TABLE II : FLOODS CHARACTERISTICS

Site number	Stream	Observ. site	Year	Date of the max	Maximal dis m^3s-1	Climatic origine	Condition disc est	Qual. of the sect	Precis. $\pm m^3s-1$	Anteced precip.	Depth mm	Duration days
				FLOODS CHARACTERISTICS					DISCHARGE ESTIMATION			
1	2	3	4	5	6	7	8	9	10	11	12	13
1	Yarmouk	Adasiya	1954	02-08	1310	1						
			1967	03-06	650	1						
2	Yarmouk	Maqarin	1969	03-20	330	1						
			1971	04-13	283	1						
3	Wadi Zerqa	Deir Alla	1965	01-19	525	1						
			1963	02-11	300	1						
4	Zerqa	Jerash Bridge	1971	04-13	352	1						
			1965	01-19	209	1						
5	Zerqa	Sukhneh	1971	12-06	60	1						
6	Zerqa	Dhuleil	1972	04-09	87	1						
7	Wala	Bridge	1971	12-07	704	1						
			1971	04-13	445	1						
8	Mojib	Kerak road Bridge	1971	11-13	1890	1						
			1965	01-19	1590	1						

KENYA

TABLE I : IDENTIFICATION OF OBSERVATION SITES AND CHARACTERISTICS OF BASINS

| | OBSERVATION SITE | | | | | | | CHARACTERISTICS OF BASIN | | | | | | |
Site number	River basin	Stream	Observ. site		Coordinates Lat. Long.		Period	Area km²	Slope	Soil	Cover	Regime	Mean precip. mm	Mean disc. m³s-1
1	2	3	4	5	6		7	8	9	10	11	12	13	14
1GD1	Victoria Lake (Nile)	Nyando	Near Ahero	1	S 00:10	E 34:55	1948 60 1960 69 (1)	2700			B C	10	1300	15.2
1	Tana	Tana	Garissa	1	N 00:27	E 39:42	1933 75	42220			C	90 11		151

(1) From 1960 to 1969 discharges computed by correlation with a station upstream : 1GD4 = 2520 sqkm.

KENYA

TABLE II : FLOODS CHARACTERISTICS

| | FLOODS CHARACTERISTICS | | | | | | DISCHARGE ESTIMATION | | | | | |
Site number	Stream	Observ. site	Year	Date of the max	Maximal dism³s-1	Climatic origine	Condition disc est	Qual. of the sect	Precis. ±m³s-1	Anteced precip.	Depth mm	Duration days
1	2	3	4	5	6	7	8	9	10	11	12	13
1GD1	Nyando	Near Ahero	1964 1961 1962	04 11 05	400 341 294	1						
1	Tana	Garissa	1961 1951 1967	05-04	3570 1300 1200	1 1 1						

LAOS POPULAR DEMOCRATIC REPUBLIC/REPUBLIQUE POPULAIRE DEMOCRATIQUE DU LAOS

TABLE I : IDENTIFICATION OF OBSERVATION SITES AND CHARACTERISTICS OF BASINS

	OBSERVATION SITES								CHARACTERISTICS OF BASIN					
Site number	River basin	Stream	Observ. site		Coordinates Lat. Long.		Period	Area km²	Slope	Soil	Cover	Regime	Mean precip. mm	Mean disc. m³s-1
1	2	3	4	5	6		7	8	9	10	11	12	13	14
1	Mekong	Mekong	Vientiane	1	N 17:56	E 102:37	1913 79	299000	A B C D E F		A B C E	90 00 10	1000 2000	4600
2	Mekong	Mekong	Paksé	1	N 15:07	E 105:48	1924 79	545000	A B C D E F		A B C E	90 00 10	1000 2500	10200

LAOS POPULAR DEMOCRATIC REPUBLIC/REPUBLIQUE POPULAIRE DEMOCRATIQUE DU LAOS

TABLE II : FLOODS CHARACTERISTICS

	FLOODS CHARACTERISTICS						DISCHARGE ESTIMATION					
Site number	Stream	Observ. site	Year	Date of the max	Maximal dis m³s-1	Climatic origine	Condition disc est	Qual. of the sect	Precis. ±m³s-1	Anteced precip.	Depth mm	Duration days
1	2	3	4	5	6	7	8	9	10	11	12	13
1	Mekong	Vientiane	1966	09-04	26000	1	A1B1	B1B	2000	3	750	31
2	Mekong	Paksé	1978	08-17	57800	1	A1B1	B1B	5000	3	950	31

Information kindly transmitted by the Committe for coordination of investigation of the lower Mekong basin.

TABLE I : IDENTIFICATION OF OBSERVATION SITES AND CHARACTERISTICS OF BASINS

	OBSERVATION SITES						CHARACTERISTICS OF BASIN						
Site number	River basin	Stream	Observ. site		Coordinates Lat. Long.	Period	Area km²	Slope	Soil	Cover	Regime	Mean precip. mm	Mean disc. m³s-1
1	2	3	4	5	6	7	8	9	10	11	12	13	14
10105	Mano	Mano	Mano Mines	1	N W 07:21 11:08	1958 61 70 1975 79	5540	E	D	A	00	2500	221
30104	St. Paul	St. Paul	Willker Bridge	1	N W 07:21 09:30	1958 78	9760	E	D	A	00	2000	263

TABLE II : FLOODS CHARACTERISTICS

	FLOOD CHARACTERISTICS						DISCHARGE ESTIMATION					
Site number	Stream	Observ. site	Year	Date of the max	Maximal dism³s-1	Climatic origine	Condition disc est	Qual. of the sect	Precis. ±m³s-1	Anteced precip.	Depth mm	Duration days
1	2	3	4	5	6	7	8	9	10	11	12	13
10105	Mano	Mano Mines	1960	08-19	1610	1	A1B1	A1A	80			
			1959	09-24	1590	1	A1B1	A1A	80			
			1977	09-01	1450	1	A1B1	A1A	80			
30104	St. Paul	Willker Bridge	1960	09-25	1800	1	A1C1	A1A	150			
			1971	10-06	1770	1	A1C1	A1A	150			
			1975	09-25	1510	1	A1C1	A1A	100			

TABLEAU I : IDENTIFICATION DES POINTS D'OBSERVATIONS ET CARACTERISTIQUES DES BASSINS

	POINT D'OBSERVATION							CARACTERISTIQUES DU BASSIN					
N° du point	Bassin fluvial	Rivière	Point d'observ.		Coordonnées Lat. Long.	Période	Surface km²	Relief	Sol	Végét.	Régime	Pluie moyenne mm	Module m³s-1
1	2	3	4	5	6	7	8	9	10	11	12	13	14
060105	Mananara	Mananara	Maroangaty	1	S 22:56 E 46:58	1955 76	14160	F	C	C	00	1100	230
560110	Namorona	Nanomorona	Vohiparara	1	S 21:14 E 47:24	1951 75	445	F	C	A	00	1750	13
452003	Mananjary	Yvoanana	Fatihita	1	S 21:02 E 47:45	1956 76	835	F	C	A	00	1850	49
450105	Mananjary	Mananjary	Antsindra	1	S 20:59 E 47:44	1955 75	2260	F	C	A	00	1900	127
240110	Faraony	Faraony	Vohilava	1	S 21:46 E 47:55	1960 75	1987	F	C	A	00	2500	115
090110	Mangoro	Mangoro	Mangoro Gare	1	S 18:53 E 48:06	1956 76	3600	F E	C	A B	00	1300	90
280109	Ivondro	Ivondro	Ringaringa	1	S 18:11 E 49:15	1952 75	2545	F	C	A	00	1500	108
662509	Rianila	Vohitra	Andekaleka (Rogez)	1	S 18:48 E 48:36	1952 75	1873	F	C	A	00	1550	71
660105	Rianila	Rianila	Brickaville	1	S 18:50 E 49:04	1951 68	5880	F E	C	A C	00	2100	360
710103	Sambirano	Sambirano	Ambanja	1	S 13:41 E 48:27	1952 76	2980	F	C	A C	00	1700	124
010105	Betsiboka	Betsiboka	Ambodiroka	1	S 16:56 E 46:57	1957 75	11800	F E D	C	C	10	1520	288
010221	Betsiboka	Ikopa	Antsatrana	1	S 17:25 E 46:52	1948 75	18550	F E D	C	C	10	1600	446
010224	Betsiboka	Ikopa	Bevomanga	1	S 18:48 E 47:19	1949 73	4250	F E D	C	C	10	1400	79
012311	Betsiboka	Sisaony	Andramasina	1	S 19:04 E 47:33	1957 70	318	F E	C	C	10	1300	6
011215	Betsiboka	Andromba	Tsinjony	1	S 19:08 E 47:31	1953 70	350	F E	C	C	10	1500	9
080105	Mangoky	Mangoky	Banian	1	S 25:48 E 44:12	1956 65	50000	F30 E70	C B	C	11 10	900	430
070103	Mandrare	Mandrare	Amboasary	1	S 25:02 E 46:27	1951 73	12430	F10 E90	C	C	11 10	720	60

MADAGASCAR

TABLEAU II : CARACTERISTIQUES DES CRUES

	CARACTERISTIQUES DE LA CRUE						EVALUATION DES DEBITS					
N° du point	Rivière	Point d'observ.	Année	Date du maximum	Débit max m³s-1	Origine	Base et mode éval	Qual. de la séch.	Précis. ±m³s-1	Anteced	Hauteur	Durée jours
1	2	3	4	5	6	7	8	9	10	11	12	13
060105	Mananara	Maroangaty	1970	02-26	3530	1	A24C	A1A	400	3		
			69	02-14	2730	1	A24C	A1A	400	3		
560110	Namorona	Vohiparara	1970	02-23	1100	1	A24C	A1A	300	3		
			54	01-15	500	1	A34C	A1A	250	3		
			59	03-29	470	1	A24C	A1A	250	3		
452003	Ivoanana	Fatihita	1970	02-24	1030	1	A24C	A1A	300	3		
			59	03-28	870	1	A24C	A1A	250	3		
450105	Mananjary	Antsindra	1959	03-28	2050	1	A24C	A1A	350	3		
			70	02-23	1720	1	A24C	A1A	200	3		
240110	Faraony	Vohilava	1945	02	4500	1	C4C	A1A	600	3		
			1970	02-23	1700	1	A24C	A1A	200	3		
090110	Mangoro	Mangoro Gare	1959	03-28	2700	1	A24C	A1A	300	3	800	10
			75	03-13	1300	1	A24C	A1A	200	3		
280109	Ivondro	Ringaringa	1956	02-06	3050	1	A24C	A1A	500	3	750	4
			1971	01-21	3050	1	A24C	A1A	500	3		
			1959	03-25	2850	1	A24C	A1A	200	3	800	10
662509	Vohitra	Andekaleka	1959	03-28	5000	1	A24C	A1A	1000	3	800	10
			1964	03-08	2670	1	A24C	A1A	500	3		
			1949	03-08	2240	1	A24C	A1A	500	3	400	1
660105	Rianila	Brickaville	1959	03-27	9000	1	A24C	A1A	1000	3	800	10
			64	03-11	8800	1	A24C	A1A	1000	3		
710103	Sambirano	Ambanja	1925	02	8000	1	C5D	B1B	U	3		
			1957	02-07	6400	1	A24C	B1B	1000	3		
			1959	03-28	5000	1	A24C	B1B	1000	3		

TABLEAU II : CARACTERISTIQUES DES CRUES

				CARACTERISTIQUES DE LA CRUE						EVALUATION DES DEBITS		
N° du point	Rivière	Point d'observ.	Année	Date du maximum	Débit max m³s-1	Origine	Base et mode éval	Qual. de la séch.	Précis. ±m³s-1	Anteced	Hauteur	Durée jours
1	2	3	4	5	6	7	8	9	10	11	12	13
010105	Betsiboka	Ambodiroka	1927	03-04	22000	1	D5C1	A1A	3000			
			1959	03-28	18000	1	A2C1	A1A	2000	3		
			1972	02-14	13000	1	A2C1	A1A	1000	3		
			1965	01-15	12020	1	A2C1	A1A	500	3		
010221	Ikopa	Antsatrana	1972	02-15	5000	1	A2C1	A1A	500	3		
			1973	02-26	3800	1	A2C1	A1A	500	3		
			1966	02-21	3270	1	A2C1	A1A	500	3		
010224	Ikopa	Bevomanga	1959	03-30	728	1	A2B1	A1A	100	3	240	7
			1970	01-07	550	1	A2B1	A1A	50	3	340	13
			1972	02-07	464	1	A2B1	A1A	50	3		
012311	Sisaony	Andramasina	1977	02-02	470	1	A2C1	A1A	50	3		
			1959	03-27	250	1	A2B1	A1A	20	3	240	7
			1975	03-13	183	1	A2B1	A1A	20	3	330	13
			1965	12-22	165	1	A2B1	A1A	20	3		
011215	Andromba	Tsinjony	1959	03-28	202	1	A2B1	A1A	15	3	210	7
			1958	01-24	167	1	A2B1	A1A	15	3	270	13
			1957	03-20	156	1	A2B1	A1A	15	3		
080105	Mangoky	Banian	1933	02-05	38000	1	D (1)		U			
			1904	01-28	37000	1	D (1)		U			
			1970	01-18	27700	1	A2C1	C1B	2000	3	105	3
											300	15
070103	Mandrare	Amboasary	1971	02-02	16000	1	A2C1	D2C	3000	3		
			1970	02-25	6800	1	A2C1	D2C	800	3		
			1963	02-05	5300	1	A2C1	D2C	500	3		

(1) estimé d'après les données pluviométriques.

MALAWI

TABLE I : IDENTIFICATION OF OBSERVATION SITES AND CHARACTERISTICS OF BASINS

	OBSERVATION SITES							CHARACTERISTICS OF BASIN						
Site number	River basin	Stream	Observ. site		Coordinates Lat. Long.		Period	Area km²	Slope	Soil	Cover	Regime	Mean precip. mm	Mean disc. m³s-1
1	2	3	4	5	6	7	8	9	10	11	12	13	14
1	Nyassa Lake	Shire (including) (Ruo)	Chiromo	1	S 16:33	E 35:10	1953 75	154000				00 10 11		
2	Shire	Ruo	Swazi Estate	1	S 15:30	E 36:00		202	F			10		
3	Shire	Ruo	Sankulani	1	S 16:22	E 35:15		4840	F E D			10		

MALAWI

TABLE II : FLOODS CHARACTERISTICS

	FLOODS CHARACTERISTICS						DISCHARGE ESTIMATION					
Site number	Stream	Observ. site	Year	Date of the max	Maximal dism³s-1	Climatic origine	Condition disc est	Qual. of the sect	Precis. ±m³s-1	Anteced precip.	Depth mm	Duration days
1	2	3	4	5	6	7	8	9	10	11	12	13
1	Shire	Chiromo	1974	03-31	1780	1			U			
2	Ruo	Swazi Estate	1960	01-06	850	1			U			
3	Ruo	Sankulani	1956	04-06	5525	1			U			

TABLE I : IDENTIFICATION OF OBSERVATION SITES AND CHARACTERISTICS OF BASINS

	OBSERVATION SITES							CHARACTERISTICS OF BASIN					
Site number	River basin	Stream	Observ. site		Coordinates Lat. Long.	Period	Area km²	Slope	Soil	Cover	Regime	Mean precip. mm	Mean disc. m³s-1
1	2	3	4	5	6	7	8	9	10	11	12	13	14
1	Kelantan	Kelantan	Guillemard Bridge	1	N E 05:46 102:09	1949 80	11900	F E D		A D E	00	2500	513
2	Trengganu	Trengganu	Kampong Tanggol	1	N E 05:08 103:03	1947 80	3380	F E D		A D E	00	3300	154
3	Pahang	Pahang	Temerloh	1	N E 03:27 102:26	1963 80	19000	D30 C30 B40		A70 D25 E 5	00	2100	560
4	Johore	Johore	Rantau Panjang	1	N E 01:47 103:45	1964 80	1130	C60 A40		A60 D30 E10	00	2400	45
5	Perak	Perak	Iskandar Bridge	1	N E 04:49 100:58	1915 80	7770	F E D		A D E	00	2150	159
6	Klang	Klang	Kuala Lumpur Sulaiman Bridge	1	N E 03:09 101:42	1910 80	457	F E D		A D E	00	2300	14.0

TABLE II : FLOODS CHARACTERISTICS

		FLOODS CHARACTERISTICS						DISCHARGE ESTIMATION				
Site number	Stream	Observ. site	Year	Date of the max	Maximal dis m³s-1	Climatic origine	Condition disc est	Qual. of the sect	Precis. ±m³s-1	Anteced precip.	Depth mm	Duration days
1	2	3	4	5	6	7	8	9	10	11	12	13
1	Kelantan	Guillemard Bridge	1967	01-07	16300	1	A2C5	A1A	2400			
			1973	12-10	15140	1	A1C5	A1A	2250			
			1951	01-24	7200	1	A	A1A				
2	Trengganu	Kampong Tanggol	1967	01-06	12500	1	A1B					
			1966	12-30	10500	1	A1B					
			1972	12-18	7100	1	A1B					
3	Pahang	Temerloh	1971	12-13	6710	1	A2D1	A1A	1000			
			1967	03-14	5490	1	A1D1	A1A	500			
4	Johore	Rantau Panjang	1969	12-12	575	1	A1C1	A1B	110			
			1964	03-01	392	1	A1B1	A1B	40			
5	Perak	Iskandar Bridge	1967	01-06	6300	1	A1B					
			1967	11-27	2800	1	A1B					
			1969	12-01	2500	1	A1B					
6	Klang	Sulaïman Bridge	1971	01-05	670	1	A1D1	A1A	100			
			1972	11-17	290	1	A1B1	A1A	50			

TABLEAU I : IDENTIFICATION DES POINTS D'OBSERVATIONS ET CARACTERISTIQUES DES BASSINS

		POINT D'OBSERVATION						CARACTERISTIQUES DU BASSIN					
N° du point	Bassin fluvial	Rivière	Point d'observ.		Coordonnées Lat. Long.	Période	Surface km²	Relief	Sol	Végét.	Régime	Pluie moyenne mm	Module m³s-1
1	2	3	4	5	6	7	8	9	10	11	12	13	14
27152005	Niger	Sankarani	Gouala	1	N 11:58 W 08:13	1954 79	35300	B	C	B	10 11	1500	390
27150142	Niger	Niger	Koulikoro	1	N 12:52 W 07:34	1907 79	120000	C	C	B	10 11	1600	1505
27160105	Niger	Bani	Beneni Kegny	1	N 13:23 W 04:55	1951 79	116000	B A	C	C	10 11	1200	565
27161205	Niger	Bagoe	Pankourou	1	N 11:27 W 06:35	1956 79	31800	C	C	B	10 11	1400	215
27150118	Niger	Niger	Diré	1	N 16:16 W 03:23	1924 79	340000	A B C	C	B	10 11		1090
1	Niger	Dounfing	Bassin représentatif	4	N 12:41 W 08:02	1955 56	17.5	D	C	B	10	1150	
2	Niger	Koumbaka	B.R. II	4	N 13:52 W 04:08	1956 57	30.4	C	C	C	11	570	0.09

MALI

TABLEAU II : CARACTERISTIQUES DES CRUES

			CARACTERISTIQUES DE LA CRUE				EVALUATION DES DEBITS					
N° du point	Rivière	Point d'observ.	Année	Date du maximum	Débit max m³s-1	Origine	Base et mode éval	Qual. de la séch	Précis. ±m³s-1	Anteced	Hauteur	Durée jours
1	2	3	4	5	6	7	8	9	10	11	12	13
27152005	Sankarani	Gouala	1969	09-11	2250	1	A1B1	A2B	50			
			1979	09-15	2140	1	A1B1	A2B	50			
27150142	Niger	Koulikoro	1925	10-05	9670	1	A1B1	A1A	100			
			1924	10-05	9410	1	A1B1	A1A	100			
			1967	10-12	9340	1	A1B1	A1A	100			
27160105	Bani	Beneni Kegny	1924	10-14	3600	1	A (1)		200	(1) calculé à partir d'une station voisine		
			1953	10-13	3450	1	A1C1	A2B	100			
27161205	Bagoe	Pankourou	1964	09-22	2300	1	A2C1	A1A	100			
			1967	09-07	1680	1	A1B1	A1A	20			
27150118	Niger	Diré	1955	12-06	2750	1	A1B1	B2B	100			
			1954	12-21	2730	1	A1B1	B2B	100			
			1957	12-18	2680	1	A1B1	B2B	100			
1	Dounfing	Bassin représentatif	1955	08-27	47	1	A1C1	A1A	10	3	90	<1
2	Koumbaka	B.R. II	1956	08-12	221	1	A1C1	A1A	30		99	<0.2

MARTINIQUE (FRANCE)

TABLEAU I : IDENTIFICATION DES POINTS D'OBSERVATIONS ET CARACTERISTIQUES DES BASSINS

		POINT D'OBSERVATION					CARACTERISTIQUES DU BASSIN						
N° du point	Bassin fluvial	Rivière	Point d'observ.		Coordonnées Lat. Long.	Période	Surface km²	Relief	Sol	Végét.	Régime	Pluie moyenne mm	Module m³s-1
1	2	3	4	5	6	7	8	9	10	11	12	13	14
351210	Lezarde	Rivière Blanche	Pont Alma	1	N 14:42 W 61:06	1962 72	4.31	F	C	A	00	5500	0.59
350170	Lezarde	Lezarde	Soudon	1	N 14:39 W 61:00	1961 72	62.5	E	C	A	00	4000	3.34
060160	Capot	Capot	Saut Babin	1	N 14:49 W 61:06	1951 72	34.1	E	C	A	00	4300	3.32

MARTINIQUE (FRANCE)

TABLEAU II : CARACTERISTIQUES DES CRUES

	CARACTERISTIQUES DE LA CRUE						EVALUATION DES DEBITS					
N° du point	Rivière	Point d'observ.	Année	Date du maximum	Débit max m³s-1	Origine	Base et mode éval	Qual. de la séch	Précis. ±m³s-1	Anteced	Hauteur mm	Durée jours
1	2	3	4	5	6	7	8	9	10	11	12	13
351210	Rivière Blanche	Alma	1970	08-20	120	1	A4C5	C1B	20	3	280	1
			1967	09-07	80	1	A4C5	C1B	10	3	340	1
			1966	11-20	57	1	A4C5	C1B	10	3	110	1
350170	Lézarde	Soudon	1970	08-20	800	1	A4C5	C1B	100	3	280	1
			1967	09-07	525	1	A4C5	C1B	75	3	350	1
			1963	09-25	480	1	A4C5	C1B	75	3	220	1
060160	Capot	Saut Babin	1963	09-24	480	1	A4C5	A1B	50	3	250	1
			1967	09-07	410	1	A4C5	A1B	40	3	300	1
			1970	08-20	370	1	A4C5	A1B	40	3	250	1

TABLEAU I : IDENTIFICATION DES POINTS D'OBSERVATIONS ET CARACTERISTIQUES DES BASSINS

	POINT D'OBSERVATION							CARACTERISTIQUES DU BASSIN					
N° du point	Bassin fluvial	Rivière	Point d'observ.	Coordonnées Lat.	Long.	Période	Surface km²	Relief	Sol	Végét.	Régime	Pluie moyenne mm	Module m³s-1
1	2	3	4	5	6	7	8	9	10	11	12	13	14
1	Sénégal	Boudamé Ghorfa	Ouled Addet	4	N 15:38 W 12:33	1964 66	1125	B	B30 C40 D30	C	11 20	475	2.32
2	Sénégal	Djajibine Ghorfa	Djajibine	4	N 15:46 W 12:32	1964 67	148	B	D90 C10	C	11 20	475	.40
3	Sénégal	Gorgol Noir	Foum Gleita	1	N 16:10 W 12:40	1958 61 1970 78	8950	A B	B20 C70 D10	C	11 20	380	10
4	Sénégal	Gorgol Blanc	Gleita Tor	1	N 17:04 W 12:41	1958 59	3770	A B	B20 C70 D10	C	11 20	300	1
5	Gorgol Blanc	Dionaba	Dionaba	4	N 17:06 W 12:38	1958 59	116	B	B20 C60 D20	C	11 20	300	0.07
6	Sénégal	Moktar Seloumbo	B.R. Station 1	4	N 17:47 W 12:15	1957 59	12.2	D	B30 C60 D10	C	11 20	230	0.011
7	Sahara	Tamourt en Naaje	Legdeim	1	N 17:57 W 12:12	1956 61 1969 1972 74	6190	D		C	11 20	230	1.71
8	Sahara	Ketchi	Tachounda	1	N 17:05 W 13:55	1958 63	3420	A B		C	11 20	300	1.
9	Sénégal	Karakoro	Barrage de Lehbile	1	N 17 W 12	1960	143	B		C	11 20	320	

TABLEAU II : CARACTERISTIQUES DES CRUES

N° du point	Rivière	Point d'observ.	Année	Date du maximum	Débit max m³s-1	Origine	Base et mode éval	Qual. de la séch	Précis. ±m³s-1	Anteced	Hauteur	Durée jours
		CARACTERISTIQUES DE LA CRUE					EVALUATION DES DEBITS					
1	2	3	4	5	6	7	8	9	10	11	12	13
1	Boudamé	Ouled Addet	1965	08-13	200	1	A2C3	B1B	30		103.5	1
2	Djajibine	Djajibine	1964	07-13	392	1	A1C2	A1A	30		112	1
3	Gorgol noir	Foum Gleita	1958		172	1	A1C2	A1A	30			
4	Gorgol blanc	Gleita Tor	1958		65	1	A2C2	A1A	10			
5	Dionaba	Dionaba	1958	07-31	19	1	A1B2	A1A	1		53.5	1
6	Moktar	B.R. Station 1	1959	08-27	80	1	A2C3	A1B	10		57.3	1
7	Tamourt en Naaje	Legdeim	1969		120	1	A5C3	B1B	20			
8	Ketchi	Tachounda	1960		122	1	A2C3	B1B	20			
9	Karakoro	Lehbilé	1960	08-12	170	1	A5D4	B1B	30			

TABLE I : IDENTIFICATION OF OBSERVATION SITES AND CHARACTERISTICS OF BASINS

OBSERVATION SITE							CHARACTERISTICS OF BASIN						
Site number	River basin	Stream	Observ. site		Coordinates Lat. Long.	Period	Area km²	Slope	Soil	Cover	Regime	Mean precip. mm	Mean disc. m³s-1
1	2	3	4	5	6	7	8	9	10	11	12	13	14
18500000 0000A070 F0021200	Balsas (P)	Balsas	Presa el Infiernillo	2	N 18:17 W 101:54	1963 71	109440	F 2 E 3 C75 B20	A 9 B43 C 9 D39	A51 B39 C 1 D 2 E 7	10 90	975	635
16800000 00000000 H1850600	Coahuayana (P)	Coahuayana	Estacion callejones	1	N 19:20 W 103:50	1949 75	6835	F 5 E15 C80	B41 C59	A80 B16 C 1 E 3	10 90	940	58
1	Cihuatlan (P)	Cihuatlan	Sitio Paso del Mojo	3	N 19:19 W 104:18		1370	F 5 E95	C	A20 B80	10 90	1375	
11500000 00000000 H1801800	Acaponeta (P)	Acaponeta	Estacion Acaponeta	1	N 22:29 W 105:21	1945 75	5090	F10 E15 C75	B25 C75	A17 B83	10 90	1245	42
11300000 00000000 H2002500	Baluarte (P)	Baluarte	Estacion Baluarte II	1	N 22:59 W 105:51	1947 75	4655	F 8 E 9 C53 B30	C	A70 B30	10 90	1315	65
10700000 0000A300 F0022500	Culiacan (P)	Humaya	Presa A. Lopez Mateos	1	N 25:05 W 107:23	1963 75	10980	F10 D50 C40	C73 D27	A33 B67	10 90	970	10
10200000 H3952500	Fuerte	Fuerte	Estacion Huites	1	N 26:54 W 108:21	1941 75	26020	F 5 E25 C70	C	A 1 B99	10 90	790	124
10200000 00000000 H1902500	Fuerte (P)	Fuerte	Estacion San Blas	1	N 26:06 W 108:45	1941 50	33590	F 5 E20 C75	B37 C63	A18 B62 E20	10 90	762	159
2	Yaqui (P)	Yaqui	Sitio Los Limones	3	N 27:45 W 109:26		70130	D 2 C38 B60	B59 C41	B50 D10 E40	70 90	545	
3	Arroyo San Bartolo (P)	Arroyo San Bartolo	Sitio Cerca Poblado San Bartolo	3	N 23:45 W 109:48		81	F20 E80	B50 C50	A80 B20	70	350	
28500000 00000000 H3982000	Papaloapan (A)	Papaloapan	Estacion Papaloapan	1	N 18:10 W 96:05	1947 75	21235	D10 C90	A 1 B54 C 5 D40	A62 B31 E 7	10 90	1700	695
26500335 00000000 H2003000	Panuco (A)	Tempoal	Estacion Tempoal	1	N 21:32 W 98:23	1954 75	5275	F 5 E10 C85	B40 C60	A90 B 8 E 2	10 70 90	1585	97
24500106 17000000 H0121900	Bravo (A)	San Juan	Estacion el Cuchillo	1	N 25:43 W 99:16	1930 75	8795	F10 E10 B80	C86 D14	B83 C10 E 7	70	691	23

(P) Pacific ocean (A) Atlantic ocean

TABLE II : FLOODS CHARACTERISTICS

				FLOODS CHARACTERISTIC			DISCHARGE ESTIMATION					
Site number	Stream	Observ. site	Year	Date of the max	Maximal disc m³s-1	Climatic origine	Condition disc est	Qual. of the sect	Precis. ±m³s-1	Anteced precip.	Depth mm	Duration days
1	2	3	4	5	6	7	8	9	10	11	12	13
18500000 0000A070 F0021200	Balsas	Presa el Infiernillo	1967	09-27	25200	1						
16800000 00000000 H1850600	Coahuanaya	Callejones	1959	10-27	17000	1	B4D4	B1C	2500	2	198	2
			1968	09-13	3550	1	A1CO	B1C	350	3	72	1
			1964	10-04	3016	1	A1CO	B1B	300			
1	Cihuatlan	Paso del Mojo	1959	10-27	13500	1				2	213	2
11500000 00000000 H1801800	Acaponeta	Acaponeta	1968	09-13	16000	1	A1BO	B1A	1300	2	145	2
			1972	11-24	7050	1	A1CO	B1B	700	2	164	1
			1965	09-27	6150	1	A1CO	B1B	600	2	92	2
11300000 00000000 H2002500	Baluarte	Baluarte II	1968	09-13	14140	1	A1A1	B1A	700	1	244	1
			1972	11-23	10300	1	A1CO	B1B	1000	2	215	1
			1948	09-10	9000	1	A1BO	B1A	700			
10700000 0000A300 F0022500	Humaya	Presa A. Lopez Mateos	1973	02-22	12680	1						
10200000 00000000 H3952500	Fuerte	Huites	1960	01-12	15000	1	D2CO	B1B	2200			
			1943	12-09	14375	1	A1CO	B1B	1400			
			1949	01-15	10000	1	A1CO	B1B	1000			
			1973	02-22	7960	1	A1A1	B1A	400	1	82	2
10200000 00000000 H1902500	Fuerte	San Blas	1943	12-10	12675	1	D2CO	B1B	1900			
2	Yaqui	Los Limones	1914	12	11330	1						
3	Arroyo San Bartolo	San Bartolo	1976	09-30	3000	1				1	425	1
28500000 00000000 H3982000	Papaloapan	Papaloapan	1969	09-11	6850	1				1	99	2
			1958	10-15	6825	1				2	100	1
			1950	10-13	6228	1				2	80	1
26500335 00000000 H2003000	Tempoal	Tempoal	1955	09-30	6000	1	A1CO	B1B	600	?	425	2
			1974	09-24	4950	1	A1BO	B1A	400	3	257	2
			1956	09-14	4425	1	A1CO	B1B	450	2	302	2
24500106 17000000 HO121900	San Juan	El Cuchillo	1938	08-29	6760	1	A1BO	B1A	540			
			1967	09-23	5540	1	A1CO	B1B	550	1	170	2
			1945	10-04	3360	1	A1CO	B1B	340			
			1973	06-24	3355	1	A1CO	B1B	340	3	127	1

TABLEAU I : IDENTIFICATION DES POINTS D'OBSERVATION ET CARACTERISTIQUES DES BASSINS

	POINT D'OBSERVATION							CARACTERISTIQUES DU BASSIN					
N° du point	Bassin fluvial	Rivière	Point d'observ.		Coordonnées Lat. Long.	Période	Surface km²	Relief	Sol	Végét	Régime	Pluie moyenne mm	Module m³s-1
1	2	3	4	5	6	7	8	9	10	11	12	13	14
182-17	Moulouya	Moulouya	Dar el Caïd	1	N 33:13 W 03:52	28 ans	24420	F40 E10 B50	D	B20 C20 D60	30	300	30
89-11	Moulouya	Moulouya	Melg el Ouidane	1	N 34:35 W 03:00	19 ans	48000	F50 E10 B35	D	B20 C20 D60	30	350	35
612- 4	Loukkos	Loukkos	M'Douar	1	N 35:00 W 05:30	1969 80	667	E80 D20	D	B40 C40 D20	50	800 1500	20
609-09	Sebou	Ouergha	Mjara	1	N 34:33 W 05:16	1933 44 1949 80	6190	F25 E25 C50	D	A10 C45 D45	50	1070	106
1540-15	Sebou	Sebou	Azib Soltane	1	N 34:19 W 05:30	1959 80	16150	F10 E30 D60	A30 C70	A20 D80	50	575	68
1475-37	Oum er Rbia	Oum er Rbia	Dechra el oued	1	N 32:42 W 05:54	27 ans	3330	F40 E40 D15	C70 A20 D10	B60 C15 D15	50	450	30
35-27	Oum er Rbia	Oum er Rbia	Imfout Barrage	1	N 32:44 W 07:57	40 ans	30600	F45 D50	B50 D50	B20 C 5 D50	50	550	110
1675-44	Tensift	Tensift	Abadla	1	N 31:41 W 08:31	1969 80	10150	F25 D35 C40	C	B10 C30 D30 E30	30	415	14
220-79	Massa	Massa	Tankist	1	N W 09:23	1950 69	3780	E			30	295	4.03
867-48	Ziz	Ziz	Foum Zaabel	1	N 32:06 W 04:37	11 ans	3975	F80 E10 B10	A B	B50 E30 C20	20	200	4.32
628-48	Guir	Guir	Tazzouguert	1	N 32 W 03:45	20 ans	2370	F35 E30 D15 C15	D	E95	20	120	2
37-49	Bou Anane	Bou Anane	Ben Yati	1	N 32 W 03	10 ans	7070	F20 E40 D20 C15	D	E95	20	125	4.57

TABLEAU II : CARACTERISTIQUES DES CRUES

	CARACTERISTIQUES DE LA CRUE						EVALUATION DES DEBITS					
N° du point	Rivière	Point d'observ.	Année	Date du maximum	Débit max m³s-1	Origine	Base et mode eval	Qual. de la séch	Précis. ±m³s-1	Anteced	Hauteur	Durée jours
1	2	3	4	5	6	7	8	9	10	11	12	13
182-17	Moulouya	Dar el Caïd	1963	05-27	5170	1	A1B4	B1B	400			
			1975	04-19	2030	1	A1B5	B1B	200			
89-11	Moulouya	Melg el Ouidane	1963	05-27	7200	1	A1B4	B2C	700			
			75	04-20	3300	1	A1B5	B2C	300			
612- 4	Loukkos	M'Douar	1977	01-23	3500	1	A1C5	B1B	400	3	100 200	1
609-09	Ouergha	Mjara	1950	12-29	7950	1	D5C4	C1C	800			
			1963	12-18	7030	1	A2C4	C1C	700			
1540-15	Sebou	Azib Soltane	1963	01-07	3350	1	A2C4	C1B	250			
			1960	01-16	2930	1	A2C4	C1B	250			
1475-37	Oum er Rbia	Dechra el oued	1963	12-18	1440	4	A1C4	C1B	150			
35-27	Oum er Rbia	Imfout	1963	12-21	3850 (1)	4	A1D6	A1A	300	3		
1675-44	Tensift	Abadla	1949		2800		C5D5	XOX	500			
220-79	Massa	Tankist	1957	12-15	2800	1	A2C4	A1B	200			
867-48	Ziz	Foum Zaabel	1965	11-06	4500 (2)	1	A1C5	A1B	500			
			1975	04-19	1360	1	A1A3	A1B	70			
628-48	Guir	Tazzouguert	1962	09-25	3300	1	A2C4	B1B	300			
37-49	Bou Anane	Ben Yati	1967	11-16	5000	1	A2C4	B1B	500			
			1975	05-04	2560		A2C4	B1B	250			

(1) crue naturelle reconstituée.
(2) observée à Aït Athmane 4310 km².

TABLE I : IDENTIFICATION OF OBSERVATION SITES AND CHARACTERISTICS OF BASINS

	OBSERVATIONS SITES							CHARACTERISTICS OF BASIN					
Site number	River basin	Stream	Observ. site		Coordinates Lat. Long.	Period	Area km²	Slope	Soil	Cover	Regime	Mean precip. mm	Mean disc m³s-1
1	2	3	4	5	6	7	8	9	10	11	12	13	14
E393	Maputo	Maputo	Fronteiraw	1	S E 26:51 32:08	1966 70	15750				40 11	800	56
E10	Umbeluzi	Umbeluzi	Goba	1	S E 26:12 32:07	1951 70	3100				40	800	10
E23	Incomati	Incomati	(1)	1	S E 25:26 32:00	1952 70	21200				11 40	1300	70
E117	Limpopo	Elefantes	Tiobine	1	S E 23:53 32:10	1967 70	68400				11 40	500	30
E47	Save	Save	(2)	1	S E 21:06 34:41	1961 70	101000				11 40	500	130
E188	Buzi	Buzi	Estaquinha	1	S E 19:57 34:09	1967 70	26300				11	800	78
E65	Pungoè	Pungoè	Pungoè II	1	S E 18:33 33:15	1957 70	3100				11	1300	55
E320	Zambèze	Zambèze	Teté	1	S E 16:09 33:35	1955 70	940000				11 10	700	2590
E91	Licungo	Licungo	Mocuba	1	S E 16:50 36:59	1956 70	20400				11	1500	190
E140	Monapo	Monapo	Monapo	1	S E 14:54 40:19	1960 70	6000				11	1100	22
E128	Lurio	Lurio	Namapa	1	S E 13:41 39:51	1956 70	56200				11	1100	230

(1) ancien nom : Ressano Garcia.
(2) ancien nom : Villafranca do Save.

TABLE II : FLOODS CHARACTERISTICS

	FLOOD CHARACTERISTICS						DISCHARGE ESTIMATION					
Site number	Stream	Observ. site	Year	Date of the max	Maximal dism³s-1	Climatic origine	Condition disc est	Qual. of the sect	Precis. ±m³s-1	Anteced precip.	Depth mm	Duration days
1	2	3	4	5	6	7	8	9	10	11	12	13
E393	Maputo	Fronteiraw	1967	10-02	920	1	A1B2	B1B	100	3		
E10	Umbeluzi	Goba	1966	01-07	1600	1	A1B2	A1A	50	3		
E23	Incomati		1955	02-13	1670	1	A1B2	B1B	150	3		
E117	Elefantes	Tiobine	1969	03-17	3100	1	A1B2	B1B	400	3		
E47	Save		1969	03-20	3350	1	A1B2	B1A	600	3		
E188	Buzi	Estaquinha	1969	03-19	970	1	A1B2	B1B	200	3		
E65	Pungoè	Pungoè II	1962	03-17	2720	1	A1B2	A1A	250	3		
E320	Zambèze	Teté	1958		17000	1						
E91	Licungo	Mocuba	1963	02-10	2730	1	A1B2	B1A	250	3		
E140	Monapo	Monapo	1965	01-31	512	1	A1B2	B1A	50	3		
E128	Lurio	Namapa	1963	02-18	4420	1	A1B2	A1A	500	3		

TABLE I : IDENTIFICATION OF OBSERVATION SITES AND CHARACTERISTICS OF BASINS

	OBSERVATION SITES						CHARACTERISTICS OF BASIN						
Site number	River basin	Stream	Observ. site		Coordinates Lat. Long.	Period	Area km²	Slope	Soil	Cover	Regime	Mean precip. mm	Mean disc m³s-1
1	2	3	4	5	6	7	8	9	10	11	12	13	14
03570	Rhine	Rhine	Lobith	2	N E 51:51 06:06	1901 1976	160000 (1)	F10 E20 C20 B20 A30	B30 C50 D20	D90 E10	50 90	910	2200
03860	Meuse	Meuse	Borgharen	2	N E 50:52 05:41	1911 1976	21000 (2)	E10 C30 B30 A30	B40 C50 D10	D90 E10	50	750	250

(1) : entire basin 185000 km².

(2) : entire basin 32000 km².

TABLE II : FLOODS CHARACTERISTICS

	FLOOD CHARACTERISTICS						DISCHARGE ESTIMATION					
Site number	Stream	Observ. site	Year	Date of the max	Maximal dism³s-1	Climatic origine	Condition disc est	Qual. of the sect	Precis. ±m³s-1	Anteced precip.	Depth mm	Duration days
1	2	3	4	5	6	7	8	9	10	11	12	13
03570	Rhine	Lobith	1926	01-04	12000	4	A1B4	B1A	500	3 (1) 3 (2)	140 64/241 9/53	Dec. Dec. 3
			1920	01-18	11400	4	A1B4	B1A	500	3 (1) 3 (2)	184 73/378 78/287	Dec. Dec. Jan.
			1970	02-27	9900	4	A1B4	B1A	500	3 (1) 3 (2)	286 72/251	24 21/24
								(1) Zurich		(2) Rhein provinz		
03860	Meuse	Borgharen	1926	01-01	3000	1	A1B4	A1A	100	3	96/176	25
			1970	02-23	2170	1	A1B4	A1A	100	3 (1) 3 (2)	96/243 159	Feb. Feb.
			1920	01-15	2090	1	A1B4	A1A	100	3 (2)	80	Dec.
								(1) Belgium		(2) France.		

TABLEAU I : IDENTIFICATION DES POINTS D'OBSERVATIONS ET CARACTERISTIQUES DES BASSINS

	POINT D'OBSERVATION						CARACTERISTIQUES DU BASSIN						
N° du point	Bassin fluvial	Rivière	Point d'observ.		Coordonnées Lat. Long.	Période	Surface km²	Relief	Sol	Végét.	Régime	Pluie moyenne mm	Module m³s-1
1	2	3	4	5	6	7	8	9	10	11	12	13	14
050101	Dumbéa	Dumbéa Est	Barrage	4	S E 22:09 166:31	20 ans	56	F	C80 D20	A10 B50 C40	10	2700	3.5
520101	Tontouta	Tontouta	Mine Liliane	1	S E 21:57 166:18	14 ans	380	E	C80 D20	A10 B50 C40	10	1900	15
330101	Ouenghi	Ouenghi	Pont R T 1	1	S E 21:54 116:07	28 ans	240	E	C80 D20	A20 B50 C30	10	1700	8.5
260101	Néra	Boghen	Aval Arémo	1	S E 21:36 165:39	35 ans	114	E	C40 D60	A40 B30 C30	10	1700	3.8
080102	Houailou	Houailou	Carovin	1	S E 21:17 165:26	32 ans	270	E	C50 D50	A10 B40 C50	10	1900	12
470301	Téméla	Faténaoué	Témala	1	S E 20:54 164:45		113	E	B10 C40 D50	A10 B50 C40	10	1500	2.2
040101	Diahot	Diahot	Bondé St. Anne	1	S E 20:26 164:26	35 ans	290	E	C50 D50	A20 B50 C30	10	2000	8.8
551001	Yaté	Rivière des Lacs	Goulet	1	S E 22:14 166:51	26 ans	61 69	D	B30 C70	A10 B30 C60	00	3000	5.1
550101	Yaté	Yaté	Yaté Barrage	1	S E 22:09 166:52	34 ans	435	D	B20 C70 D10	A20 B30 C50	00	2900	34
370101	Ouinné	Ouinné	Embouchure	1	S E 21:59 166:40		143	E	C80 D20	A60 B20 C20	00	3500	13
310101	Ouaième	Ouaième	Derniers Rapides	1	S E 20:38 164:50	35 ans	330	E	C50 D50	A50 B30 C20	00	3000	21

TABLEAU II : CARACTERISTIQUES DES CRUES

	CARACTERISTIQUES DE LA CRUE								EVALUATION DES DEBITS			
N° du point	Rivière	Point d'observ.	Année	Date du maximum	Débit max m³s-1	Origine	Base et mode evalla	Qual. de séch	Précis. ±m³s-1	Anteced	Hauteur mm	Durée jours
1	2	3	4	5	6	7	8	9	10	11	12	13
050101	Dumbea Est	Barrage	1969	02-02	1200	1	A2C6	A1A	120			
			1981	12-24	830	1	B4C6	A1A				
520101	Tontouta	Mine Liliane	1975	03-08	3900	1	A2C2	A1A	400			
			1981	12-24	3600	1	A2C2	A1A	400			
330101	Ouenghi	Pont R T 1	1975	03-08	2100	1	A1C2	B1C	200			
			1981	12-24	1650	1	A1C2	B1C	150			
			1974	02-04	1600	1	A1C2	B1C	120			
260101	Boghen	Aremo	1948	03	2000	1	A2C2	A1A	200			
			1975	03-07	1500	1	A1B2	A1A	100			
			1969	02-02	1300	1	A1B2	A1A	100			
080102	Houailou	Carovin	1951	02	2500	1	B4C2	A1A	400			
			1981	12-24	2500	1	A1C2	A1A	250			
			1955	03-05	2500	1	B4C2	A1A	200			
			1966	03-29	2300	1	B4C2	A1A	200			
470301	Faténaoué	Témala	1923		1800	1	B5C4	B1B	250			
			1948		1400	1	B4C4	B1B	200			
			1951	02	1400	1	B4C4	B1B	200			
			1981	12-24	1300	1	A2C4	B1B	200			
040101	Diahot	Bondé	1981	12-24	5000	1	A2C4	B1B	700			
			1948	01	4500	1	B4C4	B1B	600			
			1972	02-06	3700	1	A2C4	B1B	400			
			1976	01-17	2950	1	A2C4	B1B	300			
551001	Rivière des Lacs	Goulet	1968	01-19	600	1	A1B3	A1A	60			
			1981	12-25	505	1	A1B3	A1A	50			
550101	Yaté	Yaté barrage	1981	12-25	5700	1	A1E	A1A	300			
			1937	11-30	3100	1	A2D6	A1A	300			
			1937	04-24	2500	1	A2D6	A1A	250			
370101	Ouinné	Embouchure	1975	03-08	4000	1	B5C4	A1A	400			
			1981	02-13	3100	1	B4C2	A1A	300			
			1981	12-24	2800	1	B4C2	A1A	280			
310101	Ouaième	Derniers Rapides	1981	12-24	10400	1	A2C4	A1A	2000		1692 (1)	1
			1948	03	7300	1	B5C4	A1A	1400			
			1972	02-06	6000	1	B4C4	A1A	1200			

(1) observé en 1 point du bassin 1050 mm en un second point.

TABLE I : IDENTIFICATION OF OBSERVATION SITES AND CHARACTERISTICS OF BASINS

OBSERVATIONS SITES							CHARACTERISTICS OF BASIN						
Site number	River basin	Stream	Observ. site		Coordinates Lat. Long.	Period	Area km²	Slope	Soil	Cover	Regime	Mean precip. mm	Mean disc m³s-1
1	2	3	4	5	6	7	8	9	10	11	12	13	14
NORTH ISLAND :													
15410	Rangitaiki	Whirinaki	Galatea	1	S 38:29 E 176:45	1958 77	534	E	B	A95 B 5	50	1730	15.2
1	Waiapu	Waiapu	Rotokautuku	1	S 38:47 E 178:22		1600	D	B		50		
2	Kopuawhara	Kopuawhara			S 38:55 E 177:55		40.4	D	B		50		
3	Mangakotukutuku				S 38:50 E 177:55		18.7	D	B		50		
4	Wairoa	Wairoa	Wairoa	1	S 39:05 E 177:33		3670	E D	B		50		
5	Esk	Esk		1	S 39:20 E 176:57		199	D	B		50		
23209	Waipawa	Otane	Glendon	1	S 39:53 E 176:35	1965 77	24.3	D	C	C	50	955	164
6	Mangakahia	Mangakahia			S 36 E 175		253	D			40		
7	Waikato	Waikato	Mercer	1	S 38:44 E 175:05		13700	D C			50		
29820	Hutt	Taita	Native	1	S 41:11 E 174:58	1955 77	0.15	D	C	A	50	1290	
29250	Ruamahanga	Ruakokpatuna Iraia		1	S 41:23 E 175:22	1969 77	15.5	D	C	A10 C90	50	1840	0.657
SOUTH ISLAND :													
8		Pelorus	Pelorus Bridge		S 41:40 E 172:20		373						
64610	Waiau-uha	Stanton	Cheddar Valley	1	S 42:38 E 173:09	1968 77	41.6	D	C	C	50	980	0.482
69621	Opihi	Rocky Gully	Rockburn	1	S 44:20 E 170:46	1964 77	22.4	D	C	C	50	800	0.294
93207	Buller	Inangahua	Blacks Point	1	S 42:07 E 171:53	1970 77	234	E	C	A77 C23	50 90	2520	16.13
9	Buller·	Buller	Berlins	1	S 41:50 E 172		5920	E D			50 90		

TABLE I : IDENTIFICATION OF OBSERVATION SITES AND CHARACTERISTICS OF BASINS

| OBSERVATIONS SITES | | | | | | | CHARACTRISTICS OF BASIN | | | | | | |
Site number	River basin	Stream	Observ. site	Coordinates Lat. Long.		Period	Area km²	Slope	Soil	Cover	Regime	Mean precip. mm	Mean disc m³s-1
1	2	3	4	5	6	7	8	9	10	11	12	13	14
10	Hokitika	Hokitika	Kanieri	1	S E 42:50 170:58		1040	F E			50 90		
11	Haast	Haast	Roaring Billy	1	S E 43:55 169:30		1020	F E			50 90		
12	Hollyford	Hollyford			S E 44:30 168:05		64.5	F			50 90		

TABLE II : FLOODS CHARACTERISTICS

	FLOOD CHARACTERISTICS						DISCHARGE ESTIMATION					
Site number	Stream	Observ. site	Year	Date of the max	Maximal dism³s-1	Climatic origine	Condition disc est	Qual. of the sect	Precis. ±m³s-1	Anteced precip.	Depth mm	Duration days
1	2	3	4	5	6	7	8	9	10	11	12	13
NORTH ISLAND :												
15410	Whirinaki	Galatea	1965 1967 70	02-13	632 310 307	1 1 1	A1C1 A1C1 A1C1	C1B C1B C1B		3	191	3
1 (3)	Waīapu	Rotokautuku	1924	05	6500	1			U			
2	Kopuawhara		1938	02	960	1			U			
3	Mangakotukutuku		1938	02	685	1			U			
4	Wairoa	Wairoa	1948	05-15	11400	1			U			
5	Esk		1938	04-25	1830	1			U		250	1
23209	Otane	Glendon	1974	06-16	37.31	1	A1B1	A1A		1	192	1
6	Mangakahia		1917	02	2015	1			U			
7	Waikato	Mercer	1907 1953	02	1700 1390	1 1			U U			
29820	Taita	Native	1975	12-20	2.17	1	A1A1	A1A	0.17	3	290	2
29250	Ruakokpatuna	Iraia	1971	08-17	120	1	A1B1	A1A		1	192	1
SOUTH ISLAND :												
8	Pelorus	Pelorus Bridge	1954	02	1680	1			U			
64610	Stanton	Cheddar Valley	1974	09-04	117.8 (2)	1	A1C1	B1B		3	140	1
69621	Rocky Gully	Rockburn	1972	05-16	51.6	1	A1C1	B1B		1	109	1
93207	Inangahua	Blacks point	1974	04-14	977	1	A1C1	B1B		3	109	1
9	Buller	Berlins	1926 1950	05 11	10000 (1) 10000	1 1			2000 2000			
10	Hokitika	Kanieri	1967	03-11	5550	1			U			
11	Haast	Roaring Billy	1979 1950	12-02 05	7690 7075	1 1			U			
12	Hollyford		1952	02	1040	1			U			

(1) largest floods since 1871   (2) largest flood since 1923
(3) The stations with code index correspond to stations well instrumented
    The stations with the number corresponding to the order of sequency
    present heavy floods (often historical) with very rough estimation.

TABLEAU I : IDENTIFICATION DES POINTS D'OBSERVATIONS ET CARACTERISTIQUES DES BASSINS

	POINT D'OBSERVATION						CARACTERISTIQUES DU BASSIN						
N° du point	Bassin fluvial	Rivière	Point d'observ.		Coordonnées Lat. Long.	Période	Surface km²	Relief	Sol	Végét.	Régime	Pluie moyenne mm	Module m³s-1
1	2	3	4	5	6	7	8	9	10	11	12	13	14
50127	Niger	Niger	Niamey	1	N 13:40 E 02:05	1934 79	700000		(1)		$^{10}/_{11}$	(1)	970
1	Lake Tchad	Komadougou	Bagara	1	N 13:17 E 12:36	1962 79	115000	A	B C D	C D	11	800	18.5
51806	Niger	Gorouol	Dolbel	1	N 14:37 E 00:18	1961 79	7500	B	C D	C	11	500	8.4
54515	Niger	Maggia	Tsernaoua	1	N 13:53 E 05:20	1954 79	2525	B	C D	C	11	500	1.9
56706	Niger	Goulbi de Maradi	Madarounfa	1	N 13:19 E 07:10	1956 79	5400	A B	C D	C D	11	550	6.5
2	Niger	Teloua	Azel	1	N 17:03 E 08:03	10 ans	1360	F E D	D	C E	$^{11}/_{20}$	150	0.63
3	Niger	Tamgak	S1	4	N 19:10 E 08:40	1975 79	620	F	D	E	20	45	0.19

(1) aucune signification.

TABLEAU II : CARACTERISTIQUES DES BASSINS

			CARACTERISTIQUES DE LA CRUE							EVALUATION DES DEBITS		
N° du point	Rivière	Point d'observ.	Année	Date du maximum	Débit max m³s-1	Origine	Base et mode éval	Qual. de la séch.	Précis. ±m³s-1	Anteced	Hauteur mm	Durée jours
1	2	3	4	5	6	7	8	9	10	11	12	13
50127	Niger	Niamey	1970	02-01	2360	1	A1B1	B1A	100			
			1968	02-09	2320							
			1956	02-22	2160	1	A1B1	B1A	100			
1	Komadougou	Bagara	1964	12-19	86	1	A1B1	B1B	8			
			1962	12-18	78	1	A1B1	B1B	7			
			1970	01-02	60	1	A1B1	B1B	6			
51806	Gorouol	Dolbel	1978	08-06	213	1	A1B1	A1A	10			
			1977	07-24	120	1	A1B1	A1A	10			
			1961	09-07	118	1	A1B1	A1A	10			
54515	Maggia	Tsernaoua	1961	08-30	210	1	B5C	A1B	+40 −30			
			1974	08-06	140	1	A2B1	A1B	10			
			1964	07-22	85	1	A2B1	A1B	10			
56706	Goulbi de Maradi	Madarounfa	1961	08-12	1300	1	(2)	C1B	200			
			1963	08-23	1050	1	A2C1	C1B	100			
			1964	08-09	750	1	A2C1	C1B	60			
2	Teloua	Azel	1978	07-28	460	1	A1A1	B1B	30			
			1980	07-14	420	1	A1A1	B1B	30			
			1958		400	1	B5C	B1B	100			
3	Tamgak	S1	1977	08-04	1100	1	A1C3	B1B	200			
			1976	09-10	830	1	A1C3	B1B	100			

(2) déterminé par correlation.

TABLE I : IDENTIFICATION OF OBSERVATION SITES AND CHARACTERISTICS OF BASINS

	OBSERVATION SITES						CHARACTERISTICS OF BASIN						
Site number	River basin	Stream	Observ. site		Coordinates Lat. Long.	Period	Area km²	Slope	Soil	Cover	Regime	Mean precip. mm	Mean disc m³s-1
1	2	3	4	5	6	7	8	9	10	11	12	13	14
1	Niger	Benue	Yola	1	N 09:15 E 12:30	1929 30 1938 39 1941 57 1967 71	107000				10 11	1160	740
2	Niger	Benue	Makurdi	1	N 07:45 E 08:27	1931 67 1970 77	305000				10 11	1240	3150
3	Niger	Niger	Lokoja	1	N 07:50 E 06:47	1915 1977	1080000 (1)				10 11 20		6100
4	Niger	Niger	Onitsha	1	N 06:09 E 06:45	1914 66 1970 77	1100000 (1)				10 11 20		6600

(1) estimation of the active part of the basin.

TABLE II : FLOODS CHARACTERISTICS

	FLOOD CHARACTERISTICS						DISCHARGE ESTIMATION					
Site number	Stream	Observ. site	Year	Date of the max	Maximal dis m³s-1	Climatic origine	Condition disc est	Qual. of the sect	Precis. ±m³s-1	Anteced precip.	Depth mm	Duration days
1	2	3	4	5	6	7	8	9	10	11	12	13
1	Benue	Yola	1970		8035	1						
			1948		6700	1						
			1969		6090	1						
			1943		5850	1						
			1955		5600	1						
2	Benue	Makurdi	1970		14600 (1)	1						
			1975		14200	1						
			1960		14100	1						
			1954		14000	1						
			1948		13900	1						
3	Niger	Lokoja	1969		27140	1			2000			
			1915		27000	1						
			1925		26500	1						
			1955		26400	1						
4	Niger	Onitsha	1955 (2)		23000	1			2000			
			1954		23000	1						
			1962		22900	1						
			1957		22400	1						

(1) perhaps the maximum of 1969 exceeded the 1970 maximum.

(2) 1969 is missing.

TABLE I : IDENTIFICATION OF OBSERVATION SITES AND CHARACTERISTICS OF BASINS

	OBSERVATION SITES						CHARACTERISTICS OF BASIN						
Site number	River basin	Stream	Observ. site		Coordinates Lat. Long.	Period	Area km²	Slope	Soil	Cover	Reg.	Mean precip. mm	Mean disc m³s-1
1	2	3	4	5	6	7	8	9	10	11	12	13	14
374-0	Klara	Engera	Engeren	1	N 61:03 E 12:36	1911 75	394	D	C70 D30	(1) A 70 C 30	61	850	7.4
395-0/1960-0	Glomma	Glomma	Langnes	1	N 59:36 E 11:07	1901 76	40013	F15 D25 C60	C60 D40	A 60 C 35 D 5	61 90	750	660
458-0	Dramselv	Snarumselv	Krøderen	1	N 60:08 E 09:47	1889 1964	5094	F 5 D85 C10	C45 D55	A 45 C 55	61 90	1000	120
518-11/12	Nidelv	Nidelv	Lunde Mølle	1	N 58:24 E 08:38	1900 76	3841	D	C75 D25	A 75 C 25	61 90	1250	120
560-11/12	Fedeelv	Fedeelv	Refsti	1	N 58:17 E 06:49	1898 1975	211	D	C65 D35	A 65 C 35	50	1750	9.8
919-0	Hellelandselv	Hellelandselv	Gya	1	N 58:36 E 06:21	1933 73	60	D	C25 D75	A 25 C 75	50	3100	5.3
603-0	Kløvteitelv	Kløvtveitelv	Kløvtveitvatn	1	N 60:58 E 05:18	1922 76	4.4	F	C25 D75 (2)	A 5 C 75 L 20	50	4800	0.63
622-11	Loelv	Loelv	Lovatn	1	N 61:51 E 06:53	1901 76	231	F	C15 D85	A 15 C 85	50 90	2300	15
640-0	Aura	Aura	Eikesdalsvatn	1	N 62:38 E 08:07	1902 74	1091	F20 D80	C10 D90	A 10 C 90	50 90	1500	41
661-0	Gaula	Gaula	Haga-bru	1	N 63:04 E 10:17	1908 76	3080	D	C45 D55	A 40 C 55 D 5	50 90	1900	160
685-0	Argardselv	Argardselv	Øyungen	1	N 64:15 E 11:05	1917 76	235	D	C55 D45	A 55 C 45	50	1100	5.8
726-0	Strandvassa	Strandvassa	Stranda	1	N 67:32 E 14:53	1917 73	23	D50 F50	C60 D40	A 60 C 40	50	1750	1.1
756-0	Salangselv	Salangselv	Vassas	1	N 68:53 E 17:53	1914 76	580	D20 F80	C35 D65	A 35 C 65	50	1350	22
764-0	Altaelv	Altaelv	Stengelsen	1	N 69:52 E 23:18	1915 69	6173	D20 C80	C30 D70	A 30 C 70	80	450	76
775-0	Pasvikelv	Pasvikelv	Bjørnvatn	1	N 69:31 E 30:06	1911 72	18150	D10 C80 B10	C65 D35	A 65 C 35	80	400	170

(1) A should be considered here as A and B.

(2) L : lake

TABLE II : FLOODS CHARACTERISTICS

	FLOOD CHARACTERISTICS						DISCHARGE ESTIMATION					
Site number	Stream	Observ. site	Year	Date of the max	Maximal dism^3s^{-1}	Climatic origine	Condition disc est	Qual. of the sect	Precis. ±m^3s^{-1}	Anteced precip.	Depth mm	Duration days
1	2	3	4	5	6	7	8	9	10	11	12	13
374-0	Engeren	Engera	1934	05-07	117	2	A2C1	A1A	10			
			1967	05-27	112	2	A2C1	A1A	10			
			1966	05-20	102	2	A2C1	A1A	10			
395-0	Glomma	Langnes	1967	06-06	3540	2	A2C1	A1A	350			
			1966	05-26	3225	2	A2C1	A1A	320			
458-0	Snarumselv	Krøderen	1916	05-12	1100	2	A2C1	A1A	110			
			1927	06-30	1090	2	A2C1	A1A	110			
			1917	05-31	1040	2	A2C1	A1A	100			
518-11/12	Nidelv	Lunde Mølle	1953	11-04	1150	1	A2C1	A1A	110			
			1949	11-24	1130	1	A2C1	A1A	110			
560-11/12	Fedeelv	Refsti	1929	10-25	132	4	A2C1	A1A	13			
			1898	11-03	125	4	A2C1	A1A	12			
919-0	Hellelandselv	Gya	1957	12-20	128	4	A2C1	A1A	13			
			1963	10-11	128	4	A2C1	A1A	13			
603-0	Kløtveitelv	Kløtveitvatn	1975	09-25	2.82	4	A2C1	A1A	0.3			
			1953	10-11	2.82	4	A2C1	A1A	0.3			
			1923	09-11	2.49	4	A2C1	A1A	0.2			
622-11	Loelv	Lovatn	1941	07-14	145	2	A2C1	A1A	14			
			1901	07-25	133	2	A2C1	A1A	13			
640-0	Aura	Eikesdalsvatn	1923	07-13	495	2	A2C1	A1A	50			
			1905	06-22	410	2	A2C1	A1A	40			
661-0	Gaula	Haga bru	1940	08-24	2975 ?	1	A2C1	A1A	300			
			1944	06-10	1600	2	A2C1	A1A	160			
			1935	06-28	1570	2	A2C1	A1A	160			
			1934	05-06	1475	2	A2C1	A1A	150			
685-0	Argardselv	Øyungen	1932	01-28	520	4	A2C1	A1A	50			
			1953	03-25	335	4	A2C1	A1A	30			
726-0	Strandvassa	Stranda	1971	08-26	20.2	1	A2C1	A1A	2			
			1956	01-06	19.8	4	A2C1	A1A	2			
756-0	Salangselv	Vassas	1959	10-07	407	1	A2C1	A1A	40			
			1939	06-21	227	2	A2C1	A1A	20			
			1917	06-16	217	2	A2C1	A1A	20			
764-0	Altaelv	Stengelsen	1920	05-23	1350	2	A2C1	A1A	130			
			1917	06-18	1270	2	A2C1	A1A	125			
			1968	06-08	1190	2	A2C1	A1A	120			
775-0	Pasvikelv	Bjornvatn	1952	06-04	825	2	A2C1	A1A	80			
			1949	05-20	740	2	A2C1	A1A	70			
			1943	05-16	670	2	A2C1	A1A	60			

PAKISTAN

TABLE I : IDENTIFICATION OF OBSERVATION SITES AND CHARACTERISTICS OF BASINS

	OBSERVATIONS SITE							CHARACTERISTICS OF BASIN					
Site number	River basin	Stream	Observ. site		Coordinates Lat. Long.	Period	Area km^2	Slope	Soil	Cover	Regime	Mean precip. mm	Mean disc. m^{3}s-1
1	2	3	4	5	6	7	8	9	10	11	12	13	14
1	Indus	Indus	Attock	1	N 33:54 E 72:15	1868 1978	264000	F E D C			90 10		
2	Indus	Indus	Kotri	1	N 25:20 E 68:20	1901 1978	945000	F E D C B A			90 10 11		
3	Indus	Chenab	Marala	1	N 32:35 E 74:35	1925 78	34000	F E D C			90 10		
4	Indus	Chenab	Panjnad	1	N 29:20 E 71:01	1922 78	280000	F E D C B A			90 10 11		
5	Chenab	Jhelum	Mangla	1	N 32:55 E 73:40	1922 78	29000	F E D C			90 10		
6	Chenab	Ravi	Jassar	1	N 32:10 E 75:20	1948 78	(10000)	F E D			90 10		
7	Chenab	Sutlej	Suleimanki	1	N 30:20 E 73:45	1928 78	65000	F E D C B			90 10		

TABLE II : FLOODS CHARACTERISTICS

	FLOOD CHARACTERISTICS						DISCHARGE ESTIMATION					
Site number	Stream	Observ. site	Year	Date of the max	Maximal dis $m^3s{-}1$	Climatic origine	Condition disc est	Qual. of the sect	Precis. $\pm m^3s{-}1$	Anteced precip.	Depth mm.	Duration days.
1	2	3	4	5	6	7	8	9	10	11	12	13
1	Indus	Attock	1929		23200	4						
			1882		20900	4						
			1924		19500	4						
			1878		19100	4						
2	Indus	Kotri	1956		27800 (1)	4						
			1955		22400	4						
			1973		22200	4						
			1976		21650	4						
3	Chenab	Marala	1959		24600	4						
			1957		23200	4						
			1954		23150	4						
			1973		21760	4						
4	Chenab	Panjnad	1973		22700	4						
			1976		19900	4						
			1950		18400	4						
5	Jhelum	Mangla	1929		31100	4						
			1959		22600	4						
			1958		20400	4						
			1928		17000	4						
6	Ravi	Jassar	1955		19240	4						
			1957		9200	4						
			1966		9100	4						
7	Sutlej	Suleimanki	1955		16900	4						
			1947		10200	4						
			1950		9400	4						

(1) maximum observed at Guddu downstream of the Indus and Chenab junction : 33.280 $m^3s{-}1$ 1976.

PANAMA

TABLE I : IDENTIFICATION OF OBSERVATION SITES AND CHARACTERISTICS OF BASINS

	OBSERVATIONS SITE						CHARACTERISTICS OF BASIN						
Site number	River basin	Stream	Observ. site		Coordinates Lat. Long.	Period	Area km²	Slope	Soil	Cover	Regime	Mean precip. mm	Mean disc m³s-1
1	2	3	4	5	6	7	8	9	10	11	12	13	14
1	Chiriqui	Chiriqui	David	1	N 08:25 W 82:21	1955 80	1200	F E	C D	A30 D70	00	4030	129
2	Santa Maria	Santa Maria	San Francisco	1	N 08:13 W 80:58	1955 80	1200	E D	C D	D	00	3290	87.5
3	Grande	Grande	Rio Grande	1	N 08:26 W 80:30	1955 80	471	E	C	D	00	2200	20.9

PANAMA

TABLE II : FLOODS CHARACTERISTICS

	FLOOD CHARACTERISTICS							DISCHARGE ESTIMATION				
Site number	Stream	Observ. site	Year	Date of the max	Maximal dis m³s-1	Climatic origine	Condition disc est	Qual. of the sect	Precis. ±m³s-1	Anteced precip.	Depth mm	Duration days
1	2	3	4	5	6	7	8	9	10	11	12	13
1	Chiriqui	David	1974 1970	10-02 04-09	2980 2310	1			300 230			
2	Santa Maria	San Francisco	1955	11-13	3080	1			320			
3	Grande	Rio Grande	1960	11-21	1900	1			350			

PHILIPPINES

TABLE I : IDENTIFICATION OF OBSERVATION SITES AND CHARACTERISTICS OF BASINS

| | | OBSERVATIONS SITE | | | | | | CHARACTERISTICS OF BASIN | | | | | | |
Site number	River basin	Stream	Observ. site		Coordinates Lat. Long.		Period	Area km²	Slope	Soil	Cover	Regime	Mean precip. mm	Mean disc. m³s-1
1	2	3	4	5		6	7	8	9	10	11	12	13	14
LUSON ISLAND														
1		Agno	Carmen Rosales	1	N 15:53	E 120:35	1945 76	2210				00	>3000	125
2	Pampanga	Pampanga	San Augustin	1	N 15:10	E 120:46	1944 75	6490				00	>2000	228
3	Cagayan	Cagayan	Echague Isabella	1	N 16:36	E 121:41	1958 74	4245				00	>3000	265

PHILIPPINES

TABLE II : FLOODS CHARACTERISTICS

| | | FLOOD CHARACTERISTICS | | | | | | DISCHARGE ESTIMATION | | | | |
Site number	Stream	Observ. site	Year	Date of the max	Maximal dis m³s-1	Climatic origine	Condition disc est	Qual. of the sect	Precis. ±m³s-1	Anteced precip.	Depth mm.	Duration days.
1	2	3	4	5	6	7	8	9	10	11	12	13
LUSON ISLAND												
1	Agno	Carmen Rosales	1946		4330	1						
2	Pampanga	San Augustin	1973		2764	1						
3	Cagayan	Echague Isabella	1959		17550	1						

TABLEAU I : IDENTIFICATION DES POINTS D'OBSERVATIONS ET CARACTERISTIQUES DES BASSINS

	POINT D'OBSERVATION							CARACTERISTIQUES DU BASSIN						
N° du point	Bassin fluvial	Rivière	Point d'observ.		Coordonnées Lat. Long.	Période	Surface km²	Relief	Sol	Végét.	Régime	Pluie moyenne mm	Module m³s-1
1	2	3	4	5	6	7	8	9	10	11	12	13	14
1	Wisla (Vistule)	Wisla	Tyniec	1	N 50:01 E 19:48	1951 80	7530	F E D			90 61	885	88.5
2	Wisla	Skawa	Wadowice	1	N 50:02 E 19:27	1921 80	835	F E D			90 61	1005	11.5
3	Wisla	Dunajec	Nowy Sacz	1	N 49:38 E 20:43	1921 80	4340	F E D			90 61	875	61.5
4	Wisla	San	Radomys'l	1	N 50:41 E 21:56	1921 80	16800	E D C			61	720	134
5	Wisla	Wieprz	Lubartow	1	N 51:30 E 22:39	1951 80	6360	C B			61	585	21.8
6	Wisla	Pilica	Bialobrezegi	1	N 51:40 E 20:57	1951 80	8670	C B			61	625	46
7	Wisla	Bug	Wyszkow	1	N 52:35 E 21:27	1921 80	39100	C B A			61	555	137
8	Bug	Liwiec	Lochow	1	N 52:31 E 21:41	1931 80	2460	C B			61	555	10.2
9	Wisla	Wisla	Tczew	1	N 54:06 E 18:48	1921 80	194000				61	611	1000
10	Odra (Oder)	Nysa Klodzka	Skorogoszcz	1	N 50:49 E 17:42	1921 80	4535	F E D			90 61	725	40.5
11	Odra	Warta	Poznan	1	N 52:25 E 16:57	1951 80	39100	C B A			61	560	135
12	Warta	Prosna	Boguslac	1	N 51:54 E 17:58	1951 80	4300	B A			61	545	14.5
13	Odra	Bobr	Szprotawa	1	N 51:33 E 15:32	1948 80	2880	F E D			90 61	722	25.5
14	Odra	Odra	Gozdowice	1	N 52:46 E 14:20	1921 80	110000				61	600	510

TABLEAU II : CARACTERISTIQUES DES CRUES

	CARACTERISTIQUES DE LA CRUE								EVALUATION DES DEBITS			
N° du point	Rivière	Point d'observ.	Année	Date du maximum	Débit max m³s-1	Origine	Base et mode éval	Qual. de la séch	Précis. ±m³s-1	Anteced	Hauteur	Durée jours
1	2	3	4	5	6	7	8	9	10	11	12	13
1	Wisła	Tyniec	1970	07-19	2260	1	A2C4	B1A	230			
			1972	08-23	1980	1			200			
2	Skawa	Wadowice	1958	06-29	935	1	A1C4/5	C1B	190			
			1980	08-15	685	1			140			
3	Dunajec	Nowy Sacz	1934	07-17	3300	1		B1A				
			1958	06-30	3300	1		B1A				
			1970	07-19	2680	1	A1B4	B2B	270			
4	San	Radomys'l	1924	03-29	3340 (1)	2		B1A				
			1947	03-18	2790	2		B1A				
			1940	03-27	2720	2		B1A				
5	Wieprz	Lubartow	1964	04-06	465	2		B1A				
			1956	04-03	250	2						
			1979	03-18	245	2	A2B4	B1A	25			
6	Pilica	Białobrezegi	1967	02-08	470	2		B1A	50			
			1953	02-01	465	2		B1A	50			
7	Bug	Wyszkow	1979	03-28	2400	2	A2B4	B1A	240			
			1924	04-06	1500	2	A2B4	B1A	150			
			1958	04-17	1430	2		B1A	150			
8	Liwiec	Łochow	1979	03-25	320	2	A2C4	B1A	32			
			1953	02-24	260	2			25			
9	Wisła	Tczew	1924	04-01	9550 (2)	2						
			1940	04-02	8920	2						
			1962	06-13	7840	1						
			1979	04-01	7020	2	A2B4	B1A	700			
10	Nysa Kłodza	Skorogoszcz	1938	09-03	955	2	A1B4/5	B1A	95			
			1965	06-01	590	2	A1B4/5	B1A	59			
11	Warta	Poznan	1979	03-18	830	2	A1B4	B1A	85			
			1953	02-06	705	2			70			
12	Prosna	Bogusłav	1953	01-31	237	2						
			1979	03-11	235	2	A2B4	B1A	80			
13	Bobr	Szprotawa	1977	08-04	565	1	A2C4/5	B1A	56			
			1958	07-07	450	1	A2C4/5	B1A	45			
14	Odra	Gozdowice	1940	03-22	3720	2		B1A				
			1931	11-08	2660	1		B1A				
			1926	06-26	2450	1		B1A				

(1) la très forte crue de 1867 surestimée à l'origine a été réévaluée récemment,
le débit est inférieur à celui de la crue de 1924.

(2) la très forte crue de 1855 a été longtemps surestimée, elle a été réévaluée récemment,
le débit est inférieur à celui de la crue de 1924.

TABLEAU I : IDENTIFICATION DES POINTS D'OBSERVATIONS ET CARACTERISTIQUES DES BASSINS

	POINT D'OBSERVATION							CARACTERISTIQUES DU BASSIN					
N° du point	Bassin fluvial	Rivière	Point d'observ.		Coordonnées Lat. Long.	Période	Surface km²	Relief	Sol	Végét	Régime	Pluie moyenne mm	Module m³s-1
1	2	3	4	5	6	7	8	9	10	11	12	13	14
1	Douro	Tamega	P. Canaveses	1	N 41:12 W 08:10	1955 78	3180				$^{30}/_{50}$	1100	70
2	Douro	Paiva	Castro Daire	1	N 40:53 W 07:56	1945 78	286				$^{30}/_{50}$	1100	7.0
3	Vouga	Vouga	Pedre	1	N 40:45 W 08:18	1962 76	928				$^{30}/_{50}$	1000	20
4	Mondego	Mondego	P. de Tabua	1	N 40:22 W 08:03	1969 78	1549				$^{30}/_{50}$	1200	30
5	Tejo	Tejo	Vila Velha Da Rodao	1	N 39:42 W 08:20	67 ans	59170	F25 E35 D40	B20 C50 D30	B40 C20 D40	$^{30}/_{50}$	540	300
6	Sado	Sado	Gamitinha	1	N 38:05 W 08:24	1934 78	2720				30	620	9
7	Guadiana	Ardila	Ardila	1	N 38:10 W 07:27	1945 78	3745				30	570	13.5
8	Guadiana	Odeleire	M. Fortes	1	N 37:21 W 07:37	1961 78	290				30	860	3.0
9	Arade	Odelouca	M. Pachecos	1	N 37:18 W 08:27	1962 78	386				30	780	4.0

TABLEAU II : CARACTERISTIQUES DES CRUES

	CARACTERISTIQUES DE LA CRUE								EVALUATION DES DEBITS			
N° du point	Rivière	Point d'observ.	Année	Date du maximum	Débit max dism³s-1	Origine	Base et mode éval	Qual. of la séch	Précis. ±m³s-1	Anteced	Hauteur	Durée jours
1	2	3	4	5	6	7	8	9	10	11	12	13
1	Tamega	P. Cavaneses	1961/62		1960	1	A1B2	A1A	100	2		
2	Paiva	Castro Daire	1965/66		320	1	A1B2	A1A	30	2		
3	Vouga	Pedre	1976/77		1040	1	A1B2	A1A	100	2		
4	Mondego	P. de Tabua	1978/79		484	1	A1B2	A1A	50	2		
5	Tejo	Vila Velha Da Rodao	1876 (1)	12-07	12000	1	A1B2	A1A	1000			
6	Sado	Gamitinha	1949/50		2010	1	A1B2	A1A	150	2		
7	Ardila	Ardila	1963	02-16	1660	1	A1B2	A1A	100	2		
8	Odeleire	M. Fortes	1969	01-09	850	1	A1B2	A1A	100	2		
9	Odelouca	P. Pachecos	1968	03-04	444	1	A1B2	A1A	50	2		

(1) L'importance de la régularisation rend estrêmement difficile l'estimation des valeurs maximales récentes.

PUERTO RICO/PORTO RICO (UNITED STATES OF AMERICA/ETATS UNIS D'AMERIQUE)

TABLE I : IDENTIFICATION OF OBSERVATION SITES AND CHARACTERISTICS OF BASINS

	OBSERVATIONS SITE						CHARACTERISTICS OF BASIN						
Site number	River basin	Stream	Observ. site	Coordinates Lat.	Long.	Period	Area km²	Slope	Soil	Cover	Regime	Mean precip. mm	Mean disc. m³s-1
1	2	3	4	5	6	7	8	9	10	11	12	13	14
50046000	La Plata	La Plata	Toa Alta	1	N 18:24 W 66:15	1960 67 1969 71 1975 1979	520			A	00		8.4
50121000	Tallaboa	Tallaboa	Penuelas	1	N 18:03 S 66:43	1959 71	62.7						

PUERTO RICO/PORTO RICO (UNITED STATES OF AMERICA/ETATS UNIS D'AMERIQUE)

TABLE II : FLOODS CHARACTERISTICS

	FLOOD CHARACTERISTICS						DISCHARGE ESTIMATION					
Site number	Stream	Observ. site	Year	Date of the max	Maximal discm³s-1	Climatic origine	Condition disc est	Qual. of the sect	Precis. ±m³s-1	Anteced precip.	Depth mm.	Duration days.
1	2	3	4	5	6	7	8	9	10	11	12	13
50046000	La Plata	Toa Alta	1960 1970	09-06 10- 9	2700 2220	1 1	A1C1					
50121000	Tallaboa	Penuelas	1963 1961	08-27	413 285	1 1						

REPUBLIC OF CAPO VERDE ISLANDS/REPUBLIQUE DES ILES DU CAP VERT

TABLEAU I : IDENTIFICATION DES POINTS D'OBSERVATIONS ET CARACTERISTIQUES DES BASSINS

	POINT D'OBSERVATION							CARACTERISTIQUES DU BASSIN						
N° du point	Bassin fluvial	Rivière	Point d'observ.		Coordonnées Lat. Long.	Période	Surface km²	Relief	Sol	Végét	Régime	Pluie moyenne mm	Module m³s-1
1	2	3	4	5	6	7	8	9	10	11	12	13	14
	Ribeira Brava	Ribeira Brava	Vila de Ribeira Brava (Ile de Sao-Nicolao)	1	N 16:37 W 24:18	78 82	6.7	F	C	D50 C50	11 30	350	

REPUBLIC OF CAPO VERDE ISLANDS/REPUBLIQUE DES ILES DU CAP VERT

TABLEAU II : CARACTERISTIQUES DES CRUES

	CARACTERISTIQUES DE LA CRUE						EVALUATION DES DEBITS					
N° du point	Rivière	Point d'observ.	Année	Date du maximum	Débit max m³s-1	Origine	Base et mode éval	Qual. de la séch	Précis. ±m³s-1	Anteced	Hauteur	Durée jours
1	2	3	4	5	6	7	8	9	10	11	12	13
	Ribeira Brava	Vila de Ribeira Brava	1978	09-26	253	1	A1D5	C1B	+10 -50	3	240	0.07
			81	09-13	142	1	A1A3	C1B	14	3	128	1

TABLE I : IDENTIFICATION OF OBSERVATION SITES AND CHARACTERISTICS OF BASINS

OBSERVATIONS SITE							CHARACTERISTICS OF BASIN						
Site number	River basin	Stream	Observ. site		Coordinates Lat. Long.	Period	Area km²	Slope	Soil	Cover	Regime	Mean precip. mm	Mean disc. m³s-1
1	2	3	4	5	6	7	8	9	10	11	12	13	14
1010495	Han	Han	Goan 1	1	N 37:32 E 127:17	1917 1947	23880	F E D	Regulation begin in 1943 Regulated in 1973		60 40	1250	570
1010492 493	Han	Han	Goan 2 3	1	N 37:32 E 127:16	1954 1973	23880	F E D			60 40	1250	570
1010450	Han	Han	Indogyo Bridge	2	N 37:31 E 126:58	1918 1940 1947 48 1952 76	25050	F E D		d°	60 40	1250	(570)
3030410	Geum	Geum	Gongju	1	N 36:28 E 127:08	1917 40 1952 76	7125	F E D			40	1200	150
3010470	Geum	Geum	Gyuam	1	N 36:16 E 126:54	1916 1940 1954 1973	8275	F E D			40	1250	
2040436	Nakdong	Nakdong	Waegwan	1	N 36:00 E 128:24	1916 1940 1953 1976	11075	F E	Regulated since 1976		40	975	
2010490	Nakdong	Nakdong	Jindong	1	N 35:23 E 128:29	1924 40 1954 76	20310	F E D	Regulated since 1970		40	1050	

TABLE II : FLOODS CHARACTERISTICS

	FLOOD CHARACTERISTICS							DISCHARGE ESTIMATION				
Site number	Stream	Observ. site	Year	Date of the max	Maximal discm³s-1	Climatic origine	Condition disc est	Qual. of the sect	Precis. ±m³s-1	Anteced precip.	Depth mm.	Duration days.
1	2	3	4	5	6	7	8	9	10	11	12	13
1010495	Han	Goan 1	1925	07-18	37000	1	A2B/C1/4		3000			
			1936	08-12	25500	1	A2B1					
1010492 493	Han	Goan 2,3	1972 1965	08-19 07-16	30000 27000	1 1	A2B1 A1B1	A1A	3000			
1010450	Han	Indogyo Bridge	1925 1972 1965 1966	07-18 08-19 07-16 07-26	34400 30000 26000 25900	1 1 1 1	A2B/C1 A1B1 A1B1 A1B1	B1A	3000 3000 2000 2000			
3030410	Geum	Gongju	1934 1958 1925	07-24 07-05 07-13	9770 8510 8030	1 1 1	A2C3 A2C3 A2C3	B1A	1500 1200 1000			
3010470	Geum	Gyuam	1969 1958 1971	08-08 07-06 07-27	10800 8530 7800	1 1 1	A1 A1 A1	B1/2A	1200 1000 800			
2040436	Nakdong	Waegwan	1920 1934 1921	07-21 07-24 07-12	11520 9740 9290	1 1 1	A2C1 A2C1 A2C1	B1A	1000 1000 900			
2010490	Nakdong	Jindong	1936 1934	08-29 07-25	13070 >12600	1 1	A2C3 A2C3	B1/2B				

REUNION ISLAND/ILE DE LA REUNION (FRANCE)

TABLEAU I : IDENTIFICATION DES POINTS D'OBSERVATIONS ET CARACTERISTIQUES DES BASSINS

	POINT D'OBSERVATION						CARACTERISTIQUES DU BASSIN						
N° du point	Bassin fluvial	Rivière	Point d'observ.		Coordonnées Lat. Long.	Période	Surface km²	Relief	Sol	Végét.	Régime	Pluie moyenne mm	Module m³s-1
1	2	3	4	5	6	7	8	9	10	11	12	13	14
21-01-05	Roches	Roches	Grand Bras (Abondance)	1	S E 21:01 55:40	15 ans	23.8	F	C	A	00	5000	3.5
04-01-09	Marsouins	Marsouins	Gingembre (Takamaka)	1	S E 21:05 55:37	26 ans	27.5	F	B	A60 B40	00	4500	4.5
22-01-05	Langevin	Langevin	Passerelle	1	S E 21:20 55:39	30 ans	36	F	B	B75 D15 E10	00	3500	2.5
1	Galets	Galets	Prise d'eau Canal Savannah	3	S E 21:03 55:18		105	F	B		00		

REUNION ISLAND/ILE DE LA REUNION (FRANCE)

TABLEAU II : CARACTERISTIQUES DES CRUES

	CARACTERISTIQUES DE LA CRUE						EVALUATION DES DEBITS					
N° du point	Rivière	Point d'observ.	Année	Date du maximum	Débit max m³s-1	Origine	Base et mode éval	Qual. de la séch	Précis. ±m³s-1	Anteced	Hauteur	Durée jours
1	2	3	4	5	6	7	8	9	10	11	12	13
21-01-05	Roches	Grand Bras	1952	03-18	750	1	B4D4	A1C	100			
			1980	01-27	570	1	A1D4	A1C	75			
04-01-09	Marsouins	Gingembre	1948	01-27	600	1	B4D4	A1C	100			
			1980	01-27	590	1	A1D4	A1B	50			
			1952	03-18	550	1	B4D4	A1C	100			
22-01-05	Langevin	Passerelle	1944	04	550	1	C5D4	A1B	75			
			1960	01-19	400	1	B4D4	A1B	50			
			1952	03-18	200	1	B4D4	A1B	25			
1	Galets	Prise d'eau Canal Savannah	1958	03-19	1800	1	B5D4	C1B	300	2	2033	2

TABLE I : IDENTIFICATION OF OBSERVATION SITES AND CHARACTERISTICS OF BASINS

	OBSERVATIONS SITE							CHARACTERISTICS OF BASIN						
Site number	River basin	Stream	Observ. site		Coordinates Lat. Long.		Period	Area km²	Slope	Soil	Cover	Regime	Mean precip. mm	Mean disc. m³s−1
1	2	3	4	5	6		7	8	9	10	11	12	13	14
1	Dunarea (Danube)	Someş	Satu Mare	1	N 47:48	E 22:53 77	1925	15200	F E		A45 C40 D15	90 70	770	114
2	Dunarea	Mureş	Tg Mureş	1	N 46:32	E 24:35 77	1950	4050	F E		A60 C40	90 70	810	33.5
3	Dunarea	Tirnava Mare	Odorhei	1	N 46:17	E 25:17 77	1956	657	F E		A60 C40	90 70	815	5.45
4	Dunarea	Tirnava Mare	Topa	1	N 46:15	E 25 77	1955	1670	F E		A60 C40	90 70	730	8.1
5	Dunarea	Laslea	Laslea	1	N 46:10	E 24:30 77	1964	83	E D		A35 D15 C50	70	650	0.395
6	Dunarea	Mureş	Arad	1	N 45:14	E 20:11 77	1925	27600	F E D C		A37 D53 C10	90 70	730	154
7	Dunarea	Dunarea	Orşova	1	N 44:43	E 22:24 77	1834	575000	F E D C B A			90 70	881	6370
8	Dunarea	Jiu	Cîmpum lui Neag	1	N 45:20	E 23:04 77	1957	140	F		A70 C30	90 70	1080	3.42
9	Dunarea	Jiu	Podari	1	N 44:30	E 23:32 77	1950	9240	F E D C B		A40 D40 C20	90 30	790	86.5
10	Dunarea	Argeş	Budeşti	1	N 44:10	E 26:27 77	1950	9370	F E D C B		A35 D35 C30	90 30	671	50.0
11	Dunarea	Ialomita	Coşereni	1	N 44:42	E 26:35 77	1950	6470	F E D C B		A40 C20 D40	90 30	710	36.0
12	Dunarea	Buzău	Nehoiu	1	N 45:23	E 26:17 77	1949	1570	F E D		A80 C20	90 30	840	19.2

TABLE I : IDENTIFICATION OF OBSERVATION SITES AND CHARACTERISTICS OF BASINS

	OBSERVATIONS SITE							CHARACTERISTICS OF BASIN					
Site number	River basin	Stream	Observ. site		Coordinates Lat. Long.	Period	Area km²	Slope	Soil	Cover	Regime	Mean precip. mm	Mean disc. m³s-1
1	2	3	4	5	6	7	8	9	10	11	12	13	14
13	Dunarea	Siret	Lungoci	1	N E 45:33 27:30	1951 77	36500	F E D B C A		A45 C15 D40	90 30	660	152
14		Iris	Cocargea	1	N E 44:08 28:01	1960 77	10.5	A		C30 D70	30	400	0.007

TABLE II : FLOODS CHARACTERISTICS

	FLOOD CHARACTERISTICS						DISCHARGE ESTIMATION					
Site number	Stream	Observ. site	Year	Date of the max	Maximal $discm^3s^{-1}$	Climatic origine	Condition disc est	Qual. of the sect	Precis. $\pm m^3s^{-1}$	Anteced precip.	Depth mm.	Duration days.
1	2	3	4	5	6	7	8	9	10	11	12	13
1	Someş	Satu Mare	1970	05-15	3340	1				3	67.5	1
			1940	03-19	2600	2						
			1932	04-07	2350	2						
2	Mureş	Tg. Mureş	1970	05-13	1210	1				3	53	1
			1958	02-17	565	2						
3	Tirnava Mare	Odorhei	1970	05-13	305	1				3	50	1
			1956	04-26	140	1						
4	Tirnava Mare	Topa	1970	05-14	700	1				3	56.8	1
			1956	04-25	451	1						
5	Laslea	Laslea	1967	04-01	22.7	1				2	23.4	1
6	Mureş	Arad	1970	05-18	2320	1				3	35	1
			1932	04-07	2150	2						
7	Dunarea (Danube)	Orşova	1895	04-17	15900	2						
			1888	05-17	15500	2						
			1897	06-07	15400	2						
			1940	04-13	15100	2						
8	Jiu	Cîmpul lui Neag	1966	07-27	237	1						
			1961	11-07	210	1				1	40	1
9	Jiu	Podari	1972	10-11	2000	1				3	35.6	1
			1953	01-09	1500	1						
10	Argeş	Budeşti	1972	10-12	1540	1				2	70	1
			1956	04-05	900	2						
11	Ialomita	Coşereni	1972	10-06	1170	1					47.4	1
			1971	05-08	939	1				2	68.5	1
12	Buzău	Nehoiu	1971	07-02	1320	1				3	70	1
			1969	07-13	1120	1						
13	Siret	Lungoci	1970	05-19	3190	1				3	31	1
			1969	07-18	2670	1				3	52	1
			1971	05-31	2550	1						
14	Iris	Cocargea	1972	07-20	97.5	1						

RWANDA

TABLEAU I : IDENTIFICATION DES POINTS D'OBSERVATIONS ET CARACTERISTIQUES DES BASSINS

	POINT D'OBSERVATION							CARACTERISTIQUES DU BASSIN					
N° du point	Bassin fluvial	Rivière	Point d'observ.	Lat.	Coordonnées Long.	Période	Surface km²	Relief	Sol	Végét	Regime	Pluie moyenne mm	Module m³s-1
1	2	3	4	5	6	7	8	9	10	11	12	13	14
180 204	Akagera	Nyabarongo (1)	Kigali	1	S 01:57	E 30:00	1955 74	8900	F E D C		A B C D	00	1400	73
180 104	Nil	Akagera	Rusumo	1	S 02:23	E 30:47	1955 74	30200	F E D C B		A B C D	00	1200	200

(1) La source du Nyabarongo est considérée comme la source du Nil.

RWANDA

TABLEAU II : CARACTERISTIQUES DES CRUES

	CARACTERISTIQUES DE LA CRUE						EVALUATION DES DEBITS					
N° du point	Rivière	Point d'observ.	Année	Date du maximum	Débit max m³s-1	Origine	Base et mode éval	Qual. de la séch	Précis. ±m³s-1	Anteced	Hauteur	Durée jours
1	2	3	4	5	6	7	8	9	10	11	12	13
180 204	Nyabarongo	Kigali	1963	05-	400	1	A2C2	B	50			
180 104	Akagera	Rusumo	1963 1964 1970	07-01 05-05 04-14	685 637 600	1 1 1	A1C2	A	70			

TABLEAU I : IDENTIFICATION DES POINTS D'OBSERVATIONS ET CARACTERISTIQUES DES BASSINS

	POINT D'OBSERVATION						CARACTERISTIQUES DU BASSIN						
N° du point	Bassin fluvial	Rivière	Point d'observ.		Coordonnées Lat. Long.	Période	Surface km²	Relief	Sol	Végét.	Régime	Pluie moyenne mm	Module m³s-1
1	2	3	4	5	6	7	8	9	10	11	12	13	14
26 01 03	Sénégal	Sénégal	Bakel	1	N 14:54 W 12:27	1903 80	218000	C10 B20 A70	C	B40 C60	11 10	400 1600	730
26 16 09	Sénégal	Falémé	Kidira	1	N 14:27 W 12:13	1930 42 1951 78	28900	C20 B30 A50	C	B65 C35	11 10	800 1500	180
1	Gambie	Gambie	Kédougou	1	N 12:33 W 12:11	1970 80	7550	E 5 D10 C40 B45	C	B	10 11	1300 1700	120
2	Gambie	Gambie	Goulombo	1	N 13:28 W 13:44	1953 78	42000	C20 B30 A50	C	B	10 11	1000 1700	300
3	Casamance	Casamance	Kolda	1	N 12:53 W 14:56	1967 78	3700	B	B	B80 D20	10 11	1100 1300	4.
4	Rio Geba	Kayanga	Pont de Niapo	1	N 12:51 W 14:04	1962 1967 69 1976 78	1755	B	B	B	10 11	1100 1300	2.
5	Panetior	Panetior	Sebikotane	4	N 17:08 W 14:44	1962	93.2	C	B50 C50	C70 D30	11	625	0.126

SENEGAL

TABLEAU II: CARACTERISTIQUES DES CRUES

			CARACTERISTIQUES DE LA CRUE						EVALUATION DES DEBITS			
N° du point	Rivière	Point d'observ.	Année	Date du maximum	Débit max m³s-1	Origine	Base et mode éval	Qual. de la séch	Précis. ±m³s-1	Anteced	Hauteur mm	Durée jours
1	2	3	4	5	6	7	8	9	10	11	12	13
26 01 03	Sénégal	Bakel	1906	09-15	9340	1	A2B1	A2B	500			
			1922	09-25	9070	1	A2B1	A2B	450			
			1958	08-29	8170	1	A1B1	A2B	400			
			1950	09-06	7630	1	A1B1	A2B	300			
26 16 09	Falémé	Kidira	1961	09-08	3120	1	A1B1	A1A	100	3	300	12
			1964	09-07	2860	1	A1B1	A1A	100	3	130	5
1	Gambie	Kédougou	1970	08-09	1131	1	A1B1	A1B	80			
			1975	09-20	1020	1	A1B1	A1B	60			
2	Gambie	Goulombo	1961	09-18	2160	1	A3B/C1	A1B	200			
			1964	10-07	2060	1	A3B/C1	A1B	200			
3	Casamance	Kolda	1969	09-05	116	1	A1C1	B2B		3	219	3
4	Kayanga	Pont de Niapo	1967	10-07	135	1	A1C1	A1B				
5	Panetior	Sebikotane	1962 (2)	08-26	41.3	1	A1B1	A1A		3 (1)	104	1

(1) 96.8 la veille.

(2) Période de retour de l'ordre de 10 ans.

SIERRA LEONE

TABLE I : IDENTIFICATION OF OBSERVATIONS SITES AND CHARACTERISTICS OF BASINS

	OBSERVATIONS SITE						CHARACTERISTICS OF BASIN						
Site number	River basin	Stream	Observ. site		Coordinates Lat. Long.	Period	Area km²	Slope	Soil	Cover	Regime	Mean precip. mm	Mean disc. m³s-1
1	2	3	4	5	6	7	8	9	10	11	12	13	14
R5	Rokel or Seli	Seli	Badala	2	N 09:19 W 11:32		2525	D C		C	00		1.2 (1)
R6 M10	Rokel or Seli	Seli	Bumbuna	1	N 09:02 W 11:45		3990	D C		B	00		1.5 (1)
R9	Jong	Pampana	Old Mototoka Bridge	1	N 08:40 W 11:52		2410	C		B	00		0.5 (1)
R13	Sewa	Sewa	Sewa Bridge	1	N 08:34 W 11:16		6870	C		A	00		4.8 (1)
R15	Sewa	Bundoyo	Palima	1	N 08:06 W 11:19		361	C		B	00		0.24 (1)
R16	Sewa	Maboa	Dodo	1	N 08:09 W 11:09		57	A		B	00		0.07 (1)
R17	Moa	Moa	Moa Bridge	1	N 07:49 W 11:10		1750	C		A	00		9.6 (1)

(1) perhaps underestimated.

SIERRA LEONE

TABLE II : FLOODS CHARACTERISTICS

	FLOODS CHARACTERISTICS							DISCHARGE ESTIMATION				
Site number	Stream	Observ. site	Year	Date of the max	Maximal discm³s-1	Climatic origine	Condition disc est	Qual. of the sect	Precis. ±m³s-1	Anteced precip.	Depth mm.	Duration days.
1	2	3	4	5	6	7	8	9	10	11	12	13
R5	Seli	Badala	1974	10-03	503	1	A1B2					
R6	Seli	Bumbuna	1970	09-03	1164	1	A1B2					
R9	Pampana	Old Mototoka Bridge	1974	08-25	511	1	A1B2					
R13	Sewa	Sewa Bridge	1974	10-06	730	1	A2B2					
R15	Bundoyo	Palima	1974	10-04	160	1	A1B2					
R16	Maboa	Dodo	1975	09-21	16.7	1	A1B2					
R17	Moa	Moa Bridge	1974	10-07	2942	1	A1B2					

SOCIALIST REPUBLIC OF VIETNAM/RÉPUBLIQUE SOCIALISTE DU VIETNAM

TABLE I : IDENTIFICATION OF OBSERVATION SITES AND CHARACTERISTICS OF BASINS

	OBSERVATIONS SITE							CHARACTERISTICS OF BASIN					
Site number	River basin	Stream	Observ. site	Coordinates Lat. Long.		Period	Area km²	Slope	Soil	Cover	Regime	Mean precip. mm	Mean disc. m³s-1
1	2	3	4	5	6	7	8	9	10	11	12	13	14
1	Mékong	Mékong	My Thuan 1	N 10:14	E 105:54	1960 78	Distributary 1						
2	Mékong	Bassac	Chan Doc 1	N 10:43	E 105:07	1960 78	Distributary 2						
3	Dong Haï	Da Nhim	Dran 1	N 11:57	E 108:35	1925 45	752	F E D	C	B C D	10 90	1850	23
4	Song Koï	Song Koï	Vietri 1	N 21:13	E 105:18		113000	F E D C			10 90		

SOCIALIST REPUBLIC OF VIETNAM/RÉPUBLIQUE SOCIALISTE DU VIETNAM

TABLE II : FLOODS CHARACTERISTICS

	FLOOD CHARACTERISTICS						DISCHARGE ESTIMATION					
Site number	Stream	Observ. site	Year	Date of the max	Maximal discm³s-1	Climatic origine	Condition disc est	Qual. of the sect	Precis. ±m³s-1	Anteced precip.	Depth mm.	Duration days.
1	2	3	4	5	6	7	8	9	10	11	12	13
1	Mékong	My Thuan	1961	10-21	23000	1	A1B1	B2B	2500	3	500	31
2	Bassac	Chan Doc	1961	10-15	8150	1	A1B1	B2B	1000	3	500	31
3	Da Nhim	Dran	1932	05-04	3500	1	A2C1	B1B	500			
4	Song Koï	Vietri	1945		32500	1	XOXO	XOX	2500			

Information for 1 and 2 kindly transmitted by the Committee for coordination of investigations of the lower Mekong basin.

TABLE I : IDENTIFICATION OF OBSERVATION SITES AND CHARACTERISTICS OF BASINS

	OBSERVATIONS SITE						CHARACTERISTICS OF BASIN						
Site number	River basin	Stream	Observ. site		Coordinates Lat. Long.	Period	Area km²	Slope	Soil	Cover	Regime	Mean precip. mm	Mean disc. m³s-1
1	2	3	4	5	6	7	8	9	10	11	12	13	14
A2	Pienaars	Waterkloof Spruit	Pretoria Country Club	3	S 25:46 E 28:13	45 years	5	E	B 5 C95	A60 C30 E10	11	780	
A2	Krokodil	Pienaars	Road N4	3	S 25:45 E 28:22	75 years	243	C	B10 C90	A10 C30 D50 E10	11	750	
A2M06	Krokodil	Pienaars	Klipdrift	1	S 25:23 E 28:19	1905 76	1030	C	C20 D80	B20 C40 D25 E15	11	700	1.04
B6M01	Olifants	Blyde	Willemsoord	1	S 24:40 E 30:48	1910 76	518	C	A30 B20 C20 D30	A40 B50 D10	40	1240	6.23
B7M02	Olifants	Ngwabitsi	Tours	1	S 24:05 E 30:16	1949 73	58	E	B20 C60 D20	A10 B60 C20 D 5 E 5	11	830	0.50
C1M01	Orange	Vaal	Standerton	1	S 26:57 E 29:15	1905 76	8185	A B C	C70 D30	B10 C60 D30	11	780	17.15
C3M03	Vaal	Harts	Taung	1	S 27:34 E 24:45	1923 76	10990	C B	A10 B20 C50 D20	C60 D25 E15	11	540	1.15
D2M01	Orange	Caledon	Jammersdrift	1	S 29:43 E 26:59	1922 72	13420	E D C B	B30 C40 D30	B10 C50 D20 E20	11	793	39.9
D1M01	Orange	Stormberg Spruit	Diepkloof	1	S 31:00 E 26:20	1912 80	2400	C B	D	B30 C40 E30	11	485	
D3M03	Orange	Orange	Doring bult outspan Vluytjes Kraal	1 1	S 29:48 E 24:26	1915 48 1948 76	93280	E D C B	B55 C40 D 5	B 5 C50 D15 E30	11	627	242.5
D6	Brak	Meltonwold Spruit	Aspeling Dam	3	S 31:26 E 22:46		127	C	D	C10 D10 E80	11	230	
D6R02	Orange	Ongers	Smartt Dam Syndicate	1	S 30:37 E 23:18	1922 47 1965 74	13390	C B	D	B25 D20 E55	11	260	

TABLE I : IDENTIFICATION OF OBSERVATIONS SITES AND CHARACTERISTICS OF BASINS

	OBSERVATIONS SITE				Coordinates		Period	Area km²	Slope	Soil	Cover	Regime	Mean precip. mm	Mean disc. m³s-1
Site number	River basin	Stream	Observ. site		Lat.	Long.								
1	2	3	4	5	6		7	8	9	10	11	12	13	14
D7M08	Orange	Orange	Buchuberg	1	S 29:02	E 22:11	1925 1932 80	342970	E D C B A	B20 C25 D55	C25 D45 E30	11	540	
E2M06	Olifants	Kruis	Nooit Gedacht	1	S 33:09	E 19:22	1929 70	40	D	C10 D90	A 5 B35 C45 D10 E 5	30	815	0.212
E2M02	Olifants	Doring	Aspoort	1	S 32:30	E 19:32	1923 76	6905	D C	C10 D90	B 5 C80 D 5 E10	11 30	220	9.2
G2M08	Eerste	Jonkershoek	Kleinplaas	1	S 33:59	E 18:57	1947 76	20	F	C40 D60	A40 C40 E20	30	2610	0.83
H4	Breeriver	Willem Nels	3 km from Robertson	3	S 33:47	E 19:52	80 years	32	F E			30	600	0.30
J1	Gouritz	Buffels	S A R Bridge at Laingsburg	3	S 33:12	E 20:51	80 years	3070	E D			30	180	1.00
J3M04	Gouritz	Olifants	Kromlaagte	1	S 33:29	E 23:01	1923 76	4305	D C	C15 D85	C70 D15 E15	30	255	0.56
L9R01	Gamtoos	Loerie	Loerie dam	3	S 33:52	E 25:02	14 years	147	D C			30	700	1.10
M2	Indian Ocean	Van Stadens	Van Stadens Pars	3	S 33:55	E 25:12	73 years	74				30	800	0.80
M2	Algoa Bay	Shark	Port Elizabeth	3	S 33:59	E 25:39	12 years	9	E	C50 D50	C60 E40	40	600	
N3	Sundays	Blyde	Near Pearston	3	S 32:28	E 25:14		130	C D	D	B10 C10 D20 E60	40	430	
Q1M01	Great Fish	Great Fish	Katkop	1	S 31:54	E 25:29	1918 73	9090	C D	B 5 C30 D65	B10 C60 D15 E15	40	370	1.18
Q3M04	Great Fish	Pauls	Spitzkop	1	S 32:02	E 25:31	1926 48 1973 80	873	C D	D	C90 E10	40	400	

TABLE I : IDENTIFICATION OF OBSERVATIONS SITES AND CHARACTERISTICS OF BASINS

	OBSERVATIONS SITE							CHARACTERISTICS OF BASIN					
Site number	River basin	Stream	Observ. site		Coordinates Lat. Long.	Period	Area km²	Slope	Soil	Cover	Regime	Mean precip. mm	Mean disc. m³s-1
1	2	3	4	5	6	7	8	9	10	11	12	13	14
S6M01	Great Kei	Kubusi	Stutter Heim	1	S 32:35 E 27:22	1947 74	91	D E	A10 C25 D65	A55 C10 D15 E15	90 40	990	0.46
T5M07	Mzimkulu	Mzimkulu	Umzimkulu	1	S 30:16 E 29:57	1931 76	3645	D C	B10 C50 D40	A20 C30 D40 E10	40 90	1030	31
U1M03	Mkomanzi	Mkomanzi	Mkomanzi Drift	1	S 30:11 E 30:46	1951 80	4375	D C	B60 C40	A10 B30 D50 E10	40 90	960	
V6M02	Tugela	Tugela	Tugela Ferry	1	S 28:45 E 30:26	1927 43 1946 67 1969 76	12860	F E D C	B10 C40 D50	B 5 C70 D20	90 40	920	88
V5M02	Tugela	Tugela	Mandini	1	S 29:10 E 31:24	1925 1956 80	28490	F E D C B	B15 C35 D50	A20 B20 C50 D10	90 40	960	
W3R01	Hluhluwe	Hluhluwe	Hluhluwe Dam	1	S 28:07 E 32:11	1963 1965 80	735	C B	B50 D50	B30 C15 D45 E15	40	860	
X1M01	Komati	Komati	Hoogenoeg	1	S 26:02 E 30:59	1909 76	5445	D C	B40 C50 D10	A10 C55 D35	40	915	18.5

TABLE II : FLOODS CHARACTERISTICS

	FLOOD CHARACTERISTICS						DISCHARGE ESTIMATION					
Site number	Stream	Observ. site	Year	Date of the max	Maximal discm³s-1	Climatic origine	Condition disc est	Qual. of the sect	Precis. ±m³s-1	Anteced precip.	Depth mm.	Duration days.
1	2	3	4	5	6	7	8	9	10	11	12	13
A2	Waterkloof Spruit	Pretoria Country Club	1935	12	141	1			U			
A2	Pienaars	Road N4	1978	01-28	1250	1	B4D6		375			
A2M06	Pienaars	Klipdrift	1914	11-26	1220 (1)	1	A1C1	A1B	360			
			1909	01-22	785	1	A1C1	A1B	250			
B6M01	Blyde	Willemsoord	1915	02-13	477 (1)	1	A1B1	A1B	100			
			1923	02-14	448	1	A1B1	A1B	100			
			1918	02-14	358	1	A1B1	A1B	90			
B7M02	Ngwabitsi	Tours	1956	02-17	530 (2)	1	A1C1	A1B	U			
			1953	02-23	198	1	A1C1	A1B	U			
C1M01	Vaal	Standerton	1911	01-12	2285	1	A1C1	A1B	200			
			1923	01-28	2060	1	A1C1	A1B	200			
			1975	02-15	1920	1	A1C1	A1B	200			
C3M03	Harts	Taung	1931	03-02	566 (3)	1	A1C1	A1B	60			
			1929	03-05	510	1	A1C1	A1B	50			
			1975	01-26	450	1	A1C1	A1B	45			
D2M01	Caledon	Jammersdrift	1934	01-03	3680 (3)	1	A1C1	A1B	370	3	37	
			1976	01-06	3680	1	A1C1	A1B	370			
			1923	02-14	2170	1	A1C1	A1B	220	3	109	
D1M01	Stormberg Spruit	Diepkloof	1925	03-22	2690	1	A1C1		U			
			1974	02-28	1685	1	A1D4		500			
D3M03	Orange	Doringbult Outspan	1925	03-24	11100 (2)	1	A1D4		2200			
			1967	02-03	8920	1	A1D4		1500			
			1934	01-05	6825	1	A1D4		1000			
D6	Meltonwold Spruit	Aspelingdam	1961	03-27	453	1			45			
D6R02	Ongers	Smart Syndicate Dam	1961	03-28	6940	1	A1D6		1000			
			1974	03-05	980	1	A1D6		150			
D7M08	Orange	Buchuberg	1925	03-26	16230	1	A1D4		3000			
			1974	03-06	9000	1	A1D4		2000			
			1934	01-06	7560	1	A1D4		1500			
E2M06	Kruis	Nooit Gedacht	1945	06-21	67	1	A1C1	A1B	7			
			1957	07-14	61		A1C1	A1B	6		91	
			1942	06-20	31		A1C1	A1B	3			
E2M02	Doring	Aspoort	1925	06-17	2125 (4)				U			
			1967	06-10	1700		A1C1		250	3	79	

(1) return period 140 years   (2) return period 60 years   (3) return period 100 years   (4) return period 85 years.

TABLE II : FLOODS CHARACTERISTICS

	FLOOD CHARACTERISTICS						DISCHARGE ESTIMATION					
Site number	Stream	Observ. site	Years	Date of the max	Maximal disc m³s-1	Climatic origine	Condition disc est	Qual. of the sect	Precis. ±m³s-1	Anteced precip.	Depth mm.	Duration days.
1	2	3	4	5	6	7	8	9	10	11	12	13
G2M08	Jonkershoek	Kleinplaas	1955	02-18	74 (5)	1	A1B1	A1B	7			
			1950	04-26	72	1	A1B1	A1B	6			
H4	Willem Nels	3 km from Roberston	1981	01-25	590	1	B2D4		180		240	3
J1	Buffels	S A R Bridge at Lainsburg	1981	01-25	5680	1	B2D6		570		162	3
J3M04	Olifants	Kromlaagte	1953	02-23	1060	1	A3C1	A1B	100			
			1956	03-16	975	1	A3C1	A1B	100			
			1961	03-28	827	1	A3C1	A1B	80	3	36	
L9R01	Loerie	Loerie Dam	1981	03-26	1750	1	A2E		510			
M2	Van Stadens		1981	03-26	1110	1	B2D4		110			
M2	Shark	Port Elisabeth	1968	09-01	218	1	B3D4		60			
N3	Blyde	Near Pearston	1922	01-11	1165	1	B3D4		360			
Q1M01	Great Fish	Katkop	1974	03-01	2640	1	A3D4		800			
			1950	05-18	1120	1	A3D4	A1B	300			
Q3M04	Pauls	Spitzkopf	1974	03	2500	1	A1D4		750			
			1976	03-21	285	1	A1C1		85			
			1955	02-04	280	1	A1B1		85			
S6M01	Kubusi	Stutter Heim	1948	04-19	129	1	A1B1		13	3	159	
			1953	10-22	67	1	A1B1		7	3	170	
T5M07	Mzimkulu	Umzimkulu	1959	05-18	3795		A3D4		1000	3	276	
			1939	02-23	2295	1	A3D4		600			
			1976	03-04	1500		A3C1		150	3	89	
U1M03	Mkomanzi	Mkomanzi drift	1959	05-17	6230		A3D4		U			
			1976	03-21	2740		A1B1		U			
V6M02	Tugela	Tugela Ferry	1943	04-25	4615 (7)	1	A1B1		460	3	127	
			1955	02-09	4080	1	A1B1		410	3	81	
			1930	03-08	3245	1	A1B1		325			
V5M02	Tugela	Mandini	1925	03	15100	1	A1D4	A1A	U			
			1967	02-08	4680	1	A1B1	A1A	U			
			1975	02-16	4590	1	A1B1	A1A	U			
W3R01	Hluhluwe	Hluhluwe Dam	1963	07-04	3060	1	A1D4/D3		900			
			1977	02-07	550		A1D6		150			
X1M01	Komati	Hoogenoeg	1939	02-07	3415 (8)	1	A1C1	A1A	U			
			1918	02-21	2495	1	A1C1	A1A	U			
			1974	02-08	1990	1	A1C1	A1A	U			

(5) return period 60 years   (6) return period 45 years   (7) return period 100 years   (8) return period 800 years.

TABLEAU I : IDENTIFICATION DES POINTS D'OBSERVATIONS ET CARACTERISTIQUES DES BASSINS

	POINT D'OBSERVATION						CARACTERISTIQUES DU BASSIN						
N° du point	Bassin fluvial	Rivière	Point d'observ.		Coordonnées Lat. Long.	Période	Surface km²	Relief	Sol	Végét.	Régime	Pluie moyenne mm	Module m³s-1
1	2	3	4	5	6	7	8	9	10	11	12	13	14
E609	N de Espana	Mino	Rabade	1	N 43:09 W 07:30	49 ans	999				50	1250	39.2
E629	N de Espana	Mino	Los Peares	1	N 42:58 W 07:32	25 ans	4580				50	1250	129
E631	N de Espana	Mino	Orense (Pte. Mayor)	1	N 42:21 W 07:50	33 ans	12930				50	1140	270
E769	N de Espana	Sil	San Pedro	1	N 42:27 W 06:52	51 ans	7985				50	1180	161
E 1	Ebro	Ebro	Miranda	1	N 42:41 W 02:57	63 ans	5480				70	760	61.9
E 11	Ebro	Ebro	Zaragoza	1	N 41:39 W 00:50	69 ans	40430				70	615	245
E 27	Ebro	Ebro	Tortosa	1	N 40:49 W 00:33	51 ans	84230				70 30 90	630	548
E 4	Ebro	Arga	Peralta	1	N 42:20 W 01:48	58 ans	2705				90 70	1300	56.6
E 5	Ebro	Aragon	Caparroso	1	N 42:21 W 01:30	63 ans	5470				90 70	1115	79.2
E101	Ebro	Aragon	Yesa	1	N 42:37 W 01:12	61 ans	2190				90 70	1240	42.7
E17	Ebro	Cinca	Fraga	1	N 41:32 E 00:18	47 ans	9610				90 30	790	85.3
E25	Ebro	Segre	Seros	1	N 41:27 E 00:23	33 ans	12780				90 30	765	101
E 2	Duero	Duero	Garray	1	N 41:48 W 02:30	62 ans	1500				70	770	12.1
E54	Duero	Duero	Villamarciel	1	N 41:32 W 04:50	54 ans	36570				70	610	145
E93	Duero	Duero	Puento Pino	1	N 41:35 W 06:10	32 ans	63160				70	625	292
E43	Duero	Pisuerga	Cabezon de P.	1	N 41:44 W 04:37	43 ans	14285				70	675	71.4
E95	Duero	Esla	Breto	1	N 41:52 W 05:44	60 ans	14430				70	840	162

TABLEAU I : IDENTIFICATION DES POINTS D'OBSERVATIONS ET CARACTERISTIQUES DES BASSINS

	POINT D'OBSERVATION						CARACTERISTIQUES DU BASSIN						
N° du point	Bassin fluvial	Rivière	Point d'observ.		Coordonnées Lat. Long.	Période	Surface km²	Relief	Sol	Végét.	Régime	Pluie moyenne mm	Module m³s-1
1	2	3	4	5	6	7	8	9	10	11	12	13	14
E 2	Llobregat	Cardoner	Manresa	1	N 41:41 E 01:50	63 ans	1332				30	725	6.31
E23	Llobregat	Llobregat	Castellvell	1	N 41:39 E 01:52	57 ans	3295				30	755	18.3
E 5	Llobregat	Llobregat	Martorell	1	N 41:28 E 01:56	51 ans	4560				30	735	21.6
E29	Francoli	Francoli	La Riba	1	N 41:19 E 01:12	23 ans	450				30	490	1.58
E 6	Gaya	Gaya	Querol	1	N 41:26 E 01:25	35 ans	123				30	540	0.40
E 1	Tajo	Tajo	Peralejos	1	N 40:36 W 01:57	31 ans	410				70 90	950	5
E12	Tajo	Tajo	La Portusa	1	N 39:42 W 04:15	10 ans	27170				70	560	91
E19	Tajo	Tajo	Alcantara	1	N 39:43 W 06:57	61 ans	52170				70	675	274
E52	Tajo	Jarama	Mejorada	1	N 40:24 W 03:30	55 ans	7005				70	650	32
E127	Tajo	Tietar	Rosarito	1	N 40:07 W 05:20	37 ans	1755				70	1200	30
E140	Tajo	Alagon	Coria	1	N 39:59 W 06:30	10 ans	4015				70	950	33
E32	Jucar	Jucar	Cuenca	1	N 40:04 W 02:08	63 ans	985				30	870	11.8
E36	Jucar	Jucar	Los Frailes	1	N 39:09 W 01:44	60 ans	5400				30	575	25.1
E45	Jucar	Jucar	Alcira	1	N 39:09 W 00:26	65 ans	19685				30	510	33.7
E112	Jucar	Gabriel	Cofrentes	1	N 39:15 W 01:05	63 ans	4695				30	570	21.9
E25	Jucar	Turia	La Presa	1	N 39:31 W	57 ans	6295				30	535	15.8

TABLEAU I : IDENTIFICATION DES POINTS D'OBSERVATIONS ET CARACTERISTIQUES DES BASSINS

	POINT D'OBSERVATION						CARACTERISTIQUES DU BASSIN							
N° du point	Bassin fluvial	Rivière	Point d'observ.		Coordonnées Lat. Long.	Période	Surface km²	Relief	Sol	Végét.	Régime	Pluie moyenne mm	Module m³s-1
1	2	3	4	5	6	7	8	9	10	11	12	13	14
E 4	Guadiana	Guadiana	La Cubeta	1	N W 38:59 02:52	47 ans	855				70	480	2.98
E14	Guadiana	Guadiana	Villanueva de la Serena	1	N W 39:01 05:46	59 ans	34770				70	525	62.6
E18	Guadiana	Guadiana	Badajoz Pte. Las Palmas	1	N W 38:53 06:55	64 ans	48515				70	520	99.1
E203	Guadiana	Ciguela	Buenavista	1	N W 39:18 03:20	30 ans	9930				70	600	4.19
E105	Guadiana	Zujar	Villanueva de la Serena	1	N W 39:01 05:45	44 ans	8510				70	555	20.4
E 1	Segura	Segura	E. Fuensanta	1	N W 38:29 02:11	50 ans	1220				30	845	10.6
E 6	Segura	Segura	Almadenes	1	N W 38:14 01:36	48 ans	7110				30	545	17.5
E 30	Segura	Segura	Guardamar	1	N W 38:06 00:38	48 ans	14925				30	430	4.8
E 1	Guadalquivir	Guadalquivir	Arroyo Maria	1	N W 38:11 02:49	36 ans	585				30	1180	7.86
E 70	Guadalquivir	Guadalquivir	Cordoba	1	N W 37:51 04:47	29 ans	25450				30	650	77.2
E 72	Guadalquivir	Guadalquivir	Alcala del Rio	1	N W 37:31 06:00	44 ans	47000				30	655	185.
E 47	Guadalquivir	Genil	Puente Genil	1	N W 37:23 04:45	59 ans	6160				30	665	31.0
E 1	S. de Espana	Guadiaro	Corchado	1	N W 36:32 05:22	64 ans	570				30	1070	11.3
E 19	S. de Espana	Guadalhorce	Gobantes	1	N W 36:57 04:46	36 ans	965				30		3.23
E 14	S. de Espana	Guara	C. del Monte	1	N W 36:52 04:08	41 ans	119				30	690	1.05
E 23	S. de Espana	Nacimiento	El Chono	1	N W 37:05 02:37	31 ans	615				30	430	0.29
E 73	S. de Espana	Almanzora	Sta. Barbara	1	N W 37:21 01:57	13 ans	1850				30	380	1.16

TABLEAU II : CARACTERISTIQUES DES CRUES

	CARACTERISTIQUES DE LA CRUE							EVALUATION DES DEBITS				
N° du point	Rivière	Point d'observ.	Année	Date du maximum	Débit max m³s-1	Origine	Base et mode éval	Qual. de la séch	Précis. ±m³s-1	Anteced	Hauteur mm	Durée jours
1	2	3	4	5	6	7	8	9	10	11	12	13
E609	Mino	Rabade	1947	02-22	810							
			1959	12-12	391							
E629	Mino	Los Peares	1959	12-27	2095							
			1962	03-31	1050							
E631	Mino	Orense	1959	12-27	5700							
			1962	03-31	4990							
E769	Sil	Sam Pedro	1962	03-31	3450							
			1959	12-27	2900							
E 1	Ebro	Miranda	1959	12-13	1315							
			1929	11-15	1300							
E 11	Ebro	Zaragoza	1961	01-02	4130							
			1889	02-18	3800							
			1892	02-06	3790							
E 27	Ebro	Tortosa	1907	10-24	12000							
			1937	10-29	10000							
			1961	01-05	4580							
E 4	Arga	Peralta	1915	04-11	2050							
			1930	11-28	1600							
E 5	Aragon	Caparroso	1966	11-09	2320							
			1960	12-31	1650							
E101	Aragon	Yesa	1966	11-09	1560							
			1937	10-27	1310							
E 17	Cinca	Fraga	1907	10-23	3900							
			1937	10-26	2600							
E 25	Segre	Seros	1907	10-24	5200							
			1937	10-25	3400							
E 2	Duero	Garray	1967	11-18	263.5							
			1969	03-17	234.5							
E 54	Duero	Villamarciel	1933	03	2350							
			1970	01-12	1900							
			1969	03-19	1690							
E 93	Duero	Puento Pino	1962	01-03	7690							
			1966	02-21	5480							
E 43	Pisuerga	Cabezon de P.	1962	01-03	1650							
			1960	02-19	1340							

TABLEAU II : CARACTERISTIQUES DES CRUES

	CARACTERISTIQUES DE LA CRUE					EVALUATION DES DEBITS						
N° du point	Rivière	Point d'observ.	Année	Date du maximum	Débit max m³s-1	Origine	Base et mode éval	Qual. de la séch	Précis. àm³s-1	Anteced	Hauteur mm	Durée jours
1	2	3	4	5	6	7	8	9	10	11	12	13
E 95	Esla	Breto	1962	01-03	4860							
			1966	02-21	3300							
			1959	12-28	2350							
E 2	Cardoner	Manresa	1907	10-17	1140							
			1942	04-28	582							
			1940	10	385							
E 23	Llobregat	Castellvell	1907	10-17	2700							
			1971	09-20	2300							
E 5	Llobregat	Martorell	1971	09-20	3080							
			1907	10-17	2785							
			1940	10-18	2200							
E 29	Francoli	La Riba	1930	10-19	1580							
			1966	11	590							
E 6	Gaya	Querol	1921	08-17	310							
			1969	04-05	141							
E 1	Tajo	Peralejos	1947	03-04	216							
			1948	01-28	149							
E 12	Tajo	La Portusa	1972	11-05	969							
E 19	Tajo	Alcantara	1941	01-26	11000							
			1947	03-08	9300							
			1935	12-28	7160							
E 52	Jarama	Mejorada	1970	01-11	1240							
			1947	03-05	1010							
			1948	01-30	970							
E127	Tietar	Rosarito	1936	02	1290							
			1955	01-21	1065							
E140	Alagon	Coria	1972	02-03	1720							
E 32	Jucar	Cuenca	1941	01	632 ?							
			1966	01-20	585 ?							
E 36	Jucar	Los Frailes	1941	01	690 ?							
E 45	Jucar	Alcira (1)	1923	10-21	1040 ?	M. Pardé mentionne une crue de 10000-12000 m³s-1						
			1916	11-29	1000 ?	près d'Alcira (BV : 17260 km²) en 1864.						
E112	Gabriel	Cofrentes	1923	10-30	800							
			1941	01	700							
			1976	08-28	605							

TABLEAU II : CARACTERISTIQUES DES CRUES

	CARACTERISTIQUES DE LA CRUE					EVALUATION DES DEBITS						
N° du point	Rivière	Point d'observ.	Année	Date du maximum	Débit max m³s-1	Origine	Base et mode éval	Qual. de la séch	Précis. ±m³s-1	Anteced	Hauteur mm	Durée jours
1	2	3	4	5	6	7	8	9	10	11	12	13
E 25	Turia	La Presa	1957	10-14	3700							
			1949	09-28	2300							
			1967	10-23	920							
E 4	Guadiana	La Cubeta	1970	02-16	30.5							
			1966	10-30	28.5							
E 14	Guadiana	Villanueva de la Serena	1947	03-05	5000							
			1970	01-12	3190							
E 18	Guadiana	Badajoz	1877	12-07	10000							
			1947	03-06	8000							
			1970	01-13	5430							
E203	Ciguela	Buenavista	1947	03-09	34.7							
			1956	04-02	32.2							
E105	Zugar	Villanueva de la Serana	1961	12-31	3000							
			1963	02-17	2050							
			1947	03-05	1940							
E 1	Segura	E. Fuensanta	1947	03-08	363							
			1960	02-15	327							
E 6	Segura	Almadenes	1946	04-22	785							
			1947	03-09	380							
E 30	Segura	Guardamar	1946	04-22	269							
			1966	10-12	223							
E 1	Guadalquivir	Arroyo Maria	1963	02-18	310							
			1915	02-21	305							
E 70	Guadalquivir	Cordoba	1947	03-06	3500							
			1916	12-19	3500							
			1916	01-04	3400							
E 72	Guadalquivir	Alcala del Rio	1925	12-22	6800							
			1912	02-10	6700							
			1924	03-30	6000							
E 47	Genil	Puente Genil	1963	02-17	790							
			1947	02-04	655							
			1921	09-21	655							
E 1	Guadario	Corchado	1948	01-27	325							
			1963	02-16	293							
			1926	10-30	277							
E 19	Guadalhorce	Gobantes	1969	10-04	200							
			1961	11-28	200							
			1958	12-22	200							

TABLEAU II : CARACTERISTIQUES DES CRUES

	CARACTERISTIQUES DE LA CRUE					EVALUATION DES DEBITS						
N° du point	Rivière	Point d'observ.	Année	Date du maximum	Débit max m³s-1	Origine	Base et mode éval	Qual. de la séch	Précis. ±m³s-1	Anteced	Hauteur mm	Durée jours
1	2	3	4	5	6	7	8	9	10	11	12	13
E 14	Guaro	C. del Monte	1968	09-30	142							
			1970	01-13	140							
E 23	Nacimiento	El Chono	1946	11-11	220							
			1942	12-28	99.3							
			1965	08-15	79.2							
E 73	Almanzora	Santa Barbara	1973	10-19	5600							

SRI LANKA

TABLE I : IDENTIFICATION OF OBSERVATION SITES AND CHARACTERISTICS OF BASINS

	OBSERVATIONS SITE							CHARACTERISTICS OF BASIN						
Site number	River basin	Stream	Observ. site		Coordinates Lat. Long.	Period	Area km²	Slope	Soil	Cover	Regime	Mean precip. mm	Mean disc. m³s-1
1	2	3	4	5	6	7	8	9	10	11	12	13	14
1	Kelani	Kelani	Glencourse	1	N 07:02 E 80:16	1944 71	2310	F E D		A 9 C13 D78	00	4050	246
2	Walawe	Walawe	Embilipitiya	1	N 06:21 E 80:54	1942 64	2490	E D C		A40 C11 D49	00	2140	68.2
3	Malwathu	Malwathu	Kapachchi	1	N 08:36 E 80:16	1944 73	3300	C B			00	1490	26.4
4	Mahaweli	Mahaweli	Manampitiya	1	N 07:55 E 80:05	1941 71	10600	F E D		A44 C10 D46	00	2510	343

SRI LANKA

TABLE II : FLOODS CHARACTERISTICS

	FLOOD CHARACTERISTICS						DISCHARGE ESTIMATION					
Site number	Stream	Observ. site	Year	Date of the max	Maximal discm³s-1	Climatic origine	Condition disc est	Qual. of the sect	Precis. ±m³s-1	Anteced precip.	Depth mm	Duration days
1	2	3	4	5	6	7	8	9	10	11	12	13
1	Kelani	Glencourse	1967 1968 1971	05-20	3790 3080 2040	1 1 1						
2	Walawe	Embilipitiya	1947 1963	08-15 01-11	2250 1870	1 1						
3	Malwathu	Kapachchi	1957 1948	12-26 01-01	6510 2730	1 1						
4	Mahaweli	Manampitiya	1960 1961 1964	02-22 01-15 01-03	5920 3740 3620	1 1 1						

TABLE I : IDENTIFICATION OF OBSERVATIONS SITES AND CHARACTERISTICS OF BASINS

	OBSERVATIONS SITE							CHARACTERISTICS OF BASIN					
Site number	River basin	Stream	Observ. site		Coordinates Lat. Long.	Period	Area km²	Slope	Soil	Cover	Regime	Mean precip. mm	Mean disc. m³s-1
1	2	3	4	5	6	7	8	9	10	11	12	13	14
1	Nile	Blue Nile	Roseires	1	N 11:52 E 34:23	1922 75	210 000	F E D C B		B C D	90 00		1580
2	Nile	Bahr el Jebel (White Nile)	Malakal	1	N 09:35 E 31:40	1912 75	1080 000 (2)	F E D C B A (1)		A B D	90 00	2)	890
3	Nile	Bahr el Jebel (White Nile)	Mongalla	1	N 05:12 E 31:46	1905 75	450 000	F E D C B (1)		A B D	90 00	1100	840

(1) lakes (Victoria, Kyoga, etc...).
(2) no physical signification.

SUDAN/SOUDAN

TABLE II : FLOODS CHARACTERISTICS

	FLOOD CHARACTERISTICS						DISCHARGE ESTIMATION					
Site number	Stream	Observ. site	Year	Date of the max	Maximal discm³s-1	Climatic origine	Condition disc est	Qual. of the sect	Precis. ±m³s-1	Anteced precip.	Depth mm.	Duratio days.
1	2	3	4	5	6	7	8	9	10	11	12	13
1	Blue Nile	Roseires	1946 1917 (1)	08-21	11300	1	A2A1					
2	Bahr el Jebel	Malakal	1964 (2)		2430	1	A3B					
3	Bahr el Jebel	Mongalla	1964 1917 1963	10-15 10-05 05-15	2900 (3) 2840 2800	1 1 1	A3C1 A3B1 A3C1	C1B C1B C1B	580 300 560			

(1) discharge less than for the 1946 flood but unknown because of the lack of measurement.
(2) discharge certainly exceeded in 1878 (see Egypt).
(3) slightly underestimated, one observation each 10 days.

TABLE I : IDENTIFICATION OF OBSERVATIONS SITES AND CHARACTERISTICS OF BASINS

	OBSERVATIONS SITE						CHARACTERISTICS OF BASIN							
Site number	River basin	Stream	Observ. site		Coordinates Lat. Long.	Period	Area km²	Slope	Soil	Cover	Regime	Mean precip. mm	Mean disc. m³s-1
1	2	3	4	5	6	7	8	9	10	11	12	13	14
1	Götaälv	Klarälven	Edsforsens krv 1703	1	N 60:04	E 13:34	1910 80	8580	E D C		A	90 80	700	128
2	Götaälv 108	Götaälv	Sjötorp 243	1	N 58:50	E 13:59	1807 1937	46800	E D C B		A	90 80 61 50	690	539
3	Fyllean 100	Esmaan	Gardsilt 1207	1	N 56:42	E 13:09	1927 80	55	B		A	50	1000	1.28
4	Rönnean 96	Bäljanea	Klippan 2 1635	1	N 56:09	E 13:07	1890 1980	239	B A		A	50	790	3.30
5	Vesanan K 86/87	Vesanan	Halabäck 736	1	N 56:07	E 14:37	1927 80	4.7	B A		A	61	600	0.03
6	Motala 67	Dummean	Risbro 818	1	N 57:51	E 14:02	1915 42	50	B		C	61	650	0.61
7	Motala 67	Velenan	Velen 2 1662	1	N 58:43	E 14:18	1937 80	45	B		A	61	650	0.36
8	Motala 67	Motala	Motala 154	1	N 58:32	E 15:03	1858 1939	6360	B A		A	61	600	42.4
9	Motala 67	Motala	Norsholm 172	1	N 58:31	E 15:59	1873 1927	13200	B A		A	61	580	85.8
10	Noorström 61	Vattholmaan	Vattholma 563	1	N 60:01	E 17:44	1916 80	284	B A		A	61	570	2.16
11	Dalälven 53	Dalälven	Norslund 121	1	N 60:24	E 15:41	1851 1918	25300	B C A		A	80 61	675	349
12	Ljusnan 48	Tännan	Lillglän 1083	1	N 62:38	E 12:08	1932 80	63	C		C	80 90	800	1.26
13	Ljusnan 48	Ljusnan	Sveg 106	1	N 62:02	E 14:23	1914 61	8490	D C B		A	80 90	655	121
14	Ljungan 42	Giman	Gimdalsby 97	1	N 62:50	E 15:40	1910 80	2180	B		A	80	575	17.6
15	Indalsälvan 40	Areälven	O. Norn 1328	1	N 63:28	E 12:48	1900 80	2390	D C B		A	90 80	935	63.3
16	Umeälv 28	Vindelälven	Sorsele 56	1	N 65:33	E 17:31	1909 80	6110	D C B		A	90 80	755	122

TABLE I : IDENTIFICATION OF OBSERVATIONS SITES AND CHARACTERISTICS OF BASINS

	OBSERVATIONS SITE						CHARACTERISTICS OF BASIN						
Site number	River basin	Stream	Observ. site	Coordinates Lat. Long.		Period	Area km²	Slope	Soil	Cover	Regime	Mean precip. mm	Mean disc. m³s-1
1	2	3	4	5	6	7	8	9	10	11	12	13	14
17	Umeälv 28	Vindelälven	Renfors 1545	1 N 64:13	E 19:42	1911 80	11900	D C B A		A	90 80	750	207.5
18	Raneälv 7	Raneälv	Niemisel 20	1 N 66:01	E 22:00	1900 80	3770			A	80	540	39.5
19	Törneälv 1	Törneälv	Jukkasjärvi 3	1 N 67:51	E 20:37	1915 67	6000	D C B		A	90 80	535	101.8
20	Törneälv 1	Muonjoälv	Kallio 589	1 N 67:13	E 23:35	1911 80	14300	C B A		A	90 80	500	158.7

TABLE II : FLOODS CHARACTERISTICS

				FLOOD CHARACTERISTICS					DISCHARGE ESTIMATION			
Site number	Stream	Observ. site	Year	Date of the max	Maximal discm³s-1	Climatic origine	Condition disc est	Qual. of the sect	Precis. ±m³s-1	Anteced precip.	Depth mm.	Duration days.
1	2	3	4	5	6	7	8	9	10	11	12	13
1	Klarälven	Edsforsens	1916	05-13	1320	2			100			
			1931	05-21	1020	2			80			
			1924	06-05	876	2			60			
2	Götaälv	Sjötorp	1927	11-05	836	1			50			
			1910	06-02	829	2			50			
			1860	11-22	817	1			50			
3	Esmaan	Gardsilt	1970	04-24	17.4	2			1.5			
			1955	12-29	14.9	1			1.3			
			1959	01-24	14.4	2			1.3			
4	Bäljanea	Klippan 2	1963	11-23	43	1			6			
			1893	03-08	41	2			6			
			1970	04-20	37	2			5			
5	Vesanan	Halabäck	1936	04-13	1.05	2			0.05			
			1946	03-23	0.96	2			0.05			
			1942	04-10	0.70	2			0.04			
6	Dummean	Risbro	1927	06-29	15	1			3			
			1937	04-06	10.9	2			2			
			1941	04-14	8.9	2			2			
7	Velenan	Velen 2	1977	05-04	3.9	2			0.3			
			1966	05-05	2.97	1			0.3			
			1951	04-20	2.7	2			0.25			
8	Motala	Motala	1867	06-05	100	1			20			
			1924	08-07	91	1			18			
			1927	07-25	91	1			18			
9	Motala	Norsholm	1913	01-04	224	2			30			
			1912	12-31	215	1			30			
			1877	05-05	210	2			28			
10	Vattholmaan	Vattholma	1922	05-02	25	2			2			
			1924	05-11	24	2			2			
			1966	05-04	22	2			2			
11	Dalälven	Norslund	1860	06-01	2640	2			400			
			1916	05-18	2410	2			400			
			1899	05-25	2030	2			320			
12	Tännän	Lillglän	1934	05-08	39	2			5			
			1944	06-10	33	2			4			
			1973	06-01	29	2			4			
13	Ljusnan	Sveg	1916	05-12	1150	2			100			
			1924	05-27	1090	2			90			
			1959	05-02	1080	2			90			
14	Giman	Gimdalsby	1945	05-06	127	2			10			
			1966	05-25	125	2			10			
			1916	05-21	124	2			10			

TABLE II : FLOODS CHARACTERISTICS

		FLOOD CHARACTERISTICS						DISCHARGE ESTIMATION				
Site number	Stream	Observ. site	Year	Date of the max	Maximal discm^{3}s-1	Climatic origine	Condition disc est	Qual. of the sect	Précis. ±m^{3}s-1	Anteced precip.	Depth mm.	Duration days.
1	2	3	4	5	6	7	8	9	10	11	12	13
15	Areälven	O. Norn	1934	05-11	715	2			100			
			1976	05-26	560	2			80			
			1938	06-04	560	2			80			
16	Vindelälven	Sorsele	1938	06-07	1370	2			50			
			1971	06-05	1280	2			50			
			1922	06-23	1230	2			50			
17	Vindelälven	Renfors	1938	06-09	1650	2			150			
			1945	06-21	1500	2			150			
			1971	06-08	1480	2			150			
18	Raneälv	Niemisel	1934	05-11	763	2			50			
			1910	05-16	700	2			50			
			1906	05-10	685	2			50			
19	Törneälv	Jukkasjarvi	1918	07-08	653	2			100			
			1952	06-26	648	2			100			
			1943	06-24	633	2			100			
20	Muonjoälv	Kallio	1968	06-10	1720	2			250			
			1917	06-07	1650	2			250			
			1920	05-22	1600	2			250			

SWITZERLAND/SUISSE

TABLEAU I : IDENTIFICATION DES POINTS D'OBSERVATIONS ET CARACTERISTIQUES DES BASSINS

	POINT D'OBSERVATION						CARACTERISTIQUES DU BASSIN						
N° du point	Bassin fluvial	Rivière	Point d'observ.		Coordonnées Lat. Long.	Période	Surface km²	Relief	Sol	Végét.	Régime	Pluie moyenne mm	Module m³s−1
1	2	3	4	5	6	7	8	9	10	11	12	13	14
1	Rhein	Medelser Rhein	Disentis	1	N 46:42 E 08:51	1962 75	128				90 50 (1)		0.96
2	Rhein	Rhein	Schmitter	1	N 47:27 E 09:40	1962 75	6122				90 50		228
3	Rhein	Rhein	Basel	1	N 47:33 E 07:36	1808 75	35925	F50 E20 D20 C 5 B 5	B25 C25 D50		90 50		1027
4	Ticino	Moesa	Lumino	1	N 46:14 E 09:04		471						
5	Ticino	Ticino	Bellinzona	1	N 46:12 E 09:01	1921 75	1515				90 50		68.9

(1) débit résiduel dès 1962.

SWITZERLAND/SUISSE

TABLEAU II : CARACTERISTIQUES DES CRUES

	CARACTERISTIQUES DE LA CRUE						EVALUATION DES DEBITS					
N° du point	Rivière	Point d'observ.	Année	Date du maximum	Débit max m³s−1	Origine	Date et mode éval	Qual. de la séch	Précis. ±m³s−1	Anteced	Hauteur mm	Durée jours
1	2	3	4	5	6	7	8	9	10	11	12	13
1	Medelser Rhein	Disentis	1954	08−21	350	1	A1B1	B1A	50			
2	Rhein	Schmitter	1927 1954	09−25 08−22	3100 2600	4 4	A1B1 A1B1	B1A B1A	100 100			
3	Rhein	Basel	1876 1852	06−13 09−18	5700 5650	4 1	A1D4 C4D4	B1A B1A	200 200			
4	Moesa	Lumino	1951	08−08	900	1	A1B1	B1A	50			
5	Ticino	Bellinzona	1868	09−28	2500	1	C4D4	B1A	80			

201

TABLE I : IDENTIFICATION OF OBSERVATIONS SITES ANS CHARACTERISTICS OF BASINS

	OBSERVATIONS SITE							CHARACTERISTICS OF BASIN					
Site number	River basin	Stream	Observ. site		Coordinates Lat. Long.	Period	Area km²	Slope	Soil	Cover	Regime	Mean precip. mm	Mean disc. m³s-1
1	2	3	4	5	6	7	8	9	10	11	12	13	14
1	Mekong	Mekong	Chiang Saen	1	N 20:16 E 100:06	1960 74	189000	F E D C			90 10	1960	3030
2	Mekong	Mekong	Mukdahan	1	N 16:32 E 104:42	1959 74	391000	F E D C B			90 10	1510	8210
3	Nam Chi	Nam Chi	Yasothorn	1	N 15:47 E 104:08	1960 74	43100	E D C B		A D			254
4	Nam Chi	Nam Mun	Ubon	1	N 15:13 E 104:52	1950 74	104000	E D C B		A D		1590	603
5	Nam Chi	Sai Yai	Ban Saphan Hin	1	N 14:08 E 101:44	1963 74	636	E D		A D		2060	18.3
6		Lam Takong	Khao Yai	1	N 14:26 E 101:22	1964 74	60.7	D C B		A		2190	1.38

THAILAND/THAILANDE

TABLE II : FLOODS CHARACTERISTICS

	FLOOD CHARACTERISTICS						DISCHARGE ESTIMATION					
Site number	Stream	Observ. site	Year	Date of the max	Maximal discm³s-1	Climatic origine	Condition disc est	Qual. of the sect	Precis. ±m³s-1	Anteced precip.	Depth mm.	Duration days.
1	2	3	4	5	6	7	8	9	10	11	12	13
1	Mekong	Chiang Saen	1966	09-03	23600	1						
2	Mekong	Mukdahan	1966	09-15	36200	1						
3	Nam Chi	Yasothorn	1962	10-10	1930	1						
4	Nam Mun	Ubon	1950	10-18	4790	1						
5	Sai Yai	Ban Saphan Hin	1967	08-17	316	1						
6	Lam Takong	Khao Yai	1965	10-12	144	1						

TOGO

TABLEAU I : IDENTIFICATION DES POINTS D'OBSERVATIONS ET CARACTERISTIQUES DES BASSINS

	POINT D'OBSERVATION						CARACTERISTIQUES DU BASSIN						
N° du point	Bassin fluvial	Rivière	Point d'observ.		Coordonnées Lat. Long.	Période	Surface km²	Relief	Sol	Végét.	Régime	Pluie moyenne mm	Module m³s-1
1	2	3	4	5	6	7	8	9	10	11	12	13	14
271103	Volta	Oti	Mandouri	1	N 10:51 E 0:51	1959 81	29100	C 5 B25 A70	C	C	11	900 1200	95.3
276106	Volta	Oti	Mango	1	N 10:18 E 0:28	1953 81	35650	C 4 B20 A76	C	C	11	900 1200	132
273910	Volta	Kara	Lama Kara	1	N 09:32 E 01:11	1954 81	1560	C10 B90	C	B50 C50	10	1300 1400	22.4
274006	Volta	Kéran	Titira	1	N 10:00 E 01:07	1962 81	3695	D 5 C50 B45	C	B50 C50	10	1300 1400	41.5
275105	Volta	Mo	Boungoulou 1	1	N 09:01 E 0:41	1965 81	2700	E30 D40 C30	C	A 5 B95	10	1500 1300	
278103	Volta	Kpelou	Kpesside 1	1	N 09:38 E 00:57	1962 81	417	D20 C80	C	B	10	1400	7.1
279061	Volta	Dayes	Dzogbegan	4	N 07:15 E 0:41	1963 81	52	C	C	B	10	1550	0.74
279070	Volta	Koza	Rte Tchitchao	3	N 09:42 E 01:10		25	E	B	B	10	1400	
279042	Volta	Hidenwou	Kandé Grand Bassin	4	N 09:57 E 01:04	1962 64	25	D	C	C	11	1300	0.5
400109	Mono	Mono	Correkopé	1	N 07:48 E 01:18	1953 81	9950	B A	C	C	10	1400 1100	66
400117	Mono	Mono	Tététou	1	N 07:01 E 01:32	1951 81	20500	E 5 D10 B10 A75	C	C	10	1600 1000	120
401009	Mono	Anié	Anié Pont CFT	1	N 07:44 E 01:12	1964 81	3650	E10 C90	C	C	10	1500 1100	30.2

TABLEAU II : CARACTERISTIQUES DES CRUES

	CARACTERISTIQUES DE LA CRUE						EVALUATION DES DEBITS					
N° du point	Rivière	Point d'observ.	Année	Date du maximum	Débit max m³s-1	Origine	Date et mode éval	Qual. de la séch	Précis. ±m³s-1	Anteced	Hauteur mm	Durée jours
1	2	3	4	5	6	7	8	9	10	11	12	13
271103	Oti	Mandouri	1970	09-22	860	1	A3B1	B1B	100			
			1964	09-25	835	1	A3B1	B1B	100			
			1962	09-17	835	1	A3B1	B1B	100			
271106	Oti	Mango	1962	09-21	1750	1	A2B1	B1B	50			
			1970	09-27	1710	1	A2B1	B1B	50			
			1957	09-28	1620	1	A2B1	B1B	50			
273910	Kara	Lama Kara	1951	09-02	2300	1	D5C1	A1A	200			
			1956	09-03	1370	1	A3C1	A1A	100			
			1963	08-27	770	1	A3C1	A1A	50			
274006	Kéran	Titira	1964	09-03	1475	1	A3C1	A1A	100			
			1962	09-01	1175	1	A5C1	A1A	+500 -0			
			1969	09-08	1160	1	A3C1	A1A	100			
275105	Mo	Boungoulou	1979	09-07	1180	1	A3C1	A1A	50			
			1967	09-29	845	1	A3C1	A1A	+200 -50			
			1966	08-30	820	1	A3C1	A1A	50			
278103	Kpélou	Kpéssidé	1967	09-09	391	1	A3C1	A1A	50			
			1978	08-18	390	1	A3C1	A1A	50			
			1964	09-03	318	1	A3C1	A1A	50			
279061	Dayes	Dzogbegan	1979	09-04	605	1	A1C1	A1B	7			
			1968	10-21	475	1	A1C1	A1B	5			
279070	Koza	Rte de Tchitchao	1951	08-31	550 (1)	1	C4DO		100		235	2
279042	Hidenwou	Kandé Grd.Bassin	1962	08-28	105	1	A1B1	A1A	10	2	123	0.5
400109	Mono	Correkopé	1957	09-10	890	1	A3B1	A1B	20			
			1970	09-21	835	1	A1B1	A1B	20			
400117	Mono	Tététou	1968	09-07	1310	1	A3C1	A1A	100			
			1963	07-30	1255	1	A3C1	A1A	100			
			1960	09-29	1240	1	A3C1	A1A	100			
401009	Anié	Anié Pont CFT	1967	09-17	1180	1	A1C1	B1B	+200 -50			
			1969	09-09	915	1	A1C1	B1B	50			

(1) Période de retour supérieure à 100 ans.

TABLEAU I : IDENTIFICATION DES POINTS D'OBSERVATIONS ET CARACTERISTIQUES DES BASSINS

	POINT D'OBSERVATION							CARACTERISTIQUES DU BASSIN					
N° du point	Bassin fluvial	Rivière	Point d'observ.		Coordonnées Lat. Long.	Période	Surface km²	Relief	Sol	Végét.	Régime	Pluie moyenne mm	Module m³s-1
1	2	3	4	5	6	7	8	9	10	11	12	13	14
1	Joumine	Joumine	Jebel Antra	1	N 36:53 E 09:40	1952 80	235	E D	D	B C D	30	870	3
2	Mejerda	Mejerda	Ghardimaou	1	N 36:26 E 08:25	1948 80	1480	E D C	B C D	B C D	30	680	5.25
3	Mejerda	Mellègue	P.K. 13	1	N 36:08 E 08:32	1923 80	9000	E D C	B C D	B C D	30	400	5.0
4	Mejerda	Mejerda	Bou Salem	1	N 36:37 E 08:58	1925 80	16230	E D C	B C D	B C D	30	440	21.4
5	Miliane	Miliane	Cheylus	1	N 36:34 E 10:01	1945 80	1420	D C		C D	30	450	1.44
6	Merguellil	Merguellil	Haffouz	1	N 35:36 E 09:42	1966 80	651	D C		B C D	30	400	0.55
7	Zéroud	Zéroud	Sidi Saad	1	N 35:24 E 09:36	1945 80	8950	E D C		B C D E	30	200 600	2.2
8	Sidi Aïch	Bou Haya	Pont G.P. 15	1	N 35:00 E 08:37	1965 80	370	D C		C D E	30	300	
9	Bayech	Bayech	Gafsa	3	N 34:24 E 08:38		6360	C B		E	30/20	250	0.8
10	Oudrane	Leben	Maknassy	3	N 34:35 E 09:38		1060	C		E D	30/20	205	0.08
11	Zita	Zita I			E 34:08 09:48	1972 78	3.2	D		E	20	160	
12	Oum Zessar	Oum Zessar	Koutine	1	N 33:30 E 10:24	1976 80	285	E D		E	20	180	

TABLEAU II : CARACTERISTIQUES DES CRUES

			CARACTERISTIQUES DE LA CRUE				EVALUATION DES DEBITS					
N° du point	Rivière	Point d'observ.	Année	Date du maximum	Débit max m³s-1	Origine	Base et mode éval	Qual. de la séch	Précis. ±m³s-1	Anteced	Hauteur mm	Durée jours
1	2	3	4	5	6	7	8	9	10	11	12	13
1	Joumine	Jebel Antra	1962	10-20	235	1					175	1
2	Mejerda	Ghardimaou	1973	03-28	2370	1	A1C1/3	B1B	200		176	1
			1976		1013	1	A1C1/3	B1B	100			
			1958	01-18	660	1	A1C1/3	B1B	70			
3	Mellègue	P.K. 13	1969	09-29	4480	1	A1C1/3	C1C	500			
			1957	10-06	3340	1	A1C1/3	C1C	400			
			1948	02-28	2000	1	A1C1/3	C1C	250			
4	Mejerda	Bou Salem	1973	03-29	3180	1	A1C1	C1B	300			
			1931	12-14	2060	1	A1C1	C1B	200			
			1940	01-26	1780	1	A1C1	C1B	200			
5	Miliane	Cheylus	1969	10-22	1800	1			200			
6	Merguellil	Haffouz	1969	09-24 27	2890	1		C1C	400			
7	Zéroud	Sidi Saad	1969	09-27	17050	1	A1B1/3	C1C (1)	2000		200	1
8	Bou Haya	Pont G.P. 15	1969	10-28	1600	1			250		100	1
9	Bayech	Gafsa	1973	12-13	2500	1			500		125	1
10	Leben	Maknassy	1969	10-07	3500	1			700		237	1
11	Zita	Zita I	1973	12-12	131	1	A1C1	B1B	13		159	1
12	Oum Zessar	Koutine	1973	03-04 05	1475	1			200		142	1

(1) B. pour les très fortes crues : le seuil rocheux de la station est dégagé.

TABLE I : IDENTIFICATION OF OBSERVATIONS SITES AND CHARACTERISTICS OF BASINS

	OBSERVATIONS SITE						CHARACTERISTICS OF BASIN						
Site number	River basin	Stream	Observ. site		Coordinates Lat. Long.	Period	Area km²	Slope	Soil	Cover	Regime	Mean precip. mm	Mean disc. m³s-1
1	2	3	4	5	6	7	8	9	10	11	12	13	14
302	Kocadero	M. Kemalpasa	Döllük	1	N 39:58 E 28:31	1940 79	5630				30		64
902	Sakarya	Köprüçay	Beskonak	1	N 38:53 E 31:11	1939 79	1942				70		86
1501	Kizilirmak	Kizilirmak	Yamula	1	N 38:53 E 35:15	1938 79	15580				70		66
1401	Yesilirmak	Kelkit	Fatli	1	N 40:28 E 37:00	1938 79	10050				70/30		69
1714	Göksu	Göksu	Karahacili	1	N 36:24 E 33:49	1961 79	10065				30		123
1801	Seyhan	Göksu	Himmetli	1	N 37:52 E 36:03	1935 79	2600				70		31
2119	Firat (Euphrates)	Firat	Kemahbogazi	1	N 39:41 E 39:24	1953 79	10356				90/70		80
2605	Dicle (Tigris)	Dicle	Diyarbakir	1	N 37:53 E 40:14	1945 79	5655				90/70		73

TABLE II : FLOODS CHARACTERISTICS

	FLOOD CHARACTERISTICS						DISCHARGE ESTIMATION					
Site number	Stream	Observ. site	Year	Date of the max	Maximal discm³s-1	Climatic origine	Condition disc est	Qual. of the sect	Precis. ±m³s-1	Anteced precip.	Depth mm.	Duration days.
1	2	3	4	5	6	7	8	9	10	11	12	13
302	M. Kemalpasa	Döllük	1962	12-19	2940	1	A1B1	B1A	290			
			1940	12-26	1735	1	A1B1	B1A	175			
			1970	03-30	1570	1	A1B1	B1A	160			
902	Köpruçay	Beskonak	1976	12-13	2200	1	A1B1	B1A	220			
			1953	10-25	1620	1	A1B1	B1A	160			
			1966	01-21	1485	1	A1B1	B1A	150			
1501	Kizilirmak	Yamula	1968	03-14	900		A1B1	B1A	90			
			1940	04-04	755		A1B1	B1A	75			
			1952	04-04	745		A1B1	B1A	75			
1401	Kelkit	Fatli	1968	04-16	905		A1B1	B1A	90			
			1960	04-27	800		A1B1	B1A	80			
			1964	03-06	775		A1B1	B1A	80			
1714	Göksu	Karahacili	1963	12-19	1550	1	A1B1	B1A	155			
			79	01-04	1250		A1B1	B1A	125			
1801	Göksu	Himmetli	1968	03-13	560		A1B1	B1A	55			
			1979	01-03	550		A1B1	B1A	55			
			1975	04-29	320		A1B1	B1A	30			
2119	Firat	Kemahbogazi	1968	04-19	1160		A1B1	B1A	116			
			1969	04-29	770		A1B1	B1A	77			
2605	Dicle	Diyarbakir	1974	03-15	3250		A1B1	B1A	325			
			66	01-26	2640		A1B1	B1A	265			

TABLE I : IDENTIFICATION OF OBSERVATIONS SITES AND CHARACTERISTICS OF BASINS

| | OBSERVATIONS SITE | | | | | | CHARACTERISTICS OF BASIN | | | | | | |
Site number	River basin	Stream	Observ. site		Coordinates Lat. Long.	Period	Area km²	Slope	Soil	Cover	Regime	Mean precip. mm	Mean disc. m³s-1
1	2	3	4	5	6	7	8	9	10	11	12	13	14
1	Nile	Kyoga Nile	Paraa	1	N 02:17 E 31:34		340000	(1)		A B C	90 10 00	1150	960
2	Nile	Semliki	Bwera Mule	1	N 00:56 E 30:00		8000	(1)		A B C	90 10 00		148
3	Kyoga Nile	Kafu	Kampala-Masindi Road	1	N 01:33 E 32:03	1952 70	15490	A(1) B C		B C	10	1200	20

(1) Lakes and swamps

TABLE II : FLOODS CHARACTERISTICS

| | FLOOD CHARACTERISTICS | | | | | | DISCHARGE ESTIMATION | | | | | |
Site number	Stream	Observ. site	Year	Date of the max	Maximal discm³s-1	Climatic origine	Condition disc est	Qual. of the sect	Precis. ±m³s-1	Anteced precip.	Depth mm.	Duration days.
1	2	3	4	5	6	7	8	9	10	11	12	13
1	Kyoga Nile	Paraa	1917 1964 1963	11 11 06	2100 2000 1780	1 1 1						
2	Semliki	Bwera Mule	1963 1917	05 11	500 < 500	1 1						
3	Kafu	Kampala-Masindi Road	1967 1963	12 06	179 161	1 1						

TABLE I : IDENTIFICATION OF OBSERVATIONS SITES AND CHARACTERISTICS OF BASINS

	OBSERVATIONS SITE					CHARACTERISTICS OF BASIN							
Site number	River basin	Stream	Observ. site		Coordinates Lat. Long.	Period	Area km²	Slope	Soil	Cover	Regime	Mean precip. mm	Mean disc. m³s-1
1	2	3	4	5	6	7	8	9	10	11	12	13	14
EUROPEAN PART OF URSS													
1	Petchora Sea	Petchora	Ust-Tsilma	1	N 65:28 E 52:15	1932 79	248000		B C D	A90	80 81	735	3400
2	White Sea	Mezen	Maloniso-gorskaya	1	N 64:57 E 45:40	1920 79	56400		B D	A89	80	690	650
3	Severnaya Dvina (Northern Dvina)	Vaga	Filiayevskaya	1	N 61:14 E 42:15	1938 79	13200		B D	A91	61	725	109
4	Ladoga Lake	Volkhov	VI Hydro-electric Power station	1	N 59:54 E 32:28	1944 79	79800		C D		61	800	520
5	Baltic Sea (Gulf of) (Finland)	Neva	Novosaratovka	1	N 59:48 E 30:43	1959 79	218000		B D		61	800	2520
6	Volma and Msta rivers	Verebushka	Oksochi	1	N 58:42 E 32:48	1945 79	96.3	B	B D	A64	61	700	0.94
7	Ilmen lake	Lovat	Khoyam	1	N 57:08 E 31:17	1911 79	14700		B D	A85	61	650	97
8	Baltic Sea (Gulf of Riga)	Zapadnaya Dvina (Western Dvina)	Daugavpils	1	N 55:53 E 26:41	1881 1979	64600		B D		61	800	450
9	Baltic Sea	Neman	Smalininkaï	1	N 55:01 E 22:31	1811 1978	81200		B D		61	850	540
10	Black Sea	Dnieper	Smolensk	1	N 54:48 E 32:07	1881 1979	14100	A	B C D	A36 D40	61	630	95
11	Dnieper	Pripiat	Mozir	1	N 51:58 E 29:14	1881 1979	101000	A	B C D	A35	61	550	377
12	Dnieper	Desna	Tchernigov	1	N 51:27 E 31:21	1884 1970	81400		D		61	540	325
13	Black Sea	Dnieper	Kiev	1	N 50:30 E 30:27	1876 1970	328000				61	610	1380
14	Dnieper	Golovesnia	Pokoschichi	1	N 51:53 E 32:44	1928 70	29.5	E		A15	61	580	0.17
15	Black Sea	Dniester	Zaleschiki	1	N 48:33 E 25:45	1877 70	24600				90/70	565	225

TABLE I : IDENTIFICATION OF OBSERVATIONS SITES AND CHARACTERISTICS OF BASINS

	OBSERVATIONS SITE						CHARACTERISTICS OF BASIN						
Site number	River basin	Stream	Observ. site		Coordinates Lat. Long.	Period	Area km²	Slope	Soil	Cover	Regime	Mean precip. mm	Mean disc. m³s-1
1	2	3	4	5	6	7	8	9	10	11	12	13	14
16	Black Sea	Southern Bug	Alexandrovka	1	N 47:33 E 31:11	1923 70	46200			A93	70	425	85
17	Azov Sea	Don	Razdorkskaya	1	N 47:30 E 40:40	1881 1951	378000		C D		70	405	665
18	Don	Medveditsa	Archedinskaya	1	N 49:49 E 43:10	1928 79	33700	C	D	A 5 D75 E	70	400	64
19	Gorky Reservoir (Volga)	Unzha	Makariev	1	N 57:54 E 43:40	1896 1978	18500		B C D	A80 D 4 E	61	525	167
20	Volga	Oka	Murom	1	N 55:39 E 42:02	1881 1978	188000			B	61	550	910
21	Kuibyshev Reservoir (Volga)	Kama	Volosnitskoye	1	N 59:31 E 52:42	1929 78	9750		D		61	600	69
22	Caspian Sea	Volga	Volgograd Hydroelectric Power station	1	N 48:46 E 44:43	1879 1955	1350000				70 61	450	8380
23	Caspian Sea	Ural	Kushum	1	N 50:51 E 51:17	1915 79	190000		B D		70 90	350	310
CAUCASIA													
24	Kuban	Teberda	Teberda	1	N 43:16 E 41:38	1927 79	505	D	D	A10 D E 1	90 30	1780	27
25	Black Sea	Rioni	Sakochiadze	1	N 42:13 E 41:48	1928 79	13300	F	D		90 30	1900	400
26	Vostochny-Lake Manych	Kalaus	Svetlogorsk	1	N 45:14 E 42:47	1930 79	4540	D	D	A 5 D60 E20	70	475	3
27	Caspian Sea	Terek	Odzhonikidze	1	N 43:04 E 44:36	1912 79	1490	F	D	A10 D E 1	90	850	3440
SIBERIA													
28	(Kaz.) Irtysh	Ishim	Tselinograd	1	N 51:07 E 71:28	1933 69	7400	A	B D	A 1 E 0.3	70	300	5.9
29	(Kaz.) Irtysh	Ishim	Petropavlovsk	1	N 54:58 E 69:07	1932 67	106000		B D	A27	70	310	59.3
30	Ob	Biya	Biysk	1	N 52:31 E 85:16	1894 1979	36900		D		90	640	480

TABLE I : IDENTIFICATION OF OBSERVATIONS SITES AND CHARACTERISTICS OF BASINS

OBSERVATIONS SITE							CHARACTERISTICS OF BASIN						
Site number	River basin	Stream	Observ. site		Coordinates Lat. Long.	Period	Area km²	Slope	Soil	Cover	Regime	Mean precip. mm	Mean disc. m³s⁻¹
1	2	3	4	5	6	7	8	9	10	11	12	13	14
31	Tom	Usa	Mezhdurechensk	1	N 53:39 E 88:06	1936 79	3320	D	B C D	A75	61	550	150
32	Ob	Tym	Napas	1	N 59:54 E 81:55	1936 79	24500		C D	A71	61	530	190
33	Kara Sea Arctic Ocean	Ob	Salekhard	1	N 66:34 E 66:32	1930 79	2430000				61 80 81	415	12500
34	Arctic Ocean	Pur	Samburg	1	N 67:05 E 78:09	1936 79	95100				80	450	890
35	Krasnoyarsk Reservoir (Yeniseï)	Abakan	Abaza	1	N 52:35 E 90:10	1932 79	14400		D	A75	61 90	1270	300
36	Krasnoyarsk Reservoir (Yeniseï)	Tuba	Bugurtak	1	N 53:46 E 92:46	1911 79	31800		D	A58	61 90	1110	760
37	Lake Baïkal (Yeniseï)	Selenga	Mostovoï	1	N 52:01 E 107:24	1934 78	440000				70 80 90	400	940
38	Selenga	Khilok	Maleta	1	N 50:46 E 108:15	1936 78	25700		C D	A76 D 5	90	410	73
39	Lake Baïkal	Bolshaya Rechka	Posolskaya	1	N 51:46 E 106:27	1929 78	565	D	C D	A99	61	840	12.7
40	Kara Sea Arctic Ocean	Yeniseï	Yeniseisk	1	N 58:28 E 92:03	1902 66	1400000				61 90	500	7720
41	Yeniseï	Graviyka	Igarka	1	N 67:31 E 86:37	1938 79	323	A	D	A 7	80	705	5.13
42	Lena	Vitim	Romanovka	1	N 53:07 E 112:47	1944 78	18200		C D	A75	90 80	440	77
43	Aldan (Lena)	Timpton	Nagorny	1	N 55:59 E 124:45	1926 78	615	C	C D		80 90	600	9.4
44	Laptev Sea Arctic Ocean	Lena	Kusur	1	N 70:42 E 127:39	1935 78	2430000				80 90	215	1650
45	Lena	Ebitiem	Ebitem	1	N 70:22 E 127:57	1937 77	1000	D	C D		81	380	13.5
46	East Siberian Sea Arctic Ocean	Indigirka	Vorontsovo	1	N 69:35 E 147:21	1937 78	305000				80 90	420	1560

UNION OF SOVIET SOCIALIST REPUBLICS/UNION DES REPUBLIQUES SOCIALISTES SOVIETIQUES

TABLE I : IDENTIFICATION OF OBSERVATIONS SITES AND CHARACTERISTICS OF BASINS

OBSERVATIONS SITE							CHARACTERISTICS OF BASIN						
Site number	River basin	Stream	Observ. site		Coordinates Lat. Long.	Period	Area km²	Slope	Soil	Cover	Regime	Mean precip. mm	Mean disc. m³s-1
1	2	3	4	5	6	7	8	9	10	11	12	13	14
47	East Siberian Sea	Kolyma	Ust-Srednekan	1	N 67:27 E 152:43	1933 78	99400		D	F	80 90	390	725
48	Kolyma	Khasyn	Kolyma-Road km 79	1	N 64:22 E 151:18	1941 78	682	D	D		80	600	8.75
49	Chukotsk Sea Arctic Ocean	Anguelma	Mouth of the brook Shoumny	1	N 67:40 E 178:30	1944 76	26700		D		81	400	275
50	Bay of Cross Bearing Sea	Brook Izyskatelsky	1.6 km upstream of the Mouth	1	N 66:22 E 179:15	1947 78	13.2	D	D		81	450	.35
51	Zeya (Amur)	Dep	Rychkovo	1	N 53:25 E 127:55	1942 79	8440	B	D	A75	61	650	74
52	Amur	Ussuri	Kirovski	1	N 45:01 E 133:39	1927 79	24400			A95	61	800	234
53	Okhotsk Sea	Amur	Komsomolsk	1	N 50:38 E 137:07	1933 79	1730000				61	700	9990
54	Japan Sea	Razdolnaya (Suifun)	Terekhovka	1	N 43:47 E 131:58	1928 79	15500			A50 D18	61	800	76
KAZAKHSTAN-UZBEKISTAN													
55	Aral Sea	Syr Darya	Tiumen-Aryk	1	N 44:03 E 67:03	1930 60	219000		B		71 90	200	700
56	Aral Sea	Amu Darya	Chatly	1	N 42:17 E 59:42	1931 60	450000		B		71 90	200	1400

(see Irtysch 28 - 29).

TABLE II : FLOODS CHARACTERISTICS

FLOOD CHARACTERISTICS							DISCHARGE ESTIMATION					
Site number	Stream	Observ. site	Year	Date of the max	Maximal discm³s-1	Climatic origine	Condition disc est	Qual. of the sect	Precis. ±m³s-1	Anteced precip.	Depth mm.	Duration days.
1	2	3	4	5	6	7	8	9	10	11	12	13
1	Petchora	Ust-Tsilma	1952	06-08	39500	2	A1B1	A				
			1934	06-06	34600	2	A1B1	A				
			1966	06-02	33400	2	A1B1	A				
2	Mezen	Maloniso-gorskaya	1952	06-02	9530	2	A1B1	A				
			1966	06-26	9040	2	A1B1	A				
			1923	05-26	8820	2	A1B1	A				
3	Vaga	Filyaevskaya	1961	05-16	2100	2	A1B1	A				
			1957	03-05	2090	2	A1B1	A				
			1974	05-12	1900	2	A1B1	A				
4	Volkhov	VI Hydro-electric power station	1966	05-04	2730	2	A1B1	A				
			1946	05-07	2110	2	A1B1	A				
5	Neva	Novosaratovka	1955	07-23	4590	2	A1B1	A				
			1924	06-15	4510	2	A1B1	A				
			1958	06-06	4470	2	A1B1	A				
6	Verebushka	Oksochi	1955	05-09	25.8	2	A1B1	A				
			1968	04-07	20.8	2	A1B1	A				
			1978	04-16	20.6	2	A1B1	A				
7	Lovat	Khoyam	1931	04-23	2130	2	A1B1	A				
			1962	04-12	1720	2	A1B1	A				
			1948	04-09	1560	2	A1B1	A				
8	Zapadnaya Dvina	Daugavpils	1931	04-30	6930	2	A1B1	A				
			1956	04-27	6230	2	A1B1	A				
			1951	04-07	5230	2	A1B1	A				
9	Neman	Smalininkaï	1829	04-12	6820	2	A1B1	A				
			1958	04-21	6580	2	A1B1	A				
			1827	03-13	6240	2	A1B1	A				
10	Dnieper	Smolensk	1908	05-01	1820	2	A1B1	B				
			1931	05-01	1720	2	A1B1	B				
			1958	04-28	1650	2	A1B1	B				
11	Pripiat	Mozir	1895	04-22	5670	2	A1B1	B				
			1888	04-05	5100	2	A1B1	B				
			1889	04-25	4700	2	A1B1	B				
12	Desna	Tchernigov	1970	04-20	8000	2						
13	Dnieper	Kiev	1931	05-02	23100	2						
			1970	04-21	18500	2						
			1917	04-22	17500	2						
14	Golovesnia	Pokoschichi	1951	03-26	28	2						
15	Dniester	Zaleschiki	1971	04-04	8040	1						
			1969	06-10	5970	1						

TABLE II : FLOODS CHARACTERISTICS

	FLOOD CHARACTERISTICS						DISCHARGE ESTIMATION					
Site number	Stream	Observ. site	Year	Date of the max	Maximal discm³s-1	Climatic origine	Condition disc est	Qual. of the sect	Precis. ±m³s-1	Anteced precip.	Depth mm.	Duration days.
1	2	3	4	5	6	7	8	9	10	11	12	13
16	Southern Bug	Aleksandrovka	1932	04-08	5320	2						
17	Don	Rasdorskaya	1917	04-26	13500	2	A1B1	B				
			1942	05-13	13100	2	A1B1	B				
18	Medveditsa	Archedinskaya	1929	05-05	2070	2	A1B1	B				
			1948	04-23	1960	2	A1B1	B				
19	Unzha	Makariev	1947	05-05	2520	2	A1B1	A				
			1957	05-08	2520	2	A1B1	A				
			1974	05-16	2330	2	A1B1	A				
20	Oka	Murom	1926	04-30	18500	2	A1B1	A				
			1932	04-24	17200	2	A1B1	A				
			1970	04-24	13000	2	A1B1	A				
21	Kama	Volosnitskoye	1957	05-06	1100	2	A1B1	A				
			1968	05-15	1020	2	A1B1	A				
			1974	05-11	1000	2	A1B1	A				
22	Volga	Volgograd	1926	05-29	51900	2	A1B1	A				
			1919	05-25	46700	2	A1B1	A				
			1929	06-05	45500	2	A1B1	A				
23	Ural	Kushum	1957	04-27	14000	2	A1B1	C				
			1942	05-09	13500	2	A1B1	C				
			1922	04-20	11900	2	A1B1	C				

CAUCASIA

24	Teberda	Teberda	1975	06-29	396	2	A1C1	B	U			
			1936	07-08	319	2	A1C1	B				
25	Rioni	Sakochiadze	1977	08-19	3520	4	A1B1	C				
			1978	04-10	3510	4	A1B1	C				
			1963	06-12	3000	4	A1B1	C				
26	Kalaus	Svetlogorsk	1964	06-13	500	1	A1B1	C				
			1932	04-13	435	1	A1B1	C				
			1954	04-01	257	2	A1B1	C '				
27	Terek	Odzhonikidze	1967	03-06	424	2	A1B1	B				
			1953	08-17	369	2	A1B1	B				
			1961	07-29	365	2	A1B1	B				

SIBERIA

28	Ishim (Kaz.)	Tselinograd	1948	04-16	1200	2	A1B1	C				
			1949	04-19	1080	2	A1B1	C				
29	Ishim (Kaz.)	Petropavlovsk	1941	04-23	3760	2	A1BA	B				
			1948	05-08	3750	2	A1B1	B				
			1942	05-14	3340	2	A1B1	B				
30	Biya	Biysk	1969	04-30	5770	2	A1B1	A				
			1937	05-12	5040	2	A1B1	A				
			1936	06-15	4790	2	A1B1	A				

TABLE II : FLOODS CHARACTERISTICS

	FLOOD CHARACTERISTICS								DISCHARGE ESTIMATION				
Site number	Stream	Observ. site	Year	Date of the max	Maximal disc m³s-1	Climatic origine	Condition disc est	Qual. of the sect	Precis. ±m³s-1	Anteced precip.	Depth mm.	Duration days.
1	2	3	4	5	6	7	8	9	10	11	12	13
31	Usa	Mezhdurechensk	1958	06-02	2590	2	A1B1	A				
			1945	07-21	2520	1	A1B1	A				
32	Tym	Napas	1970	06-12	1180	2	A1B1	A				
			1979	06-04	1170	2	A1B1	A				
			1960	06-07	1070	2	A1B1	A				
33	Ob	Salekhard	1979	08-10	44800	2	A1B1	A				
			1971	07-04	43800	2	A1B1	A				
			1941	08-07	41800	2	A1B1	A				
34	Pur	Samburg	1948	06-08	7940	2	A1B1	A				
			1976	06-10	7930	2	A1B1	A				
35	Abakan	Abaza	1969	05-29	6700	2	A1B1	A				
			1932	06-22	5800	1	A1B1	A				
			1954	05-19	4230	2	A1B1	A				
36	Tuba	Bugurtak	1966	06-09	10500	2	A1B1	A				
			1965	05-22	8240	2	A1B1	A				
			1916	06-02	7750	2	A1B1	A				
37	Selenga	Mostovoï	1936	06-11	7620	1	A1B1	B				
			1973	07-29	7210	1	A1B1	B				
			1940	08-06	6480	1	A1B1	B				
38	Khilok	Maleta	1939	04-23	935	2	A1B1	B				
			1968	05-08	830	2	A1B1	B				
			1938	09-07	795	1	A1B1	B				
39	Bolshaya Rechka	Posolskaya	1942	07-15	445	1	A1B1	B				
			1971	07-20	335	1	A1B1	B				
			1944	07-28	192	1	A1B1	B				
40	Yeniseï	Yeniseisk	1937	05-18	57400	2	A1B1	A				
			1923	05-13	46600	2	A1B1	A				
			1941	05-26	44700	2	A1B1	A				
41	Graviyka	Igarka	1958	06-15	212	2	A1B1	A				
			1961	06-25	197	2	A1B1	A				
42	Vitim	Romanovka	1949	08-26	3400	1	A1B1	A				
			1948	07-20	2930	1	A1B1	A				
			1971	07-31	2920	1	A1B1	A				
43	Timpton	Nagorny	1958	07-16	698	1	A1C1	A				
			1934	05-25	510	2	A1B1	A				
			1963	06-08	423	2	A1B1	A				
44	Lena	Kusur	1967	06-08	189000	2	A1B1	A				
			1962	06-06	166000	2	A1B1	A				
			1948	06-13	165000	2	A1B1	A				

TABLE II : FLOODS CHARACTERISTICS

				FLOOD CHARACTERISTICS					DISCHARGE ESTIMATION				
Site number	Stream	Observ. site	Year	Date of the max	Maximal discm³s-1	Climatic origine	Condition disc est	Qual. of the sect	Precis. ±m³s-1	Anteced precip.	Depth mm.	Duration days.
1	2	3	4	5	6	7	8	9	10	11	12	13
45	Ebitiem	Ebitem	1952	08-04	748	1	A1B1	A				
			1966	06-16	661	2	A1B1	A				
			1962	09-08	650	1	A1B1	A				
46	Indigirka	Vorontsovo	1967	06-15	11700	2	A1B1	A				
			1941	06-08	11500	2	A1B1	A				
			1968	05-31	11200	2	A1B1	A				
47	Kolyma	Ust-Srednekan	1939	08-24	17800	2	A1B1	A				
			1956	06-15	13000	2	A1B1	A				
			1951	06-14	11800	2	A1B1	A				
48	Khasyn	Kolyma Road km 79	1950	07-19	514	1	A1B1	A				
			1963	10-03	513	1	A1B1	A				
			1975	08-27	478	1	A1B1	A				
49	Anguema	Mouth of the Brook Shoumny	1962	06-24	6790	2	A1B1	A				
			1973	06-25	6240	2	A1B1	A				
			1957	06-16	5780	2	A1B1	A				
50	Brook Izyskatelsky	1.6 km upstream of the mouth	1959	09-14	54	1	A1B1	A				
			1963	07-25	24	1	A1B1	A				
51	Dep	Rychkovo	1964	07-07	3970	1	A1B1	A				
			1953	02-12	2000	1	A1B1	A				
52	Ussuri	Kirovski	1950	07-24	10300	1	A1B1	B				
			1927	08-13	9380	1	A1B1	B				
			1938	09-03	6610	1	A1B1	B				
53	Amur	Komsomolsk	1959	09-20	38900	1	A1B1	B				
			1951	09-21	38200	1	A1B1	B				
			1957	09-17	35500	1	A1B1	B				
54	Razdolnaya (Suifun)	Terekhovka	1943	08-30	5780	1	A1B1	B				
			1938	08-31	5580	1	A1B1	B				
			1950	07-24	4840	1	A1B1	B				

KAZAKHSTAN-UZBEKISTAN

28 Ishim   29 Ishim   (see Siberia)

55	Syr Darya	Tiumen-Aryk	1934	06-30	2730	4	A1B1	D				
			1936	06-09	2420	4	A1B1	D				
			1952	05-19	2130	4	A1B1	D				
56	Amu Darya	Chatly	1958	07-27	6900	4	A1B1	D				
			1934	07-15	6600	4	A1B1	D				
			1953	07-22	5950	4	A1B1	D				

TABLE I : IDENTIFICATION OF OBSERVATIONS SITES AND CHARACTERISTICS OF BASINS

	OBSERVATIONS SITE					CHARACTERISTICS OF BASIN							
Site number	River basin	Stream	Observ. site		Coordinates Lat. Long.	Period	Area km²	Slope	Soil	Cover	Regime	Mean precip. mm	Mean disc. m³s−1
1	2	3	4	5	6	7	8	9	10	11	12	13	14
7002	Findhorn	Findhorn	Forres	1	N 57:36 W 03:39	1958 81	780	C	B36 B64	C70 D30	50	1200	18.
8006	Spey	Spey	Boat O'brig	1	N 57:33 W 03:08	1952 80	2860	D	C D	C100	50	1150	77.1
12001	Dee	Dee	Cairnton Woodend	1	N 57:03 W 02:36	1929 80	1370	B	B33 C 1 D66	C80 D15 E 5	50	1150	35.7
24003	Wear	Wear	Stanhope	1	N 54:44 W 02:01	1958 79	172	D	D	C	50	1320	3.56
25002	Tees	Tees	Dent Bank	1	N 54:37 W 02:06	1959 71	217	D	C12 D88	C	50	1720	7.66
27021	Humber	Don	Doncaster	1	N 53:31 W 01:08	1868 1980	1260	C	C D	C50 D50	50	800	14.4
28070	Trent	Burbage Brook	Burbage	1	N 53:19 W 01:36	1925 80	9.1	D	D	C	50	1000	0.19
28009	Humber	Trent	Colwick (Trent Bridge)	1	N 52:57 W 01:04	1883 80	7490	C		C70 D30	50	785	71.2
29003	Lud	Lud	Louth	1	N 53:22 W 00:00	1966 81	55.1	C	A	C10 D90	50	680	0.39
38007	Lee	Canons Brook	Harlow	1	N 51:46 W 00:04	1950 80	21.4	B	D	C80 D20	50	640	0.10
39001	Thames	Thames	Teddington	1	N 51:26 W 00:19	1882 74	9670	C B		C60 D40	50	735	75.4
45005	Otter	Otter	Dotton	1	N 50:41 W 03:17	1962 81	203	B	A52 C48	C15 D80 E 5	50	1005	3.16
46003	Dart	Dart	Austins Bridge	1	N 50:29 W 03:45	1958 81	248	C	A26 B24 D50	C80 D20	50	1820	11.2
46005	Dart	East Dart	Bellever	1	N 50:35 W 03:53	1964 81	21.5	E	D	C	50	2100	1.20
46806	Avon	Avon	Intake	1	N 50:27 W 03:51	1939 57	14	E	D	C	50	2200	
51901	West Lyn	West Lyn	Lynmouth	1	N 51:13 W 03:49	1952 80	23.5		B85 D15	C20 D80	50	1250	

TABLE I : IDENTIFICATION OF OBSERVATIONS SITES AND CHARACTERISTICS OF BASINS

	OBSERVATIONS SITE						CHARACTERISTICS OF BASIN						
Site number	River basin	Stream	Observ. site		Coordinates Lat. Long.	Period	Area km²	Slope	Soil	Cover	Regime	Mean precip. mm	Mean disc. m³s-1
1	2	3	4	5	6	7	8	9	10	11	12	13	14
53004	Avon	Chew	Compton Dando	1	N 51:22 W 02:30	1958 80	130	B	A22 C55 D23	C10 D90	50	1015	0.99
54001	Severn	Severn	Bewdley	1	N 52:23 W 02:19	1923 80	4325	A	A22 B28 D50	C20 D75 E 5	50	945	61.9
54013	Severn	Clywedog	Cribynan	1	N 52:27 W 03:33	1959 65	57	D	B36 D64	A60 C30 D10	50	1805	2.22
54043	Severn	Severn	Upton	1	N 52:03 W 02:11	1955 80	6990	C		C65 D35	50	850	93
55008	Wye	Wye	Cefn Brwyn	1	N 52:26 W 03:43	1950 80	10.4	D		C	50	2530	0.73
55007	Wye	Wye	Erwood	1	N 52:05 W 03:20	1937 81	1280	B	B57 D43	A10 C70 D20	50	1425	34.9
56006	Usk	Usk	Trallong	1	N 51:57 W 03:31	1963 81	184	C	B53 D47	A10 C80 D10	50	1710	6.14
57004	Cynon	Cynon	Abercynon	1	N 51:39 W 03:20	1960 81	109	C	D	A10 C70 D15 E 5	50	1800	
60001	Towy	Towy	Ty Castell Farm	1	N 51:51 W 04:11	1958 81	1090	B	B70 D30	A15 C45 D40	50	1570	39.4
71001	Ribble	Ribble	Salmesbury	1	N 53:46 W 02:37	1960 80	1145	B	D	C25 D70 E 5	50	1325	33.9
71804	Hodder	Dunsop	Footholme	1	N 53:58 W 02:31	1959 67	24.9	E	D	C	50	1810	
77001	Esk	Esk	Netherby	1	N 55:02 W 02:57	1961 79	840	B	C35 D65	A10 C65 D25	50	1500	22.7
83802	Irvine	Irvine	Kilmarnock	1	N 55:36 W 04:30	1913 80	218	C		C80 D20	50	1250	5.87

TABLE II : FLOODS CHARACTERISTICS

	FLOOD CHARACTERISTICS						DISCHARGE ESTIMATION					
Site number	Stream	Observ. site	Year	Date of the max	Maximal disc m³s-1	Climatic origine	Condition disc est	Qual. of the sect	Precis. ±m³s-1	Anteced precip.	Depth mm.	Duration days.
1	2	3	4	5	6	7	8	9	10	11	12	13
7002	Findhorn	Forres	1970	08-16	2400	1	AOXO					
			1981	09-20	955	1	A1BO					
			1981	10-03	650	1	A1BO					
8006	Spey	Boat O'Brig	1970	08-17	1600	1	A1BO					
			1956	07-30	1150	1	A1BO					
			1960	08-25	980	1	A1BO					
12001	Dee	Cairnton	1829	08	1900	1	DOXO					
		Woodend	1920	10	1135	1	DOXO					
			1937	01-24	1135	1	A1CO					
24003	Wear	Stanhope	1968	03-23	224	4	A2BO					
			1976	01-02	167	4	AOBO					
25002	Tees	Dent Bank	1968	03-23	445	4	A1BO					
			1959	10-26	352	1	A1BO					
27021	Don	Doncaster	1941		348		AOB1					
			1947	03-19	347	2	A1B1					
28070	Burbage Brook	Burbage	1958	07-01	27.8	1	A1CO					
			1973	07-15	24.5	1	A1CO					
28009	Trent	Trent Bridge	1795		1420							
			1875		1270							
			1852		1130							
			1947	03-19	1110	2	AOXO					
29003	Lud	Louth	1920	05-29	152	1	D5XO					
			1968	11-02	7.35		A1BO					
38007	Canons Brook	Harlow	1958	07-01	14.2	1	A2X6					
			1977	02-20	12.3	1	A1B6					
39001	Thames	Teddington (1)	1894	11-18	1060	1	AOXO					
			1947	03-20	715	2	A1BO					
			1968	09-17	600	1	A1BO					
45005	Otter	Dotton	1968	07-10	348	1	A1CO					
			1972	12-02	130	1	AOBO					
46003	Dart	Austins Bridge	1979	12-27	550	1	AOCO					
			1960	09-30	328	1	A1B1					
46005	East Dart	Bellever	1979	12-27	67	1	AOBO					
			1967	07-22	63	1	A1BO					
46806	Avon	Intake	1944	11-16	47.9	1	A1XO					
			1956	09-27	37.4	1	A1XO					
51901	West Lyn	Lynmouth	1952	08-15	252	1	B4D4					

(1) 1821 flood exceeded 1894 flood. 1774 and 1809 flood exceeded probably the 1894 flood.

TABLE II : FLOODS CHARACTERISTICS

	FLOOD CHARACTERISTICS						DISCHARGE ESTIMATION					
Site number	Stream	Observ. site	Year	Date of the max	Maximal disc m³s-1	Climatic origine	Condition disc est	Qual. of the sect	Precis. ±m³s-1	Anteced precip.	Depth mm.	Duration days.
1	2	3	4	5	6	7	8	9	10	11	12	13
53004	Chew	Compton Dando	1968	07-10	227	1	A2XO					
			1979	05-30	67.5	1	A1BO					
54001	Severn	Bewdley	1947	03-21	671	2	A1B1					
			1946	02-10	642		A1B1					
			1960	12-06	629	1	A1B1					
54013	Clywedog	Cribynan	1964	12-12	120	1	A1C1					
			1959	10-26	88	1	A1B1					
54043	Severn	Upton	1960	01-25	540	4	A1B1					
			1960	12-07	515	1	A1B1					
			1965	12-12	490	1	A1B1					
55008	Wye	Cefn Brwyn	1973	08-05	57.1	1	A1XO					
			1957	08-05	48.8	1	A4BO					
			1971	11-20	30	1	A1BO					
55007	Wye	Erwood	1960	12-04	1205	1	A1B1					
			1979	12-27	1130	1	A1B1					
			1965	12-09	1090	1	A1B1					
55006	Usk	Trallong	1979	12-27	316	1	A1B1					
			1967	10-16	259	1	A1B1					
			1967	02-27	252	1	A1B1					
57004	Cynon	Abercynon	1979	12-27	184	1	A1B1					
			1965	12-18	146	1	A1B1					
			1981	03-21	114	1	A1B1					
60001	Towy	Ty Castell Farm	1931		1270		COXO					
			1979	12-28	844	1	A1B1					
			1981	03-22	705	1	A1B1					
71001	Ribble	Salmesbury	1980	10-27	995	1	A1B1					
			1964	12-12	915	1	A1B1					
71804	Dunsop	Footholme	1967	08-08	241	1	AODO					
			1961	08-03	32.5	1	A1B1					
77001	Esk	Netherby	1977	10-31	1110	1	A1B1					
			1964	10-06	1060	1	A1B1					
			1967	10-09	1060	1	A1B1					
83802	Irvine	Kilmarnock	1961	08-08	227	1	AOXO					
			1966	12-19	129	1	A1BO					
			1953	11-15	109	1	A2BO					

TABLE I : IDENTIFICATION OF OBSERVATIONS SITES AND CHARACTERISTICS OF BASINS

OBSERVATIONS SITE							CHARACTERISTICS OF BASIN						
Site number	River basin	Stream	Observ. site		Coordinates Lat. Long.	Period	Area km²	Slope	Soil	Cover	Regime	Mean precip. mm	Mean disc. m³s-1
1	2	3	4	5	6	7	8	9	10	11	12	13	14
MAINE													
01055000	Androscogin	Swift	Roxbury	1	N 44:39 W 70:35	1929 80	248				61	1100	5.6
MASSACHUSSETTS													
01170500	Connecticut	Connecticut	Montague City	1	N 42:35 W 72:35	1904 80	20370				61	1250	390
CONNECTICUT													
01187980	Connecticut	Farmington	Collins- Ville	1	N 41:48 W 72:56	1928 36 1938 1955 1963 77	917				60	1250	
01189500	Connecticut	Salmon	Granby	1	N 41:56 W 72:47	1946 63	173				60	1250	3.6
01208500	Housatonic	Naugatuck	Beacon Falls	1	N 41:27 W 73:04	1918 24 1928 80	671				60	1300	14.0
NEW YORK													
01335500	Hudson	Hudson	Mechanic- Ville	1	N 42:55 W 73:41	1887 1956	11660				61	1100	210
04223000	St. Lawrence	Genesee	Portage- Ville	1	N 42:34 W 78:03	1909 80	2540				60	850	36
NEW JERSEY													
01463500	Delaware	Delaware	Trenton	1	N 40:13 W 74:47	1913 80	17560				61 60	1200	333
01482500	Delaware	Salem	Woodstown	1	N 39:39 W 75:20	1941 80	38				60	1100	0.5
PENSYLVANIA													
01473100	Delaware	Zacharias	Skippak	1	N 40:12 W 75:22	1960 80	18.8				60	1100	
01570500	Susquehanna	Susquehanna	Harrisburg	1	N 40:15 W 76:53	1890 1980	62400				60	1000	980
1	Ohio	Two Mile	Port Alleghany	3	N 41:50 W 78:16		18.3				60	1100	
03036500	Ohio	Allegheny	Kittaning	1	N 40:49 W 79:32	1904 28 1934 80	23240				60	1000	444

TABLE I : IDENTIFICATION OF OBSERVATIONS SITES AND CHARACTERISTICS OF BASINS

	OBSERVATIONS SITE						CHARACTERISTICS OF BASIN						
Site number	River basin	Stream	Observ. site		Coordinates Lat. Long.	Period	Area km²	Slope	Soil	Cover	Regime	Mean precip. mm	Mean disc. m³s-1
1	2	3	4	5	6	7	8	9	10	11	12	13	14
MARYLAND													
01613000	Potomac	Potomac	Hancock	1	N 39:42 W 78:11	1932 80	10550			A D	60	1100	120
01638500	Potomac	Potomac	Point of Rocks	1	N 39:16 W 77:33	1895 1980	25000				60	1100	266
01650500	Potomac	N.W.B. Anacostia	Colesville	1	N 39:04 W 77:02	1923 80	54.6				60	1100	0.65
VIRGINIA													
01656725	Potomac	Bull run	Catharpin	1	N 38:53 W 77:34	1970 79	66.8				60	1100	1.05
01668000	Rappahannock	Rappahannock	Fredericksburg	1	N 38:19 W 77:31	1907 80	4134			A D	60	1200	47.0
02027000	James	Tye	Lovingston	1	N 37:43 W 78:59	1938 80	240				60	1100	4.4
03171500	Ohio	New	Eggleston	1	N 37:17 W 80:37	1914 79	7620				60	1100	111
NORTH CAROLINA													
02112000	Pee Dee	Yadkin	Wilkesboro	1	N 36:09 W 81:09	1903 1909 1920 1980	1280			A D	60	1300	23.3
03162500	Ohio	N.F. New	Crumpler	1	N 36:31 W 81:23	1908 16 1928 58	717			A D	60	1250	13.4
SOUTH CAROLINA													
02161500	Santee	Broad	Richtex	1	N 34:11 W 81:12	1925 80	12560				60 40	1300	177
GEORGIA													
02197000	Savannah	Savannah	Augusta	1	N 33:22 W 81:57	1883 91 1896 1906 1925 80	19450				40	1300	292
02226000	Altamaha	Altamaha	Doctortown	1	N 31:39 W 81:50	1931 80	35200			A D	40	1200	393
FLORIDA													
02313000	Withlacoochee	Withlacoochee	Holder	1	N 28:59 W 82:21	1928 29 1931 80	4730				40	1300	31

TABLE I : IDENTIFICATION OF OBSERVATIONS SITES AND CHARACTERISTICS OF BASINS

	OBSERVATIONS SITE						CHARACTERISTICS OF BASIN						
Site number	River basin	Stream	Observ. site		Coordinates Lat. Long.	Period	Area km²	Slope	Soil	Cover	Regime	Mean precip. mm	Mean disc. m³s-1
1	2	3	4	5	6	7	8	9	10	11	12	13	14
02323000	Suwannee	Suwannee	Bell	1	N 29:47 W 82:55	1932 56	25700				40	1300	240
ALABAMA													
02420000	Mobile	Alabama	Montgomery	1	N 32:25 W 86:25	1927 80	31900				40	1350	690
WEST VIRGINIA													
03071500	Ohio	Cheat	Morgantown	1	N 39:40 W 79:52	1899 1900 1902 05 1908 18 1924 25	3570			A	60	1100	90.3
.2	Ohio	Laurel	White Pine	3	N 39 W 81		6.3				60	1300	
03151000	Mississipi	Ohio	Parkersburg	1	N 39:16 W 81:34	1940 68	92200				60	1100	
03193000	Ohio	Kanawha	Kanawha Falls	1	N 38:08 W 81:13	1877 1980	21670				60	1300	356
OHIO													
03138900	Ohio	Jennings Bridge Trib.	Wooster	1	N 40:45 W 81:56	1946 1966 80	2.33				60	900	
03255000	Mississipi	Ohio	Cincinnati	1	N 39:06 W 84:31	1858 1980	1983000				60	1100	2740
03272000	Ohio	Twin	Germantown	1	N 39:38 W 84:24	1914 23 1926 80	712				60	1000	7.4
03274500	Ohio	Miami	Venice	1	N 39:18 W 84:39	1914 27 1932 33	9820				60	900	110
04191500	St. Lawrence	Auglaize	Defiance	1	N 41:14 W 84:24	1915 79	6000				60	850	48
KENTUCKY													
03282000	Ohio	Kentucky	Heidelberg	1	N 37:33 W 83:46	1925 31 1936 80	6880				60	1100	104

UNITED STATES OF AMERICA/ETATS UNIS D'AMERIQUE

TABLE I : IDENTIFICATION OF OBSERVATIONS SITES AND CHARACTERISTICS OF BASINS

OBSERVATIONS SITE							CHARACTERISTICS OF BASIN						
Site number	River basin	Stream	Observ. site		Coordinates Lat. Long.	Period	Area km²	Slope	Soil	Cover	Regime	Mean precip. mm	Mean disc. m³s-1
1	2	3	4	5	6	7	8	9	10	11	12	13	14
INDIANA													
03322000	Mississipi	Ohio	Evansville	1	N 37:58 W 87:35	1873 1980	277100				60	1100	3650
TENNESSEE													
03436500	Ohio	Cumberland	Clarksville	1	N 36:31 W 87:22	1924 44	41400				60	1300	633
03540000	Ohio	Emory	Deermont	1	N 36:02 W 84:35	1920 27	1820				60	1300	39
03541500	Ohio	Whites	Glen Alice	1	N 35:48 W 84:46	1934 78	280				60	1300	6.1
03568000	Ohio	Tennessee	Chattanooga	1	N 35:05 W 85:17	1874 1980	55430				90 60	1300	1050
03588500	Ohio	Shoal	Iron City	1	N 35:01 W 87:35	1925 80	900			A D	60	1300	18
03605000	Ohio	Tennessee	Johnsonville	1	N 36:01 W 88:00	1889 1944	99700				60	1250	1760
ILLINOIS													
03377500	Ohio	Wabash	Mount Carmel	1	N 38:24 W 87:45	1884 1980	74160				60	950	771
03611500	Mississipi	Ohio	Metropolis	1	N 37:09 W 88:44	1928 80	526000				60	1050	7700
05585500	Mississipi	Illinois	Meredosia	1	N 39:49 W 90:34	1921 80	67410				60	1000	605
MICHIGAN													
04113000	St. Lawrence	Grand	Lansing	1	N 43:45 W 84:33	1901 80	3180				61	700	23.3
04157000	St. Lawrence	Saginaw	Saginaw	1	N 43:25 W 83:58	1901 80	15700				61	700	
04164350	St. Lawrence	Highbank	Armada	1	N 42:28 W 82:51	1959 70	38.6				61	700	
VERMONT													
04285500	St. Lawrence	N.B. Winooski	Wrightsville	1	N 44:18 W 72:35	1933 80	179			A	61	900	3.8
04290500	St. Lawrence	Winooski	Essex Junction	1	N 44:29 W 73:08	1928 80	2705				61	900	48

TABLE I : IDENTIFICATION OF OBSERVATIONS SITES AND CHARACTERISTICS OF BASINS

	OBSERVATIONS SITE						CHARACTERISTICS OF BASIN						
Site number	River basin	Stream	Observ. site		Coordinates Lat. Long.	Period	Area km²	Slope	Soil	Cover	Regime	Mean precip. mm	Mean disc. m³s⁻¹
1	2	3	4	5	6	7	8	9	10	11	12	13	14
MINNESOTA													
05211000	Mississipi	Mississipi	Grand Rapids	1	N 47:14 W 93:32	1883 1980	8730				61	650	33
05325000	Mississipi	Minnesota	Mankato	1	N 44:10 W 94:00	1903 80	38600				61	700	77
WISCONSIN													
05362000	Mississipi	Jump	Sheldon	1	N 45:18 W 90:57	1915 80	1490				61	700	14.5
05370000	Mississipi	Eau Galle	Spring Valley	1	N 44:51 W 92:14	1944 80	168				61	700	0.89
IOWA													
05421200	Mississipi	Pine	Winthrop	1	N 42:28 W 91:47	1950 80	73				61	900	
05451500	Mississipi	Iowa	Marshall Town	1	N 42:04 W 92:54	1902 03 1914 27 1932 80	4050				61	850	22
05474500	Mississipi	Mississipi	Keokuk	1	N 40:24 W 91:22	1878 1980	308000				61	750	1770
05491000	Mississipi (see Missouri)	Sugar	Keokuk	1	N 40:27 W 91:28	1923 28 1930 31 1959 72	280				60	1000	
MONTANA													
06019500	Missouri	Ruby	Alder	1	N 45:11 W 112:09	1938 80	1390				90 70	700	5.0
06065500	Mississipi	Missouri	Helena	1	N 46:46 W 111:53	1922 42	43700				90 70	(500)	116
06099500	Missouri	Marias	Shelby	1	N 48:26 W 111:53	1902 07 1911 80	8400				90 70	(500)	27
06102500	Missouri	Teton	Farmington	1	N 46:53 W 112:37	1948 54 1964	272				70	(400)	4.7
06174500	Missouri	Milk	Nashua	1	N 48:08 W 106:22	1940 80	57840				70	300	21

TABLE I : IDENTIFICATION OF OBSERVATIONS SITES AND CHARACTERISTICS OF BASINS

	OBSERVATIONS SITE						CHARACTERISTICS OF BASIN						
Site number	River basin	Stream	Observ. site		Coordinates Lat. Long.	Period	Area km²	Slope	Soil	Cover	Regime	Mean precip. mm	Mean disc. m³s-1
1	2	3	4	5	6	7	8	9	10	11	12	13	14
06185200	Missouri	Missouri Trib. 3	Culbertson	1	N 48:06 W 104:31	1963 80	3.2				70	300	
06329500	Missouri	Yellowstone	Sidney	1	N 47:41 W 104:09	1910 31 1933 80	178980				90 70	400	371
12355500	Columbia	N.F. Flathead	Columbia Falls	1	N 48:30 W 114:08	1910 17 1929 80	4010			A	90 70	800	84
12356500	Columbia	Bear	Essex	1	N 48:17 W 113:26	1946 52 1964 1975 81	53			A	90 70	(800)	1.3
12357000	Columbia	M.F. Flathead	Essex	1	N 48:17 W 113:36	1939 53 1956 64	1320			A	90 70	(800)	30

NORTH DAKOTA

06340300	Missouri	Otter	Hannover	1	N 47:07 W 101:36	1965 73	111				61	400	
06342500	Mississipi	Missouri	Bismarck	1	N 46:49 W 100:49	1927 80	482800				90 61 70	400	641

COLORADO

06709500	Missouri	Plum	Louviers	1	N 39:29 W 105:00	1947 80	782			C	90 70	(500)	0.8
06710000	Missouri	South Platte	Littleton	1	N 39:37 W 105:01	1941 80	7950				90 70	600	6.6
06758000	Missouri	Kiowa	Elbert	1	N 39:13 W 104:32	1955 65	74			C	90 70	500	0.03
07099500	Missouri	Arkansas	Pueblo	1	N 38:16 W 104:39	1896 1975	12140				90 70	400	21
09034500	Colorado	Colorado	Hot Sulphur Springs	1	N 40:05 W 106:05	1905 79	2140			A	90	800	
09342500	Colorado	San Juan	Pagosa Springs	1	N 37:16 W 107:01	1910 14 1935 80	772			A	90 70	500	10

TABLE I : IDENTIFICATION OF OBSERVATIONS SITES AND CHARACTERISTICS OF BASINS

| OBSERVATIONS SITE | | | | | | | CHARACTERISTICS OF BASIN | | | | | | |
Site number	River basin	Stream	Observ. site		Coordinates Lat. Long.	Period	Area km²	Slope	Soil	Cover	Regime	Mean precip. mm	Mean disc m³s⁻
1	2	3	4	5	6	7	8	9	10	11	12	13	14
NEBRASKA													
06794710	Missouri	Bone	David City	1	N 41:17 W 97:03	1968 78	22.6				61	650	
06803900	Missouri	N.F. Wahoo	Weston	1	N 41:12 W 96:44	1951 78	112				61	700	
06810500	Missouri	Little Nemaha	Syracuse	1	N 40:38 W 96:11	1950 69	549				61	700	1.9
06828500	Missouri	Republican	Stratton	1	N 40:08 W 101:14	1950 80	(22300) (1) (9840) (2)				70	400	3.7
KANSAS													
06889000	Missouri	Kansas	Topeka	1	N 39:04 W 95:39	1902 80	146900				60 61	550	154
06889100	Missouri (see Wyoming)	Soldier	Goff	1	N 39:37 W 95:58	1964 80	5.34				60	850	0.04
07166700	Mississipi	Burnt	Reese	1	N 37:48 W 96:27	1957 69	23.0				60	850	
07169800	Mississipi	Elk	Elk Falls	1	N 37:23 W 96:11	1967 80	570				60	850	4.6
07179600	Mississipi	Four Mile	Council Grove	1	N 38:36 W 96:30	1964 77	142				60	800	
07182000	Mississipi	Cottonwood	Cottonwood Falls	1	N 38:23 W 96:36	1902 04 1932 70	3440				60	800	15
07182400	Mississipi	Neosho	Strawn	1	N 38:16 W 95:52	1902 62	7600				60	850	34
MISSOURI													
05508000	Mississipi	Salt	New London	1	N 39:37 W 91:25	1922 80	6420				60	900	47
05514500	Mississipi	Cuivre	Troy	1	N 39:01 W 90:59	1922 80	2340				60	950	21
06922500	Missouri	Osage	Warsaw	1	N 38:15 W 92:23	1916 51 (26 years)	29780				60	900	260
06925300	Missouri	Prairie	Decaturville	1	N 37:53 W 92:43	1955 80	3.83				60	1050	

(1) beginning of the observations period

TABLE I : IDENTIFICATION OF OBSERVATIONS SITES AND CHARACTERISTICS OF BASINS

	OBSERVATIONS SITE							CHARACTERISTICS OF BASIN						
Site number	River basin	Stream	Observ. site		Coordinates Lat. Long.		Period	Area km²	Slope	Soil	Cover	Regime	Mean precip. mm	Mean disc. m³s-1
1	2	3	4	5	6		7	8	9	10	11	12	13	14
06934500	Mississipi	Missouri	Herman	1	N 38:43	W 91:26	1930 80	1358000				90 70 60		2260
07010000	Mississipi	Mississipi	St. Louis	1	N 38:37	W 90:11	1861 1980	1805000				90 70 60		5010
ARKANSAS														
07061000	Mississipi	White	Batesville	1	N 35:46	W 91:38	1904 58	28650				60	1000	350
07263500	Mississipi	Arkansas	Little Rock	1	N 34:45	W 92:16	1927 70	409300				90 70 60	650	1150
07265450	Mississipi	Mississipi	Arkansas City	1	N 33:33	W 91:14	1890 93 1897 98 1900 79	2928300				90 70 60		15500
07339500	Mississipi	Rolling	De Queen	1	N 34:03	W 94:25	1948 80	471				60	1300	8.3
07340500	Mississipi (see New Mexico)	Cossatot	De Queen	1	N 34:03	W 94:13	1938 80	940				60	1300	18
MISSISSIPPI														
07275500	Mississipi	Long	Courtland	1	N 34:14	W 89:56	1940 43 1952 80	170				40	1250	
07292500	Mississipi (see Texas)	Homochitto	Rosetta	1	N 31:19	W 91:06	1951 80	1940				40	1400	32
02472500	Pascagoula	Bowie	Hattiesburg	1	N 31:26	W 89:25	1938 80	787			A D	40	1400	13
02486115	Pearl	Three Mile	Jackson	1	N 32:16	W 90:13	1962 80	2.72				40	1350	
LOUISIANA														
07355000	Mississipi	Hemphill	Hot Wells	1	N 31:18	W 92:44	1949 64	46.6				40	1400	0.8
07368000	Mississipi	Boeuf	Girard	1	N 32:29	W 91:48	1926 80	3180				40	1350	10.5
02489400	Pearl	Pushepatapa	Varnado	1	N 30:53	W 89:50	1949 65	410				40	1500	

TABLE I : IDENTIFICATION OF OBSERVATIONS SITES AND CHARACTERISTICS OF BASINS

	OBSERVATIONS SITE						CHARACTERISTICS OF BASIN						
Site number	River basin	Stream	Observ. site		Coordinates Lat. Long.	Period	Area km²	Slope	Soil	Cover	Regime	Mean precip. mm	Mean disc. m³s-1
1	2	3	4	5	6	7	8	9	10	11	12	13	14
08015500	Calcasieu	Calcasieu	Kinder	1	N 30:30 W 92:55	1922 25 1938 57 1961 80	4400				40	1500	73
08022500	Sabine	Sabine	Logansport	1	N 31:58 W 94:00	1903 68	12540				40	1000	91
TEXAS 07335500	Mississipi	Red	Arthur City	1	N 33:53 W 95:30	1905 11 1936 76	115300 100000 (2)				70 60 40	700	270
08082500	Brazos	Brazos	Seymour	1	N 33:35 W 99:16	1923 80	40240 15470 (2)				70 60	550	11
08094000	Brazos	Green S.W. n°1	Dublin	1	N 32:10 W 98:20	1955 77	10.8				40	700	2.02
08106500	Brazos	Little	Cameron	1	N 30:50 W 96:57	1916 80	18300				40 70	800	51
08153500	Colorado (of Texas)	Pedernales	Johnson City	1	N 30:17 W 98:24	1939 80	2450				70	750	5.0
08158000	Colorado	Colorado	Austin	1	N 30:15 W 97:32	1898 1980	99500				70	600	77
08187900	Guadalupe	Escondido	Kenedy S.W.S 11	4	N 28:52 W 97:51	1958 77	21.8				40	900	
08190500	Nueces	West Nueces	Bracket Ville	1	N 29:28 W 100:14	1939 50 1955 80	1800				70	500	0.97
08192000	Nueces	Nueces	Uvalde	1	N 29:07 W 99:54	1939 80	5040				70	550	3.2
08201500	Nueces	Seco	Utopia	1	N 29:34 W 99:24	1961 80	112				70	700	0.5
08364000	Rio Grande	Rio Grande	El Paso	1	N 31:48 W 106:32	1884 1889 93 1897 1975	75200				70	400	25
08447500	Rio Grande	Pecos	Comstock	1	N 29:46 W 101:21	1900 54	91410 (1)				70	300	16

(1) lower part of the basin : 9300 km² responsible for the 1954 flood .
(2) second part of the records

TABLE I : IDENTIFICATION OF OBSERVATIONS SITES AND CHARACTERISTICS OF BASINS

	OBSERVATIONS SITE						CHARACTERISTICS OF BASIN						
Site number	River basin	Stream	Observ. site		Coordinates Lat. Long.	Period	Area km²	Slope	Soil	Cover	Regime	Mean precip. mm	Mean disc m³s
1	2	3	4	5	6	7	8	9	10	11	12	13	14
08449500	Rio Grande	Devils	Del Rio	1	N 29:29 W 101:00	1910 12 1925 56	10840				70	400	16
08452500	Rio Grande	Rio Grande	Del Rio	1	N 29:20 W 100:56	1901 13 1924 54 1962 76	328800				70	(350)	112
08455000	Rio Grande (see New Mexico)	Pinto	Del Rio	1	N 29:09 W 100:43	1930 76	645				70	400	0.8
NEW MEXICO													
07227000	Mississipi	Canadian	Logan	1	N 35:21 W 103:25	1909 14 1926 79	28860				70	(400)	11
08318900	Rio Grande	San Pedro	Golden	1	N 35:14 W 106:18	1953 79	117				70 90	(400)	
08379500	Rio Grande	Pecos	Anton Chico	1	N 35:11 W 105:07	1911 15 1918 20 1929 79	2720				70 90	400	3.6
08408500	Rio Grande	Delaware	Red Bluff	1	N 32:01 W 104:13	1938 79	1780				70	300	0.4
09365000	Colorado	San Juan	Farmington	1	N 36:43 W 108:13	1924 79	18750				90 70	450	6.7
UTAH													
09180500	Colorado	Colorado	Cisco	1	N 38:49 W 109:18	1914 17 1923 79	62420				90 70 71	500	214
09274000	Colorado	Duchesne	Hanna	1	N 40:32 W 110:52	1921 23 1929 30 1946 63	202				90 70	600	
09315500	Colorado	Saleratus	Green River	1	N 38:59 W 110:15	1949 70	466			C	90 71	250	0.0
09378700	Colorado	Cottonwood	Blanding	1	N 37:34 W 109:35	1959 80	531			C	90 70	400	0.2

TABLE I : IDENTIFICATION OF OBSERVATIONS SITES AND CHARACTERISTICS OF BASINS

	OBSERVATIONS SITE						CHARACTERISTICS OF BASIN						
Site number	River basin	Stream	Observ. site		Coordinates Lat. Long.	Period	Area km²	Slope	Soil	Cover	Regime	Mean precip. mm	Mean disc. m³s-1
1	2	3	4	5	6	7	8	9	10	11	12	13	14
10242000	Great Basin	Coal	Cedar City	1	N 37:40 W 113:02	1916 19 1935 80	210				90 70	(500)	0.9
WYOMING													
06316480	Missouri	Headgate	Buffalo	1	N 44:31 W 106:10	1966 73	8.6			B	70	400	
06651800	Missouri	Sand	Orin	1	N 42:40 W 105:13	1955 1961 80	72				70	350	
09217000	Colorado	Green	Green River	1	N 41:31 W 109:27	1951 79	36300 (1) 25200 (2)				70 90	400	48
09224980	Colorado	Summers dry	Green River	1	N 41:22 W 109:39	1965 81	1100			C	71	150	
NEVADA													
09418500	Colorado	Meadow Valley	Caliente	1	N 37:33 W 114:34	1951 60 1964 80	4320			C	71	200	0.3
09419670	Colorado	Red Block	Blue Diamond	1	N 36:10 W 115:30	1962 80	21				71	200	
09419675	Colorado	Flamingo	Las Vegas	1	N 36:07 W 115:11	1966 80	223			E	71	150	
10322500	Great Basin	Humboldt	Palisade	1	N 40:36 W 116:12	1903 06 1912 80	12980				71	250	10
ARIZONA													
09380000	Colorado	Colorado	Lees Ferry	1	N 36:52 W 111:35	1921 80	289600 (1) 279000 (2)				90 70 71	(300)	505
09401000	Colorado	Little Colorado	Grand Falls	1	N 35:26 W 111:12	1925 51 1953 60	54900				71	250	7.2
09401400	Colorado	Moenkopi	Tuba City	1	N 36:01 W 111:24	1941 53 1965 78	6500 (1) 3360 (2)			C	71	250	0.4
09426000	Colorado	Bill Williams	Alamo Dam	1	N 34:14 W 113:36	1927 1929 80	12250				70 71	300	2.6

(1) Beginning of the observations period

TABLE I : IDENTIFICATION OF OBSERVATIONS SITES AND CHARACTERISTICS OF BASINS

	OBSERVATIONS SITE						CHARACTERISTICS OF BASIN						
Site number	River basin	Stream	Observ. site		Coordinates Lat. Long.	Period	Area km²	Slope	Soil	Cover	Regime	Mean precip. mm	Mean disc. m³s⁻¹
1	2	3	4	5	6	7	8	9	10	11	12	13	14
09469500	Colorado	Gila	Coolidge Dam	1	N W 33:10 110:32	1914 80	33380				70 71	300	9.6
09471000	Colorado	San Pedro	Charleston	1	N W 31:38 110:10	1916 80	3160			C	70 71	300	1.7
09471190	Colorado	Walnut Gulch (ARS W.T.S.11)	Tombstone	4	N W 31:44 100:06	1954 80	114	D E		C	70	290	
09487100	Colorado	Little Brawley	Three Points	1	N W 32:07 111:20	1968 81	30.8			C	70	300	
09515500	Colorado	Hassayampa	Wickenburg	1	N W 34:03 112:43	1925 27 1937 38 1946 80	1080			C	71	200	0.5
CALIFORNIA													
10262500	Great Basin	Mojave	Barstow	1	N W 34:54 117:01	1931 80	3340			C	70 71	250	0.7
11056500	Santa Ana	Little San Gorgonio	Beaumont	1	N W 34:02 116:57	1950 80	4.5				30	600	0.00
11066500	Santa Ana	Santa Ana	Arlington	1	N W 33:58 117:28	1927 80	2200				30	500	
11073000	Santa Ana	San Antonio	Claremont	1	N W 34:13 117:40	1918 72	43.8				30	700	0.6
11142500	Arroyo de la Cruz	Arroyo de la Cruz	San Simeon	1	N W 35:43 121:17	1951 1979	107				30	600	1.4
11187000	Sacramento	Kern	Kernville	1	N W 35:46 118:25	1951 1954 80	2610			A	90 30	800	25
11300000	Sacramento	Stanislaus	Knights Ferry	1	N W 37:53 120:36	1903 32	2520			A	90 50	1000	46
11378000	Sacramento	Sacramento	Red Bluff	1	N W 40:14 122:11	1879 88 1892 1968	24090			A B C	90 50	900	324
11407000	Sacramento	Faether	Oroville	1	N W 39:31 121:33	1901 80	9390			A B	90 50	1200	166
11433300	Sacramento	Mid. Fork American	Forest Hill	1	N W 39:00 120:46	1959 80	1360			A	90 50	1500	30

TABLE I : IDENTIFICATION OF OBSERVATIONS SITES AND CHARACTERISTICS OF BASINS

		OBSERVATIONS SITE											CHARACTERISTICS OF BASIN	
Site number	River basin	Stream	Observ. site		Coordinates Lat. Long.	Period	Area km²	Slope	Soil	Cover	Regime	Mean precip. mm	Mean disc. m³s-
1	2	3	4	5	6	7	8	9	10	11	12	13	14
11459800	San Francisco Bay	San Rafael	San Rafael	1	N 37:58 W 122:32	1973 76	3.2			E	50	800	
11474500	Eel	North F. Eel	Mina	1	N 39:56 W 123:21	1953 75	648			A	50	1100	18
11477000	Eel	Eel	Scotia	1	N 40:30 W 124:06	1911 80	8060			A B C	50	1200	207
11527550	Klamath (see Oregon)	Panther	Denny	1	N 40:54 W 123:26	1961 65	14.7			A	50	1300	
11532000	Smith	South F. Smith	Crescent City	1	N 41:48 W 124:02	1955 79 18 years	754			A	50	2000	54

IDAHO

Site number	River basin	Stream	Observ. site		Coordinates Lat. Long.	Period	Area km²	Slope	Soil	Cover	Regime	Mean precip. mm	Mean disc. m³s-
10090500	Great Basin	Bear	Preston	1	N 42:10 W 111:51	1889 1916 1944 80	11770			A	90 70	400	24
12309500	Columbia	Kootenai	Bonners Ferry	1	N 48:42 W 116:19	1928 60	33700				70 90	(600)	421
12392000	Columbia	Clark fork	Cabinet Gorge	1	N 48:05 W 116:04	1928 80	57170				90 70	(600)	633
12415000	Columbia (see Montana)	Ste. Maries	Lotus	1	N 47:20 W 116:37	1921 66	1130			A	90 61	1000	14.8
13050500	Snake	Henrys Fork	St. Anthony	1	N 43:58 W 111:40	1919 80	4580				90 70	500	54
13202000	Snake	Boise	Boise	1	N 43:37 W 116:12	1895 1916 1954 80	6940				90 70	700	33
13313000	Snake	Johnson	Yellow Pine	1	N 44:58 W 115:30	1928 80	552			A	70	700	9.9
13342500	Snake (see Washington, Oregon)	Clearwater	Spalding	1	N 46:27 W 116:50	1911 13 1924 80	24790				90 70	900	438

OREGON

Site number	River basin	Stream	Observ. site		Coordinates Lat. Long.	Period	Area km²	Slope	Soil	Cover	Regime	Mean precip. mm	Mean disc. m³s-
11501000	Klamath	Sprague	Chiloquin	1	N 42:35 W 121:51	1921 80	4090			A	70	500	16
13178000	Snake	Jordan	Jordan Valley	1	N 42:52 W 116:57	1946 52 1955 71	1140			B	70	300	5.6

TABLE I : IDENTIFICATION OF OBSERVATIONS SITES AND CHARACTERISTICS OF BASINS

	OBSERVATIONS SITE						CHARACTERISTICS OF BASIN							
Site number	River basin	Stream	Observ. site		Coordinates Lat. Long.	Period	Area km²	Slope	Soil	Cover	Regime	Mean precip. mm	Mean disc. m³s-1
1	2	3	4	5	6	7	8	9	10	11	12	13	14
14105700	Columbia	Columbia	The Dalles	1	N 45:36 W 121:10	1858 1980	614000						5470
14185900	Columbia	Quartzville	Cascadia	1	N 44:32 W 122:26	1963 80	257				90 50	1800	19.
14191000	Columbia	Willamette	Salem	1	N 44:57 W 123:03	1893 1980	18900				90 50	1400	666
14378200	Rogue	Illinois	Agness	1	N 42:31 W 124:03	1961 80	2560			A	50	2600	118
WASHINGTON													
12194000	Skagit	Skagit	Concrete	1	N 48:32 W 121:46	1925 79	7090			A	50	2400	430
12399500	Columbia	Columbia	International Boundary	1	N 48:55 W 117:47	1938 79	154600						2840
13334300	Columbia	Snake	Anatone	1	N 46:06 W 116:59	1959 80	241000				70 90	400	438
13343450	Snake	Dry	Clarkston	1	N 46:24 W 117:06	1963 77	17.7				70	400	

TABLE II : FLOODS CHARACTERISTICS

	FLOOD CHARACTERISTICS						DISCHARGE ESTIMATION					
Site number	Stream	Observ. site	Year	Date of the max	Maximal discm³s-1	Climatic origine	Condition disc est	Qual. of the sect	Precis. ±m³s-1	Anteced precip.	Depth mm.	Duration days.
1	2	3	4	5	6	7	8	9	10	11	12	13
MAINE												
01055000	Swift	Roxbury	1959	10-24	476	1	A1C1			2	74	3
			1942	06-15	416	1						
MASSACHUSSETTS												
01170500	Connecticut	Montague City	1936	03-19	6680	4	A2C1	A1A				
			1938	09-22	5520	1						
CONNECTICUT												
01187980	Farmington	Collinsville	1955	08-19	3960	1	B4D4					
			1938	09-21	1530	1						
01189500	Salmon	Granby	1955	08-19	1130	1	B4XO			3	440	
			1955	10-16	306	1						
01208500	Naugatuck	Beacon Falls	1955	08-19	3000	1	A2C1			3	340	4
			1955	10-16	861	1	A1B1					
			1948	12-31	835	1						
NEW YORK												
01335500	Hudson	Mechanicville	1913	03-28	3400	4	A1C1					
			1948	12-31	3340	1						
			1922	04-12	2060	4						
04223000	Genesee	Portageville	1972	06-23	2550	1	A4D6					
			1967	09-29	1340	1	A1C1					
NEW JERSEY												
01463500	Delaware	Trenton	1955	08-20	9320	1	A2C1					
			1903	10-11	8350	1	D5C1					
			1936	03-19	6430	4	A1C1					
01482500	Salem	Woodstown	1940	09-01	623	1	A5C4					
			1968	06-12	125	1	A1B1					
			1950	11-25	106	1						
PENSYLVANIA												
01473100	Zacharias	Skippak	1971	09-13	283	1						
			1972	06-22	166	1						
01570500	Susquehanna	Harrisburg	1972	06-24	28900	1	A2C1					
			1936	03-19	21000	1						
			1889	06-02	18500	1	D5C4					
			1894	05-22	17400	1						
			1865	03-18	16300	4						
1	Two Mile	Port Alleghany	1942	07-18	425	1	C4D4					
03036500	Allegheny	Kittanning	1913	03-26	7620	4	A4CO					
			1806	04-10	7340	4						
			1865	03-18	7140	4						

TABLE II : FLOODS CHARACTERISTICS

	FLOOD CHARACTERISTICS						DISCHARGE ESTIMATION					
Site number	Stream	Observ. site	Year	Date of the max	Maximal disc m³s-1	Climatic origine	Condition disc est	Qual. of the sect	Precis. ±m³s-1	Anteced precip.	Depth mm.	Duration days.
1	2	3	4	5	6	7	8	9	10	11	12	13

MARYLAND

01613000	Potomac	Hancock	1936	03-18	9630	1	A4C1					
			1889	05	6230	1	D5C1					
01638500	Potomac	Point of Rocks	1936	03-19	13600	1	A4C4	A1B				
			1889	06-02	13000	1	C4C4					
			1942	10-16	11800	1						
01650500	N.W.B. Anacostia	Colesville	1972	06-22	312	1	A1C1					
			1975	08-15	188	1						

VIRGINIA

01656725	Bull run	Catharpin	1972	06-22	1120	1	A5D4					
01668000	Rappahannock	Fredericksburg	1942	10-16	3960	1	A4C4					
			1937	04-26	3790	1						
			1972	06-22	3030	1						
02027000	Tye	Lovingston	1969	08-20	2270	1	A4C4					
			1972	06-21	345	1						
03171500	New	Eggleston	1940	08-14	6200	1						
			1878	09	5920	1						
			1916	07-16	5780	1						
			1977	11-07	2800	1						

NORTH CAROLINA

02112000	Yadkin	Wilkesboro	1940	08-14	4530	1	A4D1				320	
			1916	07	3290	1	C4D1					
03162500	N.F. New	Crumpler	1940	08-14	2070	1	A4D4			2	290	6
			1878	09-12	1250	1						

SOUTH CAROLINA

02161500	Broad	Richtex	1929	10-03	6460	1	A4D6					
			1928	08-17	630	1	A1C1					

GEORGIA

02197000	Savannah	Augusta	1796		10200	1	C5DO					
			1929	10-02	9910	1	A					
			1908	08-27	8690	1						
			1888	09-11	8580	1						
02226000	Altamaha	Doctortown	1925	01-23	8500	1	C4C1					
			1929	03-13	5070							

FLORIDA

02313000	Withlacoochee	Holder	1960	04-05	245	1	A1X1					
			1960	10-10	200	1						
02323000	Suwannee	Bell	1948	04-13	2330	1						
			1928	08-28	2100	1						

TABLE II : FLOODS CHARACTERISTICS

	FLOOD CHARACTERISTICS						DISCHARGE ESTIMATION					
Site number	Stream	Observ. site	Year	Date of the max	Maximal discm^3s^{-1}	Climatic origine	Condition disc est	Qual. of the sect	Precis. $\pm m^3s^{-1}$	Anteced precip.	Depth mm.	Duration days.
1	2	3	4	5	6	7	8	9	10	11	12	13

ALABAMA

02420000	Alabama	Montgomery	1886	04-01	9120	1	C5BO					
			1888	03-30	8010	1	C5BO					
			1961	02-26	8010	1	A1B1					

WEST VIRGINIA

03071500	Cheat	Morgantown	1888	07-10	4530	1						
			1924	03-29	2620	4						
			1911	01-30	2350	4						
2	Laurel	White Pine	1943	08	210	1	C4D4					
03151000	Ohio	Parkersburg	1913	03-29	16800	4						
			1943	01-01	12500	4						
			1945	03-08	12400	4						
03193000	Kanawha	Kanawha Falls	1878	09-14	9060	1	A4CO					
			1901	05-23	7960	1						
			1940	08-15	7020	1						

OHIO

03138900	Jenningsbridge Trib.	Wooster	1946	06-16	53.2	1						
			1969	07-05	19.0	1						
03255000	Ohio	Cincinnati	1937	01-26	25300	4	A1C1	practically no effect of regulation for this flood.				
			1773		23300							
			1884	02-14	20800	4						
			1945	03-07	20100	4						
03272000	Twin	Germantown	1913	03-25	1870	4	C4D4					
			1915	07-08	266	1	A4CO					
03274500	Miami	Venice	1913	03-26	10500	4						
			1920	04-21	1610	1	AOXO					
04191500	Auglaize	Defiance	1913	03	3400	4	B5C1					
			1950	02-16	1490	4	AOC1					

KENTUCKY

03282000	Kentucky	Heidelberg	1939	02-04	3400	4	A4C1					
			1957	01-30	3290	4						
			1929	03-24	3200	1						

INDIANA

03322000	Ohio	Evansville	1937	01-29	39900	4	A1C1					
			1884	02-19	26300	4						
			1883	02-19	25900	4						
			1964	03-16	25900	4						

TENNESSEE

03436500	Cumberland	Clarksville	1937	01-24	8210	4	AOXO					
			1927	01-02	6120	4						
03540000	Emory	Deermont	1929	03-23	5240	4	A1C1					
			1926	12-25	1450	1						

TABLE II : FLOODS CHARACTERISTICS

								DISCHARGE ESTIMATION				
Site number	Stream	Observ. site	Year	Date of the max	Maximal disc m³s-1	Climatic origine	Condition disc est	Qual. of the sect	Precis. ±m³s-1	Anteced precip.	Depth mm.	Duration days.
1	2	3	4	5	6	7	8	9	10	11	12	13
03541500	Whites	Glen Alice	1929	03-23	1870		A1C1					
			1973	05-27	1770	1						
			1957	11-18	1440	1						
03568000	Tennessee	Chattanooga x	1867	03-11	13000	1	C0C1	x Regulated since 1940				
			1875	03-01	11600	1	A1C1					
			1886	04-03	11100	1						
			1917	03-07	9660	1						
03588500	Shoal	Iron City	1955	03-21	3740	1	A1D1			1	230	3
			1927	03-13	1840	1	A1C1					
			1973	03-15	1750	1						
03605000	Tennessee	Johnsonville x	1897	03-24	13000	1	A0X1	x Regulated after 1897				
			1927	01-04	9690	4						
			1936	04-10	9600	1						
			1937	01-23	9000	4						
ILLINOIS												
03377500	Wabash	Mount Carmel	1913	03-30	12100	4	A4D4					
			1875	08-09	9060	1						
			1943	05-25	8640	1	A1C1					
03611500	Ohio	Metropolis	1937	02-01	52400	4	A0C1					
			1913	04-07	39600	1						
			1950	02-13	37400	4						
			1975	04-11	33700	1						
05585500	Illinois	Meredosia	1943	05-26	3480	1	A1C1					
			1979	04-19	3370	1						
MICHIGAN												
04113000	Grand	Lansing	1904	03-26	694	4	A1C1					
			1947	04-07	464	1						
04157000	Saginaw	Saginaw	1904	03-29	1930	4	A1C1					
			1916	03-31	1720	4						
04164350	Highbank	Armada	1975	04-19	53.5	1						
			1968	02-01	39.6	4						
VERMONT												
04285500	N.B. Winooski	Wrightsville	1927	11-03	487	1	C4D6					
			1934	04-12	61.5	4	A1C1					
04290500	Winooski	Essex Junction	1927	11-04	3200	1	C4D6					
			1936	03-19	1280	4	A1D6					
MINNESOTA												
05211000	Mississipi	Grand Rapids	1948	09-03	354	1	A1C1					
			1905	09-08	149	1						
			1901	04-21	148	4						
05325000	Minnesota	Mankato	1881	04-26	3120		D4X0					
			1965	04-10	2660	4	A1C1					
			1969	04-12	2170	4						

TABLE II : FLOODS CHARACTERISTICS

	FLOOD CHARACTERISTICS						DISCHARGE ESTIMATION					
Site number	Stream	Observ. site	Year	Date of the max	Maximal discm³s-1	Climatic origine	Condition disc est	Qual. of the sect	Precis. ±m³s-1	Anteced precip.	Depth mm.	Duration days.
1	2	3	4	5	6	7	8	9	10	11	12	13

WISCONSIN

Site number	Stream	Observ. site	Year	Date of the max	Maximal discm³s-1	Climatic origine	Condition disc est	Qual. of the sect	Precis. ±m³s-1	Anteced precip.	Depth mm.	Duration days.
05362000	Jump	Sheldon	1941	08-31	1300	1	A4CO					
			1967	04-01	592	4						
05370000	Eau Galle	Spring Valley	1942	09-18	930	1	C4D4					
			1954	04-15	198	4	A1B1					

IOWA

Site number	Stream	Observ. site	Year	Date of the max	Maximal discm³s-1	Climatic origine	Condition disc est	Qual. of the sect	Precis. ±m³s-1	Anteced precip.	Depth mm.	Duration days.
05421200	Pine	Winthrop	1968	07-17	685	1	AOD4					
			1950	09-21	411	1						
05451500	Iowa	Marshall Town	1918	06-04	1190	1	A4CO					
			1969	07-09	903	1	A1C1					
			1960	03-31	609	4						
05474500	Mississipi	Keokuk	1851	06-06	10200	1	D4XO					
			1973	04-24	9740	4	A1C1					
			1965	05-01	9260	1						
			1888	05-18	8890	1						
05491000	Sugar (see Missouri)	Keokuk	1905	06-09	934	1						
			1927	10-01	187	1						

MONTANA

Site number	Stream	Observ. site	Year	Date of the max	Maximal discm³s-1	Climatic origine	Condition disc est	Qual. of the sect	Precis. ±m³s-1	Anteced precip.	Depth mm.	Duration days.
06019500	Ruby	Alder	1972	06-08	48.1	2						
			1970	06-10	47.3	2	A1B1	A1B				
06065500	Missouri	Helena	1927	06-15	943	2	A1X1					
			1942	06-10	708	2						
06099500	Marias	Shelby	1964	06-09	6830	2	A4C1	(Dam failure)				
			1975	06-20	2140	2	A1C1					
			1948	06-18	1130	2						
06102500	Teton	Farmington	1964	06-08	1550	2						
			1948	06-03	78.7	2						
06174500	Milk	Nashua	1952	04-18	1280	2	AOXO					
			1978	04-05	535	2						
06185200	Missouri Trib. 3	Culbertson	1966	07-04	72.8	1	B4D4					
06329500	Yellowstone	Sidney	1921	06-21	4500	2	AOXO					
			1952	03-31	3910	2						
12355500	N.F. Flathead	Columbia Falls	1964	06-09	1960	4	A4D4					
			1974	06-18	971	2						
12356500	Bear	Essex	1964	06-08	237	4						
			1975	06-19	52.1	2						
12357000	M.F. Flathead	Essex	1964	06-08	2130	4	A4D4					
			1954	05	510	2						

TABLE II : FLOODS CHARACTERISTICS

	FLOOD CHARACTERISTICS						DISCHARGE ESTIMATION					
Site number	Stream	Observ. site	Year	Date of the max	Maximal discm³s-1	Climatic origine	Condition disc est	Qual. of the sect	Precis. ±m³s-1	Anteced precip.	Depth mm.	Duration days.
1	2	3	4	5	6	7	8	9	10	11	12	13
NORTH DAKOTA												
06340300	Otter	Hannover	1966	06-24	1280	1						
			1965	07-12	27.8	1						
06342500	Missouri	Bismarck	1952	04-06	14200	2	A1C1					
		Regulated since	1943	04-03	7990	2						
		1937	1947	03-29	7420	2						
COLORADO												
06709500	Plum	Louviers	1965	06-16	4360	1	A4D4					
			1969	05-08	125	1						
06710000	South Platte	Littleton	1965	06-16	3100	1	A4D4					
		Regulated	1973	05-06	312	4						
			1942	04-23	275	4						
06758000	Kiowa	Elbert	1935	05-30	1230	1	C4D4					
			1965	06-17	1180	1	A4D4					
			1955	08-27	8.6	1						
07099500	Arkansas	Pueblo	1921	06-03	2920	4						
			1902	08-05	850	1						
			1923	07-12	725	1						
09034500	Colorado	Hot Sulphur	1921	06-15	292	2	AOXO					
		Springs	1924	06-14	253	2	A1C1					
09342500	San Juan	Pagosa Springs	1911	10-05	708	1	A5DO					
			1927	06-29	453	2	D5XO					
			1970	09-06	186	1	A1B1					
NEBRASKA												
06794710	Bone	David City	1963	06-24	592	1						
			1978	06-22	46.7	1						
06803900	N.F. Wahoo	Weston	1963	06-24	2310	1						
			1977	08-31	311	1						
06810500	Little Nemaha	Syracuse	1950	05-09	6370	1						
			1951	06-02	810	1						
06828500	Republican	Stratton	1935	05-31	5660	1	C5D4					
			1962	07-31	759	1						
KANSAS												
06889000	Kansas	Topeka	1951	07-13	13300	1	A4D4					
		Regulated since	1903	05-30	8500	1						
		1948	1908	06-09	5670	1						
06889100	Soldier (see Wyoming)	Goff	1970	05-10	201	1	A1D4					
			1975	06-18	27.8	1						
07166700	Burnt	Reese	1965	06-09	581	1						
			1961	11-01	108	1						

TABLE II : FLOODS CHARACTERISTICS

	FLOOD CHARACTERISTICS						DISCHARGE ESTIMATION					
Site number	Stream	Observ. site	Year	Date of the max	Maximal discm³s-1	Climatic origine	Condition disc est	Qual. of the sect	Precis. ±m³s-1	Anteced precip.	Depth mm.	Duration days.
1	2	3	4	5	6	7	8	9	10	11	12	13
07169800	Elk	Elk Falls	1976	07-03	5660	1	A1C1					
			1970	04-18	830	1						
07179600	Four Mile	Council Grove	1969	06-26	1930	1						
			1974	05-14	368	1						
07182000	Cottonwood	Cottonwood Falls	1951	07-11	5520	1						
			1948	07-20	2210	1						
07182400	Neosho	Strawn	1951	07-11	11300	1	AODO					
			1948	07-21	2810	1						
			1904	07-07	2550	1						
MISSOURI												
05508000	Salt	New London	1973	04-22	3030	1	A4CO					
			1969	10-14	2250	1						
05514500	Cuivre	Troy	1941	10-05	3400	1	AOC1					
			1969	10-12	2380	1						
			1979	04-12	1550	1						
06922500	Osage	Warsaw	1943	05-22	6230	1						
			1844	06	5240	1						
			1951	07-07	3400	1						
06925300	Prairie	Decaturville	1965	09-05	62.3	1						
			1958	07-16	56.6	1						
06934500	Missouri	Herman Regulated	1844	06	25300	2	DOXO					
			1903	06-06	19100	2	AOXO					
			1951	06-07	17500	2						
07010000	Mississipi	St. Louis	1844	06-27	36800	4	D5DO					
			1903	06-10	28900	4						
			1892	05-19	26200	4						
			1927	04-26	25200	4						
ARKANSAS												
07061000	White	Batesville	1916	02-01	10800	1	C5XO					
			1915	08-22	10600	1						
07263500	Arkansas	Little Rock	1943	05-27	15200	1	A1XO					
			1938	02-21	13300	4						
			1945	04-21	13200	4						
07265450	Mississipi	Arkansas City	1927	05	70000							
			1937	02-16	61200	4						
			1912	04-16	56800	4						
			1945	04-09	54400	4						
07339500	Rolling	De Queen	1947	08-27	3120	1	C4D6					
			1971	12-10	2010	1						
07340500	Cossatot	De Queen	1968	05-13	3460	1	A1C4					
			1971	12-10	2920	1						
(see New Mexico)			1969	01-30	2120	1						

TABLE II : FLOODS CHARACTERISTICS

	FLOOD CHARACTERISTICS						DISCHARGE ESTIMATION					
Site number	Stream	Observ. site	Year	Date of the max	Maximal disc $m^3 s^{-1}$	Climatic origine	Condition disc est	Qual. of the sect	Precis. $\pm m^3 s^{-1}$	Anteced precip.	Depth mm.	Duration days.
1	2	3	4	5	6	7	8	9	10	11	12	13

MISSISSIPPI

07275500	Long	Courtland	1954	05-28	1080	1						
			1955	03-21	586	1						
07292500	Homochitto (see Texas)	Rosetta	1974	04-13	4250	1	A1C1					
			1964	10-04	3990	1						
02472500	Bowie	Hattiesburg	1900	04	1420	1						
			1974	04-14	1290	1	A5CO					
02486115	Three Mile	Jackson	1971	02-26	48.4	1						
			1974	08-30	48.1	1						

LOUISIANA

07355000	Hemphill	Hot Wells	1973		555	1						
			1953	04-29	236	1	A1C1					
			1950	02-13	112	1						
07368000	Boeuf	Girard	1931	12-26	125	1						
			1934	12-04	101	1						
02489400	Pushepatapa	Varnado	1961	02-22	1580	1	AOD6					
			1961	11-13	867	1						
08015500	Calcasieu	Kinder	1953	05-19	5150	1	A1C1					
			1923	12-23	1930	1						
08022500	Sabine	Logansport Regulated since 1961	1945	04-08	2610	1	A1X1					
			1957	05-07	1740	1						

TEXAS

07335500	Red	Arthur City	1908	05-28	11300	1						
			1938	02-19	6290	4						
			1942	04-26	5640	4						
08082500	Brazos	Seymour	1926	10-16	2700	1	A4C1					
			1926	8-29	2340	1						
08094000	Green S.W. n° 1	Dublin	1956	04-30	326	1						
			1971	05-28	115	1						
08106500	Little	Cameron	1921	09-10	18300	1	A4C1					
			1929	05-29	3910	1						
			1957	04-25	3290	1						
08153500	Pedernales	Johnson City	1952	09-11	12500	1	A4C1					
			1959	10-04	4020	1						
			1978	08-03	3600	1						
08158000	Colorado	Austin	1869	07-07	15600	1						
			1935	06-15	13600	1	A4C1					
			1938	07-25	7820	1						

TABLE II : FLOODS CHARACTERISTICS

FLOOD CHARACTERISTICS							DISCHARGE ESTIMATION					
Site number	Stream	Observ. site	Year	Date of the max	Maximal disc m³s-1	Climatic origine	Condition disc est	Qual. of the sect	Precis. ±m³s-1	Anteced precip.	Depth mm.	Duration days.
1	2	3	4	5	6	7	8	9	10	11	12	13
08187900	Escondido S.W.S. n° 11	Kenedy	1967 1965	09-21 05-19	510 140	1 1						
08190500	West Nueces	Bracketville	1935 1964 1955	06-14 09-20 09-24	15600 6970 4250	1 1 1	C4D4 A4D4 C4D4					
08192000	Nueces	Uvalde	1935 1932 1955 1964	06-14 09-01 09-24 09-20	17400 5860 5350 5320	1 1 1 1	C4D4					
08201500	Seco	Utopia	1958 1973	06-17 07-15	1490 1090	1 1	CAD4					
08364000	Rio Grande	El Paso	1905 1897 1903 1891	06-12 05-27 06-21 05-17	680 515 512 470		AOC1					
08447500	Pecos	Comstock	1954 1932 1949	06-28 09-01 07-26	26800 3280 2780	1 1 1	AOD4	(basin area corresponding to the flood) 9100 sqkm				
08449500	Devils	Del Rio	1932 1954 1948 1935	09-01 06-28 06-24 06-14	16900 16600 13500 6880	1 1 1 1	AOXO					
08452500	Rio Grande	Del Rio	1954 1932 1948 1935 1964	06-28 09-01 06-24 09-05 09-24	32300 17100 13500 6340 5470	1 1 1 1 1	AOD4					
08455000	Pinto (see New Mexico)	Del Rio	1948 1964	06-24 09-20	5270 2600	1 1	AOXO A1C1					
NEW MEXICO												
07227000	Canadian	Logan	1904 1941 1914	09-30 09-22 05-01	7870 6200 5860	1 1 1	D5C1 A5C1					
08318900	San Pedro	Golden	1955 1965	09-24 07-27	306 77.3	1 1						
08379500	Pecos	Anton Chico	1904 1937 1950	09-29 06-01 07-05	2100 1140 691	1 1	A4D4					
08408500	Delaware	Red Bluff	1955 1969	10-02 10-21	2310 1010	1 1	A4D4					
09365000	San Juan	Farmington	1927 1929 1935	06-29 08-11 09-28	1930 1360 929	4 1 1	A1C1					

TABLE II : FLOODS CHARACTERISTICS

	FLOOD CHARACTERISTICS						DISCHARGE ESTIMATION					
Site number	Stream	Observ. site	Year	Date of the max	Maximal discm³s-1	Climatic origine	Condition disc est	Qual. of the sect	Precis. ±m³s-1	Anteced precip.	Depth mm.	Duration days.
1	2	3	4	5	6	7	8	9	10	11	12	13
UTAH												
09180500	Colorado	Cisco	1884	07-04	3540	2						
			1917	06-19	2180	2	A1XO					
			1914	06-03	1870	2						
09274000	Duchesne	Hanna	1963	06-16	496	4	AOXO					
			1953	06-13	42.5	2						
09315500	Saleratus	Green River	1962	09-21	402	1	A1C1					
			1967	07-16	178	1						
09378700	Cottonwood	Blanding	1968	08-01	581	1	A1C1					
			1963	09-06	245	1						
10242000	Coal	Cedar City	1969	07-23	131	1	A4D4					
			1975	07-12	126	1						
WYOMING												
06316480	Headgate	Buffalo	1964	06-15	155	1						
06651800	Sand	Orin	1955	08-07	586	1						
			1978	05-16	155	1						
09217000	Green	Green River	1918	06-19	629	2						
			1965	09-07	476	1	A1B1					
09224980	Summers Dry	Green River	1973	07-20	394	1						
			1968	08-19	108	1						
NEVADA												
09418500	Meadow Valley	Caliente	1978	03-05	68	1	A1C1					
			1979	02-14	67	1						
09419670	Red Block	Blue Diamond	1969	01-25	212	4						
			1966	12-06	70.8	4						
09419675	Flamingo	Las Vegas	1975	07-03	111	1						
			1969	01-25	46.2	1						
10322500	Humboldt	Palisade	1910	02-28	481		D5C1					
			1962	02-12	187	4	A1C1					
			1943	02-26	177							
ARIZONA												
09380000	Colorado	Lees Ferry	1884	07-07	8500	4	D5DO					
			1921	06-18	6230	4	A1C1					
			1927	07-01	3600	4						
			1957	06-12	3570	4	A1B1					
09401000	Little Colorado	Grand Falls	1923	09-19	3400	1	DOXO					
			1929	04-05	1430	4	A1XO					
			1938	03-05	1080	4						

TABLE II : FLOODS CHARACTERISTICS

		FLOOD CHARACTERISTICS					DISCHARGE ESTIMATION					
Site number	Stream	Observ. site	Year	Date of the max	Maximal discm³s-1	Climatic origine	Condition disc est	Qual. of the sect	Precis. ±m³s-1	Anteced precip.	Depth mm.	Duration days.
1	2	3	4	5	6	7	8	9	10	11	12	13
09401400	Moenkopi	Tuba City	1929	04-04	428		D5D4					
			1972	10-19	343	1	A4C1					
09426000	Bill Williams	Alamo Dam	1891	02-21	5660							
			1916	01-19	4960							
			1927	09-04	3540			Regulated since 1969				
			1937	02-07	3540		D4B4					
09469500	Gila	Coolidge Dam	1905	11-28	4250	1						
			1916	01-20	3680			Regulated since 1929				
			1916	10-14	2100	1						
09471000	San Pedro	Charleston	1926	09-28	2780	1	AOC1					
			1940	08-13	878	1	A1C1					
09471190	Walnut Gulch	Tombstone	1957	08-17	544	1	A1XO					
			1955	07-25	343	1						
09487100	Little Brawley	Three Points	1962	09-26	391	1						
			1970	10-06	70.8	1						
09515500	Hassayampa	Wickenburg	1970	09-05	1640	1	A4D4					
			1927	02-16	767							
CALIFORNIA												
10262500	Mojave	Barstow	1938	03-03	1820	1	A1D4					
			1969	02-25	850	1						
			1943	01-23	736	1						
11056500	Little San Gorgonio	Beaumont	1969	02-25	311	1	AOX4					
			1976	09-10	12.1	1	A1B1					
11066500	Santa Ana	Arlington	1862	01-22	9060	1						
			1938	03-02	2830	1						
			1969	01-25	1160	1	AOC1					
			1980	02-18	552	1						
11073000	San Antonio	Claremont	1938	03-02	606	1	AOC1					
			1969	01-25	464	1						
			1965	12-29	73.3	1	A1B1					
11142500	Arroyo de la Cruz	San Simeon	1966	12-06	997	1						
			1969	01-19	671	1						
11187000	Kern	Kernville	1966	12-06	2100	1	C4D4					
			1950	11-19	1100	1	COXO					
			1955	12-23	833	1						
11300000	Stanislaus	Knights Ferry	1862	01-11	2830		DOXO					
			1907	03-19	1830	2	AOCO					
			1911	03-31	1700	2						
11378000	Sacramento	Red Bluff	1940	02-28	8240	4	A1C1					
			1937	12-11	7420	1						
			1909	02-03	7140	4						

TABLE II : FLOODS CHARACTERISTICS

	FLOOD CHARACTERISTICS						DISCHARGE ESTIMATION					
Site number	Stream	Observ. site	Year	Date of the max	Maximal discm³s-1	Climatic origine	Condition disc est	Qual. of the sect	Precis. ±m³s-1	Anteced precip.	Depth mm.	Duration days.
1	2	3	4	5	6	7	8	9	10	11	12	13
11407000	Faether	Oroville	1907	03-19	6510	2	XOXO					
			1955	12-23	5750	1	A1C1					
11433300	Mid. Fork American	Forest Hill	1964	12-23	8780	4	A4D4					
			1963	02-01	3200	4						
			1980	01-13	1870	4						
11459800	San Rafael	San Rafael	1973	01-16	250	1						
11474500	North F. Eel	Mina	1964	12-22	3770	1	AOX1					
			1955	12-22	1050	1						
11477000	Eel	Scotia	1964	12-23	21300	1	A4C1					
			1955	12-22	15300	1						
			1974	01-16	11000	1						
11527550	Panther	Denny	1964	12-22	396	1						
11532000	South F. Smith	Crescent City	1964	12-22	4590	1						
			1955	12-22	3060	1	A4D4					
IDAHO												
10090500	Bear	Preston	1907	06-09	241	2		Regulated throughout				
						2						
12309500	Kootenai	Bonners Ferry	1948	05-28	3710	2	A1XO					
			1956	05-22	3540	2						
12392000	Clark Fork	Cabinet Gorge	1894	06	5520							
			1972	06-10	5380							
			1948	05-31	4330	4	A1X1					
12415000	St. Maries	Lotus	1933	12-22	674	4	AOC1					
			1964	12-23	623	4	A1C1					
			1948	02-26	320							
13050500	Henrys Fork	St. Anthony	1975	06-04	326	2	A1X1					
			1974	06-06	276	2						
13202000	Boise	Boise	1896	06-14	1010	2	AOXO					
			1897	04-19	835	2		Regulated since 1915				
			1904	04-15	558	2						
13313000	Johnson	Yellow Pine	1974	06-17	176	2	A1C1					
			1956	05-27	154	2						
13342500	Clearwater	Spalding	1948	05-29	5010	2	A1B1					
			1933	12-23	4870	4						
			1957	05-20	4050	2						
OREGON												
11501000	Sprague	Chiloquin	1964	12-26	422	4	A1C1					
			1970	01-27	195	4						

TABLE II : FLOODS CHARACTERISTICS

	FLOOD CHARACTERISTICS						DISCHARGE ESTIMATION					
Site number	Stream	Observ. site	Year	Date of the max	Maximal disc m³s-1	Climatic origine	Condition disc est	Qual. of the sect	Precis. ±m³s-1	Anteced precip.	Depth mm.	Duration days.
1	2	3	4	5	6	7	8	9	10	11	12	13
13178000	Jordan	Jordan Valley	1964	12–24	213	4	A1C1					
			1971	01–17	110							
14105700	Columbia	The Dalles	1894	06–06	35100	2	A1B1					
			1948	05–31	28600	2	A1B1					
			1876		27100							
			1862		26800							
14185900	Quartzville	Cascadia	1964	12–22	1030	1	B4D4					
			1972	01–20	634	1	A1B1					
14191000	Willamette	Salem	1861	12–04	14200	1	D5C1					
			1890	02–05	12700	1						
			1881	01–16	12100	1						
			1923	01–08	9860	1	A1X0					
14378200	Illinois	Agness	1964	12–22	6370	1	A1X0					
			1966	01–06	3770	1						
WASHINGTON												
12194000	Skagit	Concrete	1815		14200		D5D4					
			1856		9910							
			1897	11–19	7790							
12399500	Columbia	International Boundary	1894	06	19300	2	D0X0					
			1948	06–12	15600	2	A1C1					
			1961	06–10	14000	2						
13334300	Snake	Anatone	1974	06–18	5520	2	A1X1					
			1971	05–29	4280	2						
			1972	06–03	3910	4						
13343450	Dry	Clarkston	1976	08–03	231	1						
			1964	06–05	21.8	1						

TABLEAU I : IDENTIFICATION DES POINTS D'OBSERVATIONS ET CARACTERISTIQUES DE BASSINS

	POINT D'OBSERVATION						CARACTERISTIQUES DU BASSIN						
N° du point	Bassin fluvial	Rivière	Point d'observ.		Coordonnées Lat. Long.	Période	Surface km²	Relief	Sol	Végét.	Régime	Pluie moyenne mm	Module m³s-1
1	2	3	4	5	6	7	8	9	10	11	12	13	14
1	Comoe	Comoe	Karfiguela	1	N 10:40 W 04:55		812	B	C	C	10	1100	
20041810	Comoe	Leraba	Yendéré	1	N 10:10 W 05:04	1965 78	5930	A		B	10	1200	33.7
20151803	Niger	Gorouol	Koriziena	1	N 14:22 W 00:02	1965 78	2500	A		C	11	400	2.36
20154003	Niger	Goudebo	Yakouta	1	N 14:05 W 00:05	1969 78	1640	A		C	11	400	1.82
20270116	Volta	Volta Blanche	Wayen	1	N 12:23 W 01:05	1965 78	20000	A		C	11	800	6.82
20270113	Volta	Volta Blanche	Niaogho	1	N 11:46 W 00:45	1965 78	30200	A		C	11	900	27.8
20270119	Volta	Volta Blanche	Yakala	1	N 11:31 W 00:42	1965 78	33000	A		C	11	950	33.2
2	Volta	Kou	Nasso	1	N 11:12 W 04:26	1961 78	405	B		C	10	1100	4.75
20270232	Volta	Volta Noire	Samendeni	1	N 11:28 W 04:28	1956 78	4580	A		C	10	1100	18
20270229	Volta	Volta Noire	Nwokuy	1	N 12:31 W 03:33	1954 78	14800	A		C	11/10	900	32.7
20270208	Volta	Volta Noire	Boromo	1	N 11:47 W 02:55	1955 78	37140	A		C	11/10	950	42.1
20270211	Volta	Volta Noire	Dapola	1	N 10:54 W 02:55	1965 78	66540	A		C	11/10	1000	116
20270320	Volta	Volta Rouge	Nobere	1	N 11:26 W 01:11	1965 78	7600	A		C	11	950	5.9
20271203	Volta	Bougouriba	Diebougou	1	N 10:56 W 03:10	1955 78	12200	A		C	10	1050	23.7
3	Mare d'Oursi	Gountouré	Bassin expérimental	4	N 14:38 W 00:25	1976 80	24.6	B	C	C	11	370	0.045
4	Mare d'Oursi	Taïma	Bassin expérimental	4	N 14:37 W 00:33	1976 80	105	C	C	C	11	370	0.146
5	Mare d'Oursi	Jalafanka	Bassin expérimental	4	N 14:36 W 00:30	1976 80	0.68	B	C	E	11	370	0.018
6	Niger	Koulouoko	Niegha	4	N 12:30 W 00:30	1960 62	1010	A	C	C	11	800	1.6

TABLEAU II: CARACTERISTIQUES DES CRUES

	CARACTERISTIQUES DE LA CRUE						EVALUATION DES DEBITS					
N° du point	Rivière	Point d'observ.	Année	Date du maximum	Débit max m^3s^{-1}	Origine	Base et mode éval	Qual. de la séch	Précis. $\pm m^3s^{-1}$	Anteced	Hauteur mm	Durée jours
1	2	3	4	5	6	7	8	9	10	11	12	13
1	Comoe	Karfiguela	1954	08-24	168	1	A2B1	A1B	25			
			1952	10-01	167	1	A2B1	A1B	25			
20041810	Leraba	Yendéré	1970	09-08	520	1	A2B1	A1B	25			
			1967	09-14	454	1	A2B1	A1B	20			
20151803	Gorouol	Koriziena	1978	08-01	180	1	A2C1	B1B	20			
			1974	07-22	69.7	1	A2B1	B1B	7			
20154003	Goudebo	Yakouta	1969	08-24	65	1	A2C1	B1A	6			
			1975	07-29	63.4	1	A2C1	B1A	6			
20270116	Volta Blanche	Wayen	1975	08-01	273	1	A1B1	A1B	15			
			1974	08-20	263	1	A1B1	A1B	15			
20270113	Volta Blanche	Niaogho	1967	08-29	430	1	A1B1	A1A	20			
			1974	08-17	380	1	A1B1	A1A	18			
20270119	Volta Blanche	Yakala	1958	08-30	535	1	A1C1	A1B	30			
			1961	09-13	515	1	A1C1	A1B	25			
2	Kou	Nasso	1959		550	1	B4D4	B1B	100			
20270232	Volta Noire	Samendeni	1961	09-06	471	1	A2C1	A1A	25			
			1970	09-05	295	1	A2B1	A1A	20			
			1963	09-06	203	1	A2B1	A1A	18			
20270229	Volta Noire	Nwokuy	1970	10-10	189	1	A1A1	A1A	10			
			1961	10-20	170	1	A1A1	A1A	10			
			1958	11-05	132	1	A1A1	A1A	8			
20270208	Volta Noire	Boromo	1975	09-15	245	1	A1B1	A1A	15			
			1962	09-14	182	1	A1B1	A1A	10			
20270211	Volta Noire	Dapola	1970	09-10	772	1	A1B1	A1A	40			
			1974	09-20	677	1	A1B1	A1A	30			
20270320	Volta Rouge	Nobere	1975	09-02	120	1	A1B1	A1B	10			
20271203	Bougouriba	Diebougou	1964	09-30	342	1	A2C1	A1A	20			
			1963	09-13	338	1	A2C1	A1A	20			
3	Gountouré	Bassin expérimental	1978	07-30	42.9	1	A1B1	A1A	2	3	71	3
4	Taïma	Bassin expérimental	1978	07-30	26	1	A1B1	A1A	1	3	65	3
5	Jalafanka	Bassin expérimental	1980	08-13	2.70	1	A1B1	A1A	0.1	3	42	1
6	Koulouoko	Niegha	1962	08-19	250 (1)	1	A1B1	A1B	15	3	219	0.5

(1) Période de retour supérieure à 15 ans.

URUGUAY

TABLE I : IDENTIFICATION OF OBSERVATIONS SITES AND CHARACTERISTICS OF BASINS

	OBSERVATIONS SITE						CHARACTERISTICS OF BASIN						
Site number	River basin	Stream	Observ. site		Coordinates Lat. Long.	Period	Area km²	Slope	Soil	Cover	Regime	Mean precip. mm	Mean disc. m³s-1
1	2	3	4	5	6	7	8	9	10	11	12	13	14
140900	Uruguay	Uruguay	Salto	1	S 31:23 W 57:58	1898 1981	244000	A90 B10	C80 C20	A28 C53 D19	40	1560	4640
540900	Uruguay	Negro	Rincon del Bonete	1	S 32:49 W 56:25	1947 78	39690	A90 B10	B 1 C23 D76	C	40	1190	525
540990	Uruguay	Negro	Paso de los Toros	1	S 32:49 W 56:30	1908 44	40400	A90 B10	B 1 C23 D76	C	40	1190	535
580100	Uruguay	Negro	Paso del Puerto	1	S 33:03 W 57:27	1952 78	62380	A93 B 7	B 1 C29 D70	C	40	1180	740
580990	Uruguay	Negro	Palmar	1	S 33:07 W 57:11	1909 44 1963 71	62870	A93 B 7	B 1 C29 D70	C	40	1160	790

URUGUAY

TABLE II : FLOODS CHARACTERISTICS

	FLOOD CHARACTERISTICS						DISCHARGE ESTIMATION					
Site number	Stream	Observ. site	Year	Date of the max	Maximal discm³s-1	Climatic origine	Condition disc est	Qual. of the sect	Precis. ±m³s-1	Anteced precip.	Depth mm.	Duration days.
1	2	3	4	5	6	7	8	9	10	11	12	13
140900	Uruguay	Salto	1959 1941 1929	04-16 05-13 10-23	33000 29420 27915	1 1 1	A1D4	A1A	1000	3		
540900	Negro	Rincon del Bonete	1959 1977	04-28	15500 (1) 4454 (2)	1 1	A2DE XOXO	XOX	1500		442	10
540990	Negro	Paso de los Toros	1918 1941	10-05 02-24	5480 5195	1 1	XOXO XOXO	XOX XOX			342	19
580100	Negro	Paso del Puerto	1959 1967 1978	04-28 07-20 03-21	11325 (2) 8795 7722	1 1 1	XOXO	XOX		2	470	10
580990	Negro	Palmar	1967	07-20	8230	1	XOXO	XOX				

(1) natural discharge computed on the basis of the level fluctuations in the reservoir of Rincon del Bonete and of the discharge by the emergency weir. The discharge occurring downstream of the dam and reduced by the reservoir was 7385 m³s-1.

(2) discharge reduced by the reservoir of Rincon del Bonete, significantly smaller than the natural discharge.

TABLE I : IDENTIFICATION OF OBSERVATIONS SITES AND CHARACTERISTICS OF BASINS

	OBSERVATIONS SITE						CHARACTERISTICS OF BASIN						
Site number	River basin	Stream	Observ. site		Coordinates Lat. Long.	Period	Area km²	Slope	Soil	Cover	Regime	Mean precip. mm	Mean disc. m³s-1
1	2	3	4	5	6	7	8	9	10	11	12	13	14
870	Orinoco (Orenoque)	Orinoco	Puente Angostura (Ciudad Bolivar)	1	N 08:08 W 64:26		836000			A C	00 11		
860	Orinoco	Orinoco	Musinacio	1	N 07:40 W 64:47		787000			A C	00 11		
796	Orinoco	Cuguni	Anacoco	1	N 06:43 W 61:07		26660			A	00		
1	Orinoco	Caroni	San Pedro		N 07:15 W 63:05	1961 78	84490	E D C B		A C	11 00		
750	Orinoco	Caura	Pie de Salto	1	N 06:15 W 64:24		27700			A	00		
022	Orinoco	Apure	San Fernando	1	N 07:76 W 67:32		119500			C A	11 90		
1	Orinoco	Arauca	El Yagual	1	N 07:29 W 68:29					C A	11 90		
915	Orinoco	Ventuari	Kanaripo	1	N 04:03 W 66:58		42200			A	00		

TABLE II : FLOODS CHARACTERISTICS

		FLOOD CHARACTERISTICS						DISCHARGE ESTIMATION				
Site number	Stream	Observ. site	Year	Date of the max	Maximal discm^{3}s-1	Climatic origine	Condition disc est	Qual. of the sect	Precis. ±m^{3}s-1	Anteced precip.	Depth mm.	Duration days.
1	2	3	4	5	6	7	8	9	10	11	12	13
870	Orinoco	Puente Angostura	1892 1976 (1) 1943	08	98120 92250 91730	1 1 1						
860	Orinoco	Musinacio	1976	08	86800	1						
796	Cuguni	Anacoco	1972	05	2380	1						
1	Caroni ?	San Pedro	1976		18145	1						
750	Caura	Pie de Salto	1972	07	6475	1						
022	Apure	San Fernando	1976	08	6825	1						
1	Arauca	El Yagual	1971	10	2075	1						
915	Ventuari	Kanaripo	1971	08	6415	1						

(1) Return period : 33 years.

TABLE I : IDENTIFICATION OF OBSERVATIONS SITES AND CHARACTERISTICS OF BASINS

	OBSERVATIONS SITE						CHARACTERISTICS OF BASIN						
Site number	River basin	Stream	Observ. site		Coordinates Lat. Long.	Period	Area km²	Slope	Soil	Cover	Regime	Mean precip. mm	Mean disc. m³s⁻¹
1	2	3	4	5	6	7	8	9	10	11	12	13	14
1	Danube	Sava	Zagreb	1	N 45:47 E 15:56	1926 76 (1)	12450	E	B	B30 C 7	90 60	1430	322
2	Danube	Sava	Slavonski Brod	1	N 45:09 E 18:00	1926 76	50860	A75 E25	B69 C11 D20	A 5 B20 C28 D37 E10	90 60	1180	1060
3	Danube	Sava	Stremska Mitrovica	1	N 44:37 E 19:36	1923 78	8065(2) 8800	A			90 60 70	650	1620
4	Sava	Drina	Foca-Most	1	N 43:31 E 18:47	1926 75	5450	E94 D 6	A25 C 5 B50 D20	A33 B16 C 9 D 7	90 30	800 1500	2.12
5	Danube	Drava	Varazdin	2	N 46:19 E 16:21	1957 76	15620	C	B	D	90 60	1200	347
6	Danube	Drava	Botovo	2	N 46:14 E 16:56	1926 76	31040	B	B	D	90 60	1100	532
7	Danube	Drava	Donji Miholjac		N 45:47 E 18:12	1926 76	37140	A	D	D	90 60	1070	552
8	Black Sea	Danube	Bezdan	1	N 45:51 E 18:51	1923 78	210250						2540
9	Black Sea	Danube	Bogojevo	1	N 45:31 E 19:04	1923 78	251590						2910
10	Black Sea	Danube	Smederevo	2	N 44:40 E 20:55	1928 78	255820						5350
11	Danube	Velika Morava	Ljubicevski Most	1	N 44:35 E 21:07	1923 78	37320				70	700	244
12	Aegean Sea	Vardar	Skopje	1	N 42:00 E 21:27	1951 76	4625	E35 D50 C10 B 5	A10 B10 C70 D10	A10 B35 C10 D15 E20	70	800 900	68.3
13	Adriatic Sea	Neretva	Zitomislici		N 43:12 E 17:47	1926 76	4180	D53 C12 B17 A18	A50 C10 B15 D25	A10 B20 C20 D10 E40	30	1250 1750	238

(1) 1942 - 44 missing.

(2) Beginning of observations period

TABLE II : FLOODS CHARACTERISTICS

				FLOOD CHARACTERISTICS					DISCHARGE ESTIMATION			
Site number	Stream	Observ. site	Year	Date of the max	Maximal discm^{3}s-1	Climatic origine	Condition disc est	Qual. of the sect	Precis. ±m^{3}s-1	Anteced precip.	Depth mm.	Duration days.
1	2	3	4	5	6	7	8	9	10	11	12	13
1	Sava	Zagreb	1964	10-26	3130	1	A1A1	B1B	50	3	180	7
			1933	09-24	2880	1	A1B1	B1B	100	1	244	6
			1926	08-10	2730	1	A2B1	B1B	100	2	127	4
2	Sava	Slavonski Brod	1974	10-31	3480	1	A1A1	A1A	50	3	121	10
			1932	04-16	3340	4	A2B1	A1A	50	3	48	6
3	Sava	Sremska Mitrovica	1974	10-26	6480		A1B1	B1A	650			
			1970	01-19	5800		A1A1	B1A	580			
			1962	04-04	5540		A1A1	B1A	550			
4	Drina	Foca Most	1952	12-16	3220(1)	1	A2C1	B2B	300	1	142	7
			1968	12-20	3160	1	A2C1	B2B	300	1	130	5
			1974	10-24	2845	1	A2C1	B2B	280	3	159	7
5	Drava	Varazdin	1966	08-21	2845	2	A1C1	B1B	200	2	84	5
			1965	09-05	2005	2	A1C1	B1B	200	2	76	2
6	Drava	Botovo	1972	07-18	2650	2	A1C1	C1C	250	1	208	7
			1966	08-22	2590	2	A1C1	C1C	250	2	78	5
7	Drava	Donji Miholjac	1972	07-22	2290	2	A2B1	A1A	50	1	206	8
			1975	07-07	2100	2	A1B1	A1A	50	3	74	3
8	Danube	Bezdan	1965	06-24	8360		A1B1	B1A	840			
			1954	07-24	6860		A1B1	B1A	690			
			1975	07-12	6570		A1B1	B1A	660			
9	Danube	Bogojevo	1965	06-15	9290		A1B1	B1A	930			
			1975	07-13	8360		A1B1	B1A	840			
			1954	07-25	7920		A1B1	B1A	790			
10	Danube	Smederevo	1962	04-18	14100		A1B1	B1A	1400			
			1965	06-25	13830		A1B1	B1A	1400			
			1970	05-29	13460		A1B1	B1A	1350			
11	Velika Morava	Ljubicevski Most	1963	02-23	2350		A1B1	B1A	230			
			1965	05-17	2340		A1B1	B1A	240			
12	Vardar	Skopje	1962	11-16	1080	1	A3C2	B2	100	3	95	20
13	Neretva	Zitomislici	1959	12-12	2080	1	A2C1	A1B	200	3	268	8
			1968	12-20	1940	1	A2C1	A1B	190	1	190	4
			1940	10-30	1755	1	A2C1	A1B	170	2	188	6

(1) 10000 m^{3}s-1 at Visegrad (11000 km^2) in 1896. V. Yevdjevic (1953).

ZAÏRE

TABLEAU I : IDENTIFICATION DES POINTS D'OBSERVATIONS ET CARACTERISTIQUES DES BASSINS

	POINT D'OBSERVATION									CARACTERISTIQUES DU BASSIN				
N° du point	Bassin fluvial	Rivière	Point d'observ.		Coordonnées Lat. Long.	Période	Surface km²	Relief	Sol	Végét.	Régime	Pluie moyenne mm	Module m³s⁻¹
1	2	3	4	5	6	7	8	9	10	11	12	13	14
1	Zaïre (Congo)	Zaïre	Boma	2	S E 05:51 13:03	1933 75	3815540				00 10	1000 2300	
2	Zaïre	Zaïre	Kinshasa Port Public	2	S E 04:18 15:18	1925 79	3747320				00 10	1000 2300	43000
3	Zaïre	Zaïre	Kisangani	2	N E 00:30 26:12	1934 78	974330				00 10	1000 2300	(6500)
4	Zaïre (Lualaba)	Zaïre	Bukama	2	S E 09:12 25:52	1933 60	63090				10	1000 1200	(322)

ZAÏRE

TABLEAU II : CARACTERISTIQUES DES CRUES

	CARACTERISTIQUES DE LA CRUE						EVALUATION DES DEBITS					
N° du point	Rivière	Point d'observ.	Année	Date du maximum	Débit max m³s⁻¹	Origine	Base et mode éval	Qual. de la séch	Précis. ±m³s⁻¹	Anteced	Hauteur mm	Durée jours
1	2	3	4	5	6	7	8	9	10	11	12	13
1	Zaïre	Boma	1961	12-20	90000	1	A3B2	X1X	2700	3		
			1969	12-11	78200	1	A3B2	X1X	2400			
			1962	12-27	76400	1	A3B2	X1X	2200			
2	Zaïre	Kinshasa	1961	12-17	81110 (1)	1	A1B2	A1B	3200			
			1962	12-27	75710 (1)	1	A1B2	A1B	3000			
			1964	12-11	71875 (1)	1	A1B2	A1B	2800			
3	Zaïre	Kisangani	1961	12-07	20130	1	A1C2	X1X	U			
			1964	05-01	17765	1	A1C2	X1X	U			
			1963	05-06	16940	1	A1C2	X1X	U			
4	Zaïre	Bukama	1957	04-06	1420	1	A3C2	X1X	U			
			1936	03-25	1275	1	A3C2	X1X	U			

(1) voir tableaux du Congo.

ZIMBABWE

TABLE I : IDENTIFICATION OF OBSERVATIONS SITES AND CHARACTERISTICS OF BASINS

	OBSERVATIONS SITE						CHARACTERISTICS OF BASIN						
Site number	River basin	Stream	Observ. site		Coordinates Lat. Long.	Period	Area km²	Slope	Soil	Cover	Regime	Mean precip. mm	Mean disc. m³s-1
1	2	3	4	5	6	7	8	9	10	11	12	13	14
1	Hunyani	Avondale vlei	Salisbury	3	S E 17:50 31:01		28	B	D	E	11	850	
2	Sanyati	Umniati	Battlefields	3	S E 18:40 29:49		5880	B	C	C	11	770	
D2	Mazoe	Umwindsi	Salisbury (1)	1	S E 17:44 31:18	50 years	241	C	C	C85 D15	11	955	70
D4	Mazoe	Dassura	Mazoe Dam	1	S E 17:34 31:00	46 years	72	D	C	C	11	870	33
D5	Zambesi	Mazoe	Mazoe Dam	1	S E 17:35 31:01	48 years	225	D	C	C	11	900	58
Z1	Zambesi	Zambesi	Livingstone (1)	1	S E 17:53 25:50	50 years	360000	B C A	C	B	11	900 ?	3500
3	Lundi	Munendi	Fort Victoria (1)	3	S E 19:40 31:06		130	C	C	C	11	710	
E_2	Lundi	Umshagashe	Fort Victoria (1)	1	S E 20:03 30:51	46 years	541	C	C	C	11	680	137
E_1	Sabi (Save)	Umtali	Umtali	1	S E 18:55 32:33	50 years	249	D	C	C	11	965	56
4	Limpopo	Limpopo	Boit Bridge	1	S E 21:13 29:59	13 years	195700	B	B30 C70	C	11	600	2120

(1) These data were received in 1977. Since this time some city names may have been changed.

TABLE II : FLOODS CHARACTERISTICS

	FLOOD CHARACTERISTICS						DISCHARGE ESTIMATION					
Site number	Stream	Observ. site	Year	Date of the max	Maximal disc m³s-1	Climatic origine	Condition disc est	Qual. of the sect	Precis. ±m³s-1	Anteced precip.	Depth mm.	Duration days.
1	2	3	4	5	6	7	8	9	10	11	12	13
1	Avondale vlei	Salisbury	1945	02	318	1	D4D5	A				
2	Umniati	Battlefields	1953	01	5660	1	D5D6	A				
D2	Umwindsi	Salisbury	1926	03	247	1	A1C6	A				
			1957	02	152	1						
D4	Dassura	Mazoe Dam	1941	01	257	1	A1C6					
			1932	03	69	1						
D5	Mazoe	Mazoe Dam	1955	02	195	1	A1C6	A				
			1953	03	131	1						
Z₁	Zambesi	Livingstone	1958	03	9340	1						
3	Munendi	Fort Victoria	1946	01	1860	1	D4D5	B				
E₂	Umshagashe	Fort Victoria	1953	02	660	1	A1C6	A				
			1939	02	569	1						
			1941	01	410	1						
E₁	Umtali	Umtali	1926	01	396	1	A1C6	A				
			1929	02	291	1						
			1939	02	216	1						
4	Limpopo	Boit Bridge	1972	01	21800	1	A1C6	A				

TABLES III Chronological series of yearly
maxima

TABLEAUX III Séries chronologiques des
valeurs maximales annuelles

ALASKA (UNITED STATES OF AMERICA/ETATS UNIS D'AMERIQUE)

- Cascade Creek. Petersburg (60 km²) (1917 – 1971) (See Unesco Catalogue)
- Salcha river. Salchaket   (5620 km²)

Année Year	Mois/Month Jour/Day	Débit Discharge m³s-1	Obs.	Année Year	Mois/Month Jour/Day	Débit Discharge m³s-1	Obs.	Année Year	Mois/Month Jour/Day	Débit Discharge m³s-1	Obs.
1949	05-28	728	A2	1960				1971	05-07	660	A1
1950	05-15	382	A2	1	08-13	632	A1	2	05-10	513	A1
1	06-16	292	A2	2	05-30	666	A1	3	06-04	326	A1
2			A2	3	06-27	450	A1	4	05-20	172	A1
3	06-26	501	A2	4	06-02	683	A1	5	05-14	711	A1
4	06-16	739	A2	5	06-20	589	A1	6	05-04	233	A1
5	07-01	620	A2	6	06-20	575	A1	7	05-20	283	A1
6	06-23	1030	A2	7	08-14	2750	A2	8	08-20	147	A1
7	05-21	799	A1	8	05-22	365	A1	9	05-03	464	A1
8	05-25	654		9	08-04	442		1980	07-02	295	A1
9	05-23	530		1970	07-17	180					

ALGERIA/ALGERIE

- Oued Isser. Remchi (1935 km²)

Année Year	Mois/Month Jour/Day	Débit Discharge m³s-1	Obs.	Année Year	Mois/Month Jour/Day	Débit Discharge m³s-1	Obs.	Année Year	Mois/Month Jour/Day	Débit Discharge m³s-1	Obs.
1948	10-31	44.3	A1	1958	10-27	87	A1	1969	02-28	45.4	A1
9				9	12-13	68.2	A1	1970	01-12	76.4	A1
1950	03-01	178		1960	12-13	48.5	A1	1	05-09	292	A1
50	12-12	388		1			A1	2	03-02	120	A1
1	10-18	72.6	A3	2	02-13	113	A1	3	03-29	1110	A1
2				3			A1	4	03-30	294	A1
3	03-16	60.5	A1	4	04-11	249	A1	5	04-22	211	A1
4	04-16	1140	A3	5	01-06	251	A1	6	02-13	46.6	A1
5	01-26	183	A1	6	05-26	12.4	A1	7	02-13	42.4	A1
6	02-27	27.6	A1	7	04-14	6.8	A1	8	01-22	13.1	A1
7			A1	8	05-11	317					

- Oued Rhumel Oued Athmania (1130 km²)

Année Year	Mois/Month Jour/Day	Débit Discharge m³s-1	Obs.	Année Year	Mois/Month Jour/Day	Débit Discharge m³s-1	Obs.	Année Year	Mois/Month Jour/Day	Débit Discharge m³s-1	Obs.
1862	07-18	500	A2	1898	03-06	600	A2	1968			
1869	07-04	8.51	A1	1899	03-19	11	A2	9	12-24	67.2	A1
1870/71		320	B2	1900	01-29	14.2	A2	1970	10-14	163	A1
1875/76		700	B2	1		204	B2	1			
1882	01-07	240	A2	2/3		46	B2	2	09-06	73.9	A1
1886	01-28	320	A2	4	01-28	8	A2	2	01-27	13.9	A1
1888	06	480	A2	4/5		17.0	B2	3	09-25	313.6	A1
1888/89		26	B2	6	01-30	550	A2	4	09-22	8	A1
1890	03-28	120	A2	7	02-16	502	A2	5	09-23	29.2	A1
1891/92		3	B2	1965	10-01	105	A1	6			
1893	02	7.5	B2	1965	08-20	30.2	A1	7	05-18	12	A1
1896	05-22	220	A2	6	08-18	42	A1	8	08-17	23.5	A1
1896/97		2.3	B2	7	11-29	1236	A1				

TABLEAU III : SERIES CHRONOLOGIQUES DES VALEURS MAXIMALES ANNUELLES
TABLE III   : CHRONOLOGICAL SERIES OF YEARLY MAXIMA

ALGERIA/ALGERIE

- Oued Guir - Djorf Torba (22500 km²)

Année Year	Mois/Month Jour/Day	Débit Discharge m³s-1	Obs.	Année Year	Mois/Month Jour/Day	Débit Discharge m³s-1	Obs.	Année Year	Mois/Month Jour/Day	Débit Discharge m³s-1	Obs.
1921/22		3050	A2	1941/42		1000	A2	1952/53		2650	A2
22/23		3050	A2	42/43		3050	A2				
23/24		1850	A2	43/44		1600	A2	1966/67		3114	A2
24/25		5400	A2	44/45		1200	A2	1967/68		6241	A2
25/26		3600	A2	45/46		1600	A2	1968/69			A2
26/27		1250	A2	46/47		1200	A2	1969/70		380	A2
27/28		3600	A2	47/48		1350	A2	1970/71		3128	A2
28/29		1000	A2	48/49		1850	A2	71/72		676	A2
29/30		1600	A2	49/50		1950	A2	72/73		1462	A2
30/31		2650	A2	1950/51		1650	A2	73/74		1967	A2
31/32		1000	A2	1951/52		2500	A2	74/75		17150	A2
32/33		1200	A2								

AUSTRALIA/AUSTRALIE

- Queensland
- Pioneer river. Pleystowe Mill (1490 km²)

Year	Jour/Day	Discharge	Year	Jour/Day	Discharge	Year	Jour/Day	Discharge
1916	09-30	3	1938	03-25	430	1960	02-22	2600
16	12-27	2450	39	02-14	385	61	02-17	675
18	01-23	9840	40	04-07	4450	62	02-25	645
19	01-21	795	41	04-04	3680	63	03-25	2480
20	05-07	170	42	02-17	3500	64	03-31	88
21	03-11	1280	42	12-30	3600	65	05-09	45
21	12-31	675	44	03-28	2920	66	01-27	275
23	06-04	155	45	03-06	140	67	06-21	355
24	02-25	875	46	03-04	6240	68	02-16	5500
25	02-04	1410	47	02-05	4820	69	02-23	130
26	01-07	118	48	02-11	325	70	02-06	7800
27	02-09	395	49	03-05	535	71	02-21	3370
28	03-02	2025	50	03-04	2730	71	12-24	2000
29	01-23	1560	51	01-11	5780	73	02-20	345
30	01-29	2970	52	06-17	51	74	03-02	3420
31	02-04	57	53	01-26	1480	75	01-16	1750
32	01-20	2870	54	02-08	5130	76	03-05	4200
33	07-13	1020	55	05-25	4250	77	03-08	3820
34	02-01	1790	56	03-31	6690	78	02-01	5120
34	11-20	200	56	12-24	1170	79	02-06	5200
36	03-13	2590	58	02-18	9440	80	01-07	5000
1937	03-13	990	59	02-17	4400	81	01-20	1290
						82	03-03	67

TABLEAU III : SERIES CHRONOLOGIQUES DES VALEURS MAXIMALES ANNUELLES

TABLE III : CHRONOLOGICAL SERIES OF YEARLY MAXIMA

AUSTRALIA/AUSTRALIE

- Queensland
- Diamantina. Birdsville (158000 km²)

Année Year	Mois/Month Jour/Day	Débit Discharge m³s-1	Obs.	Année Year	Mois/Month Jour/Day	Débit Discharge m³s-1	Obs.	Année Year	Mois/Month Jour/Day	Débit Discharge m³s-1	Obs.
1950	03	1425		1959	06	32.9		1968	06	374	
1	03	144		1960	03	173		9	04	17.8	
2	10	25.6		1	02	91.1		1970	03	118.3	
3	03	700		2	01	190		1	03	789	
4	03	78.7		3	04	630		2	04	40.6	
5	07	532		4	01	330		3	03	655	
6	04	434		5	12	14		4	02	1610	
7	03	215		6	-	-		5	12	88.6	
8	11	65		7	03	56		6	02	882	
								7	03	744	

- New South Wales
- Hunter river. Singleton (16400 km²)

Année Year	Mois/Month Jour/Day	Débit Discharge m³s-1	Obs.	Année Year	Mois/Month Jour/Day	Débit Discharge m³s-1	Obs.	Année Year	Mois/Month Jour/Day	Débit Discharge m³s-1	Obs.
1898	02	1630		1926	03-25	2300		1954	02-22	1390	
99	08	1470		27	04-17	1060		55	02-26	12500	
1900	07	670		28	07-28	530		56	03-09	1140	
01	08	67		29	09-12	1120		57	02-20	450	
02	12	220		30	06-18	4300		58	01-31	480	
03	09	780		31	07-08	1690		59	02-20	180	
04	07	1730		32	09-25	290		60	12-21	165	
05	04	54		33	10-02	440		61	12-17	230	
06	09	78		34	09-02	830		62	05-14	2100	
07	12	280		35	01-16	180		63	05-07	970	
08	03	1200		36	03-03	200		64	06-11	2750	
09	12	790		37	06-23	110		65	12-18	49	
1910	01	1710		38	02-02	76		66	11-11	77	
11	08	510		39	04-04	170		67	08-07	910	
12	07	410		40	12-22	220		68	01-14	925	
13	05-16	5100		41	01-08	670		69	11-17	470	
14	10-21	240		42	10-15	1380		70	12-31	350	
15	05-08	370		43	11-21	125		71	02-01	5400	
16	12-14	790		44	08-25	275		72	01-25	1130	
17	09-20	530		45	06-13	895		73	11-13	950	
18	01-14	98		46	04-19	1380		74	01-12	1000	
19	05-30	53		47	12-15	280		75	06-22	340	
20	07-02	1980		48	09-26	205		76	01-25	3100	
21	07-25	2500		49	06-18	4100		77	03-04	4200	
22	09-14	410		50	02-07	2250		78	01-02	190	
23	07-10	170		51	01-20	2550		79	09-13	160	
24	11-13	370		52	08-14	3300		80	03-01	22	
25	12-29	185		53	09-05	1230		81	11-04	320	
								82	03-11	630	

TABLEAU III : SERIES CHRONOLOGIQUES DES VALEURS MAXIMALES ANNUELLES
TABLE III   : CHRONOLOGICAL SERIES OF YEARLY MAXIMA

AUSTRALIA/AUSTRALIE

- Nepean river. Penrith (11000 km²)

Année Year	Mois/Month Jour/Day	Débit Discharge m³s-1	Obs.	Année Year	Mois/Month Jour/Day	Débit Discharge m³s-1	Obs.	Année Year	Mois/Month Jour/Day	Débit Discharge m³s-1	Obs.
1891	06-24	5900		1921	04-09	860		1951	09-26	1980	
2	09-25	4500		2	07-26	4900		2	07-27	8200	
3	03-09	2750		3	09-07	460		3	05-08	700	
4	03-22	4700		4	04-10	115		4	02-22	1320	
5	01-24	6100		5	06-21	13400		5	05-01	2750	
6	06	850		6	03-26	220		6	02-10	11300	
7	07-27	1900		7	04-20	1660		7	08-27	135	
8	02-15	6700		8	02-17	2100		8	02-10	645	
9	08-13	2250		9	10-14	2200		9	07-22	610	
1900	07-06	15600		1930	06-02	550		1960	12-20	175	
1	01	1100		1	07-07	1160		1	11-21	11300	
2	01	1		2	09-24	245		2	01-12	1980	
3	09	400		3	04-06	1030		3	08-30	2550	
4	07-11	10600		4	07-30	1600		4	07-12	11000	
5	04	190		5	12-05	245		5	10-19	41	
6	08	1120		6	06-26	205		6	11-09	750	
7	06	27		7	03-16	640		7	08-08	1160	
8	08	540		8	08-26	2700		8	01-15	16	
9	06	55		9	04-06	135		9	04-17	510	
1910	07-20	2500		1940	12-02	235		1970	-	-	
1	01-13	2950		1	02-05	150		1	02-11	1730	
2	07-31	3050		2	10-15	1680		2	03-10	675	
3	05-15	2250		3	05-20	5900		3	03-01	455	
4	12-31	2580		4	05-28	25		4	08-30	2800	
5	06-11	595		5	06-13	1910		5	03-13	340	
6	10-05	7900		6	04-17	280		6	10-18	1490	
7	09-21	260		7	12-15	1160		7	03-05	1770	
8	01-13	790		8	05-03	730		8	03-22	10200	
9	05-30	665		9	06-18	9500		9	01-01	4	
1920	12-13	1600		1950	03-30	3450		1980	01-04	2	

- Shoalhaven river. Welcome Reef (2770 km²)

Année Year	Mois/Month Jour/Day	Débit Discharge m³s-1	Obs.	Année Year	Mois/Month Jour/Day	Débit Discharge m³s-1	Obs.	Année Year	Mois/Month Jour/Day	Débit Discharge m³s-1	Obs.
1909	07-03	220		1934	02-23	1570		1958	07-01	865	
10	02-10	405		1935	04-16	77		9	10-21	4620	
11	01-14	575		1936	06-25	380		1960	07-14	1100	
2	07-25	900		7	03-18	130		1	11-20	1190	
3	06-23	1670		8	01-17	77		2	09-17	1380	
4	03-24	1190		9	04-06	185		3	04-29	1410	
5	09-20	390		1940	04-14	21		4	06-12	630	
6	10-05	3700		1	02-03	245		5	10-19	67	
7	11-22	290		2	10-15	508		6	11-10	1490	
8	02-01	240		3	05-20	2400		7	09-06	1300	
9	02-26	355		4	05-25	550		8	05-15	96	

AUSTRALIA/AUSTRALIE

- Shoalhaven river. Welcome Reef (2770 km²)

Année Year	Mois/Month Jour/Day	Débit Discharge m³s-1	Obs.	Année Year	Mois/Month Jour/Day	Débit Discharge m³s-1	Obs.	Année Year	Mois/Month Jour/Day	Débit Discharge m³s-1	Obs.
1920	12-13	810		5	04-09	3500		1969	11-15	450	
1	04-09	350		6	06-22	62		1970	12-11	335	
2	07-25	2050		7	02-14	410		1	02-08	750	
3	09-14	205		8	05-04	1920		2	03-09	81	
4	07-08	40		9	06-21	1040		3	11-05	265	
5	05-26	8900		1950	04-07	1290		4	08-29	3450	
6	06-04	42		1	06-22	1140		5	06-22	2950	
7	04-19	265		2	06-15	2200		1976	–	–	
8	02-16	440		3	05-06	920					
9	11-19	52		4	02-23	415					
1930	06-02	180		5	–	–					
1	05-29	360		6	02-20	785					
2	08-03	100		1957	07-11	–					
3	10-02	43									

- Murrumbidgee river. Gungadai (21100 km²)

Année Year	Mois/Month Jour/Day	Débit Discharge m³s-1	Obs.	Année Year	Mois/Month Jour/Day	Débit Discharge m³s-1	Obs.	Année Year	Mois/Month Jour/Day	Débit Discharge m³s-1	Obs.
1887	01	1600		1919	09-29	120		1950	03-23	4200	
8	12	440		1920	08-11	540		1	09-27	795	
9	09	1090		1	09-11	990		2	06-18	3350	
1890	07	600		2	07-30	2400		3	11-08	690	
1	06-28	5000		3	10-14	740		4	08-27	210	
2	09	1740		4	08-27	1160		5	08-26	1030	
3	06	540		5	05	6200		6	06-29	2100	
4	04	2000		6	06-28	430		7	07-01	135	
5	06	410		7	10-03	270		8	10-13	660	
6	06	350		8	07-21	260		9	10-23	3000	
7	01	400		9	10-01	150		1960	09-27	1390	
8	02	380		1930	10-09	340		1	12-19	900	
9	08	1170		1	06	3200		2	09-19	720	
1900	07	1920		2	09-01	1100		3	08-31	330	
1	10-30	790		3	09-03	480		4	10-05	710	
2	12	180		4	10-26	2200		5	10-15	155	
3	09-19	600		5	10-25	490		6	11-13	790	
4	01-05	400		6	07-28	670		7	03-04	170	
5	07-11	1550		7	01-22	210		8	08-11	385	
6	10-05	1640		8	08-30	130		9	06-20	590	
7	12-19	260		9	08-24	1450		1970	09-25	1300	
8	09-09	340		1940	09-24	120		1	02-12	1500	
9	06-25	870		1	01	240		2	08-30	285	
1910	09-18	320		2	07	570		3	11-07	480	
1	03	340		3	10	520		4	08-29	5500	
2	09-17	630		4	07	86		5	06-27	1480	

TABLEAU III : SERIES CHRONOLOGIQUES DES VALEURS MAXIMALES ANNUELLES
TABLE III   : CHRONOLOGICAL SERIES OF YEARLY MAXIMA

AUSTRALIA/AUSTRALIE

- Murrumbidgee river. Gungadai (21100 km²)

Année Year	Mois/Month Jour/Day	Débit Discharge m³s-1	Obs.	Année Year	Mois/Month Jour/Day	Débit Discharge m³s-1	Obs.	Année Year	Mois/Month Jour/Day	Débit Discharge m³s-1	Obs.
1913	02-07	670		1945	10	210		1976	10-18	2350	
4	03-29	210		6	07	340		7	01-28	195	
5	09-22	690		7	12	540		8	09-09	1350	
6	10-07	1740		8	05	420		9	11-07	230	
7	10-22	1320		9	10-27	450		1980	10-09	210	
8	08-10	870						1981	01-23	185	

- Victoria
- Snowy river. Jarrahmond (13420 km²)

Année Year	Mois/Month Jour/Day	Débit Discharge m³s-1	Obs.	Année Year	Mois/Month Jour/Day	Débit Discharge m³s-1	Obs.	Année Year	Mois/Month Jour/Day	Débit Discharge m³s-1	Obs.
1922	07	2270		1938	03	1270		1966	10	920	
3	09	965		9	08	1040*		7	09	380	
4	08	320*		1940	09	185		8	08	182	
5	07	2000*		1	10	220*		9	06	885	
6	10	205*		2	11	655*		1970	12	820	
7	10	415*		3	10	390		1	02	7500	
8	03	1470*		4	05	1290		2	03	91	
9	11	440*		5	04	745		3	11	875	
1930	10	475*		6	06	735		4	06	1990	
1	06	380*		7	-	-		5	06	1910	
2	07	1170*		8	05	865		6	10	1630	
3	06	840*		9	07	1110		7	07	1070	
4	01	7350*		1950	04	-		8	06	4825	
5	12	1470*		1964	08	760		9	03	250	
6	06	935*		1965	08	715		1980	01	315	
7	09	290						1981	05	280	

* daily mean max.

AUSTRIA/AUTRICHE

- Donau Wien (101700 km²) (15 highest values)

Année Year	Mois/Month Jour/Day	Débit Discharge m³s-1	Obs.	Année Year	Mois/Month Jour/Day	Débit Discharge m³s-1	Obs.	Année Year	Mois/Month Jour/Day	Débit Discharge m³s-1	Obs.
1501	08	14000	E3	1890	09-07	7750	A2	1923	02-06	7450	A1
1787	11-01	11800	E3	1892	06-11	7950	A2	1940	06-05	6500	A1
1829	06-12	6650	A2	1897	08-03	9400	A1	1949	08-18	6550	A1
1862	02-04	9850	A2	1899	09-18	10500	A1	1954	07-14	9600	A1
1883	01-05	8150	A2	1920	09-11	8000	A1	1955	07-12	6400	A1

TABLEAU III : SERIES CHRONOLOGIQUES DES VALEURS MAXIMALES ANNUELLES
TABLE III   : CHRONOLOGICAL SERIES OF YEARLY MAXIMA

BENIN

- Ouémé. Pont de Savé (23600 km²)

Année Year	Mois/Month Jour/Day	Débit Discharge m^3s-1	Obs.	Année Year	Mois/Month Jour/Day	Débit Discharge m^3s-1	Obs.	Année Year	Mois/Month Jour/Day	Débit Discharge m^3s-1	Obs.
1942	09-16	670	A1	1956	09-22	560	A1	1970	09-26	1100	A2
3	09-10	980	A2	7	09-15	2040	A2	1	09-09	1115	A2
4	10-04	1745	A2	8	10-09	56	A1	2	09-13	261	A1
5	09-16	1220	A2	9	09-30	1480	A2	3	09-15	765	A1
6	10-10	745	A2	1960	09-09	1430	A2	4	09-16	1230	A2
7	10-09	1610	A2	1	09-17	600	A1	5	10-02	765	A1
8	-	-	-	2	09-02	1220	A2	6	08-13	290	A1
9	08-28	2650	A2	3	09-03	1860	A2	7	09-19	395	A1
1950	10-10	290	A1	4	09-11	1055	A2	8	07-27	485	A1
1	09-06	795	A1	5	08-30	900	A1	9	07-09	1110	A2
2	10-16	1040	A2	6	08-21	920	A1				
3	08-03	1350	A2	7	09-20	1215	A2				
4	10-19	635	A1	8	09-12	1420	A2				
5	08-03	1580	A2	9	09-05	1100	A2				

BOLIVIA/BOLIVIE

- Rio Grande. Abapo (59000 km²)

Année	Débit	Obs.	Année	Débit	Obs.	Année	Débit	Obs.
1945	3370	A2	1955	6600	A2	1965	2260	A2
6	4160	A2	6	3320	A2	6	2130	A2
7	5240	A2	7	4170	A2	7	1850	A2
8	7930	A2	8	3480	A2	8	9240	A2
9	11360	A2	9	4700	A2	9	1510	A2
1950	9080	A2	1960	8680	A2	1970	2670	A2
1	2670	A2	1	1920	A2	1	4230	A2
2	4360	A2	2	3570	A2	2	3420	A2
3	2760	A2	3	6110	A2	3	5270	A2
4	4400	A2	4	3960	A2	4	4110	A2

BRAZIL/BRESIL

- Amazonas. Obidos (4640300 km²)

Année	Débit	Année	Débit	Année	Débit
1928	215240	1939	214680	1970	224780
9	212990	1940	192350	1	237320
1930	203180	1	199550	2	229160
1	198720	2	201220	3	222980
2	208500	3	208490	4	227990
3	207370	4	221440	5	234850
4	217500	5	203460	6	239600
5	219190	6	214960	7	229670
				1978	224680

TABLEAU III : SERIES CHRONOLOGIQUES DES VALEURS MAXIMALES ANNUELLES
TABLE III   : CHRONOLOGICAL SERIES OF YEARLY MAXIMA

BRAZIL/BRESIL

- Amazonas. Obidos (4640300 km²)

Année Year	Mois/Month Jour/Day	Débit Discharge m³s-1	Obs.	Année Year	Mois/Month Jour/Day	Débit Discharge m³s-1	Obs.	Année Year	Mois/Month Jour/Day	Débit Discharge m³s-1	Obs.
1936		191520		1953		370000	1)	1978		224680	
7		191250		1963		250000					
8		207930		1968		200000		1) with flood plain			

- Rio Sao Francisco. Juazeiro (510800 km²)

Année Year	Débit Discharge	Année Year	Débit Discharge	Année Year	Débit Discharge
1930	5385	1946	11575	1962	5400
1	7525	7	7890	3	8180
2	5510	8	6615	4	6880
3	6450	9	13265	5	6480
4	6950	1950	5510	6	6950
5	6415	1	5700	7	5070
6	4930	2	7750	8	6980
7	6320	3	5165	9	4965
8	6850	4	5385	1970	6300
9	7080	5	5135	1	5230
1940	6190	6	5910	2	5165
1	5640	7	8200	3	5245
2	5960	8	5525	7	5010
3	11060	9	4920	8	4550
4	7100	1960	8010		
5	9815	1	6480		

- Rio Parana. Guaira (802200 km²)

Année Year	Débit Discharge	Année Year	Débit Discharge	Année Year	Débit Discharge
1905	32900	1940	19910	1960	17200
1921	22420	1	15900	1	23850
2	18920	2	19030	2	17625
3	18700	3	20020	3	20130
4	18150	4	15300	4	19360
5	11160	5	17000	5	24350
6	24225	6	24350	6	25850
7	20020	7	24975	7	19140
8	14910	8	16800	8	17520
9	32920	9	16700	9	13610
1930	20240	1950	19360	1970	16500
1	30960	1	21730	1	16300
2	19250	2	20350	2	20350
3	18480	3	10820	3	22305
4	13340	4	17200	4	23010
5	18150	5	12890	5	16700
6	16200	6	17730	6	20130
7	23250	7	17940	7	28375
8	14815	8	17310	8	(20000)
9	16300	9	19250	9	(19000)
				1980	(25000)

BRAZIL/BRESIL

- Rio Taquari. Muçum (16150 km²)

Année Year	Mois/Month Jour/Day	Débit Discharge m³s-1	Obs.	Année Year	Mois/Month Jour/Day	Débit Discharge m³s-1	Obs.	Année Year	Mois/Month Jour/Day	Débit Discharge m³s-1	Obs.
1940	07-17	7740		1955	05-19	4250		1970	07-08	3270	
1	05-05	12500	?	6	04-05	9980		1	06-30	4430	
2	05-19	5300		7	09-08	6260		2	08-28	7890	
3	08-03	1920		8	06-13	6030		3	08-19	5840	
4	06-25	3940		9	06-22	9175		4	06-10	3160	
5	08-31	3260		1960	09-01	6280		5	09-11	5030	
6	01-26	10300		1	09-29	6580		6	08-09	6760	
7	08-30	2495		2		?		7	08-18	7800	
8	08-02	4415		3	10-11	5930		8	07-22	3490	
9	07-16	3500		4	09-02	3570		9	10-07	3870	
1950	10-17	8590		5	08-19	11500		1980	08-23	7330	
1	10-19	3160		6	08-05	5160		1	09-24	3970	
2	06-09	1930		7	09-20	8860		2	06-28	8410	
3	09-16	6320		8	11-07	2190		3	07-06	10170	
4	09-22	9500	?	9	09-08	2530					

BULGARIA/BULGARIE

- Maritza. Belovo (741 km²) (1911 - 1970), Mativir. Sersem Kale (386 km²) (1930 - 1970)
- Striama. Bania (833 km²) (1914 - 1970), Tchepelarska. Batchkovo (825 km²) (1912 - 1970)
- Maritza. Harmanli (19700 km²) (1914 - 1970), (See Unesco Catalogue).

CAMEROON/CAMEROUN

- Benoué. Garoua (64000 km²)

Année Year	Mois/Month Jour/Day	Débit Discharge m³s-1	Obs.	Année Year	Mois/Month Jour/Day	Débit Discharge m³s-1	Obs.	Année Year	Mois/Month Jour/Day	Débit Discharge m³s-1	Obs.
1916		>6000 ?	D3	1946		4390	A1	1963	09-04	3355	A1
1930		2260	A1	7		3080	A1	4	09-23	2710	A1
1		3860	A1	8		6000	A2	5	08-14	3440	A1
2		2955	A1	9	08-30	2260	A1	6	09-11	4170	A1
3		3860	A1	1950	09-19	1965	A1	7	09-18	2900	A1
4		3335	A1	1	09-25	2185	A1	8	09-10	3155	A1
5		4410	A1	2	09-23	2040	A1	9	08-26	3345	A1
6		3515	A1	3	09-02	2110	A1	1970	05-09	4215	A1
7			A1	4	09-03	2940	A1	1	09-11	2315	A1
8		4210	A1	5	09-08	3300	A1	2	08-31	1055	A1
9		1775	A1	6	09-19	3025	A1	3	09-19	2250	A1
1940			A1	7	09-09	2610	A1	4	08-07	1515	A1
1		3730	A1	8	09-02	1905	A1	5	09-06	4340	A1
2		2975	A1	9	09-21	3905	A1	6	08-25	1550	A1
3		3555	A1	1960		4300	A1	7	09-10	2480	A1
4		1390	A1	1	09-14	3925	A1	8	08-31	3280	A1
5		3355	A1	2	09-08	3410	A1	9	08-28	1310	A1

TABLEAU III : SERIES CHRONOLOGIQUES DES VALEURS MAXIMALES ANNUELLES
TABLE III   : CHRONOLOGICAL SEIES OF YEARLY MAXIMA

CAMEROON/CAMEROUN

- Sanaga. Edéa (131.500 km²)

Année Year	Mois/Month Jour/Day	Débit Discharge m³s-1	Obs.	Année Year	Mois/Month Jour/Day	Débit Discharge m³s-1	Obs.	Année Year	Mois/Month Jour/Day	Débit Discharge m³s-1	Obs.
1943		6110	A1	1955	10-22	7570	A1	1967	10-20	7250	A1
4		5660	A1	6	10-20	6840	A1	8	10-13	5970	A1
5		5660	A1	7		6400	A1	9	10-07	7700	A2
6		5360	A1	8	10	6770	A1	1970	11-03	7400	A2
7		5160	A1	9	10-20	6680	A1	1	10-06	5700	A2
8		6840	A1	1960		6680	A1	2	10-21	5900	A2
9	10-30	7450	A1	1		7440	A1	3	10-08	5330	A2
1950	10-03	6990	A1	2	10-14	7120	A1	4	10-11	6555	A2
1	11-05	6840	A1	3	10-25	5740	A1	5	10-28	5850	A2
2	10-16	6460	A1	4	10-06	7330	A1	6	10-23	6640	A2
3	10-15	6360	A1	5	10-21	5660	A1	7	09-17	5490	A2
4	10-28	7030	A1	6	10-30	6270	A1	8	10-01	6465	A2

Depuis 1969 débits naturels reconstitués (Régularisation).

CANADA

- Yukon territory
- Stewart. Mayo. (31600 km²)

Année Year	Mois/Month Jour/Day	Débit Discharge m³s-1	Obs.	Année Year	Mois/Month Jour/Day	Débit Discharge m³s-1	Obs.	Année Year	Mois/Month Jour/Day	Débit Discharge m³s-1	Obs.
1949	06-25	2460	A2	1960	07-30	2310	A2	1971	06-14	2640	A2
1950	06-23	1510	A2	1	06-11	3680	A2	2	06-02	2920	A1
1	07-03	910	A2	2	06-26	2730	A3	3	06-12	1910	A1
2			A2	3	05-25	2430	A2	4	05-26	1510	A1
3	05-28	2000	A2	4	06-10	4110	A3	5	06-07	3140	A1
4	05-30	1930	A2	5	06-03	1820	A2	6			A1
5	07-02	2680	A2	6	06-17	2210	A2	7	06-02	2370	A1
6	06-23	1950	A2	7	06-04	2760	A2	8	06-11	1850	A1
7	O5-26	3680	A2	8	06-14	2090	A2	9	06-05	2020	A1
8	06-09	1810	A2	9	06-13	1890	A2	1980	06-12	2060	
9	05-24	2630	A2	1970	06-07	2940	A2				

Up to 1972 maximum mean daily discharge.

- British Columbia
- Skeena. Usk (42200 km²) (1952 - 1972) (See Unesco Catalogue)

Complément

Année Year	Mois/Month Jour/Day	Débit Discharge m³s-1	Obs.	Année Year	Mois/Month Jour/Day	Débit Discharge m³s-1	Obs.	Année Year	Mois/Month Jour/Day	Débit Discharge m³s-1	Obs.
1928	06-13	3910	A2	1942	05-26	3910	A2	1951	06-15	4360	A2
9	06-08	3620	A2	3	06-24	2920	A2	1973	05-17	4670	A1
1930	06-11	5010	A2	4	05-29	2890	A2	4	10-10	5920	A1
1	06-19	4730	A2	5	05-30	4960	A2	5	06-03	3600	A1
1937	06-10	4330	A2	6	05-28	5240	A2	6	06-01	6340	A2
8	05-25	3450	A2	7			A2	7	06-17	3140	A1
9	06-17	3340	A2	8	05-26	9340	A2	8	11-02	4250	A2
1940	06-13	3540	A2	9	05-23	3790	A2	9	06-04	4190	A1
1	06-04	3030	A2	1950	06-14	6540	A2				

Up to 1952 maximum mean daily discharge.

CANADA

- Fraser. Shelley (32400 km²) (1952 - 1972) (See Unesco Catalogue)
  Complément.

Année Year	Mois/Month Jour/Day	Débit Discharge m³s-1	Obs.	Année Year	Mois/Month Jour/Day	Débit Discharge m³s-1	Obs.	Année Year	Mois/Month Jour/Day	Débit Discharge m³s-1	Obs.
1950	06-17	3710	A2	1974	06-24	3480	A1	1977	06-21	3000	A1
1951	05-18	3000	A2	5	06-08	2490	A1	8	06-10	2240	A1
1973	06-26	3340	A1	6	06-21	3280	A1	9	06-07	4080	A2

- Chilko. Redstone (6940 km²) (1928 - 1972) (See Unesco Catalogue)
  Complément.

Année	Mois/Month	Débit	Obs.	Année	Mois/Month	Débit	Obs.	Année	Mois/Month	Débit	Obs.
1973	08-10	209	A1	1976	08-09	402	A1	1979	07-24	205	A2
4	06-22	283	A1	7	08-15	268	A1				
5	07-13	311	A1	8	07-28	292	A1				

- Thompson. Spences Bridge (54900 km²) (1952 - 1972) (See Unesco Catalogue)
  Complément.

Année	Mois/Month	Débit	Obs.	Année	Mois/Month	Débit	Obs.	Année	Mois/Month	Débit	Obs.
1973	06-28	2490	A1	1976	06-22	2640	A1	1978	06-12	2350	A1
4	06-25	3570	A1	7	06-24	1790	A1	9	06-08	2170	A1
5	06-12	2970	A1								

- Chilliwack. Outlet of Chilliwack Lake (329 km²) (1924 - 1972) (See Unesco Catalogue)
  Complément.

Année	Mois/Month	Débit	Obs.	Année	Mois/Month	Débit	Obs.	Année	Mois/Month	Débit	Obs.
1973	05-19	47.6	A1	1976	07-09	69.1	A1	1978	06-06	59.5	A1
4	06-20	109	A1	7	06-09	42.5	A1	9	12-19	95.4	A1
5	12-04	96.3	A1								

- Slocan. Crescent Valley (3290 km²) (1933 - 1972) (See Unesco Catalogue)
  Complément.

Année	Mois/Month	Débit	Obs.	Année	Mois/Month	Débit	Obs.	Année	Mois/Month	Débit	Obs.
1914	06-04	331	A2	1930	06-08	262	A2	1975	06-14	377	A1
1925	05-22	464	A2	1931	05-17	283	A2	6	06-20	379	A1
6	04-30	248	A2	1932	06-15	436	A2	7	06-08	323	A1
7	06-18	456	A2	1934	05-30	470	A2	8	06-09	419	A1
8	05-27	680	A2	1973	05-25	357	A2	9	05-27	337	A1
9	06-15	360	A2	1974	06-20	708	A1				

Up to 1933 maximum mean daily discharge.

- Kettle. Ferry (5700 km²) (1931 - 1972) (See Unesco Catalogue)
  Complément.

Année	Mois/Month	Débit	Obs.	Année	Mois/Month	Débit	Obs.	Année	Mois/Month	Débit	Obs.
1929	05-24	193	A2	1974	06-16	422	A1	1977	05-03	283	A1
30	06-01	155	A2	5	06-03	388	A1	8	06-06	323	A1
1973	05-18	297	A1	6	05-11	379	A1	9	05-06	306	A1

TABLEAU III : SERIES CHRONOLOGIQUES DES VALEURS MAXIMALES ANNUELLES
TABLE III   : CHRONOLOGICAL SERIES OF YEARLY MAXIMA

CANADA

- Northwest Territories
- Mackenzie river. Fort Simpson (1270000 km²)

Année Year	Mois/Month Jour/Day	Débit Discharge m³s-1	Obs.	Année Year	Mois/Month Jour/Day	Débit Discharge m³s-1	Obs.	Année Year	Mois/Month Jour/Day	Débit Discharge m³s-1	Obs.
1939	07-06	13200	A1	1953	07-28	14100	A1	1968	07-17	17500	A1
40	07-05	15000	A1	4			A1	9	06-12	13300	A2
1	06-28	18900	A1	5	07-05	18700	A1	1970	06-14	14700	A1
2	06-14	22200	A1	6	07-17	17500	A1	1	06-21	16600	A1
3	07-14	18100	A1	7	07-03	17100	A1	2	06-04	18000	A1
4	06-16	13000	A1	8	06-10	12800	A1	3	06-21	20800	A1
5	06-14	13600	A1	9	06-09	14100	A1	4	07-21	20400	A1
6	06-17	11600	A1	1960	06-27	18500	A1	5	07-02	22000	A1
1949	06-27	16400	A1	1	05-30	23500	A1	6	07-06	18400	A1
1950	06-22	21900	A1	1965	06-10	16400	A2	7	06-07	23000	A1
1	07-06	12500	A1	6	06-21	14800	A1	8	06-11	13400	A1
2	07-03	15000	A1	7	06-03	17000	A2	9	07-07	20800	A1
								1980	06-13	12500	A1

- Alberta
- Athabasca river. Athabasca (74100 km²) (1922 - 1972) (See Unesco Catalogue)
  Complément.

Année Year	Mois/Month Jour/Day	Débit Discharge m³s-1	Obs.	Année Year	Mois/Month Jour/Day	Débit Discharge m³s-1	Obs.	Année Year	Mois/Month Jour/Day	Débit Discharge m³s-1	Obs.
1913	07-06	1670	A2	1927	06-27	2230	A2	1951	05-08	1800	A2
4	06-10	3090	A2	1929	06-13	1150	A2	1953	08-29	1830	A2
5	06-30	2760	A2	1930	06-15	1780	A2	1973	06-28	1890	A1
6	07-07	2080	A2	1938	06-18	1060	A2	4	04-28	2550	A1
7	05-24	2490	A2	1939	07-20	1250	A2	5	06-30	1850	A1
8	06-18	1470	A2	1942	07-21	1700	A2	6	08-20	1660	A1
9	06-26	1030	A2	43	06-27	2080	A2	7	06-01	2380	A1
1920	05-11	2500	A2	45	06-03	951	A2	8	07-15	2350	A1
1	06-11	1480	A2	46	06-01	1630	A2	9	07-15	2320	A1
1925	08-19	1900	A2	48	05-17	3650	A2				
6	09-05	1470	A2	49	07-24	1030	A2				

- Castle river. Near Beaver Mines (826 km²) (1945 - 1972) (See Unesco Catalogue)
  Complément.

Année Year	Mois/Month Jour/Day	Débit Discharge m³s-1	Obs.	Année Year	Mois/Month Jour/Day	Débit Discharge m³s-1	Obs.	Année Year	Mois/Month Jour/Day	Débit Discharge m³s-1	Obs.
1973	05-18	96.6	A1	1976	05-11	124	A1	1978	06-06	99.1	A1
4	06-17	171	A1	77	05-11	35.1	A1	79	05-27	113	A1
5	06-20	736	A1								

- Clearwater. Rocky Mountain House (3210 km²) (1922 - 1972) (See Unesco Catalogue)
  Complément.

Année Year	Mois/Month Jour/Day	Débit Discharge m³s-1	Obs.	Année Year	Mois/Month Jour/Day	Débit Discharge m³s-1	Obs.
1915	06-27	1110	A3	1973	05-28	98.8	A1
1923	06-02	320	A3	4	06-18	121	A1
1926	09-02	233	A3	5	06-26	45.3	A1
1949	05-24	289	A3				

TABLEAU III : SERIES CHRONOLOGIQUES DES VALEURS MAXIMALES ANNUELLES
TABLE III   : CHRONOLOGICAL SERIES OF YEARLY MAXIMA

CANADA

- Manitoba
- Sprague river. Sprague (355 km²) (1929 - 1972) (See Unesco Catalogue)
  Complément.

Année Year	Mois/Month Jour/Day	Débit Discharge m³s-1	Obs.	Année Year	Mois/Month Jour/Day	Débit Discharge m³s-1	Obs.	Année Year	Mois/Month Jour/Day	Débit Discharge m³s-1	Obs.
1973	09-26	10.5	A1	1976	06-29	5.38	A1	1978	04-19	18.5	A1
4	04-22	72.5	A1	7	09-27	2.83	A1	9	04-20	27.3	A1
5	04-29	13.9	A1								

- Québec
- St Laurent. La Salle (960000 km²)

Année Year	Mois/Month Jour/Day	Débit Discharge m³s-1	Obs.	Année Year	Mois/Month Jour/Day	Débit Discharge m³s-1	Obs.	Année Year	Mois/Month Jour/Day	Débit Discharge m³s-1	Obs.
1933	04-20	11340	A1	1950	04-06	11480	A1	1967	11-15	10500	A1
4	04-13	11890	A1	1	04-17	14570	A1	8	04-05	10700	A1
5	04-21	8490	A1	2	04-07	12790	A1	9	04-24	11300	A1
6	05-20	12280	A1	3	03-28	12060	A1	1970	05-06	10000	A1
7	04-08	11890	A1	4	04-18	12680	A1	1	04-23	13400	A1
8	03-27	12790	A1	5	04-08	12800	A2	2	05-07	13000	A1
9	04-24	11680	A1	6	05-01	10700	A2	3	03-19	13800	A1
1940	06-05	9970	A1	7	07-06	9700	A2	4	05-24	13800	A1
1	04-29	10530	A1	8	04-05	9680	A2	5	04-21	13300	A1
2	04-20	10170	A1	9	04-10	10200	A2	6	04-02	14600	A1
3	05-13	14870	A1	1960	05-20	12300	A1	7	03-16	12100	A1
4	04-26	10150	A1	1	06-17	9510	A1	8	04-14	13200	A1
5	04-05	12060	A1	2	04-10	9770	A1	9	03-26	12800	A1
6	03-17	10930	A1	3	04-05	9850	A1	1980	04-17	11500	A1
7	06-04	14270	A1	4	01-02	9170	A1				
8	03-22	11410	A1	5	12-31	8410	A1				
9	04-07	11070	A1	6	03-26	9600	A1				

- Chaudière. St Lambert (5830 km²)

Année Year	Mois/Month Jour/Day	Débit Discharge m³s-1	Obs.	Année Year	Mois/Month Jour/Day	Débit Discharge m³s-1	Obs.	Année Year	Mois/Month Jour/Day	Débit Discharge m³s-1	Obs.
1915	04-12	1140	A1	1937	10-22	804	A1	1959	11-29	623	A1
6	04-02	1010	A1	8	04-16	960	A1	1960	04-23	960	A1
7	06-19	1150	A1	9	04-24	1230	A1	1	04-24	1060	A1
8	04-04	974	A1	1940	04-05	866	A1	2	11-12	980	A1
9	04-14	1080	A1	1	04-16	1140	A1	3	11-09	1300	A1
1920	05-01	714	A1	2	04-27	1580	A1	4	04-15	1260	A1
1	03-29	767	A1	3	04-27	1230	A1	5	04-17	422	A1
2	06-19	1350	A1	4	04-24	881	A1	6	04-22	804	A1
3	05-01	1220	A1	5	04-28	1250	A1	7	12-14	765	A1
4	05-02	1120	A1	6	10-02	640	A1	8	03-30	895	A1
5	04-01	937	A1	7	05-07	1650	A1	9	04-18	1640	A1
6	05-04	1830	A1	8	05-20	1020	A1	1970	04-19	1320	A1
7	04-24	467	A1	9	04-01	507	A1	1	04-22	1220	A1
8	05-25	787	A1	1950	04-22	1130	A1	2	05-05	1360	A1
9	05-04	793	A1	1	04-11	1120	A1	3	04-24	934	A1

CANADA

- Chaudière. St Lambert (5830 km²)

Année Year	Mois/Month Jour/Day	Débit Discharge m³s-1	Obs.	Année Year	Mois/Month Jour/Day	Débit Discharge m³s-1	Obs.	Année Year	Mois/Month Jour/Day	Débit Discharge m³s-1	Obs.
1930	05-04	920	A1	1952	06-03	841	A1	1974	04-30	1680	A1
1	04-12	787	A1	3	04-01	1120	A1	5	04-21	1310	A1
2	04-11	980	A1	4	04-19	954	A1	6	08-11	1540	A1
3	05-04	1680	A1	5	04-16	1640	A1	7	04-01	1060	A1
4	04-18	1240	A1	6	05-01	889	A1	8	04-21	1100	A1
5	05-01	708	A1	7	08-05	507	A1	9	03-26	1390	A1
6	03-21	1710	A1	8	04-24	1420	A1	1980	04-11	597	A1

- Rivière Saguenay. Isle Maligne (73000 km²)

Année Year	Mois/Month Jour/Day	Débit Discharge m³s-1	Obs.	Année Year	Mois/Month Jour/Day	Débit Discharge m³s-1	Obs.	Année Year	Mois/Month Jour/Day	Débit Discharge m³s-1	Obs.
1913	11-01	2380	A2	1936	06-02	6120	A2	1959	05-17	4870	A2
14	06-04	3850	A2	7	05-17	6370	A2	1960	05-21	5720	A2
5	05-15	5070	A2	8	08-22	4450	A2	1	05-14	2830	A2
6	05-10	4640	A2	9	05-21	4420	A2	2	06-03	3850	A2
7	06-11	5660	A2	1940	05-31	6460	A2	3	06-26	2370	A2
8	05-26	6820	A2	1	10-11	3770	A2	4	05-14	5150	A2
9	05-28	7930	A2	2	05-10	5830	A2	5	09-03	2820	A2
1920	05-30	9060	A2	3	05-31	6460	A2	6	10-21	4530	A2
1	05-10	6770	A2	4	06-10	2730	A2	7	10-22	5920	A2
2	05-25	4420	A2	5	05-02	3960	A2	8	08-31	2410	A2
3	05-25	4930	A2	6	05-28	5550	A2	9	06-08	4420	A2
4	06-03	6030	A2	7	06-02	7390	A2	1970	07-26	4530	A2
5	05-23	4050	A2	8	05-20	3650	A2	1	05-15	3200	A2
6	06-09	4190	A2	9	05-29	5010	A2	2	06-07	2400	A2
7	11-07	4110	A2	1950	06-25	4930	A2	3	05-14	5610	A2
8	05-31	9260	A2	1	05-05	3600	A2	4	06-06	6260	A2
9	05-10	6480	A2	2	05-03	3820	A2	5	06-04	4110	A2
1930	05-24	5180	A2	3	05-20	3400	A2	6	05-22	8950	A2
1	05-26	4050	A2	4	03-13	4670	A2	7	05-26	4810	A2
2	09-19	4220	A2	5	05-10	4670	A2	8	06-15	5830	A2
3	05-28	5270	A2	6	06-10	3510	A2	9	05-06	4960	A2
4	05-18	4250	A2	7	06-24	4590	A2	1980	08-18	3400	A2
5	06-12	4080	A2	8	06-01	4960	A2				

- New Brunswick
- St John river. Fort Kent (14700 km²) (1934 - 1972) (See Unesco Catalogue)
  Complément.

Année Year	Mois/Month Jour/Day	Débit Discharge m³s-1	Obs.	Année Year	Mois/Month Jour/Day	Débit Discharge m³s-1	Obs.	Année Year	Mois/Month Jour/Day	Débit Discharge m³s-1	Obs.
1927	04-24	1880	A2	1933	05-05	3310	A2	1976	04-22	2710	
8	05-08	2550	A2	1973	04-30	3850	A1	7	04-24	2780	
9	05-06	2210	A2	4	05-02	3680	A3	8	05-11	2730	
1930	05-05	2730	A2	5	05-13	2250		9	04-30	4280	
1	04-24	1370	A2								
2	04-24	1940	A2								

Up to 1933 maximum mean daily discharge.

TABLEAU III : SERIES CHRONOLOGIQUES DES VALEURS MAXIMALES ANNUELLES

TABLE III   : CHRONOLOGICAL SERIES OF YEARLY MAXIMA

CANADA

- St Francis. Outlet Glasier Lake (1350 km²) (1952 – 1972) (See Unesco Catalogue)
  Complément.

Année Year	Mois/Month Jour/Day	Débit Discharge m³s-1	Obs.	Année Year	Mois/Month Jour/Day	Débit Discharge m³s-1	Obs.	Année Year	Mois/Month Jour/Day	Débit Discharge m³s-1	Obs.
1973	04-30	343	A1	1975	05-14	260	A1	1977	04-25	240	A1
4	05-16	323	A1	6	04-05	227	A1	8	05-13	247	A1
								1979	04-30	428	A1

- Nova Scotia
- Northeast Margaree. Margaree Valley (368 km²) (1943 – 1972) (See Unesco Catalogue)
  Complément.

Année Year	Mois/Month Jour/Day	Débit Discharge m³s-1	Obs.	Année Year	Mois/Month Jour/Day	Débit Discharge m³s-1	Obs.	Année Year	Mois/Month Jour/Day	Débit Discharge m³s-1	Obs.
1973	05-05	189	A1	1975	12-11	493		1977	06-04	490	
4	12-03	217	A1	6	11-06	303		8	05-10	241	
								1979	01-03	266	

- New Foundland
- Rocky river. Near Colinet (285 km²) (1949 – 1972) (See Unesco Catalogue)
  Complément.

Année Year	Mois/Month Jour/Day	Débit Discharge m³s-1	Obs.	Année Year	Mois/Month Jour/Day	Débit Discharge m³s-1	Obs.	Année Year	Mois/Month Jour/Day	Débit Discharge m³s-1	Obs.
1973	10-28	143	A1	1975	08-28	120	A1	1977	12-29	96	A1
4	08-31	237	A1	6	02-23	150	A1	8	12-19	135	A1
								1979	10-15	85.1	A1

CENTRAL AFRICAN REPUBLIC/REPUBLIQUE CENTRAFRICAINE

- Oubangui. Bangui (500000 km²)

Année Year	Mois/Month Jour/Day	Débit Discharge m³s-1	Obs.	Année Year	Mois/Month Jour/Day	Débit Discharge m³s-1	Obs.	Année Year	Mois/Month Jour/Day	Débit Discharge m³s-1	Obs.
1890	10-28	8440	A1	1930	10-18	10400	A1	1956	10-19	10100	
1	11-19	14500	A1	1	10-16	9610	A1	7	11-19	8800	
2	10-13	13700	A1	2	10-08	11400	A1	8	10-25	10200	
4	–	11500	A1	3	11-03	11800	A1	9	09-29	9260	
1908	11-06	12000	A1	4	11-10	9970	A1	1960	10-15	11300	
9	10-16	11300	A1	5	10-23	11600	A1	1	11-02	14400	
1910	10-26	11700	A1	6	11-01	11800	A1	2	11-05	12900	
1	10-26	10300	A1	7	11-03	9820	A1	3	10-29	9150	
2	–	>10930	A1	8	10-23	12400	A1	4	10-30	14100	
3	10-25	6420	A1	9	11-15	11700	A1	5	11-03	9780	
4	10-28	11900	A1	1940	10-30	9510	A1	6	09-25	9950	
5	11-16	9210	A1	1	11-14	10600	A1	7	10-28	11300	
6	10-23	15800	A1	2	09-27	11400	A1	8	10-25	9280	
7	11-01	13500	A1	3	10-08	9260	A1	9	10-09	12000	
8	09-05	7320	A1	4	11-07	8180	A1	1970	11-08	10800	
9	10-25	10100	A1	5	10-25	11100	A1	1	09-18	7860	
1920	11	>10800	A1	6	10-03	11100	A1	2	11-08	9170	
1	10-29	8400	A1	7	10-21	10400	A1	3	11-06	7030	

TABLEAU III : SERIES CHRONOLOGIQUES DES VALEURS MAXIMALES ANNUELLES
TABLE III   : CHRONOLOGICAL SERIES OF YEARLY MAXIMA

CENTRAL AFRICAN REPUBLIC/REPUBLIQUE CENTRAFRICAINE

- Oubangui. Bangui (500000 km²)

Année Year	Mois/Month Jour/Day	Débit Discharge m^3s-1	Obs.	Année Year	Mois/Month Jour/Day	Débit Discharge m^3s-1	Obs.	Année Year	Mois/Month Jour/Day	Débit Discharge m^3s-1	Obs.
1922	11-12	11700	A1	1948	09-26	12400	A1	1974	10-15	10800	
3	11-05	11400	A1	9	10-20	11300	A1	5	10-26	12700	
4	10-31	11900	A1	1950	10-08	11700	A1	6	11-04	8820	
5	11-19	10200	A1	1	11-06	10400	A1	7	10-22	8990	
6	11-05	12000	A1	2	10-07	9460	A1	8	11-11	9670	
7	10-30	7660	A1	3	10-28	7530	A1	9	11-12	7680	
8	09-30	9460	A1	4	10-19	10000	A1	1980	11-06	9820	
9	10-24	11600	A1	5	11-07	11700	A1				

CHAD/TCHAD

- Chari. N'Djamena (600000 km²)

Année Year	Mois/Month Jour/Day	Débit Discharge m^3s-1	Obs.	Année Year	Mois/Month Jour/Day	Débit Discharge m^3s-1	Obs.	Année Year	Mois/Month Jour/Day	Débit Discharge m^3s-1	Obs.
1933	10	>4080	A3	1948	10	4020	A2	1963	10-05	3670	A1
34	10	>4000	A3	9	10-28	3450	A2	4	11-06	4030	A1
35	10	>3110	A3	1950	11	4380	A2	5	10-08	2570	A1
36	10-29	4400	A2	1				6	10-20	3230	A1
37	11-12	2590	A2	2	11-07	3520	A1	7	11-08	3830	A1
38	11-03	4520	A2	3	11-07	3780	A1	8	10-26	2770	A1
39	11-01	3520	A2	4	11-15	4450	A1	9	10-23	2850	A1
1940	11-04	2260	A2	5	11-10	4730	A1	1970	10-25	3940	A1
1	09-27	2190	A2	6	11-07	4440	A1	1	10-16	3410	A1
2	10-18	3400	A2	7	10-18	2690	A1	2	09-14	1430	A1
3	11-02	3610	A2	8	11-05	2800	A1	3	10-13	2130	A1
4	11-03	3120	A2	9	11-05	3910	A1	4	10-29	3270	A1
5	11-07	3520	A2	1960	11-20	4010	A1	5	11-11	3870	A1
6	11-12	4540	A2	1	11-08	5160	A1	6	10-27	2720	A1
7				2	11-10	4650	A1	7	10-21	2840	A1

CHINA/CHINE

- Henan
- Huanghe. Shanxian (688000 km²)

Année Year	Mois/Month Jour/Day	Débit Discharge m^3s-1	Obs.	Année Year	Mois/Month Jour/Day	Débit Discharge m^3s-1	Obs.	Année Year	Mois/Month Jour/Day	Débit Discharge m^3s-1	Obs.
1843	08	36000	E2	1932	08-12	8020	B2	1946	07-21	10800	B2
1919	07-28	11200	B2	3	08-10	22000	B2	7	08-20	7450	B2
1920	10-05	5590	A1	4	08-10	8000	A1	8	10-03	5100	B2
1	07-13	7850	B2	5	08-07	13300	A1	9	07-26	10800	B2
2	07-25	5490	B2	6	09-05	12000	A1	1950	07-21	6160	B2
3	08-04	8220	B2	7	08-10	11500	B2	1	08-16	10500	B2
4	08-04	3220	B2	8	10-13	8150	B2	2	08-19	5950	A1
5	08-11	10700	B2	9	07-26	7290	B2	3	08-27	12100	A1

276

CHINA/CHINE

- Henan
- Huanghe. Shanxian (688000 km²)

Année Year	Mois/Month Jour/Day	Débit Discharge m³s-1	Obs.	Année Year	Mois/Month Jour/Day	Débit Discharge m³s-1	Obs.	Année Year	Mois/Month Jour/Day	Débit Discharge m³s-1	Obs.
1926	08-10	5960	B2	1940	07-13	10600	B2	1954	09-05	13900	A1
7	08-20	4520	B2	1	08-22	5220	B2	5	09-18	6960	A1
8	07-18	3650	B2	2	08-04	17700	B2	6	07-24	7330	A1
9	08-06	8500	B2	3	09-28	9690	B2	7	07-19	6400	A1
1930	07-09	5340	B2	4		7850	B2	8	08-22	9540	A1
1	09-04	4240	B2	5		7300	B2				

- Hubei
- Changjiang. Yichang (1010000 km²)

Année Year	Mois/Month Jour/Day	Débit Discharge m³s-1	Obs.	Année Year	Mois/Month Jour/Day	Débit Discharge m³s-1	Obs.	Année Year	Mois/Month Jour/Day	Débit Discharge m³s-1	Obs.
1153	07-31	94000		1909	07-13	61100	B2	1944	09-16	37600	B2
1227	08-01	98100		1910	09-20	44000	B2	5	09-06	67500	B2
1560	08-25	98000		1	08-16	49100	B2	6	07-09	62100	B2
1693		81000		2	07-09	46100	B2	7	08-07	50500	B2
1788	07-23	86000	E2	3	07-15	53300	B2	8	07-21	57600	B2
1796	07-18	84000		4	08-11	45100	B2	9	07-10	58100	B2
1860	07-18	92500	E2	5	09-24	40200	B2	1950	07-10	59700	A1
1870	07-20	110000	E2	6	07-05	42600	B2	1	07-14	53600	A1
1877	08-08	33900	C2	7	07-27	61000	B2	2	07-16	54900	A1
8	07-12	57200	C2	8	09-13	50200	B2	3	08-07	49100	A1
9	07-11	57200	C2	9	07-20	61700	B2	4	08-06	66800	A1
1880	07-22	50200	C2	1920	07-25	61500	B2	5	07-18	54400	A1
1	09-22	41600	C2	1	07-17	64800	B2	6	06-30	57500	A1
2	09-29	48100	C2	2	08-13	63000	B2	7	07-22	53700	A1
3	07-10	54700	C2	3	07-23	56600	B2	8	08-25	60200	A1
4	07-02	41900	C2	4	08-24	42700	B2	9	08-17	54700	A1
5	07-12	42100	C2	5	09-09	40800	B2	1960	08-07	52300	A1
6	09-06	47500	C2	6	08-15	60800	B2	1	07-03	53800	A1
7	09-13	48800	C2	7	06-26	43300	B2	2	07-11	56200	A1
8	07-31	57400	C2	8	08-02	50700	B2	3	07-14	44400	A1
9	08-04	51200	C2	9	09-21	36400	B2	4	09-15	50200	A1
1890	08-04	52200	B2	1930	09-13	48000	B2	5	07-17	49000	A1
1	07-17	57700	B2	1	08-10	64000	B2	6	09-05	59800	A1
2	07-15	64600	B2	2	09-03	41900	B2	7	07-04	42600	A1
3	07-16	56000	B2	3	06-22	49100	B2	8	07-07	57500	A1
4	09-25	44800	B2	4	07-29	45900	B2	9	09-06	42700	A1
5	07-31	55800	B2	5	07-07	56900	B2	1970	08-01	46100	A1
6	09-04	71100	B2	6	08-07	62300	B2	1	08-20	34400	A1
7	07-28	52000	B2	7	07-21	61900	B2	2	05-15	35400	A1
8	08-09	60600	B2	8	07-24	61200	B2	3	07-05	51900	A1
9	09-25	46800	B2	9	08-01	53600	B2	4	08-13	61600	A1
1900	07-28	33000	B2	1940	08-14	40900	B2	5	10-05	45700	A1
1	07-21	57900	B2	1	08-08	57400	B2	6	07-22	49600	A1

TABLEAU III : SERIES CHRONOLOGIQUES DES VALEURS MAXIMALES ANNUELLES
TABLE III   : CHRONOLOGICAL SERIES OF YEARLY MAXIMA

CHINA/CHINE

- Hubei
- Changjiang. Yichang (1010000 km²)

Année Year	Mois/Month Jour/Day	Débit Discharge m³s-1	Obs.	Année Year	Mois/Month Jour/Day	Débit Discharge m³s-1	Obs.	Année Year	Mois/Month Jour/Day	Débit Discharge m³s-1	Obs.
1902	09-23	43500	B2	1942	07-09	29800	B2	1977	07-11	40200	A1
3	08-04	56300	B2	3	07-13	44300	B2	8	07-08	42500	A1
4	08-23	42400	B2					1981		72000	
5	08-14	64400	B2								
6	08-16	46300	B2								
7	09-01	48500	B2								
8	07-04	61800	B2								

- Hebei
- Luanhe river. Luanxian (44100 km²)

Année Year	Mois/Month Jour/Day	Débit Discharge m³s-1	Obs.	Année Year	Mois/Month Jour/Day	Débit Discharge m³s-1	Obs.	Année Year	Mois/Month Jour/Day	Débit Discharge m³s-1	Obs.
1886	08	35000	E2	1950	08-03	4320	B2	1965	07-20	1610	B1
1929	08-06	21500	B2	1	08-16	2560	B2	6	07-29	6360	B1
1930	08-05	25000	B2	2	07-25	3000	B2	7	08-21	4540	A1
1	08-14	726	A1	3	08-20	5140	B2	8	08-20	407	A1
2	07-27	1520	A1	4	08-11	4960	A1	9	08-13	7070	B1
3	08-02	2290	B2	5	08-17	5660	B1	1970	08-09	1980	A1
4	07-07	3440	B2	6	08-11	2390	B1	1	07-20	820	B1
5	07-25	2440	B2	7	08-13	1500	B1	2	07-29	738	A1
6	07-22	863	A1	8	07-15	13800	B1	3	08-22	3530	B1
7	08-06	1670	B2	9	07-22	24000	B1	4	08-10	2820	B1
1942	07-21	1370	B2	1960	08-08	1300	B2	5	08-13	3930	B1
1946	08-11	1380	A1	1	08-22	1050	B1	6	07-25	3680	B1
7	07-03	1380	A1	2	07-27	34000	B1	7	08-03	5820	A1
8	07-26	1420	B2	3	08-19	550	B1	8	07-29	6760	B1
9	08-15	28500	B2	4	08-14	12900	B1	9	07-28	9340	B1

- Taïwan
- Choshui. Chi-Chi (2304 km²)

Année Year	Mois/Month Jour/Day	Débit Discharge m³s-1	Obs.	Année Year	Mois/Month Jour/Day	Débit Discharge m³s-1	Obs.	Année Year	Mois/Month Jour/Day	Débit Discharge m³s-1	Obs.
1941	06-16	4325	A2	1958	07-16	4470	A2	1967	07-11	6900	A2
2	08-19	5750	A2	9	08-08	5900	A2	8	09-30	2320	A2
3	07-18	4950	A2	1960	08-01	10500	A2	9	09-27	3500	A2
1947	06-16	5070	A2	1	09-29	3400	A2	1970	09-07	6160	A2
1951	04-11	5365	A2	2	08-06	2960	A2	1	09-23	3840	A2
2	07-30	4125	A2	3	09-11	6670	A2	2	08-17	3990	A2
1955	09-03	5900	A2	4	06-09	573	A2	3	10-10	4000	A2
6	09-18	9900	A2	5	08-19	3600	A2	4	06-18	2720	A2
7	06-07	5300	A2	6	06-09	2680	A2	5	09-23	3450	A2

TABLEAU III : SERIES CHRONOLOGIQUES DES VALEURS MAXIMALES ANNUELLES

TABLE III   : CHRONOLOGICAL SERIES OF YEARLY MAXIMA

COLOMBIA/COLOMBIE

- Rio Magdalena. Puerto Berro (74410 km²)

Année Year	Mois/Month Jour/Day	Débit Discharge m³s-1	Obs.	Année Year	Mois/Month Jour/Day	Débit Discharge m³s-1	Obs.	Année Year	Mois/Month Jour/Day	Débit Discharge m³s-1	Obs.
1936	05-26	4290	A1	1950	06-09	6360	A1	1964			
7	06-01	5020	A1	1	11-11	4830	A1	1965	11-24	5910	A1
8	05-02	6420	A1	2	05-07	4925	A1	6	11-30	5660	A1
9	11-06	5870	A1	3	11-29	6060	A1	7	06-05	5450	A1
1940	10-28	4195	A1	4	11-21	5460	A1	8	10-22	5620	A1
1	05-14	3670	A1	5	11-01	5680	A1	9	10-10	6365	A1
2	05-06	6850	A1	6	11-01	6160	A1	1970	11-01	6570	A1
3	11-05	5870	A1	7	06-01	6560	A1	1	05-26	6370	A1
4	11-03	6060	A1	8	05-03	4450	A1	2	05-23	6100	A1
5	05-22	6060	A1	9	05-08	5020	A1	3	11-19	6300	A1
6	05-23	4735	A1	1960	11-04	5130	A1	4	11-26	5245	A1
7	10-16	5570	A1	1	11-08	5130	A1	5	11-14	5710	A1
8	04-22	4925	A1	2	05-04	4640	A1	6	05-03	5100	A1
9	11-09	5350	A1	3	05-12	5870	A1				

CONGO

- Congo. Brazzaville Beach (voir ZAIRE)
- Sangha. Ouesso (158350 km²)

Année Year	Mois/Month Jour/Day	Débit Discharge m³s-1	Obs.	Année Year	Mois/Month Jour/Day	Débit Discharge m³s-1	Obs.	Année Year	Mois/Month Jour/Day	Débit Discharge m³s-1	Obs.
1952	11-07	3400	A1	1961	11-01	4000	A2	1971	11-04	3790	A1
3	11-01	3400	A1	2	10-02	4720	A2	2	10-29	3220	A1
4	10-26	3650	A1	3	11-20	3910	A1	3	11-07	2920	A1
5	11-07	4010	A2	4	11-08	4110	A2	4	11-10	4340	A2
6	11-12	3450	A1	5	11-04	3780	A1	5	10-27	3900	A1
7	11-25	4660	A2	6	11-24	4200	A2	6	11-01	3200	A1
8	11-05	2580	A1	7	11-02	4050	A2	7	11-23	3250	A1
9	11-10	4600	A2	8	11-04	3650	A1	8	11-11	3630	A1
1960	11-06	4730	A2	9	11-10	3940	A1	9	11-10	2760	A1
				1970	11-09	4390	A2				

- Kouilou. Sounda Kakamoeka (55340 km²)

Année Year	Mois/Month Jour/Day	Débit Discharge m³s-1	Obs.	Année Year	Mois/Month Jour/Day	Débit Discharge m³s-1	Obs.	Année Year	Mois/Month Jour/Day	Débit Discharge m³s-1	Obs.
1950	05	4090	D2	1961	03-13	3060	A2	1971	12-04	1660	A1
1952	12-06	3180	A1	2	05-08	2500	A1	2	11-19	1960	A1
3	04-25	3070	A1	3	04-08	1830	A1	3	05-05	2410	A1
4	04-03	2300	A1	4	04-28	3120	A2	4	04-17	1940	A1
5	05-29	2975	A1	5	05-09	2440	A1	5	03-10	1860	A1
6	12-22	1900	A1	6	05-10	3560	A2	6	04-29	2060	A1
7	03-09	2100	A1	7	03-27	2990	A2	7	03-16	2430	A2
8	12-16	1350	A1	8	03-07	1532	A1	8	09-28	1540	A1
9	05-05	2140	A1	9	04-23	2380	A1	9	05-12	2670	A2
1960	11-22	2550	A1	1970	05-07	2580	A2				

COSTA RICA

- <u>Reventazon. Angostura</u> (1340 km²)

Année Year	Mois/Month Jour/Day	Débit Discharge m³s-1	Obs.	Année Year	Mois/Month Jour/Day	Débit Discharge m³s-1	Obs.	Année Year	Mois/Month Jour/Day	Débit Discharge m³s-1	Obs.
1954	10-25	950	A1	1964	09-19	695	A1	1974	12-04	1230	A1
5	10-14	1670	A1	5	06-13	600	A1	5	12-14	1260	A1
6	10-14	960	A1	6	12-26	925	A1	6	01-18	665	A1
7	-	-	-	7	06-05	570	A1	7	08-18	520	A1
8	11-11	335	A1	8	09-19	875	A1	8	06-06	370	A1
9	06-22	370	A1	9	11-24	1660	A1	9	05-04	660	A1
1960	10-08	510	A1	1970	04-09	3800	B1	1980	12-13	825	A1
1	12-26	635	A1	1	09-23	685	A1				
2	11-04	1060	A1	2	12-24	935	A1				
3	12-09	670	A1	3	12-10	1000	A1				

CUBA

- <u>Buey. San Miguel</u> (73 km²)

Année Year	Mois/Month Jour/Day	Débit Discharge m³s-1	Obs.	Année Year	Mois/Month Jour/Day	Débit Discharge m³s-1	Obs.	Année Year	Mois/Month Jour/Day	Débit Discharge m³s-1	Obs.
1960	06-09	166	A1	1967	06-02	148	A1	1974	04-26	146	A1
1	10-23	135	A1	8	12-12	118	A1	5	09-19	144	A1
2	10-27	184	A1	9	06-09	193	A1	6	11-07	195	A1
3	10-07	2060	A2	1970	05-22	165	A1	7			
4	08-26	402	A1	1	05-24	84	A1	8	01-13	213	A1
5	05-16	147	A1	2	05-20	471	A1	9	04-25	469	A1
6	09-30	542	A1	3	10-18	588	A1				

CZECHOSLOVAKIA/TCHECOSLOVAQUIE

- Smedava.Bily Potok (26.1 km²) (1956 - 1972) (See Unesco Catalogue)
  No flood exceeding 69 m³s-1 since 1972 up to 1980
- Celadenka. Celadna (31.1 km²) (1952 - 1972) (See Unesco Catalogue)
  No flood exceeding 63 m³s-1 since 1972 up to 1980
- Ostravice. Sance (146 km²) (1926 - 1972) (See Unesco Catalogue)
  No flood exceeding 220 m³s-1 since 1972 up to 1980
- Kamenice. Josefuv dul (26 km²) (1912 - 1970) (See Unesco Catalogue)
  No flood exceeding 106 m³s-1 since 1970 up to 1980
- Cidlina. Novy Bydzov (452 km²) (1932 - 1969) (See Unesco Catalogue)
  No flood exceeding 54.6 m³s-1 since 1969 up to 1980
- Berounka. Krivoklat (7422 km²) (1890 - 1970) (See Unesco Catalogue)
  No flood exceeding 897 m³s-1 since 1970 up to 1980
- Vltava. Kamyk na Vltavou (12200 km²) (1890 - 1954) (See Unesco Catalogue)
  No flood exceeding 1970 m³s-1 since 1970 up to 1980
- Labe. Decin (51100 km²) (1845 - 1970) (See Unesco Catalogue)

Complément

Année	Débit	Obs.	Année	Débit	Obs.	Année	Débit	Obs.
1970	1425	A1	1973	422	A1	1977	2126	A1
1	842	A1	4	838	A1	8	1293	A1
2	691	A1	5	1970	A1	9	1439	A1
			6	1444	A1	1980	1769	A1

TABLEAU III : SERIES CHRONOLOGIQUES DES VALEURS MAXIMALES ANNUELLES
TABLE III : CHRONOLOGICAL SERIES OF YEARLY MAXIMA

CZECHOSLOVAKIA/TCHECOSLOVAQUIE

- Zdechovka. Zdechov (4.08 km²) (1958 - 1972) (See Unesco Catalogue)
  No flood exceeding 13 m³s-1 since 1972 up to 1980
- Becva. Teplice (1280 km²) (1920 - 1972) (See Unesco Catalogue)
  No flood exceeding 650 m³s-1 since 1972 up to 1980
- Morava. Kromeriz (7010 km²) (1916 - 1972) (See Unesco Catalogue)
  No flood exceeding 681 m³s-1 since 1972 up to 1980
- Dyje. Doini Vestomice (11700 km²) (1921 - 1972) (See Unesco Catalogue)
  No flood exceeding 815 m³s-1 since 1972 up to 1980
- Vah. Lubochna (2130 km²) (1921 - 1972) (See Unesco Catalogue)
  No flood exceeding 618 m³s-1 since 1972 up to 1980
- Lubochnianka. Lubochna (118 km²) (1931 - 1972) (See Unesco Catalogue)
  No flood exceeding 51.3 m³s-1 since 1972 up to 1980
- Turiec. Martin (827 km²) (1931 - 1972) (See Unesco Catalogue)
  One flood exceeding 184 m³s-1 since 1972 up to 1980 : 188 m³s-1 10 - 22 1974
- Kysuca. Cadca (484 km²) (1920 - 1972) (See Unesco Catalogue)
  No flood exceeding 433 m³s-1 since 1972 up to 1980

DEMOCRATIC PEOPLE'S REPUBLIC OF KOREA/REPUBLIQUE POPULAIRE DEMOCRATIQUE DE COREE

- Teadonggang. Mirim (12175 km²)

Année Year	Mois/Month Jour/Day	Débit Discharge m³s-1	Obs.	Année Year	Mois/Month Jour/Day	Débit Discharge m³s-1	Obs.	Année Year	Mois/Month Jour/Day	Débit Discharge m³s-1	Obs.
1958	07-29	3900	A1	1966	07-21	10600	A1	1974	08-31	8470	A1
59	07-10	4540	A1	7	08-29	29000	A1	5	09-03	6040	A1
1960	08-02	5920	A1	8	08-20	7430	A1	6	08-01	10900	A1
1	09-05	5110	A1	9	07-31	11500	A1	7	08-08	727	A1
2	09-08	16500	A1	1970	09-09	5510	A1	8	07-15	5710	A1
3	07-19	18000	A1	1	07-07	6870	A1	9	08-02	8840	A1
4	07-09	15800	A1	2	08-18	15700	A1	1980	07-23	1120	A1
5	08-06	7630	A1	3	09-01	9380	A1	1	07-05	5680	A1

FEDERAL REPUBLIC OF GERMANY/REPUBLIQUE FEDERALE D'ALLEMAGNE

- Rhein. Maxau (50345 km²)

Année Year	Mois/Month Jour/Day	Débit Discharge m³s-1	Année Year	Mois/Month Jour/Day	Débit Discharge m³s-1	Année Year	Mois/Month Jour/Day	Débit Discharge m³s-1
1824	11-10	4080	1939	09-18	3390	1956	03-05	2860
1852	09	4160	1940	06-16	3000	7	02-27	3910
1876	06	4340	2	03-14	3010	8	02-27	3400
1880	10-11	4210	2	06-19	2160	9	01-25	2290
1881	08-09	4230	3	10-21	2000	9	08-15	2680
1882	12-28	4620	4	11-26	4330	1960	08-19	2050
1912	12-01	4010	5	06-25	2970	2	01-15	2850
1930	11-24	2930	7	03-24	2230	2	06-16	2030
1	07-13	2880	7	07-10	3550	4	05-07	2310
2	06-25	2870	8	06-14	1470	4	06-13	3650
3	12-09	2080	9	09-10	1500	6	02-11	3300
4	10-31	3060	1950	11-29	3160	6	12-27	2590
6	01-15	3500	2	04-03	2950	7	09-24	3980

TABLEAU III : SERIES CHRONOLOGIQUES DES VALEURS MAXIMALES ANNUELLES
TABLE III   : CHRONOLOGICAL SERIES OF YEARLY MAXIMA

FEDERAL REPUBLIC OF GERMANY/REPUBLIQUE FEDERALE D'ALLEMAGNE

- Rhein. Maxau (50345 km²)

Année Year	Mois/Month Jour/Day	Débit Discharge m³s-1	Obs.	Année Year	Mois/Month Jour/Day	Débit Discharge m³s-1	Obs.	Année Year	Mois/Month Jour/Day	Débit Discharge m³s-1	Obs.
1937	02-24	2600		1952	06-29	3690		1968	08-29	2800	
7	06-16	2950		4	08-25	2880		1970	02-25	4400	
1938	05-25	3220		1955	01-17	4340					

- Rhein. Rees (159680 km²)

Année Year	Mois/Month Jour/Day	Débit Discharge m³s-1	Obs.	Année Year	Mois/Month Jour/Day	Débit Discharge m³s-1	Obs.	Année Year	Mois/Month Jour/Day	Débit Discharge m³s-1	Obs.
1845	04-03	11490 (1)		1941	01-29	7970		1955	01-20	9500	
1850	02	10560 (1)		2	03-22	8790		6	03-08	7620	
1882	12	11580 (1)		3	01-18	3260		7	03-02	6950	
1926	12- 1	12200		4	02-08	3750		8	03-01	9140	
1930	11-27	8740		5	02-16	8510		8	12-01	5460	
2	01-12	5720		6	02-11	8910		1959	10-15	3570	
2	11-02	4270		7	03-16	5940		1961	02-05	5840	
4	01-25	2880		8	01-03	9320		2	04-05	5910	
5	02-09	5470		9	03-20	2830		3	03-15	3830	
6	01-18	5580		1950	02-15	4370		3	11-24	5530	
7	02-27	7290		1	01-24	6850		5	03-29	6380	
8	01-16	4630		2	04-03	7420		6	01-06	7800	
8	10-22	5870		2	12-26	8000		6	12-16	7630	
9	12-02	8500		3	10-05	3840		8	01-19	7610	
								9	03-18	5350	
								1970	02-26	9950	

(1) Rhein. Andernach.

FINLAND/FINLANDE

- Kemijoki. Taivalkoski (50820 km²) (1912 - 1971) (See Unesco Catalogue)
  One flood exceeding 3860 m³s-1 since 1970 up to 1979 : 4824 m³s-1 05 - 26 - 1973.

FRANCE

- Rhône. Beaucaire (96500 km²)

Année Year	Mois/Month Jour/Day	Débit Discharge m³s-1	Obs.	Année Year	Mois/Month Jour/Day	Débit Discharge m³s-1	Obs.	Année Year	Mois/Month Jour/Day	Débit Discharge m³s-1	Obs.
1845	11-13	6440	A2	1891	09-22	7800	A2	1937	03-24	6520	A2
6	10-19	8710	A2	2	02-23	5920	A2	8	12-12	4650	A2
7	04-16	7260	A2	3	03-01	4460	A2	9	11-06	5300	A2
8	04-21	7720	A2	4	11-18	4660	A2	1940	11-18	5970	A2
9	10-17	5620	A2	5	01-17	5420	A2	1	06-11	6280	A2
1850	11-28	4660	A2	6	11-02	9060	A2	2	11-01	5470	A2
1	02-04	5970	A2	7	02-07	5700	A2	3	10-26	5550	A2
2	08-13	6600	A2	8	11-27	5850	A2	4	11-29	6880	A2
3	10-30	7300	A2	9	01-19	5880	A2	5	02-16	5260	A2

FRANCE

- Rhône. Beaucaire (96500 km²)

Année Year	Mois/Month Jour/Day	Débit Discharge m^3s-1	Obs.	Année Year	Mois/Month Jour/Day	Débit Discharge m^3s-1	Obs.	Année Year	Mois/Month Jour/Day	Débit Discharge m^3s-1	Obs.
1854	06-03	5580	A2	1900	09-30	8940	A2	1946	09-07	4600	A2
5	10-21	7540	A2	1	11-22	6400	A2	7	03-08	5570	A2
6	05-31	11640	E	2	04-03	6180	A2	8	01-29	6780	A2
7	11-26	6100	A2	3	10-30	6240	A2	9	11-21	5320	A2
8	11-28	5380	A2	4	02-21	5230	A2	1950	11-21	5560	A2
9	11-05	6230	A2	5	11-21	4680	A2	1	11-22	9170	A2
1860	09-27	5930	A2	6	11-08	6020	A2	2	12-02	4890	A2
1	07-16	5160	A2	7	11-10	8500	A2	3	10-15	6060	A2
2	12-03	5800	A2	8	01-01	4200	A2	4	12-11	7180	A2
3	01-08	7140	A2	9	11-12	4660	A2	5	01-22	7240	A2
4	10-28	8100	A2	1910	12-08	8660	A2	6	03-22	5470	A2
5	12-05	6510	A2	1	11-25	4560	A2	7	03-01	5980	A2
6	03-20	6120	A2	2	02-10	5040	A2	8	12-22	7920	A2
7	03-29	5960	A2	3	03-18	6400	A2	9	12-11	6400	A2
8	10-04	6860	A2	4	11-04	7480	A2	1960	10-08	7970	A1
9	01-02	4560	A2	5	06-25	5500	A2	1	12-13	4440	A1
1870	09-28	5650	A2	6	03-17	5940	A2	2	01-16	3950	A1
1	09-08	4970	A2	7	05-21	7850	A2	3	11-07	7100	A1
2	10-24	9060	A2	8	01-24	5700	A2	4	03-27	5810	A1
3	03-19	7000	A2	9	01-07	8280	A2	5	12-09	4600	A1
4	12-04	4230	A2	1920	01-03	4790	A2	6	02-23	4910	A1
5	09-13	5080	A2	1	05-24	2120	A2	7	03-10	4300	A1
6	03-17	5400	A2	2	04-19	5630	A2	8	02-25	4760	A1
7	06-03	6600	A2	3	12-02	7010	A2	9	02-25	4995	A1
8	11-30	5960	A2	4	10-06	7600	A2	1970	01-11	5510	A1
9	04-18	6020	A2	5	02-16	6180	A2	1	03-22	4470	A1
1880	11-10	4500	A2	6	12-02	7280	A2	2	02-19	4880	A1
1	04-06	3720	A2	7	03-14	5630	A2	3	12-25	4790	A1
2	09-29	8390	A2	8	10-29	7090	A2	4	11-30	3840	A1
3	01-01	6060	A2	9	06-09	3330	A2	5	09-16	3930	A1
4	06-04	3770	A2	1930	06-28	6000	A2	6	11-10	8690	A1
5	11-23	5920	A2	1	03-12	6000	A2	7	10-24	8125	A1
6	11-12	10200	A2	2	05-09	6000	A2	8	02-27	7800	A1
7	12-13	5300	A2	3	11-21	7140	A2	9	10-28	6680	A1
8	12-31	7460	A2	4	05-01	4600	A2	1980	02-06	4520	A1
9	01-01	8760	A2	5	11-14	9600	A2	1	12-19	6110	A1
1890	02-24	7260	A2	6	01-02	7820	A2	1982	11-09	8025	A1

TABLEAU III : SERIES CHRONOLOGIQUES DES VALEURS MAXIMALES ANNUELLES
TABLE III : CHRONOLOGICAL SERIES OF YEARLY MAXIMA

FRANCE

- Isère. Grenoble (5720 km²)

Année Year	Mois/Month Jour/Day	Débit Discharge m³s-1	Obs.	Année Year	Mois/Month Jour/Day	Débit Discharge m³s-1	Obs.	Année Year	Mois/Month Jour/Day	Débit Discharge m³s-1	Obs.
1651	11-12	2500		1897	08-23	725		1937	06-20	840	
1673	11	1800		8	06-25	625		1940	09-16	830	
1711	02-11	1460		9	01-14	815		1944	11-25	910	
1733	09-14	1900		1901	04-06	675		1946	09-01	450	
1740	12-22	2000		2	07-10	740		8	06-20	830	
1764	06-10	1460		4	05-23	608		1950	11-17	730	
1778	10-27	1800		5	08-29	495		1	07-16	710	
1816	05-31	1010		6	06-01	690		2	11-26	675	
1840	11-26	950		7	06-13	605		5	02-09	880	
1856	05-31	1120		8	05-13	598		7	06-15	830	
1859	11-02	1800		9	10-06	445		8	06-27	715	
1877	06-07	850		1910	06-26	900		1960	10-06	790	
1878	05-25	1000		1	06-10	520		1	12-12	825	
1879	06-30	710		2	05-15	625		3	06-28	640	
1880	10-24	660		3	06-02	560		8	09-21	980	
1	08-28	580		4	07-23	810		1970	04-19	555	
2	11-27	900		5	07-28	675		1	05-09	428	
3	06-05	638		6	12-26	710		2	11-14	520	
5	11-30	660		7	05-28	640		3	07-25	760	
6	11-08	540		8	12-24	880		4	06-29	720	
7	06-03	660		9	06-13	775		7	05-20	520	
8	08-01	860		1920	09-24	810		8	06-09	710	
9	06-14	580		2	05-26	840		1980	06-15	661	
1890	06-29	670		3	05-09	445					
1	10-21	340		4	05-01	810					
2	06-04	590		5	09-24	340					
3	10-05	475		6	06-01	710					
4	10-26	340		7	06-02	580					
5	11-13	760		8	10-22	800	(1)				
1896	09-26	630		9	06-10	780					

On peut admettre que pour les maximaux annuels manquants postérieurs à 1877 le débit est inférieur à 800 m³s-1.

(1) D'après M. PARDE cette crue aurait atteint 1000 m³s-1 environ.

- Seine. Paris (44300 km²) (Pont de la Tournelle 1732-1853), (Pont Royal 1854-1879), (Paris Austerlitz).

Année	Débit	Année	Débit	Année	Débit
1732-33	665	1741-42	565	1750-51	1740
4	625	3	800	2	745
5	1400	4	1055	3	910
.6	570	5	710	4	985
7	725	6	795	5	705
8	800	7	1395	6	1320
9	870	8	1110	7	1145
1739-40	870	9	1355	8	1180
1	2160	1749-50	650	9	780

TABLEAU III : SERIES CHRONOLOGIQUES DES VALEURS MAXIMALES ANNUELLES
TABLE III : CHRONOLOGICAL SERIES OF YEARLY MAXIMA

FRANCE

- <u>Seine. Paris</u> (44300 km²)

Année Year	Mois/Month Jour/Day	Débit Discharge m³s-1	Obs.	Année Year	Mois/Month Jour/Day	Débit Discharge m³s-1	Obs.	Année Year	Mois/Month Jour/Day	Débit Discharge m³s-1	Obs.
1759-60		1455		1804-05		925		1849-50		1630	
1		915		6		1480		1		1000	
2		690		7		1845		2		785	
3		485		8		1255		3		1120	
4		1815		9		1280		4		795	
5		1125		1809-10		1065		5		1355	
6		555		1		1410		6		900	
7		530		2		1220		7		1135	
8		1335		3		810		8		530	
9		1110		4		1250		9		745	
1769-70		1430		5		865		1859-60		1110	
1		1335		6		1365		1		1560	
2		1260		7		1710		2		765	
3		1040		8		1370		3		680	
4		1385		9		655		4		610	
5		925		1819-20		1520		5		1030	
6		–		1		895		6		970	
7		935		2		633		7		1490	
8		925		3		1230		8		615	
9		1100		4		810		9		970	
1779-80		965		5		1140		1869-70		–	
1		1055		6		1165		1		–	
2		1025		7		1120		2		–	
3		1395		8		945		3		(1610)	
4		1705		9		970		4		(300)	
5		515		1829-30		1025		5		(860)	
6		845		1		1220		6		1810	
7		880		2		730		7		1375	
8		1145		3		915		8		1010	
9		1050		4		1340		9		1500	
1789-90		740		5		660		1879-80		1495	
1		1215		6		1500		1		1310	
2		815		7		1745		2		(300)	
3		1115		8		720		3		1685	
4		680		9		1345		4		740	
5		1335		1839-40		1280		5		1070	
6		1010		1		1250		6		1495	
7		755		2		1235		7		890	
8		810		3		1210		8		1010	
9		1840		4		1555		9		1550	
1799-00		570		5		890		1889-90		590	
1		1040		6		1445		1		650	
2		1995		7		1370		2		1040	
3		820		8		1510		3		950	
4		855		9		1080		4		560	

TABLEAU III : SERIES CHRONOLOGIQUES DES VALEURS MAXIMALES ANNUELLES
TABLE III   : CHRONOLOGICAL SERIES OF YEARLY MAXIMA

FRANCE

- <u>Seine. Paris</u> (44300 km²)

Année Year	Mois/Month Jour/Day	Débit Discharge m³s-1	Obs.	Année Year	Mois/Month Jour/Day	Débit Discharge m³s-1	Obs.	Année Year	Mois/Month Jour/Day	Débit Discharge m³s-1	Obs.
1894-95		740		1923-24		2010		1952-53		1345	
6		1130		5		1230		4		331	
7		1495		6		1655		5		2120	
8		560		7		1035		6		590	
9		740		8		1150		7		1300	
1899-00		890		9		770		8		1500	
1		950		1929-30		765		9		1700	
2		680		1		1685		1959-60		455	
3		680		2		850		1		1055	
4		1070		3		570		2		855	
5		380		4		580		3		395	
6		1140		5		1185		4		730	
7		770		6		1230		5		730	
8		1085		7		1450		6		1415	
9		745		8		770		7		1045	
1909-10		2405		9		985		8		1580	
1		1605		1939-40		1435		9		760	
2		1180		1		1630		1969-70		1655	
3		1090		2		945		1		420	
4		1265		3		1015		2		600	
5		1010		4		515		3		830	
6		1240		5		1990		4		780	
7		1240		6		670		5		740	
8		920		7		800		6		1410	
9		1650		8		1120		7		1650	
1919-20		1810		9		345		8		1200	
1		300		1949-50		680		9		1350	
2		1025		1		805		1979-80		1330	
3		1410		2		1155		1		1790	
								2		1510	

FRENCH GUYANA/GUYANE FRANCAISE

- <u>Maroni. Langa Tabiki</u> (60.900 km²)

1952	05-18	4660	A1	1962	05-02	4450	A1	1972	04-29	5850	
3	08-14	6280	A1	3	05-18	6030	A1	3	06-07	5790	
4	05-20	5050	A1	4	06-08	3460	A1	4	06-23	5200	
5	05-18	5960	A1	5	06-11	3120	A1	5	07-22	6240	
6	05-06	5060	A1	6	03-23	2260	A1	6	04-19	6640	
7	05-20	5970	A1	7	05-14	2970	A1	7	04-27	5090	
8	04-30	5790	A1	8	06-02	7000	A1	8	05-20	4240	
9	06-03	4580	A1	9	05-24	6090	A1	9	06-13	5460	
1960	06-04	6840	A1	1970	05-20	6290	A1	1980	05-04	4860	
1	06-11	4015	A1	1	04-05	5980	A1				

TABLEAU III : SERIES CHRONOLOGIQUES DES VALEURS MAXIMALES ANNUELLES
TABLE III   : CHRONOLOGICAL SERIES OF YEARLY MAXIMA

FRENCH POLYNESIA/POLYNESIE FRANCAISE

- Papenoo. Cote 45 (Tahiti) (78 km²)

Année Year	Mois/Month Jour/Day	Débit Discharge m³s-1	Obs.	Année Year	Mois/Month Jour/Day	Débit Discharge m³s-1	Obs.	Année Year	Mois/Month Jour/Day	Débit Discharge m³s-1	Obs.
1944		1500	D3	1971	12-15	435	A1	1978	05-19	925	B2
1955		900	D3	3	02-12	555	A1	9	01-13	520	A1
1968		1400	D3	4	10-16	200	B1	1980	01-27	415	A1
1969				5	01-17	320	A1	1	03-10	1125	B2
1970				6	12-04	345	A1	2	02-25	950	B2
1	01-29	700	B2	1976	12-08	480	A1	3	04-12	2200	B2

GABON

- Ogooué. Lambaréné (204000 km²)

Année Year	Mois/Month Jour/Day	Débit Discharge m³s-1	Obs.	Année Year	Mois/Month Jour/Day	Débit Discharge m³s-1	Obs.	Année Year	Mois/Month Jour/Day	Débit Discharge m³s-1	Obs.
1929/30	05-26	6070	A2	1947/48	12-03	8550	A2	1965/66	05-15	10700	A1
1930/31	05-31	9000	A2	9	12-01	11300	A1	7	11-17	9540	A1
2	05-23	9750	A2	1949/50	11-25	11300	A2	8	11-14	10900	A1
3	12-21	7700	A2	1				9	12-07	8350	A1
4	12-13	7800	A2	2				1969/70	12-04	9300	A1
5	11-19	13400	A2	3				1	11-04	10900	A1
6	12-02	7980	A2	4	11-21	8200	A1	2	12-03	10000	A1
7	04-18	9700	A2	5	12-02	6610	A1	3	11-26	7810	A1
8	12-28	9550	A2	6	11-27	8700	A1	4	11-25	8810	A1
9	05-31	9250	A2	7	12-14	9050	A1	5	11-20	9180	A1
1939/40	12-07	13000	A2	8	12-14	9500	A1	6	11-21	9900	A1
1	12-05	7650	A2	9	05-15	9240	A1	7	12-22	11300	A1
2	12-19	5850	A2	1959/60	11-30	10600	A1	8	11-15	12100	A1
3	05-23	7550	A2	1	11-27	11500	A1	9	11-27	8440	A1
4	05-23	9850	A2	2	11-17	13600	A1	1979/80	11-22	6760	A1
5	11-23	10400	A2	3	11-06	8930	A1	1	11-18	12200	A1
6	11-06	8500	A2	4	11-26	9210	A1				
7	06-01	11100	A2	5	04-27	9820	A1				

GHANA

- Volta. Senchi Halcrow (394000 km²) (1936 - 1971) (See Unesco Catalogue)
- White Volta. Pwalugu (63300 km²) (1951 - 1972) (See Unesco Catalogue)
  Complement

Année Year	Mois/Month Jour/Day	Débit Discharge m³s-1	Obs.	Année Year	Mois/Month Jour/Day	Débit Discharge m³s-1	Obs.	Année Year	Mois/Month Jour/Day	Débit Discharge m³s-1	Obs.
1973	08-20	1120	B2	1974	08-21	1425	B2	1975	09-26	856	B2
								1976	10-18	640	B2

- White Volta. Nawuni (92900 km²) (1953 - 1972) (See Unesco Catalogue)
  Complement

Année Year	Mois/Month Jour/Day	Débit Discharge m³s-1	Obs.	Année Year	Mois/Month Jour/Day	Débit Discharge m³s-1	Obs.	Année Year	Mois/Month Jour/Day	Débit Discharge m³s-1	Obs.
1973	09-01	1133	B2	1974	09-27	1765	B2	1975	09-29	1368	B2

GHANA

- Black Volta. Bamboi (134000 km²) (1950 - 1971) (See Unesco Catalogue)
  Complement

Année Year	Mois/Month Jour/Day	Débit Discharge m³s-1	Obs.	Année Year	Mois/Month Jour/Day	Débit Discharge m³s-1	Obs.	Année Year	Mois/Month Jour/Day	Débit Discharge m³s-1	Obs.
1973	09-13	563	A2	1974	09-15	1670	A2	1975	09-22	573	A2

- Oti - Saboba (50300 km²) (1953 - 1972) (See Unesco Catalogue)
  Complement

Année Year	Mois/Month Jour/Day	Débit Discharge m³s-1	Obs.	Année Year	Mois/Month Jour/Day	Débit Discharge m³s-1	Obs.	Année Year	Mois/Month Jour/Day	Débit Discharge m³s-1	Obs.
1973	09-14	1260	A2	1974	09-15	2406	A2	1975	08-15	983	A2
								1976	10-24	687	A2

- Pra. Twifo Praso (20800 km²) (1943 - 1972) (See Unesco Catalogue)
  Complement

Année Year	Mois/Month Jour/Day	Débit Discharge m³s-1	Obs.	Année Year	Mois/Month Jour/Day	Débit Discharge m³s-1	Obs.	Année Year	Mois/Month Jour/Day	Débit Discharge m³s-1	Obs.
1973	09-14	550	A1	1974	13-09	673	A1	1975	07-14	649	A1

- Pra. Mampong (378 km²) (1944 - 1971) (See Unesco Catalogue)
  Complement

Année Year	Mois/Month Jour/Day	Débit Discharge m³s-1	Obs.	Année Year	Mois/Month Jour/Day	Débit Discharge m³s-1	Obs.	Année Year	Mois/Month Jour/Day	Débit Discharge m³s-1	Obs.
1972	07-16	74	A1	1974	06-08	35	A1	1976	06-14	21	A1
1973	06-23	35	A1	1975	07-07	49	A1	1977	06-14	82	A1
								78		27	A1

GUATEMALA

- Usumacinta. Boca del Cerro (51540 km²)

Année Year	Débit Discharge m³s-1	Obs.	Année Year	Débit Discharge m³s-1	Obs.	Année Year	Mois/Month Jour/Day	Débit Discharge m³s-1	Obs.
1949	4090	A	1957	4395	A	1965		6070	A
1950	5165	A	8	4270	A	6		6075	A
1	3860	A	9	3615	A	7	10-23	6600	A
2	5590	A	1960	5250	A	8		5320	A
3	5150	A	1	4025	A	9		6145	A
4	5250	A	2	4575	A	1970		5810	A
5	5835	A	3	5300	A	1		4410	A
1956	5440	A	1964	4135	A	1972		6100	A

GUYANA/GUYANE

- Mazaruni. Apaikwa (14000 km²) (1950 - 1972) (See Unesco Catalogue)
- Potaru. Kaieteur (2640 km²) (1950 - 1972) (See Unesco Catalogue)
- Demerara. Great Falls (2460 km²) (1950 - 1972) (See Unesco Catalogue)
- Demerara. Saka (4040 km²) (1950 - 1972) (See Unesco Catalogue)

TABLEAU III : SERIES CHRONOLOGIQUES DES VALEURS MAXIMALES ANNUELLES

TABLE III : CHRONOLOGICAL SERIES OF YEARLY MAXIMA

HAWAII ISLANDS/ILES HAWAI (United States of America)/(Etats Unis d'Amérique)

- Honopou. Huelo (Mauai) (1.7 km²)

Année Year	Mois/Month Jour/Day	Débit Discharge m³s-1	Obs.	Année Year	Mois/Month Jour/Day	Débit Discharge m³s-1	Obs.	Année Year	Mois/Month Jour/Day	Débit Discharge m³s-1	Obs.
1911	09-30	3.7	A1	1935	02-25	7.5	A1	1958	10-22	8	A1
2				6	01-17	10.5	A1	1960	04-17	29	A1
2	10-14	2.18	A1	6	12-29	24.5	A1	1	04-02	5.8	A1
4	05-08	2.8	A1	8	08-24	12.5	A1	2	03-12	23	A1
5				9	02-07	39	A1	3	05-14	21.5	A1
6	05-01	21	A2	1940	08-12	13.5	A1	4	03-08	6.3	A1
7	04-30	9.3	A1	1	06-30	27.2	A1	4	11-05	10.3	A1
8	04-03	17.3	A2	2	03-08	15.8	A1	5	11-14	45	A1
8	12-03	7.2	A1	2	10-21	13.6	A1	7	08-08	12	A1
9	10-06	3.8	A1	4	08-23	2.45	A1	8	01.04	11.6	A1
1921	01-16	17.3	A2	4	12-26	7.5	A1	9	02-02	10.8	A1
2	02-01	75	A2	6	01-22	21	A1	9	12-28	30	A1
3	02-23	34	A2	6	12-17	26	A1	1971	04-23	58	A1
4	02-13	12.9	A2	8	01-25	36	A1	2	07-15	5.9	A1
4	10-16	31	A2	8	12-24	9.6	A1	3	03-11	8.1	A1
6	08-05	21	A2	1950	04-27	61	A1	4	01-31	13.1	A1
7	01-03	18.7	A2	0	11-25	4.8	A1	4	11-21	42	A1
8	09-19	4.3	A1	2	02-19	8.9	A1	6	03-04	6.1	A1
8	12-13	15.1	A2	3	03-07	31	A1	7	04-04	4.4	A1
1930	02-23	8.6	A1	4	02-26	9.6	A1	8	08-21	21	A1
0	11-18	162	A1	5	02-07	6.8	A1	8	11-14	53	A1
2	04-30	31	A1	6	02-25	48	A1	1980	04-02	15.2	A1
2	12-31	24.5	A1	7	02-06	12.5	A1				
4	04-25	8.1	A1	7	11-22	5.7	A1				

- Kawaikoi Stream. Waima (11km²) (1914 - 1972) (See Unesco Catalogue)

HUNGARY/HONGRIE

- Duna (Danube). Budapest. (185200 km²)

Année Year	Mois/Month Jour/Day	Débit Discharge m³s-1	Obs.	Année Year	Mois/Month Jour/Day	Débit Discharge m³s-1	Obs.	Année Year	Mois/Month Jour/Day	Débit Discharge m³s-1	Obs.
1946	07-15	4920	A1	1956	03-10	7490	A1	1966	07-30	6750	A1
7	03-24	6490	A1	7	07-30	5910	A1	7	06-14	5080	A1
8	01-10	6080	A1	8	07-04	6110	A1	8	10-07	4320	A1
9	05-30	6090	A1	9	08-20	6100	A1	9	06-11	3640	A1
1950	08-09	2740	A1	1960	07-29	5100	A1	1970	08-17	6010	A1
1	05-15	5190	A1	1	05-20	4450	A1	1	06-15	3440	A1
2	04-06	5750	A1	2	05-25	4900	A1	2	07-18	3860	A1
3	07-15	4320	A1	3	03-16	4750	A1	3	05-11	4540	A1
4	07-18	7960	A1	4	05-13	3680	A1	4	12-14	6190	A1
5	07-16	6045	A1	5	06-15	8310	A1	5	07-08	7325	A1

TABLEAU III : SERIES CHRONOLOGIQUES DES VALEURS MAXIMALES ANNUELLES
TABLE III   : CHRONOLOGICAL SERIES OF YEARLY MAXIMA

HUNGARY/HONGRIE

- Tisza. Szolnok (73110 km²) (1951 - 1970) (See Unesco Catalogue)
  Complement

Année Year	Mois/Month Jour/Day	Débit Discharge m³s-1	Obs.	Année Year	Mois/Month Jour/Day	Débit Discharge m³s-1	Obs.	Année Year	Mois/Month Jour/Day	Débit Discharge m³s-1	Obs.
1946	03-11	1380	A1	1950	12-23	1330	A1	1973	06-15	945	A1
7	03-31	1435	A1	1971	01-08	1310	A1	4	11-09	2000	A1
8	01-27	2330	A1	2	11-23	1220	A1	5	04-25	1765	A1
9	07-30	1265	A1								

- Tisza. Szeged (138400 km²) (1951 - 1970) (See Unesco Catalogue)
  Complement

Année Year	Mois/Month Jour/Day	Débit Discharge m³s-1	Obs.	Année Year	Mois/Month Jour/Day	Débit Discharge m³s-1	Obs.	Année Year	Mois/Month Jour/Day	Débit Discharge m³s-1	Obs.
1946	03-11	1745	A1	1950	05-23	1825	A1	1973	06-15	1520	A1
7	03-31	2015	A1	1971	01-09	1660	A1	4	11-10	2790	A1
8	01-30	2600	A1	2	01-12	2000	A1	5	07-13	2340	A1
9	07-30	1650	A1								

- Szamos. Csenger (15280 km²) (1951 - 1970) (See Unesco Catalogue)
  Complement

Année Year	Mois/Month Jour/Day	Débit Discharge m³s-1	Obs.	Année Year	Mois/Month Jour/Day	Débit Discharge m³s-1	Obs.	Année Year	Mois/Month Jour/Day	Débit Discharge m³s-1	Obs.
1946	02-10	735	A1	1950	02-17	1080	A1	1973	06-12	475	A1
7	02-17	625	A1	1971	01-02	700	A1	4	06-15	2150	A1
8	01-17	995	A1	1972	11-17	710	A1	5	04-05	745	A1
1949	07-24	650	A1								

- Sajo. Felsözsolca (6440 km²) (1951 - 1969) (See Unesco Catalogue)
  Complement

Année Year	Mois/Month Jour/Day	Débit Discharge m³s-1	Obs.	Année Year	Mois/Month Jour/Day	Débit Discharge m³s-1	Obs.	Année Year	Mois/Month Jour/Day	Débit Discharge m³s-1	Obs.
1946	03-17	76.5	A1	1950	02-19	69.5	A1	1973	02-18	70.5	A1
7	03-23	216	A1	70	03-29	210	A1	4	10-24	545	A1
8	04-14	100	A1	1	02-03	136	A1	5	04-12	375	A1
9	01-09	279	A1	2	05-19	336	A1				

- Zagyva. Jasztelek (4207 km²) (1951 - 1969) (See Unesco Catalogue)
  Complement

Année Year	Mois/Month Jour/Day	Débit Discharge m³s-1	Obs.	Année Year	Mois/Month Jour/Day	Débit Discharge m³s-1	Obs.	Année Year	Mois/Month Jour/Day	Débit Discharge m³s-1	Obs.
1946	06-26	74.1	A1	1950	02-24	155	A1	1973	07-02	165	
7	03-21	275	A1	1970	04-04	215	A1	4	10-23	655	
8	06-09	550	A1	1	03-15	115	A1	5	04-13	250	
9	08-17	320	A1	2	05-19	210	A1				

- Maros. Mako (30150 km²) (1951 - 1970) (See Unesco Catalogue)
  Complement

Année Year	Mois/Month Jour/Day	Débit Discharge m³s-1	Obs.	Année Year	Mois/Month Jour/Day	Débit Discharge m³s-1	Obs.	Année Year	Mois/Month Jour/Day	Débit Discharge m³s-1	Obs.
1946	03-08	460	A1	1950	04-20	280		1973	05-17	710	
7	02-25	715		1971	07-11	515		4	06-23	1220	
8	01-21	650		2	12-01	820		5	07-10	2320	
9	06-25	520									

TABLEAU III : SERIES CHRONOLOGIQUES DES VALEURS MAXIMALES ANNUELLES

TABLE III   : CHRONOLOGICAL SERIES OF YEARLY MAXIMA

INDIA/INDE

- Narmada. Garudeshwar (87900 km²) (1948 - 1968) (See Unesco Catalogue)
  Complement

Année Year	Mois/Month Jour/Day	Débit Discharge m³s-1	Obs.	Année year	Mois/Month Jour/Day	Débit Discharge m³s-1	Obs.	Année Year	Mois/Month jour/Day	Débit Discharge m³s-1	Obs.
1969	08-05	31260		1973	08-31	57800		1977	08-08	24700	
1970	09-06	69400		4	08-21	31900		8	08-30	40750	
1	09-08	20000		5	09-13	30480		9	08-11	27480	
2	08-19	43900		6	08-05	16370		1980	08-31	23140	

- Tapi. Kathoré (64400 km²) (1940 - 1958) (See Unesco Catalogue)
  Complement

Année Year	Mois/Month Jour/Day	Débit Discharge m³s-1	Obs.	Année year	Mois/Month Jour/Day	Débit Discharge m³s-1	Obs.	Année Year	Mois/Month jour/Day	Débit Discharge m³s-1	Obs.
1959	09-18	29500	?	1972	08-21	9180		1977			
1968	08-09	?		3		<12000		8	08-31	13625	
9	09-10	19680		4		< 2000		9	08-12	12020	
1970	08-06	36500	?	5				1980	08-11	1175	
1	09-08	20000		6							

- Krishna. Vijayawada (251360 km²)

Année Year	Mois/Month Jour/Day	Débit Discharge m³s-1	Obs.	Année year	Mois/Month Jour/Day	Débit Discharge m³s-1	Obs.	Année Year	Mois/Month jour/Day	Débit Discharge m³s-1	Obs.
1894	07-28	16400		1923	07-26	23000		1953	08-21	13500	
5	08-14	14000		4	09-05	20700		4	07-22	14500	
6	08-07	21500		5	07-23	19500		5	08-22	14200	
7	08-14	17500		6	08-15	16400		6	08-11	23400	
8	07-27	17600		7	08-02	18000		7	08-20	16800	
9	09-17	11500		8	10-02	13300		8	07-27	21000	
1900	07-20	20300		9	10-06	13100		9	07-28	19800	
1	08-16	13700		1930	07-10	11000		1960	09-25	16100	
2	07-23	16600		1	08-23	14600		1	07-24	22100	
3	10-07	39000		2	07-22	10800		2	08-20	16800	
4	07-11	15000		3	08-11	21000		3	08-31	16900	
5	07-30	13200		4	08-16	10300		4	10-02	27400	
6	07-29	13300		5	08-31	9600		5	07-28	15200	
7	08-01	18700		6	07-04	10700		6	08-05	12100	
8	09-27	15300		7	07-22	12300		7	08-06	19800	
9	07-18	14300		8	10-04	11600		8	08-14	7500	
1910	07-12	13300		9	07-18	13600		9	08-08	15500	
1	07-23	9300		1940	08-26	12400		1970	09-23	14500	
2	08-08	16700		1	07-08	13600		1	09-08	7300	
3	07-25	13700		2	07-12	15000		2	07-18	3500	
4	08-11	35900		3	07-20	11300		3	08-17	7900	
5	08-06	17000		4	07-20	14300		4	09-30	13300	

TABLEAU III : SERIES CHRONOLOGIQUES DES VALEURS MAXIMALES ANNUELLES
TABLE III   : CHRONOLOGICAL SERIES OF YEARLY MAXIMA

INDIA/INDE

- Krishna. Vijayawada (251360 km²)

Année Year	Mois/Month Jour/Day	Débit Discharge m³s-1	Obs.	Année Year	Mois/Month Jour/Day	Débit Discharge m³s-1	Obs.	Année Year	Mois/Month Jour/Day	Débit Discharge m³s-1	Obs.
1916	11-02	33500		1945	07-25	14500		1952	08-01	11500	
7	09-04	15400		6	08-14	18400		1975	10-13	18500	
8	09-03	7600		7	09-28	14400		6	08-11	14200	
9	10-01	14400		8	08-23	12300		7	08-02	6800	
1920	07-15	11700		9	09-24	32500		8	08-16	17000	
1	08-04	18300		1950	07-28	20300		9	10-01	17300	
2	07-28	14600		1	07-31	10200		1980	07-15	13500	

- Godavari. Dolaïshwaram Polavaram (307800 km²) (1941 - 1958) (See Unesco Catalogue)
  Complement

Année Year	Mois/Month Jour/Day	Débit Discharge m³s-1	Obs.	Année Year	Mois/Month Jour/Day	Débit Discharge m³s-1	Obs.	Année Year	Mois/Month Jour/Day	Débit Discharge m³s-1	Obs.
1907	07	>80000		1966	09-08	62600		1973	08-28	30200	
1959	09-17	78700		7	07-28	32100		4	08-13	16200	
1960	08-03	30000		8	08-19	26200		5	09-13	38100	
1				9	09-23	35500		6	07-23	55000	
2				1970	08-24	41300		7	08-25	35000	
3				1	09-03	16900		8	08-18	38200	
4				2	07-07	27300		9	08-07	32900	
5	09-04	16800						1980	08-05	29500	

- Mahanadi. Baramul (127000 km²) (1946 - 1968) (See Unesco Catalogue)
- Ganga. Farrakka (935340 km²) (1949 - 1967) (See Unesco Catalogue)
  Complement

Année Year	Mois/Month Jour/Day	Débit Discharge m³s-1	Obs.	Année Year	Mois/Month Jour/Day	Débit Discharge m³s-1	Obs.	Année Year	Mois/Month Jour/Day	Débit Discharge m³s-1	Obs.
1968	08-19	50000		1972	09-08	30500		1976	09-23	68500	
1969				3	09-12	51600		7	08-18	56300	
1970		<60000		4	08-31	59000		8	08-20	69000	
1	08-22	70500		5	08-29	64000		9	08-01	39500	
								1980	09-06	71300	

- Brahmaputra. Pandu (404000 km²) (1955 - 1970) (See Unesco Catalogue)
  Complement

Année Year	Mois/Month Jour/Day	Débit Discharge m³s-1	Obs.	Année Year	Mois/Month Jour/Day	Débit Discharge m³s-1	Obs.	Année Year	Mois/Month Jour/Day	Débit Discharge m³s-1	Obs.
1971	08-27	35000		1972	07-31	47730		1973	08-08	51100	
								1974	09-03	<60000	

IRAQ/IRAK

- Alfurat. Hits (264100 km²)

Année Year	Mois/Month Jour/Day	Débit Discharge m³s-1	Obs.	Année Year	Mois/Month Jour/Day	Débit Discharge m³s-1	Obs.	Année Year	Mois/Month Jour/Day	Débit Discharge m³s-1	Obs.
1932	05-22	1820	A1	1945	04-26	2510	A1	1958	04-28	2440	A1
33	05-16	2110	A1	6	05-15	3620	A1	9			

TABLEAU III : SERIES CHRONOLOGIQUES DES VALEURS MAXIMALES ANNUELLES

TABLE III : CHRONOLOGICAL SERIES OF YEARLY MAXIMA

IRAQ/IRAK

- Alfurat. Hits (264100 km²)

Année Year	Mois/Month Jour/Day	Débit Discharge m³s-1	Obs.	Année Year	Mois/month Jour/Day	Débit Discharge m³s-1	Obs.	Année Year	Mois/Month Jour/Day	Débit Discharge m³s-1	Obs.
1934	04-12	1860	A1	1947	04-07	2900	A1	1960			
35	04-25	3270	A1	8	04-25	4490	A1	1			
36	04-26	3750	A1	9	05-13	2630	A1	2			
37	04-27	3160	A1	1950	05-21	3430	A1	3			
38	05-11	4450	A1	1	04-09	2420	A1	4			
39	05-09	3720	A1	2	04-18	4570	A1	1965		3630	A3
1940	04-29	4480	A1	3	04-27	4420	A1	6		4480	A3
1	04-23	4060	A1	4	04-27	4730	A1	7		6090	A3
2	04-27	4040	A1	5	05-11	2510	A1	8		6650	A3
3	05-05	3900	A1	6	05-04	4560	A1	9		7370	A3
4	05-16	4530	A1	7	05-15	4420	A1	1970		3250	A3
								1		4910	A3
								1972		5214	A3

ITALY/ITALIE

- Adige. Boara Pisani (12000 km²) (1922 - 1960) (Voir Catalogue UNESCO)
  Complement

Année	Jour	Débit	Obs	Année	Jour	Débit	Obs	Année	Jour	Débit	Obs
1961				1966	06-11	1325	A1	1971	06-10	407	A1
2	05-27	445	A1	7	05-18	641	A1	2	06-14	808	A1
3	11-08	735	A1	8	06-09	622	A1	3	10-03	440	A1
4	04-22	259	A1	9	05-09	355	A1	4	07-01	458	A1
5	09-04	1290	A1	1970	06-19	468	A1				

- Adda. Fuentes (2600 km²) (1927 - 1960) (Voir Catalogue UNESCO)
- Dora. Baltea. Tavagnasco (3315 km²) (1929 - 1960) (Voir Catalogue UNESCO)
- Tanaro. Montecastello (7985 km²) (1933 - 1960) (Voir Catalogue UNESCO)
- Pô. Pontelagoscuro (70090 km²) (1918 - 1960) (Voir Catalogue UNESCO)
  Complement

Année	Jour	Débit	Obs	Année	Jour	Débit	Obs	Année	Jour	Débit	Obs
1961	04-27	4980	A1	1966	11-07	7360	A1	1970	01-18	3270	A1
2	11-13	4700	A1	7	03-14	2500	A1	1	03-25	4910	A1
3	11-09	6510	A1	8	11-07	7900	A1	2	03-16	5970	A1
4	04-06	5270	A1	9	05-11	6170	A1	3	06-11	3920	A1
5	10-06	6250	A1								

_ Magra.Calamazza (940km²) (1930 - 1970) (Voir Catalogue UNESCO)

  Arno. San Giovanni alla Vena (8185 km²) (1924 - 1970) (Voir Catalogue UNESCO)

Année	Jour	Débit	Obs	Année	Jour	Débit	Obs	Année	Jour	Débit	Obs
1971	01-01	448	A1	1973	09-26	318	A1	1974	03-05	395	A1
2	12-02	495	A1								

- Ombrone. Sasso d'Ombrone (2660 km²) (1926 - 1970) (Voir Catalogue UNESCO)

TABLEAU III : SERIES CHRONOLOGIQUES DES VALEURS MAXIMALES ANNUELLES

TABLE III   : CHRONOLOGICAL SERIES OF YEARLY MAXIMA

ITALY/ITALIE

- Tevere. Roma (16545 km²) (1922 - 1960) (Voir Catalogue UNESCO)
  Complement

Année Year	Mois/Month Jour/Day	Débit Discharge m³s-1	Obs.	Année Year	Mois/Month Jour/Day	Débit Discharge m³s-1	Obs.	Année Year	Mois/Month Jour/Day	Débit Discharge m³s-1	Obs.
1961	01-06	1390	A1	1966	12-06	895	A1	1971	12-01	460	A1
2	11-20	1160	A1	7	12-27	535	A1	2	11-13	670	A1
3	01-09	1160	A1	8	02-17	1115	A1	3	01-23	650	A1
4	12-30	1520	A1	9	02-17	1265	A1	4	05-01	885	A1
5	09-03	1560	A1	1970	01-17	800	A1				

- Pescara. Santa Teresa (3125 km²) (1922 - 1970) (Voir Catalogue UNESCO)
- Volturno. Cancello Anone (5550 km²) (1931 - 1960) (Voir Catalogue UNESCO)
- Agri. Tarangelo (507 km²) (1926 - 1960) (Voir Catalogue UNESCO)
- Simeto Giarretta (1830 km²) (1925 - 1967) (Voir Catalogue UNESCO)

IVORY COAST/COTE D'IVOIRE

- Cavally. Taï (13800 km²) (1955 - 1973) (Voir Catalogue UNESCO)
  Complement

Année Year	Mois/Month Jour/Day	Débit Discharge	Obs.	Année Year	Mois/Month Jour/Day	Débit Discharge	Obs.	Année Year	Mois/Month Jour/Day	Débit Discharge	Obs.
1974	10-04	730	A1	1977	10-09	1120	A1	1979	08-23	790	A1
5	09-29	725	A1	8	09-30	450	A1	1980	09-18	1370	A1
6	11-13	655	A1								

- Nce.Taï (1240 km²) (1955 - 1973) (Voir Catalogue UNESCO)
- Sassandra. Guessabo (35400 km²) (1953 - 1973) (Voir Catalogue UNESCO)
  Complement

Année Year	Mois/Month Jour/Day	Débit Discharge	Obs.	Année Year	Mois/Month Jour/Day	Débit Discharge	Obs.	Année Year	Mois/Month Jour/Day	Débit Discharge	Obs.
1974	09-23	1150	A1	1976	10-22	875	A1	1978	09-26	885	A1
5	09-25	1260	A1	7	09-19	1230	A1	9	08-27	1500	A1

- Bandama. Tiasalé (95500 km²) (1954 - 1970) (Voir Catalogue UNESCO)
  Complement

Année Year	Mois/Month Jour/Day	Débit Discharge	Obs.	Année Year	Mois/Month Jour/Day	Débit Discharge	Obs.	Année Year	Mois/Month Jour/Day	Débit Discharge	Obs.
1971		2350	B2	1975		1400	B2	1978		2300	B2
2		600	B2	6		350	B2	9		1840	B2
3		1500	B2	7		1250	B2	1980		1640	B2
4		1220	B2								

Débits naturels reconstitués.

- Comoe Aniassué (66500 km²) (1953 - 1973) (Voir Catalogue UNESCO)
  Complement

Année Year	Mois/Month Jour/Day	Débit Discharge	Obs.	Année Year	Mois/Month Jour/Day	Débit Discharge	Obs.	Année Year	Mois/Month Jour/Day	Débit Discharge	Obs.
1974	09-29	1430	A1	1977	09-25	730	A1	1979	09-25	1210	A1
5				8	08-05	370	A1	1980	09-23	1260	A1
6	11-11	340	A1								

JAPAN/JAPON

- Ishikari.Ishikari Ohhashi (12700 km²) (1954 – 1972) (See Unesco Catalogue)
  Complement

Année Year	Mois/Month Jour/Day	Débit Discharge m³s-1	Obs.	Année Year	Mois/Month Jour/Day	Débit Discharge m³s-1	Obs.	Année Year	Mois/Month Jour/Day	Débit Discharge m³s-1	obs.
1904	07-13	8350	E3	1942	03-26	3390	B2	1952	04-19	3050	B2
1933	05-06	3980	B2	3	05-08	3000	B2	1953	08-03	3170	B2
4	04-23	2690	B2	4	05-06	2090	B2	1973	08-20	4530	A1
5	05-01	2480	B2	5			B2	4	04-30	3420	A1
6	10-05	3150	B2	6	04-14	3400	B2	5	08-24	7530	A1
7	05-04	3100	B2	7		3650	B2	6	04-16	1990	A1
8	04-29	2450	B2	8	04-11	3390	B2	7	04-17	3870	A1
9	04-23	3230	B2	9	05-16	2360	B2	8	05-02	2960	A1
1940	04-28	2640	B2	1950	05-06	2500	B2	9	05-20	3140	A1
1	10-03	3500	B2	1	09-04	2400	B2	1980	04-07	2670	A1
								1	08-06	11330	A1

- Tokachi. Moiwa (8210 km²) (1954 – 1972) (See Unesco Catalogue)
  Complement

Année Year	Mois/Month Jour/Day	Débit Discharge m³s-1	Obs.	Année Year	Mois/Month Jour/Day	Débit Discharge m³s-1	Obs.	Année Year	Mois/Month Jour/Day	Débit Discharge m³s-1	obs.
1932	08-25	9390	02	1975	05-18	4170	A1	1978	06-05	1050	A1
3	09-04	2420	A1	6	10-21	1470	A1	9	10-20	2350	A1
4	08-27	1450	A1	7	11-29	1340	A1	1980	09-01	1120	A1
								1	08-06	8050	A1

- Kitakami. Kozenji (7060 km²) (1947 – 1972) (See Unesco Catalogue)
  Complement

Année Year	Mois/Month Jour/Day	Débit Discharge m³s-1	Obs.	Année Year	Mois/Month Jour/Day	Débit Discharge m³s-1	Obs.	Année Year	Mois/Month Jour/Day	Débit Discharge m³s-1	obs.
1910	09-02	4950	B2	1944	07-19	3850	B2	1977	05-17	2300	A1
1913	08-26	3850	B2	1973	11-28	800	A1	8	06-14	1200	A1
1920	08-09	4800	B2	4	08-01	2200	A1	9	08-07	4200	A1
1931	08-09	4000	B2	5	03-22	2100	A1	1980	04-07	2400	A1
1938	08-31	2900	A2	6	09-15	1600	A1	1	08-24	5300	A1

- Mogami. Shimono (3530 km²) (1913 – 1972) (See Unesco Catalogue)
  Complement

Année Year	Mois/Month Jour/Day	Débit Discharge m³s-1	Obs.	Année Year	Mois/Month Jour/Day	Débit Discharge m³s-1	Obs.	Année Year	Mois/Month Jour/Day	Débit Discharge m³s-1	obs.
1973	04-17	800	A1	1976	08-06	3400	A1	1979	07-29	1900	A1
4	04-15	1700	A1	7	09-20	1600	A1	1980	04-07	1800	A1
5	04-09	1500	A1	8	06-26	2000	A1	1	08-23	2500	A1

- Tone. Yattajima (5110 km²) (1936 – 1972) (See Unesco Catalogue)
  Complement

Année Year	Mois/Month Jour/Day	Débit Discharge m³s-1	Obs.	Année Year	Mois/Month Jour/Day	Débit Discharge m³s-1	Obs.	Année Year	Mois/Month Jour/Day	Débit Discharge m³s-1	obs.
1973	06-22	810	A1	1976	07-19	1880	A1	1979	10-19	1740	A1
4	09-01	5550	A1	7	09-19	2240	A1	1980	07-08	790	A1
5	07-13	1170	A1	8	06-28	630	A1				

TABLEAU III : SERIES CHRONOLOGIQUES DES VALEURS MAXIMALES ANNUELLES
TABLE III   : CHRONOLOGICAL SERIES OF YEARLY MAXIMA

JAPAN/JAPON

- Takara. Takara Gawa (19 km²) (1939 - 1964) (See Unesco Catalogue)
- Fuji. Shimizubata (2120 km²) (1922 - 1972) (See Unesco Catalogue)
  Complement

Année Year	Mois/Month Jour/Day	Débit Discharge m³s-1	Obs.	Année Year	Mois/Month Jour/Day	Débit Discharge m³s-1	Obs.	Année Year	Mois/Month Jour/Day	Débit Discharge m³s-1	Obs.
1973	06-27	130	A1	1976	09-09	1770	A1	1979	10-19	1990	A1
4	09-01	1900	A1	7	08-18	1820	A1	1980	09-12	460	A1
5	08-23	1730	A1	8	10-29	200	A1				

- Shinano. Ojiya (9719 km²) (1951 - 1972) (See Unesco Catalogue)
  Complement

1914	08-14	9000	A3	1975	07-14	2770	A2	1978	06-27	5870	A2
1973	04-18	2410	A2	6	04-14	2310	A3	9	07-03	3200	A2
4	04-21	3120	A3	7	04-16	2730	A3	1980	04-07	2830	A3

- Toyo. Ishida (545 km²) (1919 - 1972) (See Unesco Catalogue)
  Complement

1973	10-14	730	B2	1976	08-09	1730	B2	1979	10-19	4360	B2
4	07-07	3780	B2	7	11-17	1170	B2	1980	04-14	620	B2
5	08-23	2380	B2	8	09-16	930	B2				

- Nagara Shusetsu (1610 km²) (1925 - 1972) (See Unesco Catalogue)
  Complement

1973	06-27	1010	B2	1976	09-09	6390	B2	1979	06-29	3380	B2
4	08-26	3500	B2	7	11-17	1490	B2	1980	07-30	2720	B2
5	08-23	4200	B2	8	06-20	1350	B2				

- Yodo. Hirakata (7280 km²)

1885	07-02	4280	C2	1963	06-07	1250	A1	1973	05-03	1115	
1896	09-08	4240	C2	1964	07-20	955	A1	4	07-26	2740	
1944	10-08	4970	C2	1966	07-02	2440	A1	5	08-23	2770	
1949	07-29	4880	C2	7	07-10	3080	A1	6	09-10	3390	
1952	06-24	4200	A1	8	08-30	1700	A1	7	06-25	1570	
1955	10-21	1124	A1	9	07-09	2060	A1	8	06-23	2410	
1957	06-28	2740	A1	1970	06-16	2640	A1	9	06-30	2280	
1962	07-28	2620	A1	1	09-07	2100	A1				

(See Table II - the values in UNESCO Catalogue were is slightly corrected).

- Kizu. Kamo (1456 km²)

1938	08-02	1015	B1	1952	06-24	1900	A1	1966	07-09	880	A1
9	10-17	335	B1	3	09-25	5400	B1	7	07-10	1320	A1

TABLEAU III : SERIES CHRONOLOGIQUES DES VALEURS MAXIMALES ANNUELLES
TABLE III   : CHRONOLOGICAL SERIES OF YEARLY MAXIMA

JAPAN/JAPON

- Kizu. Kamo (1456 km²)

Année Year	Mois/Month Jour/Day	Débit Discharge m³s-1	Obs.	Année Year	Mois/Month Jour/Day	Débit Discharge m³s-1	Obs.	Année Year	Mois/Month Jour/Day	Débit Discharge m³s-1	Obs.
1940	06-27	635	B1	1954	09-18	1800	A1	1968	07-06	680	A1
1	06-29	380	B1	5	10-20	1080	A1	9	07-09	480	A1
2	09-21	330	B1	6	09-27	4200	A1	1970	07-06	1390	A1
3	08-05	440	B1	7	06-28	1490	A1	1	09-27	1220	A1
4				8	09-26	4410	A1	2	09-17	3260	A1
5				9	09-26	6200	B1	3	08-16	670	A1
6				1960	06-22	985	A1	4	07-25	2190	A1
7				1	10-28	2930	A1	5	08-23	1360	A1
8	09-16	345	B1	2	07-28	1020	A1	6	09-09	3050	A1
9	09-23	665	B1	3	06-04	370	A1	7	06-25	1190	A1
1950	09-03	750	B1	4	06-28	350	A1	8	06-23	1205	A1
1	07-15	335	B1	5	09-18	1590	A1	9	06-29	1180	A1

- Oota. Kumura (1960 km²)

Année Year	Mois/Month Jour/Day	Débit Discharge m³s-1	Année Year	Mois/Month Jour/Day	Débit Discharge m³s-1	Année Year	Mois/Month Jour/Day	Débit Discharge m³s-1	Obs.
1954	09-26	1200	1963	07-11	3100	1972	07-12	6800	B2
5	07-07	2100	4	06-27	2700	3	04-17	380	A1
6	08-17	1400	5	07-23	4300	4	09-08	2900	A1
7	07-04	3000	6	06-20	1100	5	08-18	1800	A1
8	07-01	890	7	07-09	1100	6	09-13	5800	A1
9	07-14	2000	8	07-27	1400	7	04-28	830	A1
1960	07-08	2900	9	07-08	2600	8	09-15	1500	A1
1	10-27	920	1970	08-15	2300	9	06-29	2400	A1
2	07-05	3100	1	08-06	2000	1980	08-31	3300	A1

- Chikugo. Senoshita (2315 km²) (1950 - 1972) (See Unesco Catalogue)
  Complement

Année Year	Mois/Month Jour/Day	Débit Discharge m³s-1	Obs.	Année Year	Mois/Month Jour/Day	Débit Discharge m³s-1	Obs.	Année Year	Mois/Month Jour/Day	Débit Discharge m³s-1	Obs.
1964	06-07	2160	A1	1975	06-22	2280	A1	1978	06-11	700	A1
1973	06-27	2510	A1	6	06-23	2320	A1	9	06-30	5060	A1
4	07-18	1720	A1	7	06-17	1660	A1				

JORDAN/JORDANIE

- Yarmouk. Adasiya (6790 km²) (1954 - 1967) (See Unesco Catalogue)

MADAGASCAR

- Betsiboka. Ambodiroka (11800 km²)

Année Year	Mois/Month Jour/Day	Débit Discharge m³s-1	Obs.	Année Year	Mois/Month Jour/Day	Débit Discharge m³s-1	Obs.	Année Year	Mois/Month Jour/Day	Débit Discharge m³s-1	Obs.
1927	03-04	22000	E3	1964	02-07	2064	B3	1970	01-15	8290	A2
1958*	01-22	4090	B3	5*	01-15	12020	A2	1	01-30	8180	A2
1959	03-29	18000	A2	6*	02-19	2570	B3	2	02-14	13000	A2
1960*	03-05	2090	B3	7*	01-18	3160	B3	3	01-30	6120	A1
1*	12-09	2573	B3	8	03-14	2360	A1	4	03-15	4725	A1
2*	01-12	2450	B3	9	01-28	3910	A1				
3*	12-30	2108	B3		* Débit moyen journalier.							

TABLEAU III : SERIES CHRONOLOGIQUES DES VALEURS MAXIMALES ANNUELLES
TABLE III   : CHRONOLOGICAL SERIES OF YEARLY MAXIMA

MADAGASCAR

- Mangoky. Banian (50000 km²)

Année Year	Mois/Month Jour/Day	Débit Discharge m^3s-1	Obs.	Année Year	Mois/Month Jour/Day	Débit Discharge m^3s-1	Obs.	Année year	Mois/Month Jour/Day	Débit Discharge m^3s-1	Obs.
1904		37000	E3	1960	01-09	3030	A1	1970	01-17	27700	A2
1933		38000	E3	1		>5940	A2	1	12-24	10000	A2
1952	01-20	4330	A2	2	12-18	4983	A2	2	02-20	7330	A2
3	02-20	6300	A2	3	02-01	5310	A2	3	12-31	9400	A2
4	02-12	4410	A2	4	01-13	5550	A2	4	01-01	9200	A2
5	01-14	3250	A1	5	01-26	6620	A2	5		>8570	A2
6	01-09	9600	A1	6	12-31	4760	A2	1976	03-01	8630	A2
7	03-14	3490	A1	7	01-07	6830	A2				
8	03-06	3150	A1	8		>3041	A2				
1959	01-09	3930	A1	1969	02-07	10460	A2				

Débits observés à Bevoay depuis 1961

- Menarandra. Tranoroa

Année Year	Mois/Month Jour/Day	Débit Discharge m^3s-1	Obs.	Année Year	Mois/Month Jour/Day	Débit Discharge m^3s-1	Obs.	Année year	Mois/Month Jour/Day	Débit Discharge m^3s-1	Obs.
1952	12-04	630	A2	1959	01-01	1830	A2	1966	01-17	1510	A2
3	12-03	3230	A2	1960		1168	A2	7	02-21	1850	A2
4	01-07	2390	A2	1	01-10	3900	A2	8	12-31	1150	A2
5		>2580	A2	2		>2900	A2	9	12-29	1680	A2
6	03-08	630	A2	3		>1320	A2	1970	01-11	1960	A2
7	02-13	685	A2	4	02-03	1070	A1	1	02-03	2680	A2
1958	02-07	1290	A2	1965	01-08	1190	A1	2	01-29	2010	A2
								3	12-27	2630	A2
								4	12-29	2260	A2
								5	01-30	1410	A2
								1976	01-13	600	A2

- Mandrare. Amboasary (12430 km²)

Année Year	Mois/Month Jour/Day	Débit Discharge m^3s-1	Obs.	Année Year	Mois/Month Jour/Day	Débit Discharge m^3s-1	Obs.	Année year	Mois/Month Jour/Day	Débit Discharge m^3s-1	Obs.
1952	03-19	3150	A2	1961	01-23	5130	A2	1970	02-25	6850	A2
3	03-03	1150	A2	2	12-30	3835	A2	1	02-02	15740	A2
4	01-27	2225	A3	3	02-05	5290	A2	2	01-31	760	A1
5	01-09	4505	A2	4	12-19	2860	A2	3	12-29	680	A1
6	03-24	1310	A2	5	01-08	1640	A2	4	12-25	2400	A2
7	01-04	1712	A2	6	02-11	2620	A2	5	01-05	1720	A1
8	12-31	1800	A2	7	01-03	2320	A2	1976	12-29	500	A1
9	01-07	1190	A2	8	01-31	475	A2				
1960	12-15	4480	A2	1969	02-12	705	A2				

MALAYSIA/MALAISIE

- Kelantan. Guillemard Bridge (11900 km²) (1949 - 1969) (See Unesco Catalogue)
  Complement

Année Year	Mois/Month Jour/Day	Débit Discharge m^3s-1	Obs.	Année Year	Mois/Month Jour/Day	Débit Discharge m^3s-1	Obs.	Année year	Mois/Month Jour/Day	Débit Discharge m^3s-1	Obs.
1970	12-28	5820	A1	1974	12-29	4020	A1	1978	12-07	3290	A1
1	01-05	11250	A2	5	11-29	5670	A1	9	11-28	10400	A2

TABLEAU III : SERIES CHRONOLOGIQUES DES VALEURS MAXIMALES ANNUELLES

TABLE III : CHRONOLOGICAL SERIES OF YEARLY MAXIMA

MALAYSIA/MALAISIE

- Kelantan. Guillemard Bridge (11900 km²) (1949 - 1969) (See Unesco Catalogue)
  Complement

Année Year	Mois/Month Jour/Day	Débit Discharge m³s-1	Obs.	Année Year	Mois/Month Jour/Day	Débit Discharge m³s-1	Obs.	Année Year	Mois/Month Jour/Day	Débit Discharge m³s-1	Obs.
1972	12-18	13610	A2	1976	12-24	2610	A1	1980	12-20	1860	A1
3	12-10	15140	A2	7	01-03	2720	A1				

- Trengganu. Kampong Tanggol (3380 km²) (1947 - 1967) (See Unesco Catalogue)
  Complement

Année Year	Mois/Month Jour/Day	Débit Discharge m³s-1	Obs.	Année Year	Mois/Month Jour/Day	Débit Discharge m³s-1	Obs.	Année Year	Mois/Month Jour/Day	Débit Discharge m³s-1	Obs.
1970	01-15	2520	A1	1974	12-29	3650	A1	1978	07-12	3920	A1
1		4200	A1	5	11-28	4590	A1	9	11-27	5950	A1
2	12-18	7100	A1	6	11-29	2880	A1	1980	12-20	1990	A1
3	12-16	4690	A1	7	01-02	1890	A1				

- Perak. Iskandar Bridge (7770 km²) (1948 - 1969) (See Unesco Catalogue)
  Complement

Année Year	Mois/Month Jour/Day	Débit Discharge m³s-1	Obs.	Année Year	Mois/Month Jour/Day	Débit Discharge m³s-1	Obs.	Année Year	Mois/Month Jour/Day	Débit Discharge m³s-1	Obs.
1970	12-28	2430	A1	1974	11-24	520	A1	1978	11-03	270	A1
1	12-20	1910	A1	5	12-25	1110	A1	9	11-28	900	A1
2	12-19	1620	A1	6	01-01	490	A1	0	10-17	1230	A1
3	12-16	1770	A1	7	10-26	530	A1				

- Klang. Kuala Lumpur (457 km²) (1948 - 1967) (See Unesco Catalogue)
  Complement

Année Year	Mois/Month Jour/Day	Débit Discharge m³s-1	Obs.	Année Year	Mois/Month Jour/Day	Débit Discharge m³s-1	Obs.	Année Year	Mois/Month Jour/Day	Débit Discharge m³s-1	Obs.
1968	12-28	118	A1	1973	12-07	192	A1	1978	10-21	100	A1
9	10-23	115	A1	4	06-22	126	A1	9	06-08	82	A1
1970	01-06	97	A1	5	12-08	165	A1	1980	10-16	116	A1
1	01-05	670	A2	6	04-22	82	A1				
2	11-17	289	A1	7	10-08	150	A1				

MALI

- Niger. Koulikoro (120000 km²)

Année Year	Mois/Month Jour/Day	Débit Discharge m³s-1	Obs.	Année Year	Mois/Month Jour/Day	Débit Discharge m³s-1	Obs.	Année Year	Mois/Month Jour/Day	Débit Discharge m³s-1	Obs.
1907	09-20	4230	A1	1931	09-25	6400	A1	1955	09-29	7240	A1
8	10-06	5510	A1	2	09-19	7610	A1	6	09-30	6190	A1
9	09-11	6870	A1	3	09-13	7280	A1	7	09-21	7380	A1
1910	09-12	4750	A1	4	09-09	5880	A1	8	10-09	5560	A1
1	09-06	6670	A1	5	09-30	5740	A1	9	09-28	7070	A1
2	09-21	5540	A1	6	10-06	7360	A1	1960	09-30	6670	A1
3	09-18	3580	A1	7	09-12	5060	A1	1	09-18	6290	A1
4	10-04	4400	A1	8	10-06	6350	A1	2	09-25	7940	A1
5	09-17	5200	A1	9	10-06	5610	A1	3	10-23	7360	A1
6	09-28	5980	A1	1940	18-10	3940	A1	4	10-05	6760	A1
7	09-19	6820	A1	1	09-20	6150	A1	5	10-03	5880	A1
8	09-18	4900	A1	2	09-10	4840	A1	6	09-21	5740	A1

MALI

- Niger. Koulikoro (120000 km²)

Année Year	Mois/Month Jour/Day	Débit Discharge m³s-1	Obs.	Année Year	Mois/Month Jour/Day	Débit Discharge m³s-1	Obs.	Année Year	Mois/Month Jour/Day	Débit Discharge m³s-1	Obs.
1919	09-22	5300	A1	1943	10-04	5140	A1	1967	10-12	9340	A1
1920	09-25	4900	A1	4	09-20	4840	A1	8	10-02	5310	A1
1	09-21	5300	A1	5	10-03	5150	A1	9	09-14	7860	A1
2	10-19	6330	A1	6	10-08	5510	A1	1970	09-14	5840	A1
3	10-01	5430	A1	7	10-02	6210	A1	1	09-02	5710	A1
4	10-05	9410	A1	8	10-02	6490	A1	2	09-26	3830	A1
5	10-05	9670	A1	9	09-22	6850	A1	3	08-25	4300	A1
6	09-23	6930	A1	1950	09-30	6400	A1	4	09-29	6260	A1
7	10-08	6890	A1	1	11-17	6380	A1	5	10-06	6830	A1
8	09-21	8610	A1	2	09-21	6260	A1	6	10-29	5060	A1
9	10-11	7430	A1	3	09-04	6870	A1	7	09-24	4130	A1
1930	10-09	6760	A1	4	09-21	6440	A1	8	10-04	5490	A1
								9	09-15	5910	A1

MARTINIQUE (FRANCE)

- Capot. Saut-Babin

Année Year	Mois/Month Jour/Day	Débit Discharge m³s-1	Obs.	Année Year	Mois/Month Jour/Day	Débit Discharge m³s-1	Obs.	Année Year	Mois/Month Jour/Day	Débit Discharge m³s-1	Obs.
1956	12-15	195	A3	1963	09-24	480	A3	1970	08-20	370	A3
6	10-10	116	A1	4	08-02	89.6	A1	1	08-18	126	A1
8	09-13	160	A1	5		<100	A1	2	02-01	195	A3
8	10-01	100	A1	6	12-07	93.3	A1	3			
9	11-25	81	A1	7	09-07	410	A3	4	01-30	175	A2
1960	07-10	91	A1	8	06-10	107	A1	5	10-24	107	A1
1	10-08	84	A1	9	11-27	166	A2				
2	08-19	97	A1	9	07-26	139	A1				

MEXICO/MEXIQUE

- Rio Acaponeta. Acaponeta (5090 km²)

Année Year	Mois/Month Jour/Day	Débit Discharge m³s-1	Obs.	Année Year	Mois/Month Jour/Day	Débit Discharge m³s-1	Obs.	Année Year	Mois/Month Jour/Day	Débit Discharge m³s-1	Obs.
1945	10-08	1185	B1	1956	09-14	1440	B1	1967	08-22	2100	B1
6	10-07	835	B2	7	10-21	4500	B2	8	09-13	16000	B1
7	09-11	1125	B2	8	08-06	2080	B2	9	10-12	4230	B2
8	09-10	1950	B2	9	08-03	870	B2	1970	09-27	1580	B1
9	09-19	435	B1	1960	08-17	690	B2	1	09-12	1210	B1
1950	09-06	1220	B2	1	09-12	875	B1	2	11-24	7050	B2
1	09-04	1335	B2	2	06-25	600	B1	3	09-12	2610	B1
2	06-30	1390	B2	3	09-29	2705	B1	4	07-24	655	B1
3	08-27	1560	B2	4	10-01	1690	B2	5	07-30	1700	B1
4	08-17	1040	B2	5	09-27	6150	B2				
5	09-09	2050	B1	6	08-11	1065	B2				

TABLEAU III : SERIES CHRONOLOGIQUES DES VALEURS MAXIMALES ANNUELLES
TABLE III   : CHRONOLOGICAL SERIES OF YEARLY MAXIMA

MEXICO/MEXIQUE

- Rio San Juan. El Cuchillo (8795 km²)

Année Year	Mois/Month Jour/Day	Débit Discharge m³s-1	Obs.	Année Year	Mois/Month Jour/Day	Débit Discharge m³s-1	Obs.	Année Year	Mois/Month Jour/Day	Débit Discharge m³s-1	Obs.
1930	10-18	995	B2	1946	10-09	525	B2	1961	09-15	490	B1
1	01-30	333	B1	7	08-05	1395	B2	2	10-02	585	B1
2	08-24	163	B1	8	09-15	1175	B1	3	09-22	605	B2
3	09-16	2740	B2	9	04-23	382	B1	4	05-21	350	B1
4	10-01	395	B2	1950	10-04	470	B2	5	09-25	1275	B2
5	09-23	605	B2	1	09-16	2085	B1	6	06-26	725	B2
6	07-14	1305	B2	2	06-09	165	B1	7	09-23	5540	B2
7	07-09	140	B1	3	08-27	2510	B1	8	09-11	465	B1
8	08-29	6760	B1	4	10-09	303	B2	9	10-28	470	B2
9	10-11	720	B1	5	07-10	385	B1	1970	09-13	655	B1
1940	10-30	405	B1	6	06-18	125	B2	1	10-10	650	B1
1	06-23	1195	B1	7	10-19	900	B2	2	05-19	455	B1
2	06-24	815	B1	8	09-18	1925	B2	3	06-24	3355	B2
3	09-25	675	B1	9	09-11	177	B1	4	09-23	1935	B1
4	09-08	1585	B1	1960	10-17	1680	B1	5	09-22	645	B1
5	10-04	3560	B2								

MOROCCO/MAROC

- Ouergha.Mjara (6190 km²) (1933 - 1972) (Voir Catalogue UNESCO)
  Complement

1945	12-21	>4000		1974	03-18	715	1977	05-05	1500
1947		>4000		5	05-08	1140	8	02-13	4000
1973	12-24	2250		6	01-23	5000	9	10-14	1100

- Sebou.Azib Soltane (16150 km²) (1933 - 1973) (Voir Catalogue UNESCO)
- Oum er Rbia. Imfout (30600 km²)

1939		830	1950	01-02	470	1960	12-20	550
40		1580	1	01-04	870	2	03-23	2400
1			2	11-12	640	3	02-09	1940
2	02-24	2500	3	01-27	420	3	12-21	3200
3	05-04	980	4	03-11	1930	5	01-05	580
4	03-01	640	5	02-28	500	5	10-29	420
5	01-20	146	6	02-18	1500	7	11-04	860
6	03-08	455	7	04-12	250	8	04-01	700
7	03-03	825	8	12-16	1920	9	02-28	1500
8	05-14	540	9	12-24	900	1970	01-14	1670
9	05-01	1300	0	01-17	1280			

TABLEAU III : SERIES CHRONOLOGIQUES DES VALEURS MAXIMALES ANNUELLES
TABLE III   : CHRONOLOGICAL SERIES OF YEARLY MAXIMA

MOROCCO/MAROC

- Ziz. Foum Zaabel (3975 km²)

Année Year	Mois/Month Jour/Day	Débit Discharge m³s-1	Obs.	Année Year	Mois/Month Jour/Day	débit Discharge m³s-1	Obs.	Année Year	Mois/Month Jour/Day	Débit Discharge m³s-1	Obs.
1961	11-01	255	A2	1969	07-06	163	A2	1976	05-31	245	A2
3	05-26	1410	A2	9	11-20	950	A2	6	09-22	420	A2
3	09-24	169	A2	1971	04-22	681	A2	7	10-15	95	A2
5	02-04	555	A2	1	10-20	87	A2				
5	04-06	4500	A3	2	11-29	630	A2	9	10-17	1010	A2
7	05-04	485	A2	4	04-23	123	A2				
7	11-16	1270	A2	5	04-19	1360	A2				

NETHERLANDS/PAYS-BAS

- Rhine. Lobith (160000 km²)

Année Year	Mois/Month Jour/Day	Débit Discharge m³s-1	Obs.	Année Year	Mois/Month Jour/Day	débit Discharge m³s-1	Obs.	Année Year	Mois/Month Jour/Day	Débit Discharge m³s-1	Obs.
1901	04-20	5655	A1	1927	04-12	5200	A1	1953	01-01	5050	A1
2	05-24	4815	A1	8	02-21	6490	A1	4	12-29	5755	A1
3	01-09	5460	A1	9	01-02	4345	A1	5	01-21	9510	A1
4	02-25	5805	A1	1930	11-27	9075	A1	6	03-08	7610	A1
5	10-18	3590	A1	1	03-05	6055	A1	7	03-03	6905	A1
6	03-07	6420	A1	2	01-12	5820	A1	8	03-01	9120	A1
7	03-24	5865	A1	3	07-01	4070	A1	9	01-12	5295	A1
8	05-30	4815	A1	4	01-21	2905	A1	1960	12-08	4765	A1
9	02-08	5745	A1	5	02-09	5820	A1	1	02-05	5606	A1
1910	03-02	6605	A1	6	01-18	5895	A1	2	04-05	5774	A1
1	03-03	4875	A1	7	02-28	7365	A1	3	11-25	5204	A1
2	01-14	5320	A1	8	01-18	4705	A1	4	11-22	3061	A1
3	02-06	5150	A1	9	12-03	8610	A1	5	12-22	7182	A1
4	03-19	7475	A1	1940	03-23	6835	A1	6	01-06	7443	A1
5	12-15	6550	A1	1	01-30	7940	A1	7	01-03	6632	A1
6	02-23	6955	A1	2	03-23	8475	A1	8	01-20	7334	A1
7	06-01	7475	A1	3	01-18	3220	A1	9	03-18	5267	A1
8	01-21	7750	A1	4	11-30	8295	A1	1970	02-27	9850	A1
9	12-31	9110	A1	5	02-17	8585	A1	1	01-31	3633	A1
1920	01-18	11365	A1	6	02-12	9140	A1	2	11-23	4931	A1
1	01-31	2800	A1	7	12-31	6620	A1	3	12-13	3444	A1
2	05-03	6090	A1	8	01-04	9785	A1	4	12-21	5910	A1
3	02-06	6210	A1	9	03-21	2790	A1	5	01-02	5341	A1
4	11-07	9300	A1	1950	12-07	6120	A1	6	01-27	3459	A1
5	12-31	7185	A1	1	01-25	6620	A1				
1926	01-04	12280	A1	1952	12-27	7605	A1				

TABLEAU III : SERIES CHRONOLOGIQUES DES VALEURS MAXIMALES ANNUELLES

TABLE III : CHRONOLOGICAL SERIES OF YEARLY MAXIMA

NEW CALEDONIA/NOUVELLE CALEDONIE (FRANCE)

- Yaté. Au Barrage (435 km²)

Année Year	Mois/Month Jour/Day	Débit Discharge m³s-1	Obs.	Année Year	Mois/Month Jour/Day	Débit Discharge m³s-1	Obs.	Année year	Mois/Month Jour/Day	Débit Discharge m³s-1	Obs.
1925	01-16	1300	A2	1937	04-24	2500	A2	1948		925	X0
6		475	B2	7	11-30	3100	A2	1950	03-20	2050	A2
7		<1000	X0	9	03-01	2100	B2	1	02-27	1420	A2
7	12-31	2100	A2	1940		275	B2	2		850	X0
9	02-28	1300	B2	1		255	B2	3		315	X0
1930	03-23	1350	B2	2		560	B2	4		665	X0
1		305	B2	3	03-18	1500	B2	5	03-05	1800	A2
2	10-05	1800	A2	4	01-18	1600	B2	6		<1000	X0
3	04-10	2500	A2	5		<1000	X0	7		<1000	X0
4	05-27	1800	B2	5	11-26	1800	B2	9	01-18	1500	B2
5	01-10	1800	A2	6		505	B2	1981	12-25	5700 (1)	B2
6	02-01	1150	B2	8	01-28	2200	A2				

(1) Débit naturel reconstitué.

- Boghen. Aval Aremo (114 km²)

Année Year	Mois/Month Jour/Day	Débit Discharge m³s-1	Obs.	Année Year	Mois/Month Jour/Day	Débit Discharge m³s-1	Obs.	Année year	Mois/Month Jour/Day	Débit Discharge m³s-1	Obs.
1955	03-04	970	B2	1964	11-20	60	B2	1975	03-07	1500	A1
5	12-28	570	B2	6	03-29	810	B2	6	01-07	530	A1
7	01-06	350	B2	7	03-30	1030	B2	7	02-24	370	A1
8	02-24	60	B2	8	01-19	430	B2	8	01-07	200	A1
9	01-18	400	B2	9	02-02	1300	B2	9	07-31	250	A1
1960	05-27	180	B2	1970	08-19	90	A1	1980	02-14	240	A1
1	02-07	830	B2	1	02-11	980	A1	1	02-13	1040	A1
2	07-11	480	B2	2	01-16	510	A1	1	12-24	1070	A1
3	03-11	140	B2	3	07-08	320	A1				
4	06-12	890	B2	4	02-04	730	A1				

NEW ZEALAND/NOUVELLE ZELANDE

- Whirinaki. Galatea (534 km²)

Année Year	Mois/Month Jour/Day	Débit Discharge m³s-1	Obs.	Année Year	Mois/Month Jour/Day	Débit Discharge m³s-1	Obs.	Année year	Mois/Month Jour/Day	Débit Discharge m³s-1	Obs.
1953		67.3	A2	1961		27.3	A2	1969		60	A2
4		64.9	A2	2		113	A2	1970		307	A2
5		52.6	A2	3		64.8	A2	1		117	A2
6		79.6	A2	4		133	A2	2		66	A2
7		48.7	A2	5	02-13	632	A2	3		64	A2
8		273	A2	6		183	A2	4		88	A2
9		75.9	A2	7		310	A2	5		66	A2
0		57.4	A2	8		132	A2				

NIGER

-Niger. Niamey (700000 km²)

Année Year	Mois/Month Jour/Day	Débit Discharge m³s-1	Obs.	Année Year	Mois/Month Jour/Day	Débit Discharge m³s-1	Obs.	Année Year	Mois/Month Jour/Day	Débit Discharge m³s-1	Ob
1934/35		1750	A1	1953/54		2040	A1	1966/67		1970	A1
35		1800	A1	4		2090	A1	7		2320	A1
1941/42		1500	A1	5		2160	A1	8		1920	A1
2		1450	A1	6		1730	A1	9		2360	A1
3		1620	A1	7		2060	A1	1970/71		1820	A1
4		1480	A1	8		1890	A1	1		1830	A1
5		1810	A1	9		1850	A1	2		1570	A1
6		1810	A1	1960/61		1870	A1	3		1470	A1
7		1500	A1	1		1760	A1	4		1940	A1
8		1670	A1	2		2060	A1	5		2070	A1
9		1610	A1	3		1850	A1	6		1980	A1
1950/51		1910	A1	4		2080	A1	7		1530	A1
1		1920	A1	5		1950	A1	8			
2		1970	A1								

- Gorouol. Dolbel (7500 km²)

Année Year	Mois/Month Jour/Day	Débit Discharge m³s-1	Obs.	Année Year	Mois/Month Jour/Day	Débit Discharge m³s-1	Obs.	Année Year	Mois/Month Jour/Day	Débit Discharge m³s-1	Ob
1961		118	A1	1967		104	A1	1973		84	A1
2		73	A1	8		59	A1	4		74	A1
3		96	A1	9		113	A1	5		105	A1
4		92	A1	1970		88	A1	6		64	A1
5		72	A1	1		91	A1	7		120	A1
6		117	A1	2		54	A1	8		213	A1

NIGERIA

- Niger. Onitsha (1100000 km²: active part of the basin)

Année Year	Mois/Month Jour/Day	Débit Discharge m³s-1	Obs.	Année Year	Mois/Month Jour/Day	Débit Discharge m³s-1	Obs.	Année Year	Mois/Month Jour/Day	Débit Discharge m³s-1	Ob
1950		16630	A1	1959		19490	A1	1968			
1		20010	A1	1960				9			
2		18570	A1	1		17560	A1	1970		21425	
3		19210	A1	2		22900	A1	1		19590	
4		23000	A1	3		20640	A1	2		15970	
5		23000	A1	4		22000	A1	3		14750	
6		19000	A1	5		19500	A1	4		20190	
7		22370	A1	6		21090	A1	5		20330	
8		16690	A1	7				6		14540	
								7		17350	

TABLEAU III : SERIES CHRONOLOGIQUES DES VALEURS MAXIMALES ANNUELLES
TABLE III   : CHRONOLOGICAL SERIES OF YEARLY MAXIMA

NORWAY/NORVEGE

- Glomma. Langnes (40010 km²)

Année Year	Mois/Month Jour/Day	Débit Discharge m³s-1	Obs.	Année Year	Mois/Month Jour/Day	Débit Discharge m³s-1	Obs.	Année Year	Mois/Month Jour/Day	Débit Discharge m²s-1	Obs..
1901	05-18	2010	A1	1926	06-05	2470	A1	1952	05-10	2160	A1
2	09- 4	1970	A1	7	07-07	3190	A1	3	07-15	1820	A1
3	06-06	2490	A1	8	05-09	1930	A1	4	05-28	1690	A1
4	06-08	2530	A1	9	06-01	1860	A1	5	06-10	1600	A1
5	06-26	1580	A1	1930	05-31	2310	A1	6	09-16	1600	A1
6	05-22	2410	A1	1	05-23	2830	A1	7	09-19	2420	A1
7	06-22	2410	A1	2	05-26	1900	A1	8	06-01	1450	A1
8	06-06	2750	A1	3	05-27	1350	A1	9	05-06	2130	A1
9	06-07	2380	A1	4	05-14	3220	A1	1960	07-23	2080	A1
1910	05-28	3210	A1	5	06-21	2050	A1	1	10-31	1940	A1
1	05-22	2540	A1	6	05-22	2220	A1	2	05-28	1940	A1
2	08-27	2460	A1	7	05-11	2200	A1	3	05-18	1930	A1
3	05-10	2300	A1	8	10-13	1780	A1	4	10-17	2170	A1
4	05-24	1540	A1	9	07-28	2180	A1	5	06-26	1820	A1
5	08-13	2260	A1	1940	08-28	1290	A1	6	05-26	3220	A1
6	05-16	3100	A1	1	08-19	1090	A1	7	06-06	3540	A1
7	06-06	2220	A1	2	11-03	1210	A1	8	05-05	1650	A1
8	06-30	1520	A1	3	05-18	1580	A1	9	05-19	1740	A1
9	05-20	1780	A1	4	06-18	2430	A1	1970	05-22	1540	A1
1920	05-30	2600	A1	5	06-11	1860	A1	1	05-22	1880	A1
1	06-04	1420	A1	6	09-23	1700	A1	2	06-16	2090	A1
2	05-30	1750	A1	7	05-20	1650	A1	3	06-05	2200	A1
3	07-21	1520	A1	8	09-11	1510	A1	4	10-01	1550	A1
4	06-06	2380	A1	9	06-10	2220	A1	5	05-19	2100	A1
5	06-03	2220	A1	1950	06-27	2060	A1	6	05-28	1240	A1
				1	05-30	2120	A1				

- Pasvikelv. Bjornvatn (18150 km²)

Année Year	Mois/Month Jour/Day	Débit Discharge m³s-1	Obs.	Année Year	Mois/Month Jour/Day	Débit Discharge m³s-1	Obs.	Année Year	Mois/Month Jour/Day	Débit Discharge m²s-1	Obs..
1912	06-05	440	A1	1929	05-26	460	A1	1944	11-01	370	A1
3	06-03	315	A1	1930	06-08	315	A1	5	06-16	310	A1
4	06-07	665	A1	1	06-30	450	A1	6	05-28	220	A1
5	06-20	415	A1	2	06-18	630	A1	7	05-14	275	A1
6	06-13	385	A1	3	06-10	305	A1	8	05-21	325	A1
7	06-17	625	A1	4	05-12	420	A1	9	05-20	740	A1
8	06-02	430	A1	5	06-19	465	A1	1950	04-08	209	A1
9	05-28	365	A1	6	06-09	277	A1	1	11-09	450	A1
1920	05-21	520	A1	7	06-12	211	A1	2	06-04	825	A1
1	05-24	350	A1	8	07-10	300	A1	3	05-23	545	A1
2	05-25	440	A1	9	06-03	305	A1	4	10-20	350	A1
3	05-29	335	A1	1940	09-01	360	A1	5	07-30	580	A1
4	06-10	415	A1	1	06-18	250	A1	6	05-20	320	A1
5	06-16	280	A1	2	05-11	206	A1	7	05-25	250	A1
6	05-25	320	A1	3	05-16	670	A1	8	05-31	370	A1
7	06-20	440	A1					9	05-07	420	A1
8	07-28	211	A1					1960	01-09	193	A1

305

TABLEAU III : SERIES CHRONOLOGIQUES DES VALEURS MAXIMALES ANNUELLES
TABLE III   : CHRONOLOGICAL SERIES OF YEARLY MAXIMA

PAKISTAN

- Indus. Attock (264000 km²)

Année Year	Mois/Month Jour/Day	Débit Discharge m³s-1	Obs.	Année Year	Mois/Month Jour/Day	Débit Discharge m³s-1	Obs.	Année Year	Mois/Month Jour/Day	Débit Discharge m³s-1	Obs.
1868		14300		1905		13840		1942		17370	
9		12760		6		16670		3		14600	
1870		13580		7		12760		4		14690	
1		14180		8		17000		5		15420	
2		16750		9		13300		6		12420	
3		14540		1910		13640		7		11010	
4		16300		1		14880		8		14890	
5		13840		2		14880		9		13550	
6		15050		3		14540		1950		15280	
7		12590		4		16130		1		12140	
8		19070		5		11010		2		13640	
9		12930		6		14880		3		17010	
1880		12710		7		15050		4		11230	
1		12420		8		11350		5		13580	
2		20910		9		14540		6		14290	
3		13840		1920		14690		7		13700	
4		15420		1		15250		8		18960	
5		14180		2		16130		9		15960	
6		15250		3		13840		1960		16300	
7		13840		4		19500		1		12590	
8		11290		5		14180		2		12450	
9		17710		6		12760		3		12590	
1890		15340		7		13470		4		17630	
1		12870		8		14540		5		15900	
2		17000		9		23200		6		18480	
3		16130		1930		17000		7		16550	
4		17710		1		12760		8		15510	
5		12710		2		17370		9		12900	
6		14120		3		14490		1970		10610	
7		15870		4		15280		1		12730	
8		13130		5		14710		2		11740	
9		12930		6		11740		3		15450	
1900		14180		7		12850		4		11590	
1		14540		8		13550		5		15700	
2		9590		9		14630		6		15700	
3		11800		1940		12900		7		13910	
4		13470		1		12650		8		16980	

TABLEAU III : SERIES CHRONOLOGIQUES DES VALEURS MAXIMALES ANNUELLES
TABLE III   : CHRONOLOGICAL SERIES OF YEARLY MAXIMA

POLAND/POLOGNE

- Wisla. Tyniec (7530 km²) (1951 - 1970) (See Unesco Catalogue)
  One flood exceeding 1640 m³s-1 since 1970 : 1980 m³s-1 08-23 1972

- Dunajec. Nowy Sacz (4340 km²) (1921 - 1970) (See Unesco Catalogue)
  One flood exceeding 2190 m³s-1 since 1970 up to 1980 : 2510 m³s-1 07-01 1973

- Sam. Radomys'l (16800 km²) (1921 - 1970) (See Unesco Catalogue)
  One flood exceeding 2150 m³s-1 since 1970 up to 1980 : 2260 m³s-1 07-26 1980

- Wieprz. Lubartow (6360 km²) (1951 - 1970) (See Unesco Catalogue)
  One flood exceeding 231 m³s-1 since 1970 up to 1980 : 244 m³s-1 03-18 1979

- Pilica. Bialobrezegi (8670 km²) (1951 - 1970) (See Unesco Catalogue p. 211 column (7))
  One flood exceeding 387 m³s-1 since 1970 up to 1980 : 408 m³s-1 08-27 1972

- Bug. Wyszkow (39100 km²) (1921 - 1970) (See Unesco Catalogue)
  Two floods exceeding 1140 m³s-1 since 1970 up to 1979 : 2400 m³s-1 03-28 1979, 1170 m³s-1 11-09 1974

- Liwiec. Lochow (2460 km²) (1951 - 1970) (See Unesco Catalogue)
  One flood exceeding 230 m³s-1 since 1970 up to 1980 : 318 m³s-1 03-25 1979

- Warta. Poznan (39100 km²) (1951 - 1970) (See Unesco Catalogue
  One flood exceeding 634 m³s-1 since 1970 up to 1980 : 832 m³s-1 03-18 1979

- Wisla.Tczew (194000 km²) (1921 - 1970) (See Unesco Catalogue)
  Two floods exceeding 6790 m³s-1 since 1970 up to 1980 : 7020 m³s-1 04-01 1979, 6820 m³s-1 08-03 1980

- Prosna. Boguslav (4300 km²) (1951 - 1970) (See Unesco Catalogue)
  One flood exceeding 200 m³s-1 since 1970 up to 1980 : 235 m³s-1 03-11 1979

- Odra. Gozdowice (110000 km2) (1921 - 1970) (See Unesco Catalogue)
  Two floods exceeding 1930 m³s-1 since 1970 up to 1980 : 2170 m³s-1 09-03 1977, 1970 m³s-1 03-24 1979

REPUBLIC OF KOREA/REPUBLIQUE DE COREE

- Han. Goan 1,2,3 (23900 km²)

Année Year	Mois/Month Jour/Day	Débit Discharge m³s-1	Obs.	Année Year	Mois/Month Jour/Day	Débit Discharge m³s-1	Obs.	Année year	Mois/Month Jour/Day	Débit Discharge m³s-1	Obs.
1917	09-05	7400		1933	07-30	11900		1954	07-29	10900	
8	08-17	13000		4	07-24	11100		5	07-04	9050	
9	07-07	16600		5	07-23	20900		6	07-16	13500	
1920	08-02	17300		6	08-12	25500		7	07-18	7700*	
1	07-07	8300		6	08-28	20900		8	09-06	17500*	
2	07-30	21000		7	07-20	10900		9	09-01	16800*	
2	08-23	13100		8	09-15	8600		9	07-08	14300*	
2	07-16	12400		9	05-13	1100		1960	06-29	8700*	
3	08-01	12200		1940	09-04	23100		1	07-13	6800*	
4	07-25	15000		0	07-21	18800		2	09-08	9800	

TABLEAU III : SERIES CHRONOLOGIQUES DES VALEURS MAXIMALES ANNUELLES
TABLE III   : CHRONOLOGICAL SERIES OF YEARLY MAXIMA

REPUBLIC OF KOREA/REPUBLIQUE DE COREE

- Han. Goan 1, 2, 3 (23900 km²)

Année Year	Mois/Month Jour/Day	Débit Discharge m³s-1	Obs.	Année Year	Mois/Month Jour/Day	Débit Discharge m³s-1	Obs.	Année Year	Mois/Month Jour/Day	Débit Discharge m³s-1	Obs.
1925	07-18	37000		1940	07-06	17000		1963	07-23	14900	
5	09-15	12500		1				4	08-12	14000	
6	08-06	16500		2				4	04-20	12300	
6	07-22	15300		3				5	07-16	25500	
7	07-15	14200		4				6	07-26	25100	
8	09-16	5580		5				6	07-16	15300	
9	08-18	4000		6	07-12	5300		6	09-06	11600	
1930	07-14	19700		7	08-07	14900		7	07-20	8500	
1	08-20	10800		8				8	08-24	8700	
2	08-31	14300		9				9	07-31	17300	
				1950				9	04-24	10200	
				1				1970	09-18	16250	
				2				1	08-11	9100	
				1953				2	08-19	30000	
								3	09-01	7000	

* One observation per day
  The instantaneous discharge may be underestimated
  Error 6 - 7000 m³s-1 maximum

ROMANIA/ROUMANIE

- Somes. Satu Mare (15200 km²) (1925 - 1972) (See Unesco Catalogue)

- Mures. Tg Mures (4050 km²) (1925 - 1972) (See Unesco Catalogue)

- Tirnava Mare. Odorhei (657 km²) (1956 - 1972) (See Unesco Catalogue)

- Tirnava Mare. Topa (1670 km²) (1955 - 1972) (See Unesco Catalogue)

- Laslea. Laslea (83 km²) (1964 - 1972) (See Unesco Catalogue)

- Mures. Arad (27600 km²) (1925 - 1972) (See Unesco Catalogue)

- Dunarea. Orsova (575000 km²) (1839 - 1973) (See Unesco Catalogue)

- Jiu. Cîmpul lui Neag (140 km²) (1957 - 1972) (See Unesco Catalogue)

- Jiu. Podari (9240 km²) (1950 - 1972) (See Unesco Catalogue)

- Arges. Budesti (9370 km²) (1950 - 1972) (See Unesco Catalogue)

- Ialomita. Cos,ereni (6470 km²) (1950 - 1972) (See Unesco Catalogue)

ROMANIA/ROUMANIE

- Buzäu. Nehoiu (1570 km²) (1949 - 1972) (See Unesco Catalogue)

- Siret. Lungoci (36500 km²) (1951 - 1972) (See Unesco Catalogue)

- Iris. Cocargea (10,5 km²) (1960 - 1972) (See Unesco Catalogue)

SENEGAL

- Senegal. Bakel

Année Year	Mois/Month Jour/Day	Débit Discharge m^3s-1	Obs.	Année Year	Mois/Month Jour/Day	Débit Discharge m^3s-1	Obs.	Année Year	Mois/Month Jour/Day	Débit Discharge m^3s-1	Obs.
1903	09-15	3560	A1	1928	09-17	5490	A1	1953	09-15	4180	A1
4	09-06	4790	A1	9	09-10	5490	A1	4	09-06	6610	A1
5	08-26	3630	A1	1930	09-18	4610	A1	5	10-03	5260	A1
6	08-24	9340	A1	1	09-22	4300	A1	6	09-19	6050	A1
7	09-06	2850	A1	2	08-25	4850	A1	7	09-18	5660	A1
8	09-15	4200	A1	3	09-11	5490	A1	8	08-29	8170	A1
9	09-12	5490	A1	4	09-01	5340	A1	9	09-09	5460	A1
1910	08-30	3840	A1	5	08-30	6680	A1	1960	09-20	3550	A1
1	09-03	3330	A1	6	08-22	7600	A1	1	09-11	7030	A1
2	09-16	3290	A1	7	09-16	3590	A1	2	09-05	4410	A1
3	09-16	1040	A1	8	09-16	5630	A1	3	09-09	3760	A1
4	09-16	1885	A1	9	09-02	3400	A1	4	09-09	7180	A1
5	09-29	3140	A1	1940	08-23	2760	A1	5		7080	A1
6	09-29	4200	A1	1	09-11	2890	A1	6		5500	A1
7	09-20	4960	A1	2	08-22	3590	A1	7		5850	A1
8	07-09	7300	A1	3	09-10	3480	A1	8	09-18	2900	A1
9	08-31	3560	A1	4	09-21	1740	A1	9	09-12	3780	A1
1920	09-03	5630	A1	5	08-28	6480	A1	1970	09-08	3450	A1
1	09-17	2850	A1	6	09-02	4460	A1	1	08-31	4350	A1
2	09-25	9070	A1	7	09-10	4360	A1	2	09-09	1450	A1
3	09-11	4670	A1	8	08-22	3590	A1	3	08-25	2550	A1
4	09-26	6350	A1	9	08-23	3760	A1	4		5850	A1
5	09-14	4610	A1	1950	09-06	7630	A1	5		4970	A1
6	08-07	2290	A1	1	10-07	5340	A1	6		2510	A1
7	09-08	6460	A1	2	10-06	5060	A1	7		1760	A1

SOUTH AFRICA/AFRIQUE DU SUD

- Magalies. Hartbeespoort (1207 km²)

?		1758	X3	1929	02-05	918	A2	1954	01-31	42.2	A1
1904	11-19	740	A2	9	10-28	233	A1	5	02-10	314	A1
5	11-14	660	A1	1931	02-21	309	A1	5	11-29	125	A1
7	02-04	170	A1	2	01-22	22	A1	6	10-28	62	A1
7	11-19	36.3	A1	2	12-03	112	A1	8	01-20	69.2	A1

TABLEAU III : SERIES CHRONOLOGIQUES DES VALEURS MAXIMALES ANNUELLES
TABLE III   : CHRONOLOGICAL SERIES OF YEARLY MAXIMA

SOUTH AFRICA/AFRIQUE DU SUD

- Magalies. Hartbeespoort (1207 km²) (Lat. 25:44 S, Long. 27:51 E)

Année Year	Mois/Month Jour/Day	Débit Discharge m³s-1	Obs.	Année Year	Mois/Month Jour/Day	Débit Discharge m³s-1	Obs.	Année Year	Mois/Month Jour/Day	Débit Discharge m³s-1	Obs.
1909	01-22	960	A2	1934	01-30	443	A1	1959	01-26	83.7	A1
9	11-16	1165	A2	4	12-07	292	A1	9	11-18	11.8	A1
1911	02-22	18.1	A1	6	01-13	329	A1	1960	12-20	65.1	A1
1	11-22	33.4	A1	6	11-09	623	A1	2	04-26	6.14	A1
2	12-31	26.1	A1	7	12-15	1470	A2	2	11-07	6.48	A1
3	11-14	61.5	A1	9	02-07	575	A1	3	11-13	48	A1
5	02-18	1540	A2	9	11-28	208	A1	4	12-12	41.4	A1
5	11-16	45.2	A1	1940	12-24	248	A1	6	02-05	157	A1
7	02-25	70.5	A1	1	12-11	350	A1	7	02-07	193	A1
7	11-28	757	A2	2	12-03	1172	A2	7	11-01	5.52	A1
9	01-04	47.3	A1	4	02-04	1297	A2	9	04-24	1.76	A1
9	12-12	10.9	A1	4	10-19	42.2	A1	9	11-29	239	A1
1921	01-08	105	A1	6	02-11	218	A1	1971	04-08	155	A1
1	12-10	10	A1	7	03-30	36.5	A1	2	01-21	69.8	A1
3	02-21	1130	A2	8	03-30	481	A1	2	11-06	11.6	A1
4	03-21	14.6	A1	9	01-21	101	A1	4	04-03	32.1	A1
5	03-25	498	A1	9	11-17	770	A1	5	04-13	198	A1
5	12-08	309	A1	1950	12-31	105	A1	6	05-04	382	A1
6	12-10	22	A1	1	10-25	56.4	A1	7	02-01	196	A1
8	01-12	460	A1	2	12-03	651	A1	8	03-10	358	A1
								9	03-02	36.4	A1

- Klaserie. Fleur de Lys (136 km²)

Année Year	Mois/Month Jour/Day	Débit Discharge m³s-1	Obs.	Année Year	Mois/Month Jour/Day	Débit Discharge m³s-1	Obs.	Année Year	Mois/Month Jour/Day	Débit Discharge m³s-1	Obs.
1939	02-05	793	A3	1951	11-22	11.8	A1	1965	02-19	27.8	A1
9	12-13	36.5	A2	3	03-28	81.2	A2	6	01-20	27.4	A1
1941	04-07	22	A1	4	02-05	28.2	A1	7	02-02	58.9	A2
1	12-19	18.7	A1	5	03-05	112	A2	8	02-16	9.4	A1
3	03-07	17	A1	6	03-18	271	A2	9	01-16	147	A2
4	02-02	11.3	A1	7	03-12	16.4	A1	9	10-30	4.9	A1
5	03-14	10.5	A1	8	01-10	184	A2	1971	01-21	106	A2
6	01-31	18.7	A1	9	02-19	128	A2	2	03-19	405	A2
7	01-02	6.1	A1	1960	02-02	150	A2	3	03-04	4.6	A1
8	01-01	45.1	A2	0	12-30	26.1	A1	3	12-20	114	A2
9	01-22	31.1	A2	2	01-19	15.2	A1	5	05-13	24	A1
1950	03-25	60.9	A2	2	11-22	15.7	A1	6	01-31	373	A2
1	04-23	5.5	A1	4	02-10	14	A1				

- Vaal. Standerton (8193 km²)

Année Year	Mois/Month Jour/Day	Débit Discharge m³s-1	Obs.	Année Year	Mois/Month Jour/Day	Débit Discharge m³s-1	Obs.	Année Year	Mois/Month Jour/Day	Débit Discharge m³s-1	Obs.
1905	12-12	264	A1	1932	01-14	139	A1	1958	01-20	600	A1
7	02-08	1280	A1	3	01-29	55.4	A1	8	12-05	547	A1
7	12-14	558	A1	4	01-30	863	A1	9	12-19	195	A1
9	02-13	1417	A1	4	12-12	229	A1	1960	12-19	613	A1

TABLEAU III : SERIES CHRONOLOGIQUES DES VALEURS MAXIMALES ANNUELLES
TABLE III : CHRONOLOGICAL SERIES OF YEARLY MAXIMA

SOUTH AFRICA/AFRIQUE DU SUD

- Vaal. Standerton (8193 km²)

Année Year	Mois/Month Jour/Day	Débit Discharge m³s−1	Obs.	Année Year	Mois/Month Jour/Day	Débit Discharge m³s−1	Obs.	Année Year	Mois/Month Jour/Day	Débit Discharge m³s−1	Obs.
1910	03-06	1144	A1	1936	05-24	1757	A1	1961	11-26	421	A1
1	01-12	2286	A1	7	02-13	750	A1	2	11-23	271	A1
2	02-10	240	A1	7	12-24	475	A1	4	01-29	285	A1
3	01-01	113	A1	9	02-07	1460	A1	4	11-01	681	A1
3	10-14	117	A1	9	11-29	597	A1	6	02-16	37.7	A1
5	01-15	396	A1	1941	04-08	706	A1	7	02-17	984	A1
5	11-17	486	A1	2	01-24	200	A1	7	12-20	169	A1
6	12-24	321	A1	3	07-05	291	A1	9	01-18	144	A1
8	01-01	1417	A1	4	02-04	1546	A1	9	10-20	331	A1
8	12-31	452	A1	5	03-08	211	A1	1971	04-15	139	A1
1920	01-20	90	A1	6	02-11	416	A1	1	12-03	901	A1
1	03-12	767	A1	7	01-22	238	A1	2	11-05	22.5	A1
1	11-29	1171	A1	7	12-30	331	A1	4	02-08	377	A1
3	01-28	2060	A1	8	12-09	120	A1	5	02-15	1918	A1
4	01-27	120	A1	9	12-20	523	A1	5	12-21	603	A1
5	03-25	700	A1	1951	01-03	197	A1	7	02-03	898	A1
5	11-13	100	A1	1	10-14	335	A1	7	12-01	92.8	A1
7	02-27	194	A1	3	02-25	680	A1	8	10-20	140	A1
8	03-11	154	A1	3	12-01	154	A1	1980	02-21	215	A1
9	03-11	368	A1	5	02-10	1823	A1	1	03-04	191	A1
9	12-03	761	A1	5	12-31	937	A1	2	03-09	262	A1
1931	02-05	122	A1	6	12-06	1020	A1				

- Orange. Vluytjes Kraal (92350 km²)

Année Year	Mois/Month Jour/Day	Débit Discharge m³s−1	Obs.	Année Year	Mois/Month Jour/Day	Débit Discharge m³s−1	Obs.	Année Year	Mois/Month Jour/Day	Débit Discharge m³s−1	Obs.
1914	04-07	143	A2	1933	04-07	711	A2	1951	10-31	2280	A1
5	02-22	2280	A2	4	01-05	6824	A2	3	03-02	1274	A1
5	11-29	1291	A2	4	11-22	2458	A2	4	03-30	2537	A1
7	03-18	2398	A2	6	04-03	889	A2	6	02-28	3681	A1
8	03-17	2874	A2	6	11-15	2828	A2	6	12-10	4347	A1
8	12-13	1427	A2	8	02-20	2350	A2	7	09-28	6513	A2
1920	03-06	5465	A2	9	02-25	2311	A2	9	05-19	3426	A1
1	04-03	1155	A2	1940	03-21	1943	A2	9	12-07	1535	A1
2	01-02	1359	A2	0	11-12	2155	A2	1961	04-15	1416	A1
3	02-16	4276	A2	2	03-09	2549	A2	1	12-18	3596	A1
4	03-12	3200	A2	3	05-15	2948	A2	3	01-27	2959	A1
5	03-24	11160	A2	3	11-12	3630	A2	3	11-20	1877	A1
5	11-19	765	A2	5	03-10	2251	A2	4	10-22	4539	A1
7	03-19	2418	A2	6	01-29	1603	A2	6	01-24	6400	A2
8	01-23	1308	A2	6	10-17	960	A2	7	02-03	8920	A2
8	12-25	1642	A2	8	03-13	3191	A2	8	05-20	1165	A1
9	10-03	3033	A2	8	05-01	402	A1	9	03-14	1691	A1
1931	04-20	3506	A2	1950	04-13	2427	A1	9	10-31	1429	A1
2	01-02	1812	A2	1	01-05	2832	A1				

TABLEAU III : SERIES CHRONOLOGIQUES DES VALEURS MAXIMALES ANNUELLES
TABLE III   : CHRONOLOGICAL SERIES OF YEARLY MAXIMA

SOUTH AFRICA/AFRIQUE DU SUD

- Mzimkulu. Umzimkulu (3645 km²)

Année Year	Mois/Month Jour/Day	Débit Discharge m³s-1	Obs.	Année Year	Mois/Month Jour/Day	Débit Discharge m³s-1	Obs.	Année Year	Mois/Month Jour/Day	Débit Discharge m³s-1	Obs.
1932	02-09	515	A2	1947	01-15	428	A2	1962	02-16	177	A2
3	03-09	266	A2	8	02-22	408	A2	3	01-25	336	A2
3	12-15	526	A2	8	12-27	334	A2	4	01-11	516	A2
4	12-11	530	A2	1950	01-08	526	A2	5	02-03	227	A2
6	02-08	541	A2	1	01-22	282	A2	6	01-22	216	A2
6	11-11	564	A2	2	02-22	257	A2	7	02-01	446	A2
7	12-23	317	A2	2	12-13	428	A2	7	12-23	202	A2
9	02-23	2294	A2	3	12-15	515	A2	9	04-04	96.7	A2
1940	05-05	1012	A2	5	01-31	918	A2	1970	02-08	227	A2
0	12-20	595	A2	6	03-20	746	A2	0	10-13	441	A2
2	03-03	708	A2	6	12-23	737	A2	2	02-26	402	A2
3	03-07	1245	A2	8	02-18	225	A2	3	03-20	308	A2
3	12-07	736	A2	9	05-18	3794	A2	4	02-05	860	A2
5	03-17	583	A2	1960	04-26	114	A2	5	01-30	210	A2
6	01-24	187	A2	1	04-13	261	A2	6	03-05	1450	A2

- Tugela. Mandini (28490 km²)

Année Year	Mois/Month Jour/Day	Débit Discharge m³s-1	Obs.	Année Year	Mois/Month Jour/Day	Débit Discharge m³s-1	Obs.	Année Year	Mois/Month Jour/Day	Débit Discharge m³s-1	Obs.
1925	03	15100	X3	1964	11-03	2044	A1	1974	02-07	4149	A1
1956	12-23	2407	A1	6	02-08	2156	A1	5	02-16	4594	A1
7	10-04	2752	A1	7	02-08	4678	A1	5	11-27	1067	A1
9	02-19	1358	A1	7	12-25	933	A1	6	10-04	1051	A1
1960	03-19	994	A1	9	03-02	1553	A1	8	01-25	4826	A1
0	12-31	1113	A1	1970	01-29	1337	A1	8	10-19	2046	A1
2	01-07	2133	A1	1	05-13	1606	A1	1980	02-20	435	A1
3	03-08	2397	A1	2	03-23	3056	A1	0	12-30	564	A1
4	01-11	2309	A1	3	02-09	2272	A1				

SPAIN/ESPAGNE

- Ebro. Zaragoza (40430 km2)

Année Year	Mois/Month Jour/Day	Débit Discharge m³s-1	Année Year	Mois/Month Jour/Day	Débit Discharge m³s-1	Année Year	Mois/Month Jour/Day	Débit Discharge m³s-1
1888	03-13	3760	1930	03-15	3500	1955	01-25	1480
9	02-18	3800	0	12-19	3600	6	05-29	2744
1891	01-25	3250	1	11-30	1348	7	06-25	1229
2	02-06	3790	3	03	2014	8	03-18	2003
5	01-23	3118	4	03	1502	8	12-26	2237
1906 .	11-18	3030	5	03	2906	9	12-16	2790
7	10-23	1700	6	05	2417	1961	01-02	4130
1914	02-27	1596	7	03	1673	1	11-16	2570
5	04-13	1895	7	10-28	3000	2	12-20	2390
6	02-20	1759	9	01	3058	3	12-05	1970
7	03-16	1823	1940	02	2567	5	01-23	2395
8	04-16	1623	1	01	3150	5	12-14	2260

TABLEAU III : SERIES CHRONOLOGIQUES DES VALEURS MAXIMALES ANNUELLES
TABLE III   : CHRONOLOGICAL SERIES OF YEARLY MAXIMA

SPAIN/ESPAGNE

- Ebro. Saragoza (40430 km²)

Année Year	Mois/Month Jour/Day	Débit Discharge m^3s-1	Obs.	Année year	Mois/Month Jour/Day	Débit Discharge m^3s-1	Obs.	Année year	Mois/Month Jour/Day	Débit Discharge m^3s-1	Obs.
1919	02-08	1963		1942	01	1980		1966	11-12	3154	
1920	03-20	1895		3	11-29	1200		8	01-06	2494	
1	05-19	875		6	05-13	1565		9	04-30	1495	
2	01-09	1283		7	03-07	2180		9	12-10	2031	
2	07-13	1983		8	01-31	2197		1971	04-25	1449	
3	12-25	1460		9	03-09	1475		2	02-14	1644	
5	04-28	1419		9	10-01	1825		3	02-28	1946	
6	02-16	1759		1951	03-19	1971		4	03-24	1422	
6	12-07	3175		2	02-05	3260		5	04-22	2100	
8	03-28	1755		2	12-20	1365					
8	11-11	1528		4	02-13	2470					

- Arga. Peralta (2705 km²)

Année	Mois/Month Jour/Day	Débit Discharge	Obs.	Année	Mois/Month Jour/Day	Débit Discharge	Obs.	Année	Mois/Month Jour/Day	Débit Discharge	Obs.
1907	10-23	500		1930	11-28	1600		1956	06-11	400	
09	10-28	500		1	10-26	335		8	04-13	455	
1914	02-25	995		3	01	235		8	12-24	525	
5	04-11	2050		4	04	235		9	10-30	465	
5	10-03	1245		5	03	235		1960	12-31	1200	
7	01-13	905		7	10-26	800		1	11-13	600	
7	11-18	1065		1940		760		2	12-17	580	
9	02-06	1015		1		410		3	04-12	385	
9	11-06	1175		3	01-04	650		5	01-21	515	
1921	05-12	415		3	11-27	465		6	03-01	470	
2	01-15	675		4		690		6	11-09	515	
3	02-13	410		5		500		7	12-27	515	
3	11-09	740		9	10-02	665		8	12-18	395	
5	04-26	685		1950	12-20	720		9	12-07	520	
6	02-14	880		2	02-03	855		1971	03-22	440	
6	12-06	1200		2	12-18	660		2	01-27	470	
8	03-26	660		3	10-16	910		3	02-27	445	
8	11-09	740		5	01-24	720		4	02-08	240	
1930	03-13	1500		6	05-28	525		5	05-20	435	
								5	11-19	635	

- Duero Villamarciel (36570 km²)

Année	Mois/Month Jour/Day	Débit Discharge	Obs.	Année	Mois/Month Jour/Day	Débit Discharge	Obs.	Année	Mois/Month Jour/Day	Débit Discharge	Obs.
1931	03-12	1305		1948	01-30	1650		1962	01-04	1470	
1	11-13	270		8	12-14	165		3	01-04	740	
3	03	2350		1950	05-27	170		4	02-26	1235	
4	04	660		1	03-18	940		5	03-18	455	
7	02	1225		2	04-03	785		6	04-22	1620	
7	12	1535		2	12-03	250		6	11-09	930	
9	01	1500		4	02-12	540		7	11-10	410	
1940	02	1400		5	02-19	680		9	03-19	1690	

SPAIN/ESPAGNE

- Duero. Villamarciel (36570 km²)

Année Year	Mois/Month Jour/Day	Débit Discharge m³s-1	Obs.	Année Year	Mois/Month Jour/Day	Débit Discharge m³s-1	Obs.	Année Year	Mois/Month Jour/Day	Débit Discharge m³s-1	Obs.
1942	05	415		1956	03-31	1235		1970	01-12	1900	
3	01-15	700		7	05-10	175		1	05-27	680	
3	12-23	380		8	04-04	505		2	02-13	910	
5	02-03	380		8	12-20	435		2	12-09	895	
6	05-15	745		1960	02-21	1395		5	04-26	420	
7	02-24	1115		1	01-05	1225		6	04-25	100	

- Tajo. Alcantara (52170 km²)

Année Year	Mois/Month Jour/Day	Débit Discharge m³s-1	Obs.	Année Year	Mois/Month Jour/Day	Débit Discharge m³s-1	Obs.	Année Year	Mois/Month Jour/Day	Débit Discharge m³s-1	Obs.
1935	12-28	7160		1952	04-01	3145		1965	03-13	1655	
7	01-31	6310		2	12-02	1120		6	04-16	2775	
7	11-20	5300		3	12-08	1665		7	03-10	1780	
9	01-19	5930		5	02-17	2175		8	02-22	1505	
1940	01	5705		5	12-17	3180		9	03-14	3955	
1	01-26	11000		7	02-18	900		1970	01-11	6340	
2	03	2765		8	01-29	2490		1	06-24	735	
3	02-19	3530		8	12-20	2715		2	02-17	1170	
3	11-02	1675		1960	01-27	3170		2	12-15	870	
7	03-08	9300		0	11-02	2125		4	04-26	645	
8	12-12	1480		2	01-04	3075		4	11-15	500	
9	11-21	1805		3	04-13	3810		5	12-23	650	
1951	03-14	3110		4	02-25	4250					

- Guadalquivir. Alcala del Rio (47000 km²)

Année Year	Mois/Month Jour/Day	Débit Discharge m³s-1	Obs.	Année Year	Mois/Month Jour/Day	Débit Discharge m³s-1	Obs.	Année Year	Mois/Month Jour/Day	Débit Discharge m³s-1	Obs.
1912	02-10	6700		1948	01-28	3900		1962	01-01	4050	
5	04-02	3600		1950	09-30	260		3	02-19	4800	
6	03-22	3200		1	03-15	4600		3	12-18	2500	
6	12-20	4400		2	04-01	4060		5	03-13	425	
1924	03-30	6000		3	04-23	1400		6	02-23	2580	
5	12-22	6800		4	03-17	330		7	02-19	950	
6	11-21	3120		5	02-18	955		8	03-02	880	
1936	01-27	5305		5	12-20	2680		9	03-18	2440	
7	01-01	4400		7	04-12	315		1970	01-10	3250	
1940	01-04	4600		8	03-31	290		1	05-21	620	
1	02-02	4700		8	12-23	2600		2	02-06	1320	
3	03-25	2590		1960	02-22	4000		3	01-20	425	
7	06-03	5600		0	10-25	1890		3	10-22	415	

SRI LANKA

- Kelani. Glencourse (2310 km²) (1949 - 1973) (See Unesco Catalogue)
- Walawe. Ganga. Embilipitiya (2490 km²) (1943 - 1964) (See Unesco Catalogue)
- Malwathu. Kapachchi (3300 km²) (1945 - 1971) (See Unesco Catalogue)
- Mahaweli. Manampitiya (10600 km²) (1943 - 1971) (See Unesco Catalogue)

TABLEAU III : SERIES CHRONOLOGIQUES DES VALEURS MAXIMALES ANNUELLES
TABLE III   : CHRONOLOGICAL SERIES OF YEARLY MAXIMA

SWEDEN/SUEDE

- Klarälven. Edsforsens krv. (8580 km²) (1910 - 1952) (See Unesco Catalogue)
  No flood exceeding 875 m³s-1 since 1972 up to 1980

- Götaälv. Sjötorp (46800 km²) (1807 - 1937 km²) (See Unesco Catalogue)
  No flood exceeding 1850 m³s-1 since 1972 up to 1980

- Esmaan Gardsilt (55 km²) (1928 - 1972) (See Unesco Catalogue)
  No flood exceeding 14.4 m³s-1 since 1972 up to 1980

- Bäljanea Klippan 2 (239 km²) (1890 - 1972) (See Unesco Catalogue)
  Complement

Année Year	Mois/Month Jour/Day	Débit Discharge m³s-1	Obs.	Année Year	Mois/Month Jour/Day	Débit Discharge m³s-1	Obs.	Année Year	Mois/Month Jour/Day	Débit Discharge m³s-1	Obs.
1973	12-29	11.5	A1	1976	01-22	8.4	A1	1978	03-17	17.4	A1
4	01-17	18.7	A1	7	03-06	24	A1	9	03-28	24	A1
5	01-07	11.3	A1								

- Vesanan. Halabäck (4.7 km²) (1958 - 1972) (See Unesco Catalogue)
  No flood exceeding 0.7 m³s-1 since 1972 up to 1980

- Velenan. Velen 2 (45 km²) (1938 - 1972) (See Unesco catalogue)
  One flood exceeding 2.31 m³s-1 since 1972 up to 1980 : 3.9 m³s-1 05-04 1977

- Motala. Motala (6360 km²) (1858 - 1928) (See Unesco Catalogue)

- Motala. Norsholm (13200 km²) (1873 - 1922) (See Unesco Catalogue)

- Vattholmaan. Vattholma (284 km²) (1917 - 1972) (See Unesco Catalogue)
  No flood exceeding 22 m³s-1 since 1972 up to 1980

- Dalälven. Norslund (25.300 km²) (1852 - 1918) (See Unesco Catalogue)

- Tânnan. Lillglän (63 km²) (1933 - 1972) (See Unesco Catalogue)
  Two floods exceeding 26 m³s-1 since 1972 up to 1980 : 29 m³s-1 06-01 1973, 26 m³s-1 05-24 1978

- Ljusnan. Sveg (8490 km²) (1914 - 1961) (See Unesco Catalogue)

- Giman. Gimdalsby (2180 km²) (1910 - 1972) (See unesco Catalogue)
  No flood exceeding 124 m³s-1 since 1972 up to 1980

- Arealven. Ostra Norn (2390 km²) (1901 - 1972) (See Unesco Catalogue)
  One flood exceeding 545 m³s-1 since 1972 up to 1980 : 560 m³s-1 05-26 1976

- Vindelälven. Sorsele (6110 km²) (1910 - 1972) (See Unesco Catalogue)
  No flood exceeding 1230 m³s-1 since 1972 up to 1980

- Vindelälven. Renfors (11900 km²) (1911 - 1972) (See Unesco Catalogue)
  No flood exceeding 1480 m³s-1 since 1972 up to 1980

TABLEAU III : SERIES CHRONOLOGIQUES DES VALEURS MAXIMALES ANNUELLES
TABLE III   : CHRONOLOGICAL SERIES OF YEARLY MAXIMA

SWEDEN/SUEDE

- Raneälv. Niemisel (3770 km²) (1900 - 1971) (See Unesco Catalogue)
  No flood exceeding 685 m³s-1 since 1971 up to 1980

- Törneälv. Jukkasjärvi (6000 km²) (1915 - 1967) (See Unesco Catalogue)
  No flood exceeding 633 m³s-1 since 1967 up to 1980

- Muonjoälv. Kallio (14300 km²) (1911 - 1971) (See Unesco Catalogue)
  One flood exceeding 904 m³s-1 since 1971 up to 1980 : 905 m³s-1 08-18 1974

TOGO

- Oti. Mango (35650 km²)

Année Year	Mois/Month Jour/Day	Débit Discharge m³s-1	Obs.	Année Year	Mois/Month Jour/Day	Débit Discharge m³s-1	Obs.	Année Year	Mois/Month Jour/Day	Débit Discharge m³s-1	Obs.
1953	09-13	1360	A1	1963	09-03	937	A1	1972	09-28	537	A1
4	09-28	534	A1	4	10-04	1430	A1	3	08-26	568	A1
5	08-27	1540	A1	5	09-19	406	A1	4	09-26	1128	A1
6	09-21	616	A1	6	09-22	450	A1	5	10-04	644	A1
7	09-28	1620	A1	7	10-02	651	A1	6	08-23	233	A1
8	09-22	440	A1	8	07-30	717	A1	7	09-18	532	A1
9	09-28	1220	A1	9	09-19	1510	A1	8	09-21	357	A1
1960	10-01	1240	A1	1970	09-27	1710	A1	9	09-15	765	A1
1	09-26	769	A1	1	08-31	701	A1	1980	09-15	697	A1
2	09-21	1750	A1								

TUNISIA/TUNISIE

- Mejerda. Bou Salem (16230 km²)

Année Year	Mois/Month Jour/Day	Débit Discharge m³s-1	Obs.	Année Year	Mois/Month Jour/Day	Débit Discharge m³s-1	Obs.	Année Year	Mois/Month Jour/Day	Débit Discharge m³s-1	Obs.
1925	09-29	452	A2	1943	11-06	351	A2	1961	01-28	337	A2
7	01-10	431	A2	4	09-10	196	A2	2	02-13	603	A2
8	04-04	1220	A2	6	01-27	743	A2	3	04-21	672	A2
9	03-27	1760	A2	6	12-17	911	A2	4	01-30	587	A2
1931	02-10	578	A2	7	10-11	1700	A2	5	01-22	449	A2
1	12-14	2060	A2	9	01-07	718	A2	6	04-23	685	A2
3	01-23	496	A2	1950	03-05	383	A2	7	03-09	119	A2
4	03-06	307	A2	1	05-06	191	A2	8	01-23	167	A2
5	01-03	894	A2	1	12-31	651	A2	9	01-04	118	A2
5	09-15	150	A2	2	12-07	904	A2	9	09-28	1490	A2
6	11-16	1420	A2	4	02-22	478	A2	1970		381	A2
8	02-05	310	A2	4	12-15	322	A2	1		174	A2
9	02-05	566	A2	6	02-08	465	A2	3	03	3180	A2
1940	01-26	1780	A2	7	02-03	255	A2	3		86	A2
1	05-24	231	A2	8	01-15	515	A2	4		620	A2
2	03-01	943	A2	9	03-14	1140	A2	5		210	A2
3	04-25	150	A2	1960	05-06	254	A2	6		743	A2

TABLEAU III : SERIES CHRONOLOGIQUES DES VALEURS MAXIMALES ANNUELLES
TABLE III   : CHRONOLOGICAL SERIES OF YEARLY MAXIMA

TUNISIA/TUNISIE

- Mellègue. P.K.13 (9000 km²)

Année Year	Mois/Month Jour/Day	Débit Discharge m³s-1	Obs.	Année Year	Mois/Month Jour/Day	Débit Discharge m³s-1	Obs.	Année Year	Mois/Month Jour/Day	Débit Discharge m³s-1	Obs.
1925	08-16	118	A2	1942	09-18	127	A2	1960	10-05	297	A2
6	08-28	253	A2	3	11-05	825	A2	2	02-13	300	A2
7	05-06	388	A2	4	09-09	431	A2	3	06-24	418	A2
8	05-03	1270	A2	6	01-27	863	A2	3	09-06	720	A2
8	09-15	460	A2	7	08-25	412	A2	4	10-31	1230	A2
1930	02-16	317	A2	8	02-28	2000	A2	6	05-14	392	A2
1	04-14	1030	A2	9	01-06	923	A2	7	04-22	627	A2
1	12-13	341	A2	1950	04-16	398	A2	7	09-12	950	A2
2	09-28	371	A2	1	06-02	569	A2	9	03-26	130	A2
4	04-25	277	A2	1	10-05	1000	A2	9	09-27	4480	A2
4	11-26	186	A2	3	08-05	493	A2	1970		199	A2
5	09-15	425	A2	3	10-21	244	A2	1		190	A2
6	11-15	520	A2	5	08-25	548	A2	3	03	1280	A2
8	08-27	99.8	A2	5	10-24	1060	A2	3		315	A2
9	04-16	539	A2	7	05-02	446	A2	4		1350	A2
1940	01-26	98.4	A2	7	10-06	3340	A2	5		775	A2
1	05-23	283	A2	9	06-07	1070	A2				
1	10-03	1060	A2	1960	05-05	336	A2				

TURKEY/TURQUIE

- Göksu. Himmetli (2597 km²)

Année Year	Mois/Month Jour/Day	Débit Discharge m³s-1	Année Year	Mois/Month Jour/Day	Débit Discharge m³s-1	Année Year	Mois/Month Jour/Day	Débit Discharge m³s-1
1936	05-17	173	1951	04-16	129	1966	01-25	253
7	03-16	188	2	04-06	237	7	12-16	211
8	04-12	249	3	04-14	179	8	03-13	557
9	04-08	111	4	04-17	179	9	03-18	271
1940	04-03	239	5	07-31	71	1970	03-01	128
1	03-02	146	6	04-10	110	1	04-15	90
2	03-19	178	7	03-24	226	2	04-30	194
3	04-05	228	8	03-03	279	3	04-07	92
4	03-15	195	9	03-16	125	4	03-15	201
5	04-12	133	1960	04-26	130	5	04-29	318
6	03-20	117	1	03-31	40	6	04-12	311
7	03-19	243	2	03-09	148	7	04-23	292
8	02-17	220	3	12-19	181	8	02-21	183
9	04-27	111	4	03-26	79	9	02-03	551
1950	04-14	110	5	04-19	120			

TABLEAU III : SERIES CHRONOLOGIQUES DES VALEURS MAXIMALES ANNUELLES
TABLE III   : CHRONOLOGICAL SERIES OF YEARLY MAXIMA

UGANDA/OUGANDA

- Kyoga Nile. Paraa (340000 km²)
  The following discharges are maximum monthly discharges slightly lower than instantaneous maximum discharges.

Année Year	Mois/Month Jour/Day	Débit Discharge m³s-1	Obs.	Année Year	Mois/Month Jour/Day	Débit Discharge m³s-1	Obs.	Année Year	Mois/Month Jour/Day	Débit Discharge m³s-1	Obs.
1948	09	737		1956	11	698		1964	11	1927	
9	10	571		7	08	788		5	05	1742	
1950	10	532		8	09	640		6	07	1510	
2	01	719		9	10	640		7	12	1402	
2	10	720		1960	09	890		8	07	1640	
3	06	551		2	01	1442		9	07	1625	
4	10	708		2	12	1527		0	10	1664	
5	09	720		3	06	1757					

USSR/URSS
European part of USSR

- Petchora. Ust-Tsilma (248000 km²) (1932 - 1972) (See Unesco Catalogue)
  Complement

Année Year	Mois/Month Jour/Day	Débit Discharge	Obs.	Année Year	Mois/Month Jour/Day	Débit Discharge	Obs.	Année Year	Mois/Month Jour/Day	Débit Discharge	Obs.
1973	06-01	20800	A1	1976	05-20	21500	A1	1978	07-01	23200	A1
4	06-12	25500	A1	7	05-28	19700	A1	9	05-19	23400	A1
5	06-29	16800	A1								

- Mezen. Malonisogorskaya (56400 km²) (1921 - 1972) (See Unesco Catalogue)
  Complement

Année Year	Mois/Month Jour/Day	Débit Discharge	Obs.	Année Year	Mois/Month Jour/Day	Débit Discharge	Obs.	Année Year	Mois/Month Jour/Day	Débit Discharge	Obs.
1973	05-17	4530	A1	1976	05-18	7240		1978	05-30	5380	
4	06-04	6720	A1	7	05-04	4880		9	05-11	6460	
5	05-07	4620	A1								

- Vaga. Filiayevskaya (13200 km²) (1938 - 1972) (See Unesco Catalogue)
  Complement

Année Year	Mois/Month Jour/Day	Débit Discharge	Obs.	Année Year	Mois/Month Jour/Day	Débit Discharge	Obs.	Année Year	Mois/Month Jour/Day	Débit Discharge	Obs.
1973	04-15	1060	A1	1976	05-17	1250	A1	1978	06-25	966	A1
4	05-12	1900	A1	7	04-30	1620	A2	9	05-06	1760	A1
5	04-15	848	A1								

- Verebushka. Oksochi (96.3 km²) (1946 - 1972) (See Unesco Catalogue)
  Complement

Année Year	Mois/Month Jour/Day	Débit Discharge	Obs.	Année Year	Mois/Month Jour/Day	Débit Discharge	Obs.	Année Year	Mois/Month Jour/Day	Débit Discharge	Obs.
1973	04-12	15	A1	1976	06-18	20		1978	04-16	21	A1
4	05-08	13.2	A1	7	04-26	11.2		9	04-28	12.7	A1
5	04-08	9.2	A1								

318

TABLEAU III : SERIES CHRONOLOGIQUES DES VALEURS MAXIMALES ANNUELLES

TABLE III   : CHRONOLOGICAL SERIES OF YEARLY MAXIMA

- Lovat. Khoyam (14700 km²) (1912 - 1972) (See Unesco Catalogue)
  Complement

Année Year	Mois/Month Jour/Day	Débit Discharge m³s-1	Obs.	Année Year	Mois/Month Jour/Day	Débit Discharge m³s-1	Obs.	année year	Mois/Month Jour/Day	Débit discharge m³s-1	Obs.
1973	04-10	542		1976	04-16	711		1978	04-04	822	
4	04-07	476		7	04-12	739		9	04-09	741	
5	04-15	757									

- Neva. Novosaratovka (281000 km²)

Année Year	Mois/Month Jour/Day	Débit Discharge m³s-1	Obs.	Année Year	Mois/Month Jour/Day	Débit Discharge m³s-1	Obs.	année year	Mois/Month Jour/Day	Débit discharge m³s-1	Obs.
1859	08-01	2740	A1	1899	08-26	4340	A1	1939	06-09	2460	A1
1860	06-11	2910	A1	1900	06-20	4200	A1	1940	06-05	2050	A1
1	06-13	2930	A1	1	07-03	3840	A1	1	06-23	2280	A1
2	07-03	3070	A1	2	10-04	3410	A1	2			
3	06-09	2770	A1	3	06-14	4040	A1	3	07-23	3080	A1
4	06-26	3530	A1	4	05-23	4040	A1	4	07-25	3110	A1
5	06	3500	A1	5	06-09	4080	A1	5	09-04	3080	A1
6	06-21	3240	A1	6	05-13	3970	A1	6	07-03	3740	A1
7	08-06	3860	A1	7	07-20	3060	A1	7	06-04	2980	A1
8	05-06	3990	A1	8	10-03	2740	A1	8	05-18	2660	A1
9	06-11	3040	A1	9	06-15	3000	A1	9	10-04	3000	A1
1870	06-18	3370	A1	1910	06-06	3100	A1	1950	06-12	3380	A1
1	07-03	3460	A1	1	06-18	3270	A1	1	06-13	3110	A1
2	05-31	3440	A1	2	07-06	3390	A1	2	07-07	2820	A1
3	07-05	3280	A1	3	05-13	3400	A1	3	10-07	3800	A1
4	06-15	3570	A1	4	05-28	3070	A1	4	05-12	3470	A1
5	06-19	3180	A1	5	06-15	2900	A1	5	07-23	4590	A1
6	06	2690	A1	6	05-11	2810	A1	6	06-10	3610	A1
7	08-01	2650	A1	7	05-21	3230	A1	7	06-14	3670	A1
8	09-30	3290	A1	8	06-04	3800	A1	8	06-06	4470	A1
9	08-07	4070	A1	9	05-13	3270	A1	9	06-22	4040	A1
1880	06-07	3780	A1	1920	05-26	2980	A1	1960	09-09	2840	A1
1	06-13	3970	A1	1	05-13	2640	A1	1	09-20	2780	A1
2	07-06	3230	A1	2	10-17	3200	A1	2	10-12	4040	A1
3	06-22	2810	A1	3	12-18	3640	A1	3	06-01	3920	A1
4	06-11	3260	A1	4	06-15	4510	A1	4	05-02	3030	A1
5	06-18	3000	A1	5	06-05	3580	A1	5	06-05	2690	A1
6	05-05	3000	A1	6	06-09	3540	A1	6	08-28	3470	A1
7	05-31	2810	A1	7	07-05	3210	A1	7	06-12	3560	A1
8	06-07	3440	A1	8	12-13	3630	A1	8	06-11	3430	A1
9	06-22	3590	A1	9	06-02	3900	A1	9	05-22	3320	A1
1890	08-05	2970	A1	1930	04-26	3430	A1	1970	06-13	3220	A1
1	06-15	2860	A1	1	09-26	3540	A1	1	06-11	3140	A1
2	08-19	2900	A1	2	06-16	3370	A1	2	05-08	2780	A1
3	07-03	3330	A1	3	08-06	3350	A1	3	06-17	2460	A1
4	05-24	3760	A1	4	06-25	3080	A1	4	11-30	2580	A1
5	05-27	3360	A1	5	10-26	3150	A1	5	05-26	3500	A1
6	05-15	3200	A1	6	05-24	3730	A1	6	06-08	3220	A1
7	06-06	3100	A1	7	05-29	3130	A1	7	05-25	3060	A1
8	09-05	3160	A1	8	05-22	2680	A1	8	06-14	3160	A1
								1979	06-03	2990	A1

TABLEAU III : SERIES CHRONOLOGIQUES DES VALEURS MAXIMALES ANNUELLES
TABLE III   : CHRONOLOGICAL SERIES OF YEARLY MAXIMA

USSR/URSS
European part of USSR

- Zapadnaya Dvina. Daugavpils (64600 km²)

Année Year	Mois/Month Jour/Day	Débit Discharge m³s-1	Obs.	Année Year	Mois/Month Jour/Day	Débit Discharge m³s-1	Obs.	Année Year	Mois/Month Jour/Day	Débit Discharge m³s-1	Obs.
1881	06-29	2510	A1	1914	02-13	2270	A1	1947	04-05	3530	A1
2	04-01	1770	A1	5				8	04-12	2870	A1
3	04-28	2960	A1	6	04-10	3810	A1	9	04-15	2410	A1
4	04-17	2070	A1	7				1950	04-21	1910	A1
5	04-17	1810	A1	8				1	04-07	5230	A1
6	04-09	2460	A1	9				2	10-19	1540	A1
7	04-19	1810	A1	1920				3	04-06	4070	A1
8	04-04	4220	A1	1				4	04-07	1640	A1
9	04-13	4430	A1	2	04-21	3970	A1	5	04-30	3310	A1
1890	03-29	1700	A1	3	04-23	2060	A1	6	04-27	6230	A1
1	04-22	3050	A1	4	04-07	4850	A1	7	04-11	1960	A1
2	04-23	3010	A1	5	04-04	1750	A1	8	04-24	4640	A1
3	04-14	1960	A1	6	04-25	3610	A1	9	04-15	2390	A1
4	03-22	2120	A1	7	11-14	2230	A1	1960	04-21	1750	A1
5	04-29	3390	A1	8	04-09	3470	A1	1	03-17	1450	A1
6	04-30	3980	A1	9	05-07	3970	A1	2	04-17	4320	A1
7	03-28	2270	A1	1930	03-30	1590	A1	3	04-21	3440	A1
8	04-30	2060	A1	1	04-30	6930	A1	4	04-22	2660	A1
9	04-20	2250	A1	2	04-16	2580	A1	5	04-27	3080	A1
1900	04-17	4730	A1	3	03-23	2230	A1	6	04-10	3450	A1
1	04-22	3490	A1	4	03-28	3340	A1	7	04-18	2180	A1
2	04-01	2550	A1	5	04-17	2760	A1	8	04-05	3380	A1
3	04-07	1880	A1	6	03-23	3160	A1	9	04-23	1720	A1
4	04-12	3150	A1	7	03-29	3360	A1	1970	04-25	3630	A1
5	04-28	3210	A1	8	03-26	3050	A1	1	04-09	2350	A1
6	04-17	2500	A1	9	04-08	1390	A1	2	04-15	1200	A1
7	04-24	3820	A1	1940	04-11	2530	A1	3	04-14	1550	A1
8	05-02	3800	A1	1	04-23	4660	A1	4	03-31	1110	A1
9	05-03	3170	A1	2	04-21	3040	A1	5	04-18	2020	A1
1910	04-14	1570	A1	3	06-07	1550	A1	6	04-18	1260	A1
1	04-24	2810	A1	4	04-25	2760	A1	7	04-16	2170	A1
2	04-02	2260	A1	5	04-07	2790	A1	8	04-07	2380	A1
3	03-30	2230	A1	6	04-13	2920	A1	9	04-05	2670	A1

- Neman. Smalininkäi (81200 km²)

Année Year	Mois/Month Jour/Day	Débit Discharge m³s-1	Obs.	Année Year	Mois/Month Jour/Day	Débit Discharge m³s-1	Obs.	Année Year	Mois/Month Jour/Day	Débit Discharge m³s-1	Obs.
1812	04-05	1720	A1	1868	04-15	2240	A1	1924	04-02	3460	A1
3	02-28	2320	A1	9	01-10	2370	A1	5	10-26	1160	A1
4	04-10	2080	A1	1870	04-11	6230	A1	6	01-02	3370	A1
5	04-08	1420	A1	1	03-26	3040	A1	7	03-12	2710	A1
6	04-18	3120	A1	2	04-03	2610	A1	8	04-07	2720	A1
7	04-07	1820	A1	3	03-22	2850	A1	9	05-03	2060	A1
8	03-26	1850	A1	4	03-24	1720	A1	1930	03-26	1960	A1
9	04-06	1620	A1	5	04-10	2600	A1	1	04-26	4600	A1

TABLEAU III : SERIES CHRONOLOGIQUES DES VALEURS MAXIMALES ANNUELLES

TABLE III   : CHRONOLOGICAL SERIES OF YEARLY MAXIMA

USSR/URSS

European part of USSR

- Neman. Smalininkaï (81200 km²)

Année Year	Mois/Month Jour/Day	Débit Discharge m³s-1	Obs.	Année Year	Mois/Month Jour/Day	Débit Discharge m³s-1	Obs.	Année Year	Mois/Month Jour/Day	Débit Discharge m³s-1	Obs.
1820	04-17	1670	A1	1876	03-19	2130	A1	1932	04-10	3630	A1
1	07-21	1300	A1	7	04-03	3620	A1	3	03-21	2750	A1
2	04-04	1520	A1	8	04-09	2540	A1	4	03-28	3460	A1
3	04-08	2400	A1	9	04-22	1730	A1	5	02-27	2570	A1
4	01-27	2260	A1	1880	04-04	2030	A1	6	03-18	2630	A1
5	01-05	1710	A1	1	04-19	1630	A1	7	03-18	4150	A1
6	04-17	1120	A1	2	03-14	1200	A1	8	03-22	1380	A1
7	03-13	6240	A1	3	04-13	4120	A1	9	04-02	1140	A1
8	03-29	1940	A1	4	02-03	2030	A1	1940	04-04	3400	A1
9	04-12	6820	A1	5	10-15	2140	A1	1	04-18	3850	A1
1830	03-26	1990	A1	6	04-04	3100	A1	2	04-15	3380	A1
1	04-14	1940	A1	7	04-09	2120	A1	3	02-26	1750	A1
2	05-21	1030	A1	8	04-02	5800	A1	4			
3	04-22	1140	A1	9	04-14	4680	A1	5			
4	03-02	3240	A1	1890	03-17	1550	A1	6			
5	03-18	985	A1	1	03-19	2400	A1	7	03-28	4790	A1
6	03-18	2030	A1	2	04-03	2680	A1	8	03-31	2290	A1
7	04-19	5210	A1	3	03-29	2300	A1	9	04-15	1870	A1
8	04-23	2710	A1	4	03-11	2290	A1	1950	09-18	2620	A1
9	04-30	4260	A1	5	04-13	3020	A1	1	04-06	5600	A1
1840	04-13	3900	A1	6	03-23	2280	A1	2	04-15	2360	A1
1	04-04	3420	A1	7	03-10	2800	A1	3	03-29	3100	A1
2	03-22	807	A1	8	04-08	2080	A1	4	03-29	1410	A1
3	02-06	1400	A1	9	04-19	1970	A1	5	04-18	2340	A1
4	04-16	3050	A1	1900	04-16	4290	A1	6	04-24	3690	A1
5	04-19	4310	A1	1	04-08	3420	A1	7	02-22	1730	A1
6	03-06	2980	A1	2	03-27	2660	A1	8	04-21	6580	A1
7	04-23	1590	A1	3	02-25	1820	A1	9	03-04	1740	A1
8	03-15	2120	A1	4	04-10	2710	A1	1960	03-28	3290	A1
9	04-25	2490	A1	5	04-04	2220	A1	1	03-05	1270	A1
1850	04-19	2890	A1	6	03-10	3740	A1	2	04-08	2880	A1
1	03-31	2060	A1	7	04-12	2140	A1	3	04-15	1880	A1
2	04-04	2610	A1	8	04-08	2990	A1	4	04-18	2080	A1
3	04-10	3000	A1	9	04-02	4580	A1	5	04-02	1700	A1
4	04-10	2170	A1	1910	02-28	3020	A1	6	03-05	2510	A1
5	04-07	3590	A1	1	04-04	1940	A1	7	03-15	2360	A1
6	04-14	1920	A1	2	03-09	2340	A1	8	03-28	2550	A1
7	04-04	3210	A1	3	04-24	1810	A1	9	04-11	1180	A1
8	04-02	2700	A1	4	02-07	3150	A1	1970	04-12	3370	A1
9	03-22	1700	A1	5	04-10	3160	A1	1	04-01	1650	A1
1860	04-14	3090	A1	6	01-14	3180	A1	2	12-03	837	A1
1	04-04	2720	A1	7	04-09	3870	A1	3	02-13	1190	A1
2	07-04	2990	A1	8	04-11	1810	A1	4	12-31	1560	A1

TABLEAU III : SERIES CHRONOLOGIQUES DES VALEURS MAXIMALES ANNUELLES
TABLE III   : CHRONOLOGICAL SERIES OF YEARLY MAXIMA

USSR/URSS
European part of USSR

- Neman. Smalininkaï (81200 km²)

Année Year	Mois/Month Jour/Day	Débit Discharge m³s-1	Obs.	Année Year	Mois/Month Jour/Day	Débit Discharge m³s-1	Obs.	Année Year	Mois/Month Jour/Day	Débit Discharge m³s-1	Obs.
1863	02-12	872	A1	1919	04-20	1590	A1	1975	01-09	1580	A1
4	03-12	2250	A1	1920	03-06	2480	A1	6	03-31	1410	A1
5	04-12	2790	A1	1	03-18	1540	A1	7	04-17	1260	A1
6	04-07	2730	A1	2	03-11	2860	A1	1978	03-20	1910	A1
7	04-09	4940	A1	3	03-25	2080	A1				

- Dnieper. Smolensk (14100 km²) (1881 - 1972) (See Unesco Catalogue)
  Complement

1973	04-14	369	A1	1976	04-21	451	A1	1978	04-17	419	A1
4	07-21	274	A1	7	04-22	698	A1	9	04-19	601	A1
5	04-15	527	A1								

- Pripiat. Mozir (101000 km²) (1881 - 1972) (See Unesco Catalogue)
  Complement

1973	04-14	853	A1	1976	04-18	2240	A1	1978	04-01	1820	A1
4	11-27	1520	A1	7	05-03	1190	A1	9	04-08	4310	A1
5	05-05	1770	A1								

- Don. Razdorkskaya (378000 km²) (1881 - 1951) (See Unesco Catalogue)

- Medveditsa. Archedinskaya (33700 km²) (1928 - 1972) (See Unesco Catalogue)
  Complement

1973	04-09	317	A1	1976	04-25	264		1978	04-12	569	A1
4	04-10	528	A1	7	04-18	515		9	04-24	938	A1
5	04-13	361	A1								

- Unzha. Makariev (18500 km²) (1896 - 1972) (See Unesco Catalogue)
  Complement

1973	04-20	1050	A1	1975	04-18	940	A1	1977	05-04	899	A1
4	05-16	2330	A1	6	05-17	1420	A1	8	07-01	1420	A1

- Oka. Murom (188000 km²)

1881	05-07	12700	A2	1914	04-13	4450	A1	1947	04-13	10300	A1
2	04-08	7080	A2	5	04-23	12200	A1	8	04-23	10200	A1
3	05-05	8450	A2	6	04-18	9350	A2	9	04-24	4090	A1
4	05-15	7300	A2	7	04-20	14000	A2	1950	04-22	4230	A1
5	04-24	6920	A2	8	04-25	8300	A2	1	04-10	7410	A1

TABLEAU III : SERIES CHRONOLOGIQUES DES VALEURS MAXIMALES ANNUELLES
TABLE III   : CHRONOLOGICAL SERIES OF YEARLY MAXIMA

USSR/URSS
European part of USSR

- Oka. Murom (188000 km²)

Année Year	Mois/Month Jour/Day	Débit Discharge m³s-1	Obs.	Année Year	Mois/Month Jour/Day	Débit Discharge m³s-1	Obs.	Année Year	Mois/Month Jour/Day	Débit Discharge m³s-1	Obs.
1886	04-23	7020	A2	1919				1952	05-02	8000	A1
7	04-23	9460	A2	1920	04-16	12900	A2	3	04-17	7360	A1
8	04-16	15800	A2	1	04-16	3930	A2	4	04-25	3560	A1
9	04-06	12300	A1	2	04-19	9740	A2	5	04-26	6060	A1
1890	04-08	5550	A2	3	05-04	9750	A2	6	05-05	6130	A1
1	04-11	2660	A2	4	04-24	12300	A2	7	04-26	7750	A1
2	04-25	9000	A2	5	04-15	4040	A2	8	05-06	6620	A1
3	05-03	8350	A2	6	04-30	18500	A2	9	04-20	7720	A1
4	04-25	7920	A1	7				1960	04-24	6650	A1
5	05-08	12300	A2	8	05-04	11700	A2	1	04-15	4800	A1
6	05-08	9950	A2	9	05-08	13700	A2	2	04-24	5550	A1
7	04-20	10600	A1	1930	04-06	3380	A2	3	05-01	12000	A1
8	05-07	6360	A2	1	05-06	11600	A2	4	05-01	7060	A1
9	04-24	12100	A1	2	04-24	17200	A2	5	04-24	3200	A1
1900	04-28	8120	A2	3	04-19	3420	A2	6	04-16	7770	A1
1	04-25	9950	A2	4	04-14	7580	A2	7	04-27	7250	A1
2	04-16	10500	A2	5	04-23	3700	A2	8	04-18	6650	A1
3	04-13	7900	A2	6	04-27	7620	A1	9	04-30	4470	A1
4	05-02	10500	A2	7	04-10	7600	A2	1970	04-24	13000	A1
5	05-03	6830	A2	8	04-11	6950	A1	1	04-16	5750	A1
6	04-23	6500	A2	9	04-18	6750	A1	2	04-15	4360	A1
7	04-29	8700	A2	1940	04-21	7090	A1	3	04-16	3900	A1
8	05-06	17700	A2	1	05-03	10500	A1	4	04-07	5240	A1
9	05-03	6220	A1	2	05-04	11000	A1	5	04-16	2870	A1
1910	04-25	5140	A1	3	04-21	4660	A1	6	04-24	3520	A1
1	04-25	5450	A1	4	05-09	4680	A1	7	04-17	6170	A1
2	04-20	9050	A1	5	04-22	5460	A1	8	04-12	4880	A1
3	04-05	9800	A1	6	04-24	9830	A1				

- Volga. Volgograd (1350000 km²)

Année Year	Mois/Month Jour/Day	Débit Discharge m³s-1	Obs.	Année Year	Mois/Month Jour/Day	Débit Discharge m³s-1	Obs.	Année Year	Mois/Month Jour/Day	Débit Discharge m³s-1	Obs.
1879	05-28	41000	A1	1899	05-19	43200	A1	1920	05-16	37300	A1
1880	06-10	36600	A1	1900	05-31	30600	A1	1	05-10	20400	A1
1	06-05	45400	A1	1	05-23	37700	A1	2	05-26	32800	A1
2	06-07	35100	A1	2	06-20	33000	A1	3	06-02	40000	A1
3	06-07	28900	A1	3	05-14	37800	A1	4	05-25	35800	A1
4	06-11	39400	A1	4	06-10	30500	A1	5	05-30	26400	A1
5	06-07	29500	A1	5	06-04	34800	A1	6	05-29	51900	A1
6	05-21	27000	A1	6	05-26	35900	A1	7	05-25	42800	A1
7	05-24	37000	A1	7	06-02	30200	A1	8	06-05	37800	A1
8	05-11	45200	A1	8	05-31	43500	A1	9	06-05	45500	A1
9	05-24	42500	A1	9	06-01	33200	A1	1930	05-15	22200	A1
1890	05-09	24200	A1	1910	05-28	26200	A1	1	06-02	34000	A1
1	05-04	18000	A1	1	05-29	30500	A1	2	05-25	42800	A1

TABLEAU III : SERIES CHRONOLOGIQUES DES VALEURS MAXIMALES ANNUELLES

TABLE III   : CHRONOLOGICAL SERIES OF YEARLY MAXIMA

USSR/URSS

European part of USSR

- Volga. Volgograd (1350000 km²)

Année Year	Mois/Month Jour/Day	Débit Discharge m³s-1	Obs.	Année Year	Mois/Month Jour/Day	Débit Discharge m³s-1	Obs.	Année year	Mois/Month Jour/Day	Débit Discharge m³s-1	Obs.
1892	06-02	39500	A1	1912	05-21	30000	A1	1933	05-20	22500	A1
3	06-10	33400	A1	3	05-14	28700	A1	4	05-30	29300	A1
4	05-28	32300	A1	4	06-08	42800	A1	1935	05-15	20800	A1
5	06-04	42500	A1	5	05-24	42800	A1				
6	06-05	29800	A1	6	05-24	42800	A1	1953	05-19	31000	A1
7	05-26	29600	A1	7	05-16	45700	A1	4	05-18	19400	A1
8	06-03	24000	A1	8	05-26	30000	A1	5	06-02	36300	A1
				9	05-25	46700	A1				

- Ural. Kushum (190000 km²)

Année Year	Mois/Month Jour/Day	Débit Discharge m³s-1	Obs.	Année Year	Mois/Month Jour/Day	Débit Discharge m³s-1	Obs.	Année year	Mois/Month Jour/Day	Débit Discharge m³s-1	Obs.
1912	04-23	9500	A1	1935	05-01	536	A1	1958	05-24	1700	A1
3	04-30	2380	A1	6	05-07	720	A1	9	05-09	2200	A1
4	05-15	7930	A1	7	04-22	538	A1	1960	05-10	2000	A1
5	05-07	812	A1	8	05-13	786	A1	1	04-12	840	A1
6	05-01	2450	A1	9	04-21	820	A1	2	04-23	1000	A1
7	04-15	1810	A1	1940	04-13	1190	A1	3	05-05	2400	A1
8	05-17	1320	A1	1	04-28	5780	A1	4	05-14	2500	A1
9				2	05-09	13500	A1	5	05-11	960	A1
1920				3	05-11	1490	A1	6	05-16	1450	A1
1	05-13	1440	A1	4	05-03	512	A1	7	04-17	350	A1
2	04-20	11940	A1	5	05-17	827	A1	8	04-27	800	A1
3	05-07	8220	A1	6	04-25	9200	A1	9	05-14	1200	A1
4	04-16	1520	A1	7	04-02	5210	A1	1970	04-17	10600	A1
5	05-18	1000	A1	8	04-30	8120	A1	1	05-01	7350	A1
6	05-22	4280	A1	9	05-21	2320	A1	2	05-04	1600	A1
7	05-01	6260	A1	1950	05-07	981	A1	3	04-29	790	A1
8	05-05	7080	A1	1	04-08	1060	A1	4	04-07	1500	A1
9	04-30	3740	A1	2	05-09	2330	A1	5	04-26	650	A1
1930	05-05	764	A1	3	05-13	1600	A1	6	05-10	1020	A1
1	05-01	1180	A1	4	05-08	1050	A1	7	06-18	756	A1
2	04-27	9700	A1	5	04-23	650	A1	8	05-03	1130	A1
3	05-05	565	A1	6	04-23	1300	A1	9	05-29	1240	A1
4	05-23	2290	A1	7	04-27	14000	A1				

Caucasia

- Teberda. Teberda (505 km²) (1927 - 1972) (See Unesco Catalogue)
  Complement

Année	Mois/Month	Débit	Obs.	Année	Mois/Month	Débit	Obs.	Année	Mois/Month	Débit	Obs.
1973	08-09	224		1976	07-12	176		1978	08-03	170	
4	07-25	202		7	06-07	138		9	07-30	135	
5	06-29	396									

TABLEAU III : SERIES CHRONOLOGIQUES DES VALEURS MAXIMALES ANNUELLES

TABLE III   : CHRONOLOGICAL SERIES OF YEARLY MAXIMA

USSR/URSS

Caucasia

- Kalaus. Svetlogorsk (4540 km²) (1930 - 1972) (See Unesco Catalogue)
  Complement

Année Year	Mois/Month Jour/Day	Débit Discharge m³s-1	Obs.	Année Year	Mois/Month Jour/Day	Débit discharge m³s-1	Obs.	Année Year	Mois/Month Jour/Day	Débit Discharge m³s-1	Obs.
1973	08-26	56.1	A1	1976	08-24	183	A1	1978	03-06	29.9	A1
4	03-19	94.5	A1	7	02-14	56	A1	9	08-08	52.1	A1
5	06-12	43.2	A1								

- Terek. Odzhonikidze (1490 km²) (1912 - 1972) (See Unesco Catalogue)
  Complement

Année Year	Mois/Month Jour/Day	Débit Discharge m³s-1	Obs.	Année Year	Mois/Month Jour/Day	Débit discharge m³s-1	Obs.	Année Year	Mois/Month Jour/Day	Débit Discharge m³s-1	Obs.
1973	06-22	110	A1	1976	07-19	126	A1	1978	08-19	142	A1
4	07-04	153	A1	7	06-19	110	A1	9	07-13	155	A1
5	07-12	126	A1								

Siberia

- Ishim. Tselinograd (7400 km²) (1933 - 1972) (See Unesco Catalogue)

- Ishim. Petropavlovsk (106000 km²) (1932 - 1971) (See Unesco Catalogue)

- Biya. Biysk (36900 km²) (1921 - 1972) (See Unesco Catalogue)
  Complement

Année Year	Mois/Month Jour/Day	Débit Discharge m³s-1	Obs.	Année Year	Mois/Month Jour/Day	Débit discharge m³s-1	Obs.	Année Year	Mois/Month Jour/Day	Débit Discharge m³s-1	Obs.
1973	06-06	2440	A1	1976	05-27	2640	A1	1978	04-25	2770	A1
4	04-18	2130	A1	7	05-29	3090	A1	9	04-27	2580	A1
5	05-25	2310	A1								

- Usa. Mezhdurechensk (3320 km²) (1937 - 1972) (See Unesco Catalogue)
  Complement

Année Year	Mois/Month Jour/Day	Débit Discharge m³s-1	Obs.	Année Year	Mois/Month Jour/Day	Débit discharge m³s-1	Obs.	Année Year	Mois/Month Jour/Day	Débit Discharge m³s-1	Obs.
1973	06-03	1730	A1	1976	05-25	1440	A1	1978	05-04	1270	A1
4	05-26	1310	A1	7	05-09	1940	A1	9	05-25	1710	A1
5	05-31	1790	A1								

- Tym. Napas (24500 km²) (1937 - 1972) (See Unesco Catalogue)
  Complement

Année Year	Mois/Month Jour/Day	Débit Discharge m³s-1	Obs.	Année Year	Mois/Month Jour/Day	Débit discharge m³s-1	Obs.	Année Year	Mois/Month Jour/Day	Débit Discharge m³s-1	Obs.
1973	06-12	1040	A2	1976	05-23	759	A1	1978	06-01	882	A1
4	06-03	991	A2	7	05-19	787	A1	9	06-04	1170	A1
5	06-21	942	A2								

TABLEAU III : SERIES CHRONOLOGIQUES DES VALEURS MAXIMALES ANNUELLES

TABLE III   : CHRONOLOGICAL SERIES OF YEARLY MAXIMA

USSR/URSS

Siberia

- Ob. Salekhard (2430000 km²) (1930 - 1972) (See Unesco Catalogue)
  Complement

Année Year	Mois/Month Jour/Day	Débit Discharge m³s-1	Obs.	Année Year	Mois/Month Jour/Day	Débit Discharge m³s-1	Obs.	Année Year	Mois/Month Jour/Day	Débit Discharge m³s-1	Obs.
1973	05-26	41800		1976	06-01	37100		1978	06-24	41400	
4	06-15	39500		7	05-19	35600		9	08-10	44800	
5	06-04	36100									

- Pur. Samburg (95100 km²) (1939 - 1972) (See Unesco Catalogue)
  Complement

Année Year	Mois/Month Jour/Day	Débit Discharge m³s-1	Obs.	Année Year	Mois/Month Jour/Day	Débit Discharge m³s-1	Obs.	Année Year	Mois/Month Jour/Day	Débit Discharge m³s-1	Obs.
1973	06-11	6710	A2	1976	06-10	7930	A1	1978			
4	06-18	6400	A2	7	05-31	6220	A1	9	06-18	6930	A1
5	06-17	7470	A2								

- Abakan. Abaza (14400 km²) (1932 - 1972) (See Unesco Catalogue)
  Complement

Année Year	Mois/Month Jour/Day	Débit Discharge m³s-1	Obs.	Année Year	Mois/Month Jour/Day	Débit Discharge m³s-1	Obs.	Année Year	Mois/Month Jour/Day	Débit Discharge m³s-1	Obs.
1973	06-04	3100	A1	1976	05-23	3430	A1	1978	05-25	1970	A1
4	05-24	2490	A1	7	06-19	3140	A1	9	05-24	2150	A1
5	06-01	2960	A1								

- Tuba. Bugurtak (31800 km²) (1911 - 1972) (See Unesco Catalogue)
  Complement

Année Year	Mois/Month Jour/Day	Débit Discharge m³s-1	Obs.	Année Year	Mois/Month Jour/Day	Débit Discharge m³s-1	Obs.	Année Year	Mois/Month Jour/Day	Débit Discharge m³s-1	Obs.
1973	06-06	6620	A1	1976	06-10	3290	A1	1978	06-06	5060	A1
4	05-27	5080	A1	7	06-06	4760	A1	9	05-26	5620	A1
5	06-03	6360	A1								

- Selenga. Mostovoi (440000 km²) (1934 - 1972) (See Unesco Catalogue)
  Complement

Année Year	Mois/Month Jour/Day	Débit Discharge m³s-1	Obs.	Année Year	Mois/Month Jour/Day	Débit Discharge m³s-1	Obs.	Année Year	Mois/Month Jour/Day	Débit Discharge m³s-1	Obs.
1973	07-29	7210	A1	1976	07-12	3530	A1	1978	07-05	2090	A1
4	04-26	4220	A1	7	05-14	2850	A1				
5	07-13	3630	A1								

- Khilok. Maleta (25700 km²) (1936 - 1972) (See Unesco Catalogue)
  Complement

Année Year	Mois/Month Jour/Day	Débit Discharge m³s-1	Obs.	Année Year	Mois/Month Jour/Day	Débit Discharge m³s-1	Obs.	Année Year	Mois/Month Jour/Day	Débit Discharge m³s-1	Obs.
1973	06-10	733	A1	1975	05-12	340	A1	1977	05-12	293	A1
4	06-17	408	A1	6	07-09	440	A1	8	07-04	100	A1

- Bolshaya Rechka. Posolskaya (565 km²) (1929 - 1972) (See Unesco Catalogue)
  Complement

Année Year	Mois/Month Jour/Day	Débit Discharge m³s-1	Obs.	Année Year	Mois/Month Jour/Day	Débit Discharge m³s-1	Obs.	Année Year	Mois/Month Jour/Day	Débit Discharge m³s-1	Obs.
1973	07-23	132	A1	1975	05-29	75.5	A1	1977	06-17	96.2	A1
4	05-26	92	A1	6	09-17	57.1	A1	8	07-02	116	A1

TABLEAU III : SERIES CHRONOLOGIQUES DES VALEURS MAXIMALES ANNUELLES

TABLE III   : CHRONOLOGICAL SERIES OF YEARLY MAXIMA

USSR/URSS

Siberia

- Yeniseï. Yeniseisk (1400000 km²) (1903 - 1966) (See Unesco Catalogue)

- Graviyka. Igarka (323 km²) (1938 - 1972) (See Unesco Catalogue)
  Complement

Année Year	Mois/Month Jour/Day	Débit Discharge m³s-1	Obs.	Année Year	Mois/Month Jour/Day	Débit Discharge m³s-1	Obs.	Année Year	Mois/Month Jour/Day	Débit Discharge m³s-1	Obs.
1973	06-11	79.2	A1	1976	06-11	63	A1	1978	06-10	145	A1
4	06-15	85.8	A1	7	06-01	160	A1	9	06-09	107	A1
5	06-05	85.8	A1								

- Vitim. Romanovka (18200 km²) (1944 - 1972) (See Unesco Catalogue)
  Complement

Année Year	Mois/Month Jour/Day	Débit Discharge m³s-1	Obs.	Année Year	Mois/Month Jour/Day	Débit Discharge m³s-1	Obs.	Année Year	Mois/Month Jour/Day	Débit Discharge m³s-1	Obs.
1973	07-23	2500	A1	1975	06-13	228	A1	1977	06-15	1970	A1
4	05-29	608	A1	6	08-11	914	A1	8	07-03	2480	A1

- Timpton. Nagorny (615 km²) (1926 - 1972) (See Unesco Catalogue)
  Complement

Année Year	Mois/Month Jour/Day	Débit Discharge m³s-1	Obs.	Année Year	Mois/Month Jour/Day	Débit Discharge m³s-1	Obs.	Année Year	Mois/Month Jour/Day	Débit Discharge m³s-1	Obs.
1973	07-09	306	A1	1975	05-11	182	A1	1977	05-23	185	A1
4	06-10	157	A1	6	05-21	306	A1	8	07-02	191	A1

- Lena. Kusur (2430000 km²) (1935 - 1972) (See unesco Catalogue)
  Complement

Année Year	Mois/Month Jour/Day	Débit Discharge m³s-1	Obs.	Année Year	Mois/Month Jour/Day	Débit Discharge m³s-1	Obs.	Année Year	Mois/Month Jour/Day	Débit Discharge m³s-1	Obs.
1973	06-07	133000	A1	1975	06-05	132000	A2	1977	06-08	113000	A1
4	06-11	153000	A1	6	06-10	115000	A1	8	06-13	147000	A1

- Ebitem. Ebitem (1000 km²) (1937 - 1972) (See Unesco Catalogue)
  Complement

Année Year	Mois/Month Jour/Day	Débit Discharge m³s-1	Obs.	Année Year	Mois/Month Jour/Day	Débit Discharge m³s-1	Obs.	Année Year	Mois/Month Jour/Day	Débit Discharge m³s-1	Obs.
1973	09-12	370	A1	1975	06-25	203	A1	1977	07-18	124	A1
4	06-22	282	A1	6	07-22	335	A1				

- Indigirka. Vorontsovo (305000 km²) (1937 - 1972) (See Unesco Catalogue)
  Complement

Année Year	Mois/Month Jour/Day	Débit Discharge m³s-1	Obs.	Année Year	Mois/Month Jour/Day	Débit Discharge m³s-1	Obs.	Année Year	Mois/Month Jour/Day	Débit Discharge m³s-1	Obs.
1973	06-03	5870	A1	1975	09-02	5980	A1	1977	08-10	7560	A1
4	06-04	8560	A1	6	06-30	8930	A1	8	06-08	9980	A1

- Kolyma. Ust-Srednekan (99400 km²) (1933 - 1972) (See Unesco Catalogue)
  Complement

Année Year	Mois/Month Jour/Day	Débit Discharge m³s-1	Obs.	Année Year	Mois/Month Jour/Day	Débit Discharge m³s-1	Obs.	Année Year	Mois/Month Jour/Day	Débit Discharge m³s-1	Obs.
1973	05-25	3580	A1	1975	09-05	8970	A1	1977	08-03	8130	A1
4	05-20	5640	A1	6	06-17	4800	A1	8	06-15	9420	A1

TABLEAU III : SERIES CHRONOLOGIQUES DES VALEURS MAXIMALES
TABLE III   : CHRONOLOGICAL SERIES OF YEARLY MAXIMA

USSR/URSS
Siberia

- Khasyn. Kolyma Road (682 km²) (1941 - 1972) (See Unesco Catalogue)
  Complement

Année Year	Mois/Month Jour/Day	Débit Discharge m³s-1	Obs.	Année Year	Mois/Month Jour/Day	Débit Discharge m³s-1	Obs.	Année Year	Mois/Month Jour/Day	Débit Discharge m³s-1	Obs.
1973	10-14	254	A1	1975	08-27	478	A1	1977	08-01	236	A1
4	06-18	104	A1	6	06-23	195	A1	8	07-15	220	A1

- Anguelma. Mouth of the Brook Shoumny (26700 km²) (1945 - 1972) (See Unesco Catalogue)
  complement

Année Year	Mois/Month Jour/Day	Débit Discharge m³s-1	Obs.	Année Year	Mois/Month Jour/Day	Débit Discharge m³s-1	Obs.	Année Year	Mois/Month Jour/Day	Débit Discharge m³s-1	Obs.
1973	06-25	6240	A1	1974	06-10	4030	A1	1975	06-14	2500	A1
								6	06-15	1960	A1

- Brook Izyskatelsky. 1.6 km upstream of the mouth (13.2 km²) (1947 - 1972) (See Unesco Catalogue)
  Complement

Année Year	Mois/Month Jour/Day	Débit Discharge m³s-1	Obs.	Année Year	Mois/Month Jour/Day	Débit Discharge m³s-1	Obs.	Année Year	Mois/Month Jour/Day	Débit Discharge m³s-1	Obs.
1973	09-30	16	A1	1975	09-14	21.3	A1	1977	09-13	19.6	A1
4	09-01	15.3	A1	6	07-24	18.4	A1	8	08-19	17.2	A1

- Dep. Rychkovo (8440 km²) (1942 - 1972) (See Unesco Catalogue)
  Complement

Année Year	Mois/Month Jour/Day	Débit Discharge m³s-1	Obs.	Année Year	Mois/Month Jour/Day	Débit Discharge m³s-1	Obs.	Année Year	Mois/Month Jour/Day	Débit Discharge m³s-1	Obs.
1973	07-14	743	A1	1976	06-22	464	A1	1978	02-31	407	A1
4	06-23	729	A1	7	07-28	944	A1	9	09-25	535	A1
5	07-29	442	A1								

- Ussuri. Kirovski (24400 km²) (1927 - 1972) (See Unesco Catalogue)
  Complement

Année Year	Mois/Month Jour/Day	Débit Discharge m³s-1	Obs.	Année Year	Mois/Month Jour/Day	Débit Discharge m³s-1	Obs.	Année Year	Mois/Month Jour/Day	Débit Discharge m³s-1	Obs.
1973	04-28	1590	A1	1976	04-30	696	A1	1978	05-13	344	A1
4	07-03	2950	A1	7	05-10	1400	A1	9	05-09	817	A1
5	04-20	1500	A1								

- Amur. Komsomolsk (1730000 km²)

Année Year	Mois/Month Jour/Day	Débit Discharge m³s-1	Obs.	Année Year	Mois/Month Jour/Day	Débit Discharge m³s-1	Obs.	Année Year	Mois/Month Jour/Day	Débit Discharge m³s-1	Obs.
1933	08-04	20900	A1	1949	09-22	23800	A1	1965	10-01	24300	A1
4	09-26	22300	A1	1950	05-21	18300	A1	6	09-08	23600	A1
5	06-06	24000	A1	1	09-21	38200	A1	7	09-09	22000	A1
6	08-12	27000	A1	2	08-03	18900	A1	8	06-07	16000	A1
7	08-17	24600	A1	3	08-06	35300	A1	9	09-15	23900	A1
8	09-21	29400	A1	4	09-27	13900	A1	1970	10-03	21100	A1
9	07-28	22200	A1	5	08-14	27300	A1	1	09-06	28300	A1
1940	09-04	21700	A1	6	09-25	34200	A1	2	08-25	33200	A1
1	05-25	26400	A1	7	09-17	35500	A1	3	05-11	29800	A1
2	08-05	22100	A1	8	08-08	30100	A1	4	07-13	20800	A1
3	07-23	22800	A1	9	09-20	38900	A1	5	08-18	18800	A1
4	08-14	18800	A1	1960	09-11	34300	A1	6	08-15	18100	A1
5	09-09	23800	A1	1	08-05	29400	A1	7	08-22	23400	A1

USSR/URSS
Siberia

- Amur. Komsomolsk (1730000 km²)

Année Year	Mois/Month Jour/Day	Débit Discharge m³s-1	Obs.	Année Year	Mois/Month Jour/Day	Débit Discharge m³s-1	Obs.	Année Year	Mois/Month Jour/Day	Débit Discharge m³s-1	Obs.
1946	09-15	26700	A1	1962	08-11	25500	A1	1978	08-21	20600	A1
7	10-19	25000	A1	3	09-07	29400	A1	9	05-23	15600	A1
8	06-29	24200	A1	4	08-18	26100	A1				

- Razdolnaya (Suifun). Terekhovka (15500 km²) (1928 - 1972) (See Unesco Catalogue)
  Complement

Année Year	Mois/Month Jour/Day	Débit Discharge m³s-1	Obs.	Année Year	Mois/Month Jour/Day	Débit Discharge m³s-1	Obs.	Année Year	Mois/Month Jour/Day	Débit Discharge m³s-1	Obs.
1973	05-22	588	A1	1976	04-24	83.2	A1	1978	08-21	212	A1
4	06-23	1650	A1	7	07-11	202	A1	9	08-20	857	A1
5	04-09	289	A1								

Kazàkhstan-Uzbekistan

- Syr Darya. Tiumen-Aryk (219000 km²)

Année Year	Mois/Month Jour/Day	Débit Discharge m³s-1	Obs.	Année Year	Mois/Month Jour/Day	Débit Discharge m³s-1	Obs.	Année Year	Mois/Month Jour/Day	Débit Discharge m³s-1	Obs.
1914	07-06	2090	A1	1930	06-26	1770	A1	1946			
5	05-17	1250	A1	1	07-19	2220	A1	7	05-30	890	A1
6	06-16	1010	A1	2	05-31	1580	A1	8	05-03	1270	A1
7	08-16	567	A1	3	06-10	1530	A1	9	06-02	1840	A1
8				4	06-30	2730	A2	1950	05-25	1740	A1
9	06-19	1430	A1	5	06-23	2000	A2	1	06-06	1860	A1
1920	07-18	1520	A1	6	06-09	2420	A1	2	05-19	2130	A1
1				7	05-22	1930	A1	3	06-24	1990	A1
2				8	05-21	1160	A1	4	05-08	1850	A1
3				9	05-18	1700	A1	5	06-22	1870	A1
4				1940	06-09	1570	A1	6	06-12	1530	A1
5				1	06-21	1830	A1	7	03-13	1120	A1
6				2	07-03	2070	A1	8	07-24	1840	A1
7	05-10	1020	A1	3	06-14	1340	A1	9	04-13	2090	A1
8	06-17	2260	A1	4	07-14	1010	A1	1960	06-01	2080	A1
9	05-03	1570	A1	5							

UNITED KINGDOM/ROYAUME UNI

- Spey. Boat O'Brig (2860 km²) (1951 - 1970) (See Unesco Catalogue)
  No flood exceeding 1150 m³s-1 from 1971 till 1980

TABLEAU III : SERIES CHRONOLOGIQUES DES VALEURS MAXIMALES ANNUELLES
TABLE III   : CHRONOLOGICAL SERIES OF YEARLY MAXIMA

UNITED KINGDOM/ROYAUME UNI

- Don. Doncaster (1260 km²) (1868 - 1968) (See Unesco Catalogue)
  Complement

Année Year	Mois/Month Jour/Day	Débit Discharge m³s-1	Obs.	Année Year	Mois/Month Jour/Day	Débit discharge m³s-1	Obs.	Année Year	Mois/Month Jour/Day	Débit Discharge m³s-1	obs.
1970	04-13	185	A1	1973	07-16	184	A1	1975	01-22	89	
1	04-26	142	A1	4	02-11	97	A1	6	01-02	72	
2	02-03	112	A1								

- Burbage Brook. Burbage (9.1 km²) (1927 - 1973) (See Unesco Catalogue)
  Complement

Année Year	Mois/Month Jour/Day	Débit Discharge m³s-1	Obs.	Année Year	Mois/Month Jour/Day	Débit discharge m³s-1	Obs.	Année Year	Mois/Month Jour/Day	Débit Discharge m³s-1	obs.
1973	10-10	2.05	A1	1977	02-02	3.35	A1	1980	02-07	3.21	A1
5	05-13	3.68	A1	8	01-28	1.85	A1	1	04-29	5.37	A1
6	01-01	3.20	A1	9	03-25	5.78	A1				

- Trent. Colwick (7490 km²) (1885 - 1969) (See Unesco Catalogue)
  Complement

Année Year	Mois/Month Jour/Day	Débit Discharge m³s-1	Obs.	Année Year	Mois/Month Jour/Day	Débit discharge m³s-1	Obs.	Année Year	Mois/Month Jour/Day	Débit Discharge m³s-1	obs.
1970	02-22	439	A1	1974	02-12	412	A1	1978	01-30	486	A1
1	04-25	387	A1	5	03-10	352	A1	9	02-03	442	A1
1	11-21	287	A1	5	12-02	228	A1	1980	02-09	500	A1
2	12-07	336	A1	7	02-25	957	A1	1	03-12	571	A1

- Canons Brook. Harlow (21.4 km²) (1951 - 1969) (See Unesco Catalogue)
  Three floods exceeding 10.6 m³s-1 from 1969 till 1980 : 1977   02-20   12.32 m³s-1 - 1979   05-30   11.73 m³s-1
  1978   05-05   11.58 m³s-1

- Thames. Teddington (9670 km²) (1884 - 1971) (See Unesco Catalogue)
  Complement

Année Year	Mois/Month Jour/Day	Débit Discharge m³s-1	Obs.	Année Year	Mois/Month Jour/Day	Débit discharge m³s-1	Obs.	Année Year	Mois/Month Jour/Day	Débit Discharge m³s-1	obs.
1972	03-08	312	A1	1974	11-23	531	A1	1978	01-29	310	A1
2	12-07	246	A1	5	12-02	129	A1	9	04-09	304	A1
4	02-12	380	A1	7	01-02	309	A1	9	12-29	420	A1

- Severn. Upton (6990 km²) (1956 - 1970) (See Unesco Catalogue)
  No flood exceeding 500 m³s-1 from 1970 till 1980

- Wye. Cefn Brwyn (10.4 km²) (1952 - 1973) (See Unesco Catalogue)
  No flood exceeding 48 m³s-1 from 1973 till 1980

- Irvine. Kilmarnock (218 km²) (1913 - 1967) (See Unesco Catalogue)
  No flood exceeding 129 m³s-1 from 1967 till 1980

UNITED STATES OF AMERICA/ETATS UNIS D'AMERIQUE
Massachussetts

- Connecticut. Montague City (20370 km²) (1904 - 1971) (See Unesco Catalogue)
  No flood exceeding 5520 m³s-1 from 1971 till 1979

330

UNITED STATES OF AMERICA/ETATS UNIS D'AMERIQUE
New Hampshire

- Otter Brook. Keene (110 km²) (1924 - 1957) (See Unesco Catalogue)

Pensylvania

- Susquehanna. Harrisburg (62400 km²) (1786, 1846, 1865, 1868, 1886, 1889 - 1971) (See Unesco Catalogue)
  No flood exceeding 16300 m³s-1 from 1971 till 1979

Maryland

- Potomac. Point of Rocks (25000 km²)

Année Year	Mois/Month Jour/Day	Débit Discharge m³s-1	Obs.	Année Year	Mois/Month Jour/Day	Débit Discharge m³s-1	Obs.	Année Year	Mois/Month Jour/Day	Débit Discharge m³s-1	Obs.
1889	06-02	13030	E3	1923	04-16	1153	A	1952	04-29	3597	A1
1895	04-10	1940	A2	4	05-13	7845	A	2	11-23	3342	A1
6	07-26	1586	A2	5	02-13	2521	A	4	03-03	3086	A1
7	10-01	5777	A2	6	02-27	1713	A	5	08-20	6061	A1
8	08-12	3597	A2	7	11-17	2546	A	6	04-09	1722	A1
9	03-06	3625	A2	8	05-02	4106	A	7	04-07	1960	A1
1900	03-21	1634	A2	9	04-18	5098	A	8	05-07	2039	A1
1	04-22	4560	A2	1930	10-23	3115	A	9	06-04	1577	A1
2	03-02	6202	A2	1	05-24	1042	A	1960	05-10	3512	A1
3	03-01	3115	A2	2	05-14	4475	A	1	02-21	2889	A1
4	06-01	1260	A2	3	04-21	3483	A	2	03-23	3285	A1
5	03-11	2022	A2	4	01-09	1039	A	3	03-21	3540	A1
6	03-29	2302	A2	4	12-02	3625	A	4	03-06	2464	A1
7	03-15	3370	A2	6	03-19	13590	A2	5	03-06	2770	A1
8	01-13	4305	A2	7	04-27	8779	A2	6	02-15	2019	A1
9	04-16	2351	A2	7	10-30	4956	A2	7	03-08	4078	A1
1910	06-18	4758	A2	9	02-05	3512	A2	8	03-18	2175	A1
1	09-01	3002	A2	1940	04-21	2651	A2	9	03-27	787	A1
2	02-28	2702	A2	1	04-07	1954	A2	1970	04-03	2608	A1
3	03-28	3937	A2	2	05-24	3540	A2	1	02-24	2447	A1
4	03-19	2093	A2	2	10-16	11840	A2	2	06-23	9827	A1
5	06-04	3937	A2	4	05-08	1991	A1	2	10-08	3002	A1
6	03-29	3512	A2	5	09-20	3937	A1	3	12-28	3738	A1
7	03-13	3483	A2	6	06-03	1504	A1	5	03-21	5126	A1
8	04-16	3597	A2	7	03-16	1192	A1	6	01-02	3087	A1
9	05-11	2280	A2	8	04-15	2464	A1	6	10-11	5466	A1
1920	03-06	3087	A2	9	06-20	3738	A1	8	03-16	3937	A1
1	05-06	2515	A2	1950	02-03	1832	A1	9	02-27	5041	A1
2	03-17	2231	A2	0	12-05	3625	A1	9	10-11	1968	A1

Virginia

- James. Buchanan (5370 km²) (1877,1886,1889,1893 - 1972) (See Unesco Catalogue)

TABLEAU III : SERIES CHRONOLOGIQUES DES VALEURS MAXIMALES ANNUELLES
TABLE III   : CHRONOLOGICAL SERIES OF YEARLY MAXIMA

UNITED STATES OF AMERICA/ETATS UNIS D'AMERIQUE
North Carolina

- Beetree. Swannanoa (14 km²) (1926 - 1971) (See Unesco Catalogue)

Georgia

- Altamaha. Doctortown (35200 km²) (1925 - 1971) (See Unesco Catalogue)
  No flood exceeding 3170 m³s-1 from 1971 till 1979

Alabama

- Alabama. Montgomery (31900 km²)

Année Year	Mois/Month Jour/Day	Débit Discharge m³s-1	Obs.	Année Year	Mois/Month Jour/Day	Débit Discharge m³s-1	Obs.	Année Year	Mois/Month Jour/Day	Débit Discharge m³s-1	Obs.
1886	04-01	9119	E3	1944	04-29	3993	A	1961	12-20	4220	A
1888	03-03	8015	E3	5	02-22	2605	A	3	05-04	2671	A
1928	04-25	3795	A	6	01-09	3682	A	4	04-10	5069	A
9	03-17	7250	A	7	01-23	3937	A	5	02-14	2237	A
9	11-19	3738	A	8	02-15	2860	A	6	02-18	3257	A
1930	11-19	2053	A	8	12-01	6627	A	7	08-28	2028	A
2	02-24	2642	A	1950	03-17	2283	A	8	01-12	2345	A
2	12-31	4248	A	1	04-01	3880	A	9	05-22	2351	A
4	03-06	3144	A	2	03-27	2917	A	1970	03-24	3229	A
5	03-09	2580	A	3	05-08	3200	A	1	03-06	4418	A
6	02-08	5551	A	4	01-25	2237	A	2	01-11	5523	A
7	05-07	3030	A	5	04-15	3087	A	3	04-01	3767	A
8	04-10	6061	A	6	03-17	3455	A	4	01-01	3144	A
9	08-18	3483	A	7	04-07	3937	A	5	04-03	4361	A
1940	03-16	2311	A	8	03-10	2407	A	6	04-01	3965	A
1	03-09	1051	A	9	02-17	1620	A	7	04-07	4248	A
2	03-23	3229	A	1960	04-06	2393	A	8	01-28	3710	A
3	03-23	4645	A	1	02-26	8015	A	9	04-16	7363	A
								1980	03-30	4786	A

Indiana

- Ohio. Evansville (277100 km²) (1874 - 1971) (See Unesco Catalogue)
  No flood exceeding 19900 m³s-1 from 1971 till 1979

Tennessee

- Clinch. Tazewell (3820 km²) (1862,1920 - 1967) (See Unesco Catalogue)

- Shoal. Iron City (900 km²)

1925	11-12	530	A	1944	02-09	547	A	1961	12-18	343	A1
7	03-13	1840	A	5	02-22	676	A	3	03-12	600	A1
8	03-09	592	A	6	01-08	530	A	4	03-15	267	A1
9	03-23	827	A	7	04-16	165	A	5	03-30	552	A1

TABLEAU III : SERIES CHRONOLOGIQUES DES VALEURS MAXIMALES ANNUELLES
TABLE III : CHRONOLOGICAL SERIES OF YEARLY MAXIMA

UNITED STATES OF AMERICA/ETATS UNIS D'AMERIQUE
Tennessee

- Shoal. Iron City (900 km²)

Année Year	Mois/Month Jour/Day	Débit Discharge m³s-1	Obs.	Année Year	Mois/Month Jour/Day	Débit Discharge m³s-1	Obs.	Année Year	Mois/Month Jour/Day	Débit Discharge m³s-1	Obs.
1930	03-07	334	A	1948	02-13	1728	A2	1966	02-13	185	A1
1	02-25	202	A	9	03-27	484	A	7	03-07	450	A1
2	07-07	513	A	1950	02-14	920	A	8	01-11	297	A1
2	10-17	719	A	1	02-01	770	A	9	04-10	436	A1
4	03-03	371	A	1	12-08	408	A	9	12-30	564	A1
5	03-12	589	A	3	02-12	583	A	1971	02-22	320	A1
6	04-06	592	A	4	02-20	295	A	2	01-02	326	A1
7	05-04	818	A	5	03-21	3740	A2	3	03-15	1750	A1
8	01-23	226	A	6	02-18	493	A1	4	01-11	1110	A1
9	02-15	496	A	7	01-31	541	A1	5	03-14	1510	A1
1940	04-19	623	A	7	11-18	595	A1	5	10-17	368	A1
1	07-12	153	A	9	04-19	170	A1	7	03-04	974	A1
2	02-24	90	A	1959	12-19	323	A1	8	05-08	430	A1
2	02-09	306	A	1961	03-08	886	A1	1979	09-14	739	A1

Minnesota

- Mississipi. St-Paul (95300 km²) (1867 - 1971) (See Unesco Catalogue)

Montana

- Yellowstone. Sidney (178980 km²) (1911 - 1967) (See Unesco Catalogue)

- North Fork Flathead. Columbia Falls (4010 km²)

Année Year	Mois/Month Jour/Day	Débit Discharge m³s-1	Obs.	Année Year	Mois/Month Jour/Day	Débit Discharge m³s-1	Obs.	Année Year	Mois/Month Jour/Day	Débit Discharge m³s-1	Obs.
1911	06-14	428	A2	1942	05-27	510	A1	1962	05-29	402	A1
2	05-17	331	A2	3	05-28	433	A1	3	05-31	391	A1
3	06-02	674	A2	4	05-17	222	A1	4	06-09	1960	A1
4	06-04	377	A2	5	06-02	436	A1	5	06-19	660	A1
5	06-27	242	A2	6	05-29	623	A1	6	06-01	552	A1
6	06-20	852	A2	7	05-10	666	A1	7	05-23	736	A1
1917	06-17	719	A2	8	05-24	748	A1	8	06-04	496	A1
1929	05-24	575	A1	9	05-14	564	A1	9	05-14	498	A1
1930	05-31	334	A1	1950	06-23	595	A1	1970	05-27	521	A1
1	05-17	425	A1	1	05-12	589	A1	1	05-28	629	A1
2	05-23	600	A1	2	04-28	513	A1	2	06-02	889	A1
3	06-17	691	A1	3	06-14	674	A1	3	05-18	527	A1
4	04-26	549	A1	4	05-21	892	A1	4	06-18	971	A1
5	05-24	589	A1	5	06-14	530	A1	5	06-21	869	A1
6	05-16	538	A1	6	05-22	841	A1	6	05-11	685	A1
7	05-28	394	A1	7	05-07	651	A1	7	05-11	241	A1
8	05-28	680	A1	8	05-13	578	A1	8	06-06	510	A1

TABLEAU III : SERIES CHRONOLOGIQUES DES VALEURS MAXIMALES ANNUELLES
TABLE III   : CHRONOLOGICAL SERIES OF YEARLY MAXIMA

UNITED STATES OF AMERICA/ETATS UNIS D'AMERIQUE
Montana

- North Fork Flathead. Columbia Falls (4010 km²)

Année Year	Mois/Month Jour/Day	Débit Discharge m³s-1	Obs.	Année Year	Mois/Month Jour/Day	Débit Discharge m³s-1	Obs.	Année Year	Mois/Month Jour/Day	Débit Discharge m³s-1	Obs.
1939	04-30	394	A1	1959	06-06	714	A1	1979	05-27	527	A1
1940	05-12	394	A1	1960	06-04	586	A1	1980	05-26	521	A1
1	05-03	227	A1	1	05-28	847	A1				

Michigan

- Grand River. Lansing (3180 km²)

Année Year	Mois/Month Jour/Day	Débit Discharge m³s-1	Obs.	Année Year	Mois/Month Jour/Day	Débit Discharge m³s-1	Obs.	Année Year	Mois/Month Jour/Day	Débit Discharge m³s-1	Obs.
1901	03-20	245	A	1928	04-09	88	A	1955	03-03	93	A
2	07-05	190	A	9	03-01	113	A	6	05-01	218	A
3	04-15	240	A	1930	02-22	127	A	7	05-20	116	A
4	03-26	694	A	1	06-08	46	A	8	03-01	67	A
5	06-07	363	A	2	02-13	76	A	9	03-08	132	A
6	06-10	195	A	3	04-03	127	A	1960	04-01	229	A
7	03-30	124	A	4	04-05	119	A	1	04-27	107	A
8	03-14	346	A	5	03-12	114	A	2	03-14	128	A
9	05-02	242	A	6	03-12	71	A	3	03-25	98	A
1910	03-06	183	A	7	06-27	203	A	4	05-08	45	A
1	02-18	95	A	8	02-14	200	A	5	03-06	134	A
2	04-05	263	A	9	04-19	154	A	6	03-23	85	A
3	04-05	192	A	1940	03-31	118	A	7	03-15	102	A
4	05-17	191	A	1	01-03	84	A	8	06-29	242	A
5	02-16	136	A	2	03-18	213	A	9	01-31	123	A
6	03-29	314	A	3	06-03	230	A	1970	04-09	115	A
7	04-07	161	A	4	02-27	176	A	1	02-22	155	A
8	03-15	447	A	5	05-19	210	A	2	04-19	111	A
9	03-17	218	A	6	03-07	145	A	3	01-01	174	A
1920	03-13	195	A	7	04-07	464	A	4	03-10	208	A
1	04-24	62	A	8	03-21	340	A	5	04-20	317	A
2	04-13	142	A	9	02-16	167	A	6	03-05	194	A
3	03-17	110	A	1950	04-05	234	A	7	04-06	78	A
4	03-07	117	A	1	02-21	135	A	8	03-24	132	A
5	03-21	58	A	2	04-15	176	A	9	03-07	150	A
6	03-22	195	A	3	06-08	64	A	1980	03-14	92	A
7	05-28	64	A	4	02-17	137	A				

Colorado

- Plum. Louviers (782 km²) (1942 - 1971) (See Unesco Catalogue)
  One flood exceeding 108 m³s-1 from 1971 till 1979 : 110 m³s-1 05-06 1973

UNITED STATES OF AMERICA/ETATS UNIS D'AMERIQUE

Nebraska

- Big Blue. Barneston (11500 km²) (1903,1919 - 1971) (See Unesco Catalogue)

Missouri

- Salt river. Shelbina (1250 km²) (1909,1928,1931 - 1970) (See Unesco Catalogue)

Arkansas

- Arkansas. Little Rock (409300 km²) (1923 - 1970) (See Unesco Catalogue)
  No flood exceeding 12000 m³s-1 from 1970 till 1979

Mississipi

- Mississipi. Vicksburg (2960000 km²) (1858,1885,1897,1898,1903 - 1970) (See Unesco Catalogue)

Louisiana

- Red river. Alexandria (175000 km²) (1872 - 1970) (See Unesco Catalogue)

Texas

- Rio Pecos. Comstock (91410 km² - 9300 km² participating part of the basin for the 1954 flood)

Année Year	Mois/Month Jour/Day	Débit Discharge m³s-1	Obs.	Année Year	Mois/Month Jour/Day	Débit Discharge m³s-1	Obs.	Année Year	Mois/Month Jour/Day	Débit Discharge m³s-1	Obs.
1901	09-08	260	A2	1919	09-16		A2	1937	05-10	79	A2
2	05-18	314	A2	9	10-04	148	A2	8	07-24	891	A2
3	06-29	61	A2	1921	06-13	524	A2	9	05-05	164	A2
4	09-20	495	A2	2	06-18		A2	1940	06-25	159	A2
5	04-23	412	A2	3	09-17	42	A2	1	09-18	530	A2
6	08-11	1010	A2	4	09-21	362	A2	1	10-10	405	A2
7	12-10	25	A2	5	05-28	1840	A2	3	07-15	317	A2
8	07-07	351	A2	6	07-23	124	A2	4	09-06	254	A2
9	08-01	50	A2	7	06-13	413	A2	5	07-08	247	A2
1910	09-10	735	A2	8	05-13	560	A2	5	10-07	785	A2
1	04-03	305	A2	9	06-30	113	A2	6	10-06	1840	A2
2	04-07	31	A2	9	10-14	178	A2	8	07-04	1450	A2
3	04-24	520	A2	1930	10-14	570	A2	9	07-26	2790	A2
4	05-23	263	A2	2	09-01	3280	A2	1950	07-13	1270	A2
4	10-23	1040	A2	2	10-16	180	A2	1	05-24	232	A2
6	09-01		A2	4	06-04	233	A2	2	05-27	101	A2
7	05-12	45	A2	5	09-04	2390	A2	3	08-24	419	A2
8	08-15	202	A2	6	09-27	880	A2	4	06-28	26800	A3

The return period of the 1954 flood is estimated greater than 2000 years by Baker.

- San Saba. San Saba (7880 km²) (1916 - 1971) (See Unesco Catalogue)

TABLEAU III : SERIES CHRONOLOGIQUES DES VALEURS MAXIMALES ANNUELLES
TABLE III   : CHRONOLOGICAL SERIES OF YEARLY MAXIMA

UNITED STATES OF AMERICA/ETATS UNIS D'AMERIQUE

Utah

- Virgin. Virgin (2420 km²) (1910 - 1971) (See Unesco Catalogue)

Wyoming

- Middle Crow. Hecla (67 km²) (1903 - 1967) (See Unesco Catalogue)

Arizona

- Colorado. Grand Canyon (357000 km²) (1884, 1921 - 1970) (See Unesco Catalogue)
  No flood exceeding 3300 m³s-1 from 1970 till 1979

- Salt river. Chrysotile (7400 km²) (1916, 1925 - 1970) (See Unesco Catalogue)

- San Pedro. Charleston (3160 km²)

Année Year	Mois/Month Jour/Day	Débit Discharge m³s-1	Obs.	Année Year	Mois/Month Jour/Day	Débit Discharge m³s-1	Obs.	Année Year	Mois/Month Jour/Day	Débit Discharge m³s-1	Obs.
1916	08-16	218	A2	1938	08-07	211	A2	1960	08-11	110	A2
7	08-12	368	A2	9	08-07	265	A2	1	07-30	103	A2
8	07-01	113	A2	1940	08-13	878	A2	2	07-28	101	A2
9	08-16	711	A2	1	08-16	306	A2	3	07-27	183	A2
1920	09-05	127	A2	2	07-24	81	A2	4	08-14	218	A2
1	07-19	538	A2	3	08-09	245	A2	5	09-04	118	A2
2	09-09	105	A2	4	08-18	97	A2	6	08-03	125	A2
3	08-12	147	A2	5	08-09	217	A2	7	07-26	170	A2
4	07-24	54	A2	6	08-04	340	A2	7	12-20	143	A2
5	08-06	337	A2	7	08-09	286	A2	9	07-28	111	A2
6	09-28	2780	A2	8	08-03	222	A2	1970	08-09	130	A2
6	10-09	144	A2	9	07-24	190	A2	1	08-10	168	A2
8	07-15	108	A2	1950	07-06	172	A2	2	08-26	169	A2
9	07-29	295	A2	1	07-02	162	A2	3	07-15	95	A2
1930	08-07	276	A2	2	08-17	222	A2	4	07-20	371	A2
1	08-09	694	A2	3	07-07	243	A2	5	09-14	114	A2
2	08-09	198	A2	4	08-15	668	A2	6	09-05	103	A2
3	07-22	272	A2	5	08-06	408	A2	7	08-23	147	A2
4		142	A2	6	07-18	185	A2	7	10-08	671	A2
5	08-28	244	A2	7	07-25	170	A2	9	01-18	334	A2
6	09-11	368	A2	8	08-05	238	A2	1980	08-15	28	A2
7	08-20	267	A2	9	07-27	212	A2				

California

- San Antonio. Claremont (43.8 km²)

1918	03-07	10.3	A	1936	02-02	1.64	A	1954	01-25	3.51	A
8	11-26	0.05	A	7	02-14	4.96	A	5	02-27	0.54	A

TABLEAU III : SERIES CHRONOLOGIQUES DES VALEURS MAXIMALES ANNUELLES
TABLE III : CHRONOLOGICAL SERIES OF YEARLY MAXIMA

UNITED STATES OF AMERICA/ETATS UNIS D'AMERIQUE
California

- San Antonio. Claremont (43.8 km²)

Année Year	Mois/Month Jour/Day	Débit Discharge m³s-1	Obs.	Année Year	Mois/Month Jour/Day	Débit Discharge m³s-1	Obs.	Année Year	Mois/Month Jour/Day	Débit discharge m³s-1	Obs.
1920	03-02	2.80	A	1938	03-02	606	A2	1956	01-26	1.44	A
1	03-14	1.93	A	9	09-25	10.8	A	7	01-13	2.66	A
1	12-19	28.9	A	1940	01-08	2.89	A	8	04-03	8.24	A
2	12-13	2.52	A	1	03-12	5.75	A	9	02-16	2.32	A
4	03-26	0.31	A	1	12-10	0.62	A	1960	04-27	0.25	A
5	04-06	0.45	A	3	01-23	59.5	A	1	01-26	0.12	A
6	04-05	9.86	A	4	04-08	2.89	A	2	02-11	5.15	A
7	02-16	20.3	A	4	11-11	10.6	A	3	02-09	1.02	A
8	02-04	0.28	A	5	12-23	7.08	A	4	01-21	0.26	A
9	03-10	0.21	A	6	12-26	6.37	A	5	04-30	1.02	A
1930	03-26	0.88	A	8	04-28	0.57	A	5	12-29	73.4	A
1	04-26	1.22	A	9	04-20	0.28	A	6	12-06	58.9	A
2	02-09	5.41	A	9	12-18	0.28	A	7	11-19	2.97	A
3	01-19	0.17	A	1951	04-28	0.11	A	9	01-25	464	A2
4	01-01	3.37	A	2	04-07	2.10	A	1970	03-01	1.59	A
5	04-08	2.86	A	2	12-01	0.68	A	0	11-29	5.72	A
								1	12-24	0.82	A

- Eel. Scotia (8060 km²) (1911 - 1970) (See Unesco Catalogue)
  One flood exceeding 8920 m³s-1 from 1970 till 1979 : 11000 m³s-1 01-16 1974

Idaho

- Salmon. White Bird (35100 km²) (1911 - 1971) (See Unesco Catalogue)

- Johnson. Yellow Pine (552 km²)

Année Year	Mois/Month Jour/Day	Débit Discharge m³s-1	Obs.	Année Year	Mois/Month Jour/Day	Débit Discharge m³s-1	Obs.	Année Year	Mois/Month Jour/Day	Débit discharge m³s-1	Obs.
1929	05-23	62.3	A2	1947	05-09	128	A1	1964	06-06	88.1	A1
1930	05-29	56.1	A2	8	05-27	131	A1	5	06-11	123	A1
1	05-16	41.1	A2	9	05-16	131	A1	6	05-09	50.4	A1
2	06-15	90.6	A2	1950	06-21	90.6	A1	7	06-21	90	A1
3	06-09	146	A2	1	05-28	85.5	A1	8	06-03	58.1	A1
4	04-23	59.5	A1	2	06-06	79.3	A1	9	05-25	90.6	A1
5	05-23	68.5	A1	3	06-13	104	A1	1970	06-05	115	A1
6	05-14	97.1	A1	4	05-20	118	A1	1	05-28	107	A1
7	05-19	48.7	A1	5	06-11	83.0	A1	2	06-02	128	A1
8	05-28	99.7	A1	6	05-27	154	A1	3	05-18	59.8	A1
9	04-30	58.6	A1	7	06-02	119	A1	4	06-17	176	A1
1940	05-13	82.4	A1	8	05-23	121	A1	5	06-07	83.8	A1
1	05-13	71.4	A1	9	06-06	81.6	A1	6	05-18	73.9	A1
2	05-25	71.4	A1	1960	06-03	72.5	A1	7	06-11	17.9	A1
3	05-29	96.0	A1	1	05-26	89.8	A1	8	06-08	87.5	A1
4	05-15	41.6	A1	2	06-03	77.0	A1	9	05-26	65.1	A1
5	05-10	68.8	A1	3	05-24	96.6	A1	1980	05-22	74.8	A1
6	05-28	70	A1								

UNITED STATES OF AMERICA/ETATS UNIS D'AMERIQUE
Oregon

- Columbia. The Dalles (614000 km²) (1858 - 1971) (See Unesco Catalogue)
  No flood exceeding 22300 m³s-1 from 1971 till 1979 but more unless regulated

Washington

- Skagit. Concrete (7090 km²) (1897,1909,1917,1921,1924 - 1967) (See Unesco Catalogue)
  One flood exceeding 3290 m³s-1 : 3460 m³s-1 12-04 1975

UPPER VOLTA/ HAUTE VOLTA

_ Volta Noire. Boromo (37140 km²)

Année Year	Mois/Month Jour/Day	Débit Discharge m³s-1	Obs.	Année Year	Mois/Month Jour/Day	Débit Discharge m³s-1	Obs.	Année Year	mois/Month Jour/Day	Débit Discharge m³s-1	Obs.
1955	10-15	127	A1	1963	08-29	95.7	A1	1971	09-16	130	A1
6	09-27	146	A1	4	09-23	175	A1	2	08-26	76.5	A1
7	09-15	98.1	A1	5	09-26	142	A1	3	08-04	106	A1
8	09-10	149	A1	6	10-12	90	A1	4	09-24	141	A1
9	09-01	127	B2	7	09-13	99	A1	5	09-15	245	A1
1960	08-07	139	A1	8	09-19	79	A1	6	07-04	68.1	A1
1	09-17	175	A1	9	09-18	156	A1	7	08-28	101	A1
2	09-14	182	A1	1970	09-26	127	A1	8	08-14	86.2	A1

URUGUAY

- Uruguay. Salto (244.000 km²)

Année Year	Mois/Month Jour/Day	Débit Discharge m³s-1	Obs.	Année Year	Mois/Month Jour/Day	Débit Discharge m³s-1	Obs.	Année Year	mois/Month Jour/Day	Débit Discharge m³s-1	Obs.
1898	07-02	16165	A1	1926	10-08	17324	A1	1954	10-31	20255	
9	09-03	25390	A1	7	11-20	20885	A1	5	04-28	18051	
1900	10-15	20680	A1	8	09-26	22606	A1	6	04-15	13370	
1	10-22	10700	A1	9	10-23	27915	A1	7	09-20	14771	
2	11-12	19675	A1	1930	05-11	18355	A1	8	10-15	12725	
3	06-21	17489	A1	1	09-24	10966	A1	9	04-16	33000	
4	04-06	18051	A1	2	04-28	24030	A1	1960	10-02	14923	
5	06-14	21588	A1	3	10-14	11740	A1	1	11-03	19956	
6	07-04	8346	A1	4	11-07	12965	A1	2	09-19	11295	
7	09-19	24437	A1	5	10-26	23926	A1	3	11-19	23698	
8	06-14	11316	A1	6	06-19	24358	A1	4	04-30	9878	
9	07-14	10101	A1	7	09-30	13330	A1	5	09-20	22789	
1910	04-18	14522	A1	8	05-09	19175	A1	6	07-31	21403	
1	10-13	20355	A1	9	05-27	15065	A1	7	09-03	17479	
2	08-22	17558	A1	1940	04-17	17794	A1	8	11-11	12953	
3	04-01	13109	A1	1	05-13	29418	A1	9			
4	12-10	18331	A1	2	05-28	17627	A1	1970	12-31	11850	
5	05-13	18964	A1	3	08-11	10757	A1	1	01-31	15906	

TABLEAU III : SERIES CHRONOLOGIQUES DES VALEURS MAXIMALES ANNUELLES
TABLE III   : CHRONOLOGICAL SERIES OF YEARLY MAXIMA

URUGUAY

- Uruguay. Salto (244000 km²)

Année Year	Mois/Month Jour/Day	Débit Discharge m³s-1	Obs.	Année Year	Mois/Month Jour/Day	Débit Discharge m³s-1	Obs.	Année Year	Mois/Month Jour/Day	Débit Discharge m³s-1	Obs.
1916	06-19	18868	A1	1944	10-10	8693	A1	1972	09-08	25257	A1
7	10-13	2533	A1	5	09-30	9805	A1	3	05-11	18530	A1
8	10-09	13926	A1	6	10-16	15678	A1	4	06-18	9655	A1
9	11-27	21180	A1	7	05-21	17627	A1	5	10-21	17290	A1
1920	07-02	14437	A1	8	04-20	15808	A1	6	08-07	12417	A1
1	10-07	18189	A1	9	10-07	14092	A1	7	07-30	14967	A1
2	07-05	15019	A1	1950	06-24	17770	A1	8	11-29	18264	A1
3	06-29	25166	A1	1	10-27	15500	A1	9	11-09	21791	A1
4	06-30	9885	A1	2	08-02	14950	A1	1980	11-01	16028	A1
5	05-12	20130	A1	3	10-07	21300	A1	1	02-16	11215	A1

YUGOSLAVIA/YOUGOSLAVIE

- Sava. Zagreb (12450 km²)

Année Year	Mois/Month Jour/Day	Débit Discharge m³s-1	Obs.	Année Year	Mois/Month Jour/Day	Débit Discharge m³s-1	Obs.	Année Year	Mois/Month Jour/Day	Débit Discharge m³s-1	Obs.
1926	07-10	2727	B2	1943	02-04	1580	B2	1960	12-11	1764	A2
7	09-14	1960	B2	4			B2	1	10-20	1799	A1
8	05-10	1640	B2	5	05-03	876	B2	2	01-03	2086	A2
9	11-15	1348	B2	6	11-19	876	B2	3	03-13	2141	A2
1930	10-12	2321	B2	7	03-09	1818	B2	4	10-26	3128	A1
1	03-12	1920	B2	8	11-10	2283	B2	5	12-09	1593	A2
2	04-03	1829	B2	9	11-29	1786	B2	6	12-04	2583	A1
3	09-24	2878	B2	1950	11-05	1360	B2	7	11-07	1230	A1
4	11-13	2109	B2	1	02-08	1656	B1	8	02-26	1462	A1
5	10-23	1640	B2	2	10-28	1680	B2	9	11-16	1469	A2
6	01-24	2137	B2	3	01-02	1721	B2	1970	01-07	1355	A2
7	12-17	1880	B2	4	11-12	1799	B2	1	01-23	1107	A2
8	05-23	1665	B2	5	03-26	1486	B2	2	05-17	2244	A1
9	05-24	2346	B2	6	06-03	1589	A2	3	09-27	2545	A2
1940	09-17	2044	B2	7	02-19	1120	A2	4	10-06	2709	A2
1	11-07	1592	B2	8	02-28	1654	A2	5	04-08	1910	A1
2				9	12-29	2259	A2	6	12-11	1560	A2

- Danube. Bezdan (210250 km²)

Année Year	Mois/Month Jour/Day	Débit Discharge m³s-1	Obs.	Année Year	Mois/Month Jour/Day	Débit Discharge m³s-1	Obs.	Année Year	Mois/Month Jour/Day	Débit Discharge m³s-1	Obs.
1926	07-02	6170	A	1943	06-24	4090	A	1960	08-02	4500	A
7	04-17	4190	A	4	04-27	5780	A	1	02-08	4070	A
8	02-25	3880	A	5	02-21	4800	A	2	06-01	4940	A
9	03-25	3470	A	6	07-18	4530	A	3	03-27	4700	A
1930	11-12	4490	A	7	03-28	5970	A	4	11-27	4280	A
1	04-02	3600	A	8	07-28	5550	A	5	06-24	8360	A
2	01-13	3570	A	9	08-25	5130	A	6	08-04	6370	A
3	07-24	3420	A	1950	02-17	3410	A	7	06-17	5200	A

TABLEAU III : SERIES CHRONOLOGIQUES DES VALEURS MAXIMALES ANNUELLES
TABLE III   : CHRONOLOGICAL SERIES OF YEARLY MAXIMA

YOUGOSLAVIA/YOUGOSLAVIE

- Danube. Bezdan (210250 km²)

Année Year	Mois/Month Jour/Day	Débit Discharge m³s-1	Obs.	Année Year	Mois/Month Jour/Day	Débit Discharge m³s-1	Obs.	Année Year	Mois/Month Jour/Day	Débit Discharge m³s-1	Obs.
1934	08-17	2550	A	1951	05-19	4790	A	1968	01-22	4220	
5	06-11	4440	A	2	04-09	5380	A	9	03-23	3520	
6	06-17	4590	A	3	07-18	4090	A	1970	07-20	5580	
7	03-20	4720	A	4	07-24	6860	A	1	06-17	3180	
8	01-20	4640	A	5	07-20	5400	A	2	07-21	3940	
9	12-11	5000	A	6	03-13	6220	A	3	05-14	4390	
1940	03-31	5750	A	7	08-04	5250	A	4	12-17	4550	
1	03-18	5200	A	8	07-08	4950	A	5	07-12	6570	
2	03-31	4820	A	9	08-23	5140	A	6	06-08	4030	

ZAIRE - CONGO

- Zaïre. Brazzaville. Kinshasa (3747300 km²)

Brazzaville (1902 - 1924) Kinshasa (1925 - 1980) La courbe de tarage à Kinshasa fournit des débits très légè-rement supérieurs à ceux de Brazzaville calculés à partir de jaugeages effectués immédiatement à l'amont du pool, l'écart maximum est de 5% pour la crue de 1961, 2,8% pour 60000 m³s-1.

Année Year	Mois/Month Jour/Day	Débit Discharge m³s-1	Obs.	Année Year	Mois/Month Jour/Day	Débit Discharge m³s-1	Obs.	Année Year	Mois/Month Jour/Day	Débit Discharge m³s-1	Obs.
1902	12-15	55300	A1	1928	12-12	54000	A1	1955	12-06	63340	A1
3	12-06	54850	A1	9	12-20	60470	A1	6	12-05	57060	A1
4	12-11	55400	A1	1930	12-03	50070	A1	7	12-23	56540	A1
5	12-26	52400	A1	1	12-21	50170	A1	8	12-10	44510	A1
6	12-03	61650	A1	2	11-29	58750	A1	9	12-20	60250	A1
7	12-10	47900	A1	3	12-01	52000	A1	1960	12-12	61890	A1
8	12-16	66100	A1	4	12-19	65490	A1	1	12-17	81110	A1
9	12-07	55600	A1	5	12-29	49690	A1	2	12-27	75710	A1
1910	12-16	62200	A1	6	12-09	59280	A1	3	12-19	60140	A1
1	12-23	57100	A1	7	12-18	59710	A1	4	12-11	71870	A1
2	12-05	55700	A1	8	12-09	60150	A1	5	12-23	64470	A1
3	11-29	44900	A1	9	12-20	64130	A1	6	12-11	64920	A1
4	12-22	58400	A1	1940	12-08	54290	A1	7	12-07	68280	A1
5	12-19	49000	A1	1	12-22	59280	A1	8	12-18	60360	A1
6	12-19	60700	A1	2	12-05	49030	A1	9	12-15	67700	A1
7	11-29	59200	A1	3	12-02	46460	A1	1970	12-02	67930	A1
8	12-29	45900	A1	4	11-25	55710	A1	1	12-22	55820	A1
9	12-27	46100	A1	5	11-28	60040	A1	2	11-29	59180	A1
1920	12-23	62200	A1	6	12-11	63340	A1	3	12-10	51710	A1
1	12-12	58300	A1	7	11-07	51130	A1	4	12-07	55510	A1
2	12-14	59500	A1	8	12-05	64920	A1	5	12-08	67340	A1
3	12-18	61000	A1	9	12-03	56020	A1	6	12-24	60910	A1
4	12-09	64200	A1	1950	11-27	62780	A1	7	12-10	59710	A1
5	12-20	66530	A1	1	12-21	64470	A1	8	12-12	64810	A1
6	12-03	64690	A1	2	12-01	54800	A1	9	12-10	54590	A1
7	12-07	49320	A1	3	12-08	52200	A1	1980	12-17	63080	A1
				4	12-03	55000	A1				

**Comments on
the data**

**Commentaires sur
les données**

Comments on the data presented
in this catalogue

It is not appropriate in a catalogue of this type to attempt a systematic analysis of the data published within it or to propose avenues of research that might be developed from the data. Nevertheless, some brief but very broad review may be useful. For this purpose it is necessary to define some index which permits an assessment of whether one flood is 'larger' than another one which was perhaps observed on a different river or basin area. One such index, often termed the Myer rating, is given by K where $K = Q_{max}/Area^{0.5}$. Despite its virtue of great simplicity it does not yield comparable values for catchments of below 500 km². Another alternative, and the one preferred in this publication, is to use a coefficient suggested by Francou (Francou and Rodier, 1967) given by

$$k = 10 \left[(1-(\log(Q)-6)/(\log(A)-8) \right]$$

where Q is the largest flood in $m^3 s^{-1}$; A is the catchment area in km².

This coefficient, although slightly more complicated, still permits easy depiction on log-log graph paper. Within a given hydrological regime a plot on such paper of the most extreme values of flood discharge against catchment area appears as a straight line with a value of K representative for the region. The envelope to all the largest floods of the world (up to 1960) from cachments larger than A = 100 km² is a straight line corresponding approximately to a K value of 6.

In this survey we restrict attention for the most part to floods with K coefficient exceeding 5.75. This serves for catchments larger than 100 km². A lower threshold of 5.1 is necessary for smaller basins; 39 such values are found in this catalogue. In order to include data from the very largest rivers two such, the Lena in the USSR and the Chang Jiang (Yang Tze) in China for which K values in excess of 5 have been observed, were also considered.

It should be emphasised that the maximum values of most floods quoted here are of poor precision. For more than half of the 41 selected values we have no information on measurement accuracy. In some cases the country supplying the records hesitated to include certain floods because it considered the estimation of peak discharge to be too unreliable. However, six or eight of these latter events are well-known in the world, they have been subjected to close scrutiny a posteriori, and it seems that their precision is better than 20%. Considering the 19 floods for which the precision is known, in six of them the errors are thought to exceed 10%, and for 13 the precision is around or better than 10%. Of course such estimates of errors may themselves be optimistic. In summary we can say that the precision of the flood measurement is very variable and among the 40 about 20 are known to an accuracy of ± 15%.

We appreciate very well the practical difficulties of assessing both the flows and their precision following an opportunity to observe violent floods in Tunisia in 1969, for which the K value exceeded 5. The aspect of the flow with very high waves, the obvious difference between left and right bank levels, turbulent eddying around bridges where these had not been destroyed, obstructions under the bridges, irregularities in the flow path across the flood plain due both to natural vegetation and to cultivation, and large variations in the river bed all combine to persuade the hydrologist of the impossibility of valid discharge measurement under extreme flood conditions.

It would not be warranted however to conclude that the resultant high K values are merely the outcome of errors in the discharge measurement, nor can one discount hydraulically derived velocity estimates of eight or nine $m s^{-1}$. Water velocities exceeding seven $m s^{-1}$ have been measured by skilled hydrometricians using current meters and in good conditions velocities in excess of eight $m s^{-1}$ have been measured with half-submerged floats. Furthermore, some of the 41 values have been checked against well-established procedures such as comparison with precipitation records, change in reservoir storage, etc...Overall it can be said that even if some of the 41 values are overestimated, most will not be far from the actual values.

Regarding return period, the 41 values of this sample, like the 1400 values overall from the catalogue, are not homogeneous. The return period of the Rio Pecos flood in 1954 has been assessed by Baker et al (1979), with very careful study of deposits under ideal conditions and making use of isotope dating, to be about 2000 years. For the Hanjiang and the Chang-Jiang rivers the return periods exceed 100 years. Of the 41 floods 39 were observed during the present century. This is not surprising given the recent development of the networks and the fact that prior to 1900 observations are mainly restricted to Europe and China. Within Europe, even in the Mediterranean countries, K values to date have not exceeded 5.65. However, this is not sufficient reason to assign a return period of less than 100 years for all the values where records are relatively brief, the Rio Pecos flood being a good example of the contrary. Nevertheless, it is probable that for a good many of these floods the return period is indeed less than 100 years. On the Ouaieme, for example, we have good reason to believe that the return period of the largest flood does not exceed 50 years. This is probably the lowest return period of the group of 41 floods considered here, although for the catalogue at large and especially in countries with a very recent network, it is possible that the maximum floods tabulated have a return period as low as 10 years. This is probably the case for no more than 50 values.

In Table 1 information is given about the catchment and floods for the 41 cases. The catchment areas vary from 3.2 km² up to 4,640,000 km². The corresponding maximum flood discharges in m^3s^{-1} have been plotted against catchment area in km² on a log-log scale (Fig.1). For areas larger than 100 km² the points plot close to the K = 6 straight line.

Some points lie above but not far removed from it while two, the Amazon at Obidos with K = 6.76, and the Ouaieme in New Caledonia near its estuary with K = 6.39, are considerably higher. We consider these values in more detail. The Ouaieme flood of 10.400 m^3s-1 was assessed by the slope-area method employing a Manning roughness coefficient of 0.0667.

This probably overestimates the actual roughness given the river's depth and width. Further support for such a value comes from two automatic raingauges which recorded 1693 mm and 1000 mm in 24 hours.

The hydrograph deduced from this amount of rainfall was compatible with the stated peak discharge. As regards the Amazon value it must be emphasided that for the very large rivers, basin area being 4,640,000 km² in this case, a K value of 6 does not represent a particularly excessive specific discharge, eg. 158 $ls^{-1}km^{-2}$ at 1 million km², and 69 $ls^{-1}km^{-2}$ at 4 million km². For a rainforest basin of 50,000 to 100,000 km² such specific maximum discharges are by no means unusual and it only requires that the basin response remains homogeneous with increasing catchment size for high K value to be encountered. On this assumption it is likely that had some large Amazon tributaries returned data during the 1953 flood event they would have returned even higher K values.

Very large basins are seldom homogeneous, however, and other cases do not present such high K values; for example K = 2.347 for the 3.75 million km² Zaire river. Outside the humid tropical zone a value of K = 5.197 has been observed on the Chang Jiang at Yichang for 1,010,000 km² and a value of K = 5.52 on the Lena at Kusur for A = 2,430,000 km².

It has often been noted how envelope curves tend to move upwards following major floods; we may use this sample to compare the current situation with that in 1962, 20 years ago. As shown on figure 1 an enveloping line of K = 6 as observed by Francou appeared suitable in 1962 with only the Amazon case discussed above presenting a significant departure above the line. Considering the current (1981) situation we find little evidence for an upward movement except for the addition of the Ouaieme point. Given the likelihood of this event having a return period no greater than 50 years it is probable that in the future some higher envelope than K = 6 will be needed.

Three other findings are apparent :

(a) As for the 1962 situation the limiting band of points in the 6 to 6.2 range applied to basins of 1,000 km² and above. For smaller basins the line appears to curve towards smaller discharges. This can be explained by the fact that on these smaller basins it is not the exceptional rainfall or series of rainfalls which account for the most extreme floods but the exceptional rainfall intensity during a short, possibly very short, period. Therefore the basic process which generates these extremes is different. It will also be appreciated that as the area decreases a constant K value in fact implies an increasing specific discharge.

A further explanatory factor, possibly the main one, is that the availability of data is much sparser for these smaller basins, especially for catchments below 100 km² in area.

In fact, it is in this small catchment band that some movement in the envelope line appears to be essential when data from 1962 to 1982 is added to the plot. Currently the K = 6 to 6.2 limit is valid from 80 km² rather than from 1,000 km² as hitherto.

One may enquire in this context whether the limit line could be extrapolated to yet smaller catchments. A specific extreme discharge of 100 $m^3s^{-1}km^{-2}$ for a catchment of 3 or 4 km² extent is presumably not impossible. Very little is known about the performance of small catchments in regions of high K values. One gains little information from approaching the problem through rainfall runoff computation. The runoff coefficient may approach 100% for some storms but we have little solid quantitative information on the mean intensity of violent rainstorms of below 15 minutes duration.

(b) A second finding is the apparent increase in the number of countries whose maximum discharges approach a K value of 6. This would have been made more obvious if in establishing the 1962 envelope we has restricted ourselves to the data available then as presented in M Parde's list and the UNESCO catalogue.

With this criterion the points contributing to the envelope would have derived from only Japan, Republic of Korea, China (Taïwan), USA (Texas) and perhaps the Philippines Islands. The IAHS catalogue introduces the following extra countries into the list; Democratic People's Republic of Korea, Mexico, California in USA, Madagascar, some Pacific Islands, India, Pakistan, Australia and mainland China. The impact of these additional regions would have been even more marked if, in the last four subcontinental scale countries, the survey of flood data had been extended down below the 5,000 to 10,000 km² threshold adopted by them in their national contributions to this catalogue.

However, this would have been an enormous task for countries of their size. The examples from the western part of India of the Jojri and Macchu floods (recently reported in the Hydrological Sciences Journal) demonstrate the very high K values that small streams in that area can experience.
It is to be feared that the countries of the Gulf of Mexico and possibly also New Zealand will at some time experience floods with K values near to 6. This increase in the number of countries falling in the category of high K values is primarily a reflection of the increased numbers of participating countries and the development of the networks everywhere rather than to any increase in the frequency of occurrence of such floods. Even before the recent floods in India mentioned above floods of a similar magnitude had been observed in small basins but were omitted from the catalogue due to inadequate information. It must be stressed that most of the countries in this category are subject to tropical cyclones.

(c) For those countries where discharge measurement has been practised for at least 80 to 100 years we observe that the mean K values within homogeneous regions climbs only very slowly. This stability has been used by Z. P. Kovacs to define homogeneous regions in South Africa in terms of the maximum K values.

However, we would advocate caution in carrying this approach too far in, for example, flood design. The IAHS catalogue and the envelope curves that may be deduced from it for a particular locality should be considered as one element among many in the assessment of the design flood. Nevertheless, we are convinced that regard should be paid to the magnitude of the maximum flood for the study catchment or for catchments of similar character from the catalogue when designing for very low probabilities. The precise margin between the enveloping flood and the actual design flood used in the project is a matter of judgement and should allow for the following considerations.

The designer should not only consider the envelope but also the genesis of larger floods in the basin of interest and use an appropriate estimation technique which accounts for the known properties of flood formation.

Comments on the data presented in this Catalogue

Also it should be remembered that this catalogue is not exhaustive and important countries from the hydrological point of view are missing : Burma, Angola, Chile, Afghanistan, Zambia and Tanzania. The representation of small islands in the Pacific and Atlantic might be better. Other countries are under-represented and, as has already been stated, there is need for the data from small basins to be increased for some large countries.

Although we press for further improvements to fill these gaps we do not believe it will be necessary to begin work on another global survey until near the end of the century. This is because it appears to us that the natural accumulation of data over a 20 year interval will not markedly affect the location of enveloping lines. The influence of man however is of increasing importance and this factor may give rise to an earlier updating requirement. Already in this catalogue it has been necessary to eliminate the effect of storage, or more commonly where it was not possible to make the allowance, to add the term "regulated" in Table II. Unfortunately there are cases where no mention was made of regulation and we suspect this accounts for the absence of very large floods in some records in recent years. For the future, few rivers will remain without anthropogenic modification and the task of our successors in framing the next such catalogue will be made more difficult. We wish them success.

Références :

- BAKER,V.R. CRAIG KOCHEL, Rand PATTON, P.C.- (1979) Long term flood frequency analysing using geological data Symposium of areas of low precipitation (Canberra 1979) Publication AISH 128 pp. 3-9.
- CREAGER,W.P., JUSTIN, J.D., and HIND,J. (1944) Engineering for Dams New-York.
- FRANCOU,J. et RODIER, J. (1967) Essai de classification des crues maximales observées dans le monde. Cahiers ORSTOM. Série Hydrologie - vol.IV - n° 3 - 1967 - ORSTOM Bondy - pp. 19-46.
- KOVACS, Z.P.(1980) Maximum flood peak discharges in South Africa: an empirical approach. Technical report T.R. 105 Directorate of Water affairs, Pretoria.
- OLTMAN, R.E., (1968) Reconnaissances Investigations of the Discharge and Water Quality of the Amazon River. Geological Survey Circular 552. Geological Survey. Washington.
- PARDE, M. (1961) Sur la puissance des crues en diverses parties du monde. Geographica. Ano VIII. Enero. Decembre 1961. Instituto Juan Sebastian Elcano. Facultad de Letras de Zaragoza. Zaragoza.
- UNESCO (1976) Répertoire mondial des très fortes crues. Etudes et rapports d'Hydrologie. Les Presses de l'Unesco. Paris.

Commentaires sur les données présentées dans ce répertoire

Il ne saurait être question dans un ouvrage de ce genre de tenter une analyse systématique des données qui y sont publiées ou même de suggérer des directions de recherche pour leur exploitation. Cependant on a cru utile de passer en revue rapidement les débits de crues maximales les plus élevés. A cet effet il est nécessaire de définir un indice permettant d'affirmer si une crue est plus "forte" qu'une autre observée sur un bassin versant de superficie différente. On peut utiliser un indice tel que celui qui résulte d'une formule type Myer $K = Qmax/S^{0.5}$, il présente l'avantage d'une grande simplicité, mais il ne fournit pas des valeurs vraiment comparables pour des bassins versants de moins de 500 km². Une autre solution, et c'est celle qui a été préférée ici, consiste à utiliser un coefficient proposé par Francou (Francou et Rodier 1967) défini par l'équation

$$K = 10 \left[(1 - (\log(Q) - 6) \ / \ \log(A) - 8) \right]$$

ou Q est la plus grande crue en m³s-1 et A la superficie du bassin en km².

Ce coefficient, bien que son expression soit un peu plus complexe, permet cependant une représentation facile sur du papier log-log. Pour un régime hydrologique donné en reportant sur un diagramme de ce type les valeurs extrêmes des débits de crue en fonction des superficies des bassins on trouve une ligne droite présentant une valeur de k caractéristique de la région. L'enveloppe de l'ensemble de tous les plus forts débits de crues pour le monde (observés jusqu'en 1966) pour des bassins de superficie dépassant 1000 km² est une ligne droite correspondant approximativement à une valeur de K=6.

Cette rapide revue des plus fortes crues a été limitée en principe aux crues dont les coefficients K correspondent à des valeurs dépassant 5.75. Ceci est valable pour des bassins versants dépassant 100 km².

Un seuil moins élevé de 5.1 a été jugé nécessaire pour les petits bassins versants. On a ainsi trouvé 39 valeurs dans ce catalogue. En vue d'inclure parmi ces données les débits extrêmes de très grands fleuves à fortes crues, on a considéré également les valeurs maximales de la Lena en URSS et du Chiang Jiang (Yang Tsé) en Chine pour lesquels on a observé des valeurs de K dépassant cinq.

On doit préciser ici que les valeurs maximales de la plupart des crues mentionnées dans le tableau ci-contre ont été évaluées avec une faible précision. Pour plus de la moitié de ces 41 valeurs maximales, nous n'avons pas obtenu d'information sur la précision des mesures. Dans certains cas, les pays en fournissant les relevés de débits de crues ont hésité à y incorporer certains d'entre eux car ils considéraient trop incertaine l'estimation du débit de pointe. Cependant de six à huit parmi ces 20 crues sont bien connues dans le monde, elles ont donné lieu à des contrôles à posteriori aussi sérieux que possible et il semble que la précision de l'estimation soit supérieure à 20%. Si on considère les 19 crues dont la précision est connue, pour 6 d'entre elles on pense que l'erreur peut dépasser 10% et pour les autres la précision est voisine de 10% ou même meilleure. Naturellement certaines estimations de l'erreur probable peuvent être optimistes. En conclusion on peut dire que la précision des mesures de ces débits de crues est très variable et que parmi ces 41 valeurs 20 sont connues avec une précision de 15%.

Nous avons pu nous rendre compte des difficultés pratiques pour estimer les débits de crues et la précision de leur mesure ayant eu l'occasion d'observer les fortes crues de Tunisie en 1969 pour lesquelles la valeur de K dépassait 5. L'aspect général de l'écoulement avec des vagues très élevées, la différence de niveau évidente entre la rive droite et la rive gauche, les remous turbulents entre les piles de ponts, là où ils n'avaient pas été détruits, les nombreux débris pouvant se bloquer sous les ponts, les irrégularités de l'écoulement dans les plaines d'inondation résultant de la végétation naturelle ou des cultures enfin les variations importantes du fond du lit des rivières, tout concourt à persuader l'hydrologue de l'impossibilité de procéder à des mesures de débit valables dans ces conditions extrêmes de crues.

Dans de telles conditions on peut être conduit un peu trop rapidement à la conclusion que ces fortes valeurs de K sont seulement le résultat d'erreurs dans l'estimation des débits, on peut également être sceptique devant des vitesses de huit ou neuf mètres par seconde, telles qu'elles résulteraient de calculs hydrauliques.

Mais des vitesses dépassant sept mètres par seconde ont été mesurées au moulinet par des hydrométristes confirmés et de nombreuses valeurs de vitesses d'écoulement égalant ou dépassant huit mètres par seconde ont été mesurées avec des flotteurs semi-immergés et ceci dans de bonnes conditions. En outre certaines des 41 valeurs de débits du tableau I ont été contrôlées par des moyens très sûrs tels que la comparaison avec les données des précipitations lorsqu'elles sont disponibles, les variations de volumes des réservoirs lorsque la relation entre hauteur et superficie est bien déterminée. Dans certains cas le site où ont été effectuées les estimations de débit est tel que les méthodes qui utilisent la pente superficielle et la section mouillée donnent de bons résultats. En fait on peut dire que si certaines des 41 valeurs sont surestimées, la plupart ne doivent pas être éloignées des valeurs exactes.

En ce qui concerne les périodes de retour, l'échantillon de 41 valeurs de même que l'ensemble des 1400 débits de crues maximales du catalogue n'est pas homogène. La période de retour de la crue de 1954 sur le Rio Pecos a été estimée par Baker et al. (1979) à la suite d'études minutieuses de dépôts de délaissés de crues se présentant dans de très bonnes conditions et de datations au carbone 14. Elle est voisine de 2000 ans. Pour les fleuves Hanjiang et Chang Jiang, elle excède largement 100 ans. Mais 39 valeurs maximales ont été observées au 20ème siècle. Ceci est tout à fait normal puisque les crues maximales antérieures à 1900 ont été observées surtout en Europe et en Chine. Or en Europe même pour les contrées méditerranéennes, la

valeur de K n'a pas dépassé 5.65 jusqu'à cette date, d'où l'absence de données européennes dans ce tableau I. La concentration de ces valeurs sur le 20ème siècle n'est pas une raison suffisante pour dire que la totalité des périodes de retour est inférieure à 100 ans et le cas du Rio Pecos est un bon exemple du contraire; mais il est probable que pour un bon nombre de ces 41 valeurs elle ne doit pas dépasser un siècle; par exemple pour la crue de la Ouaïeme nous avons de bonnes raisons de penser que la période de retour est inférieure à 50 ans. C'est probablement la limite inférieure pour ce groupe de 41 crues, mais pour d'autres stations du catalogue dans des pays où le réseau hydrométrique est récent, il est possible que la crue maximale observée ait une période de retour de 10 ans seulement. C'est le cas peut-être pour 50 stations ou moins.

Dans le tableau I on trouve le nom du pays, le nom du cours d'eau, de la station, le débit de la crue maximale observée, la valeur de K, et l'année de cette crue. Les superficies des bassins varient entre 3.2 et 4.640.000 km². Les débits maximaux correspondants ont été reportés sur un graphique log-log en fonction de la superficie du bassin (Fig.1). Pour A supérieur à 100 km² la plupart des points représentatifs sont très voisins de la droite K = 6. Quelques points sont au-dessus mais à faible distance sauf pour deux cours d'eau: l'Amazone à Obidos avec K = 6.76 pour 370.000 m³s-1 et 4.640.000 km², en 1953 et la Ouaïeme (Nouvelle Calédonie) près de son estuaire avec K = 6.389 pour 10.400 m³s-1 et 330 km², en 1981.

Examinons de plus près ces deux valeurs extrêmes. La dernière citée a été estimée par la méthode de la pente superficielle combinée avec la section mouillée, le coefficient de Manning adopté était égal à 0.0667, chiffre probablement plus élevé que la valeur réelle étant donné la profondeur et la largeur de la rivière pour ce débit maximum. En outre deux pluviographes enregistreurs installés sur le bassin ont relevé 1693 et 1000 mm en 24 heures. L'hydrogramme que l'on peut déduire de ces deux hyétogrammes présente un débit maximum très comparable à 10.400 m³s-1.

En ce qui concerne l'Amazone on doit préciser que pour les très grands fleuves la valeur six pour le coefficient K correspond à des débits spécifiques relativement faibles: 0.158 m³s-1 km-2 pour A=1.000.000 km² 0.069 m³s-1 km-2 pour A=4.000.000 km². Pour un bassin versant en forêt humide couvrant 50 à 100.000 km² ce débit spécifique maximum de 69 ls-1 km-2 est relativement fréquent et si le bassin reste homogène lorsque sa superficie croît, il reste à peu près constant.

Par conséquent il est probable que si certains des grands tributaires de l'Amazone avaient été observés en 1953, pour des superficies A supérieures à 500.000 km² on aurait trouvé des valeurs de K supérieures à six.

Mais de très grands bassins homogènes sont très rares. Généralement ce n'est pas le cas. Pour le Zaïre K = 2.347 pour une superficie de 3.750.000 km². En dehors de la zone tropicale humide, une valeur de K égale à 5.197 a été observée sur le Chang Jiang (Yang-Tsé) à Yichang pour une superficie de 1.100.000 km² et un débit maximum de 110.000 m³s-1 et une valeur égale à 5.52 a été relevée sur la Lena à Kusur (URSS) pour 2.430.000 km² et un débit maximum de 189.000 m³s-1.

On a souvent dit qu'une courbe enveloppe de ce genre se déplaçait vers le haut à chaque nouvelle enquête sur les crues maximales. Comparons la situation actuelle à celle de 1962, vingt ans auparavant. On constate en 1962 que la droite moyenne représentative des valeurs maximales (voir Fig.1) correspond au coefficient K = 6 comme cela a été déjà remarqué par Francou avec seulement un point éloigné de cette droite, celui correspondant à l'Amazone.

Si on considère la situation en 1981, on ne trouve actuellement aucune raison évidente de déplacer la droite enveloppe vers le haut. Mais le point représentatif de la crue de la Ouaïeme s'écarte significativement de cette enveloppe et ceci est troublant, surtout parce qu'il est difficile de dire que sa période de retour dépasse 50 ans et il est probable que dans le futur une autre enveloppe sera nécessaire mais ceci doit être examiné plus à fond et on en reparlera plus tard.

Trois autres constatations s'imposent :

a)   Si l'on part de la situation de 1962 on trouve que la ligne droite correspondant à K = 6-6.2 n'était valable seulement que pour des bassins versants de superficie dépassant 1.000 km².

Pour des bassins plus petits la limite était une ligne courbe avec des valeurs plus faibles des débits. Ceci pourrait s'expliquer par le fait que ce n'est pas une averse exceptionnelle ou une série d'averses exceptionnelles qui est responsable de la crue pour les très petits bassins mais une intensité de précipitations pendant une courte ou une très courte durée. Donc le phénomène à l'origine de cette crue est d'une autre nature. En outre, inversement à ce que l'on observe pour les très grands bassins, la valeur K constante égale à 6 correspond à des débits spécifiques peut-être trop élevés.

Mais la principale raison est la suivante: pour des bassins couvrant moins de 1.000 km² et ceci est plus net pour des superficies inférieures à 100 km² l'information disponible est plus rare que pour les grands bassins et en fait c'est pour ces bassins qu'entre 1962 et 1981 le déplacement de la limite est le plus important. Actuellement la limite de la droite K = 6-6.2 semble se situer vers 80 km² au lieu de 1.000 km². Même pour 3 ou 4 km² des débits extrêmes de 160 m³s-1 km-2 ne paraissent pas invraisemblables. On sait très peu de choses sur les crues extrêmes des bassins de ce genre pour la plupart des régions à très forte valeur de K. Si on se réfère aux intensités de précipitation en considérant un coefficient de ruissellement voisin de 100%, on n'est pas beaucoup plus avancé car pour des durées inférieures à 15 minutes ces intensités sont assez mal connues elles aussi.

b)   Un second fait qui serait beaucoup plus net si pour la courbe de 1962 on s'était basé seulement sur les données de M. Pardé et du répertoire UNESCO, c'est malheureusement l'augmentation du nombre de pays dont les débits maximaux correspondent à des valeurs de K voisines de 6. A partir des deux documents cités plus haut les pays à ranger dans cette catégorie semblaient limités au Japon, à la Corée, à la Chine (Taïwan) peut-être aux Philippines, et aux Etats-Unis, plus précisément au Texas.

La mise au point du répertoire de l'AISH permet de constater que l'ensemble de la Corée, le Mexique, aux Etats-Unis, la Californie, Madagascar, un bon nombre d'îles du Pacifique, certaines parties de l'Inde, du Pakistan, de l'Australie et de la Chine continentale doivent être ajoutées à cette liste et cela serait beaucoup plus évident si pour les quatre derniers pays le catalogue AISH avait pu utiliser les données d'un plus grand nombre de bassins de superficie inférieure à 10.000 km². Mais ceci aurait représenté une très lourde tâche pour de si grands pays. Les exemples dans la partie occidentale de l'Inde des crues du Jojri et du Macchu (dont il a été rendu compte récemment dans le Journal des Sciences Hydrologiques) montrent les très fortes valeurs de K qui peuvent être observées sur de petits cours d'eau de cette région.

Il est à craindre également que dans le golfe du Mexique d'autres pays présentent dans le futur des valeurs de K voisines de 6. Il en est de même pour la Nouvelle Zélande. Cette extension résulte davantage du grand nombre de pays consultés et de l'extension des réseaux plutôt que de l'ensemble des crues observées entre 1962 et 1981 sauf pour les petits bassins. Même avant les résentes crues en Inde mentionnées plus haut des crues du même ordre de grandeur avaient été observées sur de petits bassins mais avaient été omises dans les catalogues par suite du manque de diffusion de l'information. On doit souligner le fait que la plupart des pays de cette catégorie sont affectés par des cyclones tropicaux.

c)   De façon générale dans les pays où les débits sont observés depuis au moins 80 à 100 ans les valeurs moyennes maximales de K dans une région homogène varient très lentement avec le temps. Cette stabilité a été utilisée par Z.P. Kovacs (1980) pour définir en Afrique du Sud des zones homogènes correspondant à une même valeur de K.

Cependant nous conseillons la plus grande prudence si l'on veut suivre trop loin cette approche par exemple pour définir la crue du projet. Le catalogue AISH et les courbes enveloppes qu'on pourrait en déduire pour une région particulière ne doivent être considérées que comme de simples éléments parmi beaucoup d'autres pour la recherche de cette crue du projet et non comme une méthodologie de calcul. Nous sommes convaincus qu'on devrait examiner la crue maximale donnée par le catalogue pour le bassin que l'on étudie ou pour des bassins de caractère analogue lorsque l'on cherche à déterminer des crues de très faible probabilité. L'écart entre la crue de la courbe enveloppe et la crue de projet à adopter est une affaire de jugement et doit tenir compte des considérations suivantes :

l'Hydrologue devrait non seulement considérer l'enveloppe mais aussi la genèse des très grandes crues dans le bassin à étudier et utiliser une méthodologie d'estimation bien appropriée aux caractéristiques ainsi reconnues de la formation de ces crues.

On doit songer également au fait que ce catalogue n'est pas absolument exhaustif et que des pays importants du point de vue hydrologique n'y figurent pas tels que: le Burma, l'Angola, le Chili, l'Afghanistan, la Zambie et la Tanzanie. La représentation de petites îles dans les Océans Pacifique et Atlantique pourrait être meilleure.

D'autres pays ne sont pas représentés par un nombre suffisant de stations et comme cela a déjà été constaté il est nécessaire d'augmenter le nombre des données pour les petits bassins versants.

Bien que nous insistions pour que ces lacunes soient comblées dans le futur nous ne pensons pas qu'il sera nécessaire d'entreprendre une nouvelle enquête mondiale avant les dernières années de ce siècle. Ceci parce qu'il nous semble que la masse de données qui apparaissent au cours d'une période de 20 ans n'affecte pas de façon très sensible la position des courbes enveloppes. Cependant l'influence de l'homme est de plus en plus importante et ce facteur peut imposer une remise à jour plus proche de nous. Dans le présent catalogue il a déjà été nécessaire de corriger les débits pour tenir compte de l'effet de régularisation des réservoirs, ou plus souvent lorsqu'il n'était pas possible de procéder à cette opération, d'ajouter le mot "régularisé" dans le tableau II.

Malheureusement il y a des cas où aucune mention n'a été faite de régularisation et nous soupçonnons que ceci est la cause de l'absence de très grandes crues au cours des dernières années sur les relevés de certaines stations. Dans le futur il y a peu de rivières qui subsisterons sans aucune influence anthropogénique et la tâche de nos successeurs, pour mettre au point un nouveau catalogue tel que celui-ci, sera rendue plus difficile. Nous leur souhaitons bonne chance.

Commentaires sur les données présentées dans ce
Répertoire

Références

- BAKER,V.R. CRAIG KOCHEL, Rand PATTON, P.C. - (1979)
  Long term flood frequency analysuing using geological data Symposium of areas of low precipitation (Canberra 1979) Publication AISH 128 - pp. 3-9.
- CREAGER, W.P., JUSTIN, J.D., and HIND, J. (1944) Engineering for Dams - New York.
- FRANCOU, J. et RODIER, J. (1967) Essai de classification des crues maximales observées dans le monde. Cahiers ORSTOM. Série Hydrologie - vol. IV - n° 3 - 1967 - ORSTOM Bondy - pp. 19-46.
- KOVACS, Z.P. (1980) Maximum flood peak discharges in South Africa : an empirical approach. Technical report T.R. 105 Directorate of Water affairs, Pretoria
- OLTMAN, R.E., (1968) Reconnaissances Investigations of the Discharge and Water Quality of the Amazon River. Geological Survey Circular 552. Geological Survey. Washington.
- PARDE, M. (1961) Sur la puissance des crues en diverses parties du monde. Geographica. Ano VIII. Enero. Decembre 1961. Instituto Juan Sebastian Elcano. Facultad de Letras de Zaragoza. Zaragoza.
- UNESCO (1976) Répertoire mondial des très fortes crues. Etudes et rapports d'Hydrologie. Les Presses de l'Unesco. Paris.

Table I   Maximum floods in the world
Tableau I Crues maximales dans le monde

COUNTRY PAYS	STATION STATION	BASIN AREA SURFACE du BASSIN (Km²)	MAXIMUM DISCHARGE DEBIT MAXIMAL (m³s-1)	K VALUE VALEUR de K	YEAR ANNEE
CALIFORNIA (USA)	San Rafael San Rafael	3.2	250	5.194	1973
CALIFORNIA (USA)	L. San Gorgonio Beaumont	4.5	311	5.226	1969
HAWAI (USA)	Halawa	12	762	5.494	1965
HAWAI (USA)	Waïlua Lihue	58	2470	5.819	1963
CUBA	Buey San Miguel	73	2060	5.623	1963
TAHITI (FRANCE)	Papenoo	78	2200	5.650	1983
MEXICO	San Bartolo	81	3000	5.859	1976
N. CALEDONIA (FRANCE)	Ouinne Embouchure	143	4000	5.845	1975
TAIWAN (CHINA)	Cho Shui	259	7780	6.225	1979
N. CALEDONIA (FRANCE)	Ouaïème derniers rapides	330	10400	6.389	1981
N. CALEDONIA (FRANCE)	Yaté	435	5700	5.810	1981
U.S.A	Little Nemaha Syracuse	549	6370	5.826	1950
N. ZEALAND	Haast Roaring Billy	1020	7690	5.765	1979
CALIFORNIA (USA)	M.F. American	1360	8780	5.770	1964
MEXICO	Cithuatlan Paso del Mojo	1370	13500	6.156	1959
AUSTRALIA	Pioneer Pleystowe	1490	9840	5.840	1918
TAIWAN (CHINA)	Hualien Hualien Bridge	1500	11900	6.011	1973
JAPAN	Nyodo Ino	1560	13510	6.111	1963
JAPAN	Kiso Imujama	1680	11150	5.910	1961

Table I   Maximum floods in the World
Tableau I   Crues maximales dans le Monde

COUNTRY	STATION	BASIN AREA	MAXIMUM DISCHARGE	K VALUE	YEAR
PAYS	STATION	SURFACE du BASSIN (Km^2)	DEBIT MAXIMAL (m^3s-1)	VALEUR de K	ANNEE
TEXAS (USA)	W. Nueces Bracketville	1800	15600	6.156	1959
INDIA	Macchu	1900	14000	6.060	1979
TAIWAN (CHINA)	Tam Shui Taïpei Bridge	2110	16700	6.199	1963
JAPAN	Shingu Oga	2350	19025	6.290	1959
TEXAS (USA)	Pedernales Johnson City	2450	12500	5.873	1952
NORTHERN KOREA	Daeryong Gang	3020	13500	5.830	1975
JAPAN	Yoshino Iwazu	3750	14470	5.844	1974
PHILIPPINES	Cagayan Echague Isabella	4244	17550	5.980	1959
JAPAN	Tone Yattajima	5110	16900	5.871	1947
TEXAS (USA)	Nueces Uvalde	5504	17400	5.870	1935
CALIFORNIA (USA)	Eel Scotia	8060	21300	5.917	1964
TEXAS (USA)	Pecos Comstock	(9100)	26800	6.110	1954
MADAGASCAR	Betsiboka Ambodiroka	11800	22000	5.780	1927
NORTHERN KOREA	Toedong Gang Mirim	12175	29000	6.060	1967
SOUTHERN KOREA	Han Koan	23880	37000	6.047	1925
PAKISTAN	Jhelum Mangla	29000	31100	5.739	1929
CHINA	Hanjiang Hankang	41400	40000	5.868	1583
MADAGASCAR	Mangoky Banyan	50000	38000	5.698	1933
INDIA	Narmada Garudeshwar	88000	69400	6.210	1970
BRAZIL	Amazonas Obidos	4640000	370000	6.760	1953
USSR	Lena Kusur	2430000	189000	5.520	1967
CHINA	Chang Jiang Yitchang	1010000	110000	5.197	1870

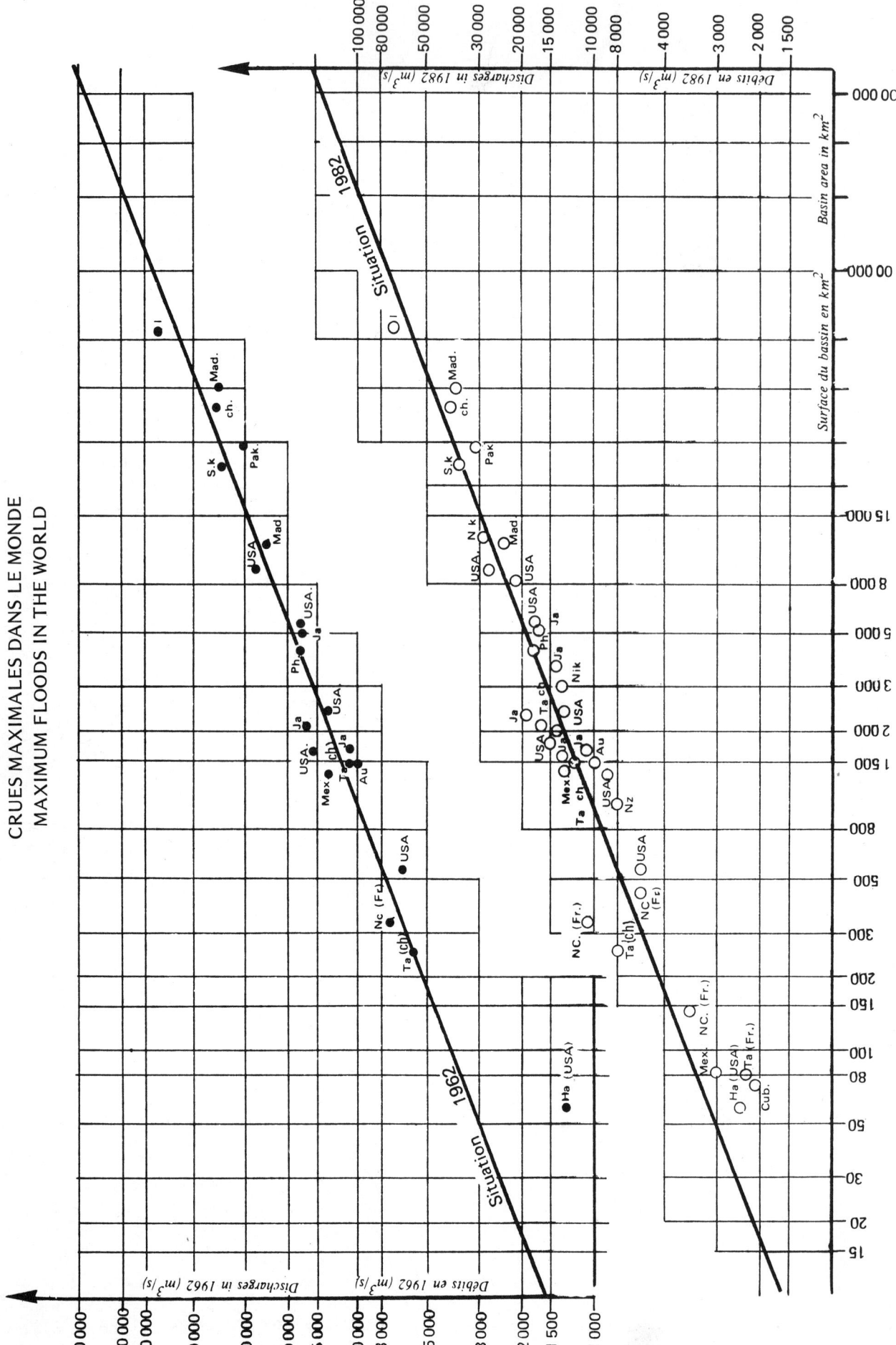

CRUES MAXIMALES DANS LE MONDE
MAXIMUM FLOODS IN THE WORLD

Fig. 1 Maximum flood discharges in the world plotted against catchment area on log-log paper/Débit maximaux de monde reportés sur un graphique log-log en fonction de la superficie du bassin.